£7.35 (147|-)

THE VEGETATION
OF SCOTLAND

To The Halden Arboretum
from William G. Strong
4-21-71

PLATE I. ALPINE LANDSCAPE. CAIRN TOUL (1292·7 m.)

Seen from Braeriach, western Cairngorms. In Scotland there is a wider range of plant habitats than anywhere else in the British Isles. The north-east face of Cairn Toul with its frost shattered rock debris and snow-beds persisting from October to May or June represents one extreme. Here plant life occurs both as lichens on rocks or as a scattered, open mosaic of montane "grass" heaths dominated by *Nardus* and *Carex bigelowii*, or by *Juncus trifidus* and characteristic, bryophyte-dominated snow-bed communities. This vegetation is, however, only comparable to the Middle-alpine zone described by Nordhagen for Scandinavia and it is doubtful if the High-alpine zone is represented, save as very local patches, in Scotland.

Photograph, R. ADAM

THE VEGETATION
OF SCOTLAND

Edited by

JOHN H. BURNETT
M.A., D.Phil., F.R.S.E.

OLIVER & BOYD
EDINBURGH AND LONDON

OLIVER AND BOYD LTD

Tweeddale Court
Edinburgh, 1
39A Welbeck Street
London, W.1

First published 1964

CONTRIBUTORS

A. J. BROOK, D.SC., F.R.S.E., Department of Botany, University of Edinburgh.

E. A. FITZPATRICK, B.SC., PH.D., Department of Soil Science, University of Aberdeen.

C. H. GIMINGHAM, B.A., PH.D., F.R.S.E., Department of Botany, University of Aberdeen.

F. H. W. GREEN, V.R.D., M.SC., F.R.MET.SOC., Speyside Research Station, The Nature Conservancy, Scotland.

J. KING, B.SC., PH.D., Hill Farming Research Organization, Edinburgh.

D. N. MCVEAN, B.SC., PH.D., C.S.I.R.O. Australia, formerly Speyside Research Station, The Nature Conservancy, Scotland.

I. A. NICHOLSON, B.SC., M.SC., Hill Farming Research Organization, Edinburgh.

D. A. RATCLIFFE, B.SC., PH.D., Monkswood Experimental Station, Abbots Ripton, formerly, The Nature Conservancy, Scotland.

D. H. N. SPENCE, B.SC., PH.D., Department of Botany, University College, Makerere, Uganda, formerly University of St. Andrews.

EDITOR

J. H. BURNETT, M.A., D.PHIL., F.R.S.E., Department of Botany, University of Newcastle upon Tyne, formerly University of St. Andrews.

EDITOR'S PREFACE

When I went to the University of St. Andrews in 1955 I knew little about the Scottish flora and less about the vegetation. On attempting to rectify this deficiency I found that no adequate account existed, the best being the papers of Robert and W. G. Smith. Valuable as these were, together with the numerous others scattered through the literature, I still felt that a single comprehensive account was desirable. Thus the idea of this book was born. A number of other botanists in Scotland shared (or could be cajoled into sharing) my view and the project was formally agreed upon at a meeting in January 1958 at the University of St. Andrews.

Our intention was to produce an account similar in general format to that of Tansley's *The British Islands and their Vegetation* but couched in terminology, and based upon descriptive methods, more akin to those of Continental ecologists and phytosociologists. We believed that this approach was important, if only because British ecologists had much to learn from and much to offer Continental workers, once the difficulty of communication could be overcome. The splendid reception of *Plant Communities of the Scottish Highlands* encourages us to believe that our attempt will be appreciated however successful it may, or may not, be. All of us owe a great debt to Duncan Poore who joined us at our first meeting and encouraged us on our way. I know that my colleagues would wish me to pay public tribute here to his inspiration and guidance.

A collection of essays as technical as these could be sufficient to daunt the heart of any prospective editor. That it has not done so is only because of the enthusiasm, willing co-operation and admirable execution of my colleagues. I thank them for their support and tolerance. I hope they share my elation that our task has been accomplished.

I must also express my especial thanks to my former colleague Dr. D. H. N. Spence (now Professor of Botany at Makerere). Without his helpful discussions and unflagging zeal I might well at times have given up or neglected the project. I must also thank Miss M. Anderson (St. Andrews) and Miss Margaret Irving (Newcastle) for clerical assistance; Miss Margaret French (Newcastle) for preparing several figures, and Mr. H. Whittle (Newcastle) for technical assistance. The publishers, Messrs. Oliver and Boyd, have been tolerant, tactful and helpful at all stages in the preparation of this book. I owe an especial debt in this matter to Mr. Thomas Jenkins, who has taught me much about book production.

J. H. BURNETT

May 1964
Department of Botany,
The University of Newcastle upon Tyne.

ACKNOWLEDGEMENTS FOR ILLUSTRATIONS

We acknowledge with thanks permission to reproduce the following figures:

Mr. P. Bannister (Fig. 41); Dr. B. A. Hulme and the University of Edinburgh (Fig. 18); Dr. S. Y. Landsberg and the University of Aberdeen (Figs. 21-24); Mr. I. A. Nicholson and the University of Durham (Fig. 19); Council of the Botanical Society of Edinburgh (Figs. 20a, b, 25, 27-29); Institute of British Geographers (Fig. 3); *Journal of Ecology*, Cambridge University Press and Blackwell's Scientific Publications (Figs. 16, 30-34, 44a, 60); *Scottish Beekeeper* (Fig. 38); *Scottish Geographical Magazine* (Fig. 43, adapted); Clarendon Press (Fig. 10, adapted); The Meteorological Office, the Nature Conservancy and Her Majesty's Stationery Office (Figs. 1, 2, 4, 5, 37, and 42 adapted); T. Nelson & Sons (Figs. 17, 39a, adapted).

Thanks are also due to the following individuals who supplied photographs:

Robert M. Adam (Plate 1); Dr. E. M. Birse (Plates 11-13, 45); Dr. J. Berry (Plate 24); Mr. E. Cormack (Plate 48); Mr. D. Jenkins (Plates 38, 47); Mr. I. Moir (Plate 41); Dr. J. C. Ritchie (Plate 44); Mr. A. Tewnian (Plate 37); the Council of the Royal Society of Edinburgh (Plates 67, 69, 71, 73, 75, 77) and the Air Ministry (Plates 78, 79).

Finally, grateful acknowledgement for the loan of blocks is due to:

Journal of Soil Science, Oxford University Press (Plates 2 and 4) The Nature Conservancy and Her Majesty's Stationery Office (Plates 22, 23, 25, 85-96) and the Hill Farming Research Organization (Plate 24).

NOTE ON NOMENCLATURE

The place names used conform to those used by the Ordnance Survey.

The plant names used in this book conforms to usage in the following works:—

CLAPHAM, A. R., TUTIN, T. G., and WARBURG, E. F. *Flora of the British Isles* (2nd. ed.), Cambridge, 1962.

WARBURG, E. F. *Census Catalogue of British Mosses* (3rd. ed.), The British Bryological Society, 1963.

JONES, E. W. "An Annotated List of British Hepatics ", *Trans. Brit. Bryol. Soc.*, **3**, 353-374, 1958.

WATSON, W. *Census Catalogue of British Lichens*, The British Mycological Society, 1953.

CONTENTS

PART I

THE PHYSICAL BACKGROUND

PART II

THE VEGETATION

THE MARITIME ZONE

4. MARITIME AND SUB-MARITIME COMMUNITIES

THE FOREST ZONE

5. WOODLAND AND SCRUB

CHAPTER 1

THE STUDY OF SCOTTISH VEGETATION

J. H. BURNETT

The study of the vegetation of Scotland was initiated by the brilliant work of Robert Smith, his elder brother W. G. Smith and their collaborators, at the end of the nineteenth century. Robert Smith's achievement was described by Tansley (1911) as "the first attempt at a scientific description of British vegetation". It is all the more tragic, therefore, that his unexpected death in August 1900 at the age of twenty-six, when apparently recovering from an operation for appendicitis, robbed Scottish vegetation studies and British ecology of their pioneer.

In the years 1898-1912 the outlines of knowledge concerning Scottish vegetation were laid down by the Smiths and their associates and, thereafter, the subject made virtually no progress for thirty to forty years. Robert Smith's achievements were great and it is worth considering briefly both them and the subsequent eclipse of vegetation studies in Scotland.

Early Vegetation studies to 1940

The study of plant life in Scotland has been dominated and to some extent is still dominated, by the richness of the flora in terms of rarities. This was first revealed in Lightfoot's *Flora Scotica* in 1778 and by the subsequent solitary and compulsive excursions of George Don, the Forfar nurseryman, in the "Caledonian Alps" (Don, 1804; Don, in Headwick, 1812), so that, to this day, the alpine rarities of Clova, Caenlochen and Lawers have an allure which blinds many botanists to the common vegetation of the hills. In the Universities this tradition was maintained, by Traill in Aberdeen, by Balfour at Edinburgh and by the founding of naturalists' societies largely devoted to the study of Scottish mountain plants (see Fletcher, 1959).

University College, Dundee, differed from the other Scottish Universities in having two men of genius and independent thought in charge of its biological departments, Patrick Geddes in botany and D'Arcy Thompson in zoology. Robert Smith, a Perthshire naturalist like Don, entered the college in 1892 as a part-time student, and finally became a lecturer in 1899. There can be little doubt that he was inspired and infected by Geddes' sociological outlook on life and biological science. Smith's interests were canalised by a visit, arranged through Geddes, to the department of Professor Charles Flahault at Montpellier. Here he learned of, and contributed to, the French school of phytogeography. He returned in the same year that Harvie Brown and J. G. Bartholomew published their 10 miles to 1 inch (1 : 625,000) "Naturalist's map of Scotland" (1895). With the enthusiastic collaboration of Bartholomew, under the joint inspiration of Flahault and Geddes, and with his field-knowledge and prodigous energy, Smith determined to commence a "Botanical Survey of Scotland". In the four years 1896-1900 he completed his great papers on the vegetation of "The Edinburgh District" and "North Perthshire" (Smith, R., 1900a, b) and most of the field work, published posthumously by his brother, on "Forfar and Fife" (1904, 1905). These papers include both descriptions of the vegetation, discussions of the important causal factors and, for each area, detailed vegetation maps showing the principal plant associations described. All this was done while he was demonstrating in zoology and virtually teaching all the botany single-handed, for Geddes was by now an absentee professor save for his summer term lectures. Before these major works, Smith published two shorter papers which show clearly his phytosociological outlook and describe his methods. The first (1898) was concerned with the associations in the immediate neighbourhood of Dundee, the Tay Basin; the second (1899) set out his working method in a region. He wrote:

"We require to know:
  a) The chief associations into which it may be divided.
  b) The particular conditions of heat, light, moisture, and food distinguishing each association.
  c) The particular adaptations or life-forms of the species of each association.
  d) The relations between the species
     1. Dominant social forms;
     2. Secondary social forms struggling for existence;
     3. Dependent species—simply protected by the presence of the dominant species or living upon the humus they form, or parasitic upon them, etc.
  e) The influence of animals and man upon (c) and (d).
  f) The general conditions of climate and of vegetation of the region compared with other regions."

This extract shows clearly how he was moving from a pure phytogeographical or regional approach to a more phytosociological and ecological treatment of vegetation. His principles are clearly to be seen in his published work where associations are described in terms of the interrelationships of the plants themselves and the interplay between geological, pedological and biotic factors with the vegetation cover (although, of course, he did not use this terminology). For example, in his account of heath vegetation the complex interrelationships of factors such as burning, recovery of the plants and their subsequent competition and the nature of the soil are discussed. On the 10th May 1900

Smith exhibited several sheets of his Botanical Survey of Scotland at the Royal Scottish Geographical Society. In the ensuing discussion he spoke of the effects on the vegetation of sheep grazing versus burning and of the dynamic balance reached. Referring to competition between oak and pine, he compared the Scottish situation with that which he had seen in the pine forests of Norway. The great importance of geology was also stressed in this discussion, especially in relation to the nature of the soil's substrate, whether solid rock or not, and it emerged that Smith, before preparing his maps, had consulted the manuscript drift maps in the Scottish geological office. The vegetation maps, prepared with all the resources and assistance of Bartholomew, the Edinburgh cartographer, were coloured and to a scale of 2 miles to 1 inch (1 : 126,720). They are so accurate that it is possible to use them to locate specific areas of interest at the present time, at least in Fife and North Perthshire.

The work of Robert Smith inspired many others in Scotland. His brother W. G. Smith, however, had obtained a post at the Yorkshire College, Leeds (now the University of Leeds), in 1897 and his subsequent accounts of arctic-alpine vegetation (1911, 1912) were based in part on the early work taken over from Robert. Marcel Hardy, a protégé of Geddes, completed a regional account of the vegetation of the Highlands (1905), more in the style of Flahault than of Smith but nevertheless including brief statements concerning the possible successional changes likely to be found in highland communities (cf. Hardy, p. 133, 1905). Shortly after, however, he too left Scotland. George West, Smith's successor, completed his arduous survey of the vegetation of the Scottish lochs (1905; 1910a, b) but, thereafter, his teaching duties became increasingly burdensome through a combination of Geddes' increasing absences and wartime conditions and he made no further contribution to vegetation studies. The other two workers in this first phase, F. J. Lewis of Liverpool and C. B. Crampton, emigrated and died respectively, shortly afterwards. F. J. Lewis developed earlier work on macro-stratigraphy of bog profiles (Geikie, 1891), so that for many years it represented the best information available in Britain on the post-glacial changes in vegetation (Lewis, 1905-7; 1911). Although his data were correlated with Scandinavian data and interpreted by Samuelsson in 1910, many years elapsed before the technique of pollen analysis was applied to Scottish sites. Carmpton was a geologist-cum-botanist, employed primarily in the Scottish Geological Survey. He was attracted by the close connexions he believed he could discern between the vegetation and the geodynamic features of the regions he surveyed, notably Caithness (Crampton, 1911, 1912). It was natural that he should be attracted, in a region such as this, to study the vegetation of areas continually exposed to change due to geodynamic factors. He contrasted such "migratory" vegetation living in unstable habitats with "stable" vegetation occurring in areas, not exposed to such changes. He noted that the "migratory" vegetation, as a whole, maintained its general nature despite change. The importance of such observations for ecology as a whole are profound and have not yet, perhaps, received proper recognition.

Thus, by 1912, inspired by the work of Robert Smith and using his methods, accounts existed of the vegetation of the Highlands, the lochs, moors, grasslands and woodlands and of the post-glacial history of Scotland. Thereafter, for almost three decades, no further major contributions were made to Scottish vegetation studies although isolated papers of importance appeared on the lochs (Mathews, 1914), Scottish beechwoods (Watt, 1931), post-glacial history (Erdtman, 1921, 1923, 1928) and on features of vegetation of importance to forestry or agriculture, e.g. Fraser (1933); Fenton (1931, 1937). The initiative passed to the English school of ecology, strengthened and organised by W. G. Smith. Scotland was virtually neglected until in 1938 and 1939 a group of workers, somewhat quixotically described as the "Cambridge Botanical Expedition to the Cairngorms", carried out valuable surveys which set the scene for the renaissance of ecological work in Scotland after the war.

Vegetation studies from 1940

This renaissance had several foci. The publication of the work of the 1938-39 expedition to the Cairngorms (Watt and Jones, 1948; Metcalfe, 1950; Burges, 1951) and of Pearsall's *Mountains and Moorlands* (1950) did much to direct attention to Scottish vegetation. A major stimulus, however, came from the controversial and comprehensive studies of Duncan Poore, first in 1952 in his native Perthshire and then, under the auspices of the Nature Conservancy, extending to the whole of the vegetation of the Highlands. The culmination of this work came ten years later with the publication of *Plant communities of the Scottish Highlands* (McVean and Ratcliffe, 1962) and was preceded by a series of important papers in which Poore's methods were described (Poore, 1954; 1955a, b, c; 1956), the general problems posed by Scottish mountain vegetation discussed and an attempt made to compare the Scottish communities with those of North-west Europe (Poore and McVean, 1957). These accounts provide comprehensive descriptions of the vegetation of the Highlands which can be related to those of Continental ecologists. This is largely due to the use of a method of describing communities devised by Poore and based upon the classification and methods used by Braun-Blanquet and Nordhagen: this method will be described later. In addition to these comprehensive studies, work was in progress on other Scottish vegetation types. At Aberdeen, where J. R. Mathews had always maintained an interest in Scottish vegetation, Gimingham commenced his important studies on moorland and maritime vegetation; the soil survey of Scotland expanded and, at the Macaulay Institute, palynological studies were developed. The Hill Farming Research Organization and the Brown Trout Research Laboratory at Pitlochry provided an impetus for the study of grasslands and the phytoplankton of the Scottish lochs, respectively. At Glasgow and St. Andrews work developed on a variety of ecological projects ranging from the Shetlands to Loch Lomond. Gregor, at the Plant Breeding Station, Roslin (Midlothian), expanded his pioneering genecological studies to cover the genecology of several communities in the Southern Uplands. Much of this work still continues but, in 1957, it seemed an appropriate moment to embark upon a comprehensive general account of Scottish vegetation. The present work is the outcome.

The present work

The object is to provide a general account of the present-day vegetation of Scotland together with relevant information concerning the climate, soils, the past history and the regional distribution of the vegetation types.

Zonation. It was decided to recognise primary zones of vegetation determined mainly by climate; two exceptions are the Maritime zone and the Aquatic zone. The former, of course, lies technically within the Forest zone but differs so greatly in its soils, climate and flora that it may conveniently be considered apart. Aquatic vegetation differs in that it may occur either in the Forest or the Montane zone but like maritime vegetation, that of lochs is so very different from other terrestrial vegetation that here again it has been convenient to treat it separately. No treatment of montane loch vegetation has been given because of lack of information.

In any area an altitudinal sequence of communities can usually be observed but the absolute altitude at which any particular community occurs is variable. In general, the altitude at which any community occurs becomes progressively lower on going from south to the north and west. Thus, for example, the highest limit of potential forest can range from 690-750 m. in the east and central Highlands to 91-135 m. in the west, e.g. about 640 m. in Cairngorms compared with 400 m. in Beinn Eighe (Poore and McVean, 1957; McVean and Ratcliffe, 1962). The causes of such altitudinal variation are many but the principal ones appear to be "oceanicity" and exposure. The former is particularly relevant when considering the east-west latitudinal variation, the latter when considering longitudinal variation, e.g. the fall in the upper limit of sub-alpine scrub on passing from the Central Highlands to the Shetlands (Spence, 1960). The Forest Zone and the Montane Zone as used in this work, therefore, are not strictly altitudinal zones and it is important that this should be realised.

Description of vegetation. Since the survey of Highland vegetation was already well advanced, using the descriptive techniques of Poore, it was decided to employ them as far as possible for describing all communities. Where this was not possible, because of absence of suitable data, e.g. maritime vegetation, or of reconnaissance studies, e.g. in the macrophytic vegetation of the lochs, an attempt has been made to arrange the communities in units more precise than those of Tansley (1949) and, wherever possible, comparable to those distinguished by Continental ecologists. For each community, named and described according to the degree to which it has been studied the intention was to provide the following information:

(a) A synoptical floristic table giving dominants and constants where possible.

(b) A description of the community, its altitudinal and edaphic range and its distribution.

(c) Its relation to other communities and its ecological history, where known. Relationships with continental communities, especially Scandinavian, were to be stressed.

Poore's methods, or an approximation to them, have been employed save in the account of the phytoplankton where they are inapplicable. It is convenient, therefore, to describe this method here. Poore has written:

"After extensive reconnaissance the worker chooses stands which are as far as possible uniform in general physiognomy, ecology and species composition, as far as these may be determined by inspection. They should also be stands of communities which are typical of the region and occur frequently in it" (Poore, p. 49, 1962). Various methods may be used to determine the homogeneity of the area but Poore describes a simple technique for determining a "minimal area" of a community. In essence, a small area, its size chosen for convenience, is marked out in the middle of the stand and the species listed. The process is repeated by doubling the area, through laying out a further quadrat alongside and touching the first, and any species not recorded in the first quadrat are added to the list. The procedure is continued, "until the number of new species added per increase of area becomes small. If the number of species continues to increase quickly with each successive increase of area, the initial choice of uniform area is at fault; if it rises suddenly in a second step it indicates that the area has passed the limits of one community into another" (Poore, p. 237, 1955a). The stand is then described by estimating by eye, the cover and abundance of each species in the list using Domin's ten-point scale or, where this proves too difficult, the Braun-Blanquet five-point scale to which the Domin scale can be converted directly (Poore, p. 253 *et seq.*, 1955b). When more than one layer is present each is estimated separately. In addition, data are collected concerning altitude, aspect, slope (if relevant), total percentage cover, height of vegetation, and the profile of a soil pit dug in the area under investigation. Once a number of areas have been so listed, the data are compared and, "By the continued examination of similarities and differences he (the ecologist) gradually builds up parallel classifications of vegetation types and environmental situations and becomes able to relate the two. As his experience grows he will be able to distinguish more finely and to draw more detailed inferences. This is the method of 'successive approximation'. The criterion which must be used to judge the validity of the inferences made is that they should be consistent with all the facts as far as they are known. . . . In this way a framework of points of reference is built up. . . . The differences that are significant will become apparent and can be subjected to more detailed and experimental examination. . . . The method of successive approximation would appear to be the most economical way of obtaining a comprehensive understanding of vegetation variation. It is *par excellence* a reconnaissance method but is not limited to reconnaissance. When the main framework is determined, more detailed investigations either of the community or of the habitat will reveal finer relationships. This, not earlier, is the proper stage for the entry of more strictly quantitative methods; for only at this stage will they produce results which are commensurate to the work they involve" (Poore, p. 38 *et seq.*, 1962).

The method was not applied strictly to the data for maritime and sub-maritime vegetation, dwarf shrub heaths in the forest-zone, the phytoplankton and macrophytic loch vegetation (Chapters 4, 7, 8 and 9 respectively). In the first two, this was because the data already compiled were so extensive that it would have delayed publication unduly if they had been re-described. However, for most of these communities the procedure was similar to that used by Poore save that the description is couched in terms of "percentage presence". This does not provide as much information as the use of a measure such as cover-abundance but it gives sufficient for valid comparisons to be made with Scandinavian authors' data. It has already been pointed out that the mode of collection of data concerning phytoplankton does not permit the use of a descriptive method such as that of Poore which is, indeed, quite inappropriate here. The study of the macrophytic vegetation of lochs, swamps and associated fens was only commenced in 1958 when there was no modern data available and no reconnaissance studies had been made. The data were collected and are expressed in the manner of Poore. However, it is not always certain that they are based on a minimal area, although every attempt was made to ensure this and, in the case of aquatic communities the estimation of cover-abundance proved difficult at times. Date for submerged vegetation beyond the limits of vision had to be based upon samples obtained with a grab. It is a remarkable testimony to Poore's claim, that his method is primarily one for reconnaissance, that it proved so successful for communities so very different from those on the Breadalbane hills where it was devised.

Finally, it may be considered how far the descriptions given are truly representative of the whole of Scotland. It must be admitted that certain areas and certain types of vegetation have been insufficiently examined. Very little information has been obtained concerning the vegetation of the Islands and they still offer a rich field of study. Similarly, little has been recorded concerning the vegetation of rivers; of lochs and lochans above 306 m.; of screes and cliffs or of the remarkable, purely bryophyte communities which occur especially in the west. Nevertheless the major vegetation types have been adequately sampled and it seems not unreasonable to claim that adequate accounts of the principal communities are now available.

Problems of classification and nomenclature

The only major problem of classification which has arisen is in connection with swamps, fens, bogs and mires. This reflects, in part, the nature of the vegetation, in part, the different interpretations of different authors. In fact, there is no great problem in the field in distinguishing the mire and bog communities from the others. In Britain, swamp and fen are terms which have virtually been defined on a regional basis. This really reflects the over-riding influence on thought of the East Anglian fens which have been intensively studied for over fifty years. Swamp is used by many British authors to describe, "the type in which the normal summer water level is above the soil surface: it is usually dominated by reeds (*Phragmites*) or by other tall grasses, sedges or rushes, often accompanied by dicotyledonous species of similar habit: the commonest kind of swamp is therefore called *reedswamp*" (Tansley, p. 634, 1949). Reedswamp occurs in Scotland but swamps dominated by *Carex* spp. are extremely widespread and those dominated by *C. rostrata* may be classified either as swamps or eutrophic mires depending largely on their location. In fact, despite floristic similarities which are not great, it is convenient to use both terms for the two kinds of communities, which occur in different regions as a result of different causal factors. The other source of confusion is the use of "swamp" by Continental authors. Here the term is used with a wider connotation than in Britain and this can be seen clearly by comparing the introduction to Chapters 9 and 10 (pp. 306-318 and pp. 426-428). In the former Spence employs the traditional British approach, in the latter, Ratcliffe's attitude is more akin to that of continental botanists. There is less confusion over the use of the term fen although Spence's usage is perhaps somewhat wider than that of Tansley (1949). There is also considerable difference in the usage of the terms descriptive of bogs and mires. For instance, in Chapter 10 the word "mire" is used to denote a soligenous bog, although it is used in a much wider sense by most continental workers. Similarly "bog" is used to cover all classes of ombrogenous bog. Although raised bog is distinguished from blanket bog, Ratcliffe (p. 428) does not consider the former to be a topogenous type, contrary to the usage in Tansley (1949). Here this distinction is not merely nomenclatural but is based upon a particular working hypothesis concerning the origin of the raised bog. There seems little doubt that the time is rapidly approaching when it will be necessary to revise the terminology of all vegetation types which occur on more or less waterlogged soil, in the light both of working hypotheses and conformation with international usage.

The principal nomenclatural problem has been the terminology to be used to define the vegetation units described. In his original papers Poore (1955a, b, c) introduced the term "nodum" to apply to abstract vegetation units of uncertain status and of any category. Once the status of the vegetation had been decided an appropriate term, based on those agreed at the 1930 International Congress (Du Rietz, 1930) could be used. However, the term nodum is particularly associated with Poore's methodology and it was felt that since not all the data had been collected in this way it might be better not to employ it in the following accounts. Usually when describing a unit of uncertain status a term of neutral connotation such as "vegetation type" or "community type" has been used. In the accounts of woodlands and montane vegetation the units described are based upon the noda determined by Poore's technique and described by McVean and Ratcliffe (1962). In this work however, McVean has now recognised them as associations although no higher groupings have been recognised. In general, wherever higher groupings have been recognised they are analogous to those of Scandinavian workers, e.g. in the account of the dwarf shrub heaths. The principal exception is in the account of the macrophytic vegetation of the lochs where it has been found necessary to develop an *ad hoc* classification to deal with the great bulk of new information which has not yet been adequately compared with that from continental accounts. Even here "sociation" and "association" are used in the internationally agreed sense, although the term "society" is used for a community type in which a species predominates seasonally or permanently as a pure stand (cf. p. 318).

The important point to recognise is that because of the similar methodology employed, the basic units (usually picked out in the text by bold side-heads) are remarkably comparable, whatever they may be called. Comparison with the units recognised by Tansley (1949) will show that the basic units used here are more natural and, on the whole, smaller. They are frequently, although by no means always, comparable with those used by recent Scandinavian workers and, in relevant cases, with those used by McVean and Ratcliffe (1962). It may be claimed that such equivalence is sufficient and that the allocation of these smaller units to higher categories may be left to those phytosociological taxonomists to whom such a pastime is rewarding. On a world scale, as in floristic taxonomy, such classification is necessary but at the field level, a more urgent task is the further investigation and analysis of the units using experimental methods.

There seems little doubt that the majority of the principal vegetation types in Scotland are described here although further investigations in the Islands and freshwaters of Scotland may add some additional types. The urgent requirement now is for an analysis of the causal factors involved in stability and change of vegetation types. Two approaches are possible. Firstly, there is that pioneered by Gregor in which the genecological analysis of the individual taxa of the community types is being developed (e.g. Gregor, 1955-62) in an attempt to analyse the genotypic adaptations relevant to life in a plant community. Secondly, there is the possibility of ecological field experiment, on a wide scale if necessary. Scotland is especially suitable for such work, at least in vegetation types such as dwarf shrub heaths, mires or bogs. Not only do vast tracts of relatively uniform stands occur but there is, in addition, a magnificent range of National Nature Reserves which cover such a large acreage that the twin requirements of experimentation and conservation can readily be met within their boundaries. Much is already being done on these lines in moorland vegetation where the economic impetus of grouseshooting has stimulated and supported financially, scientific effort. Productivity studies, of immense importance to the proper utilisation of land, are already in progress in the Aberdeen area, on Rhum and on the farms under the auspices of the Hill Farming Research Organization. All this is to the good, yet one of Scotland's greatest assets, scenically, biologically and economically—the lochs—remain relatively unstudied. Moreover, the vast acreage of bogs and mires have hardly begun to be studied analytically. Hydrological and micro-climatological analyses of the bog or mire habitats are almost non-existent and the dynamics of their growth and decay are only understood in the most general way. These problems are in urgent need of study and Scotland, of all parts of the British Isles, provides an ideal region in which such ecological work should be developed.

REFERENCES

BROWN, J. G. HARVIE   1895   *Naturalist's map of Scotland*. Edinburgh.
and BARTHOLOMEW, J. G.

BURGES, N. A.   1951   The ecology of the Cairngorms. III. The *Empetrum—Vaccinium* zone. *J. Ecol.*, 39, 271-284.

CRAMPTON, C. B.   1911   *The vegetation of Caithness considered in relation to the goleogy* Cambridge.

1912   The geological relations of stable and migratory plant formations. *Scot. Bot. Rev.*, **1**, 1-17; 57-80; 127-146.

DON, G.   1804   *Herbarium Britanicum.*

DU RIETZ, G. E.   1930   Classification and nomenclature of vegetation. *Svensk. bot. Tidskr.*, **24**, 489-503.

ERDTMAN, G.   1923   Iakttagelser från en mikropaleontologisk undersökning av nordskotska, hebridiska, orkadiska och shetländska torvmarker. *Geol. Fören. Stockh. Förh.*, **45**, 538-545.

1924   Studies in the Micropalaeontology of Post-Glacial Deposits in Northern Scotland and the Scotch Isles. *J. Linn. Soc. (Bot.).*, **46**, 449-504, with special reference to the history of the woodlands.

1928   Studies in the Postarctic History of the forests of North-western Europe. I. Investigations in the British Isles. *Geol. Fören. Stockh. Förh.*, **50**, 123-192.

FENTON, E. W.   1931   A botanical survey of grasslands in the south and east of Scotland. *J. Ecol.*, **19**, 392-409.

1937   The influence of sheep on the vegetation of hill grazing in Scotland. *J. Ecol.*, **25**, 424-430.

FLETCHER, H. R.   1959   Exploration of the Scottish Flora. *Trans. bot. Soc. Edinb.*, **38**, 30-47.

FRASER, G. K.   1933   Studies of Scottish moorlands in relation to tree growth. *Bull. For. Comm. (Lond.)*, **15**.

GEIKIE, J.   1891   *Prehistoric Europe.* London.

GREGOR, J. W.   1955-62   In, *Scottish Plant Breeding Station Report(s)*, Roslin.

HARDY, M.   1904   *Equisse de la Géographie et de la Végétation des Highlands d'Écosse.* Paris.

HEADWICK, J.   1812   *General view of the County of Angus or Forfar.* Edinburgh.

INGRAM, M.   1958   The ecology of the Cairngorms. IV. The *Juncus* zone: *Juncus trifidus* communities. *J. Ecol.*, **46**, 707-737.

LEWIS, F. J.   1905, 1906   The Plant remains in the Scottish Peat Mosses. I-IV. *Trans. Roy.*
           1907, 1911   *Soc. Edinb.*, **41**, 699-723; **45**, 335-360; **46**, 33-70; **47**, 793-833.

LIGHTFOOT, J. J.   1778   *Flora Scotica.* London.

McVEAN, D. N. and   1962   *Plant Communities of the Scottish Highlands.* H.M.S.O.,
RATCLIFFE, D. A.   London.

MATHEWS, J. R.   1914   The White Moss Loch: a study in biotic Succession. *New Phytol.*, **13**, 134-148.

METCALFE, G.   1950   The ecology of the Cairngorms. II. The Mountain Callunetum. *J. Ecol.*, **38**, 46-74.

POORE, M. E. D.   1954   *Phytosociology of the Breadalbane district of Perthshire.* Ph.D. Thesis, University of Cambridge.

1955a   The use of phytosociological methods in ecological investigations. I. The Braun-Blanquet system. *J. Ecol.*, **43**, 226-244.

1955b   — II. Practical issues involved in an attempt to apply the Braun-Blanquet system. *J. Ecol.*, **43**, 245-269.

1955c   — III. Practical application. *J. Ecol.*, **43**, 606-651.

	1956	— IV. General discussion of phytosociological problems. *J. Ecol.*, **44**, 28-50.
	1962	The method of successive approximation in descriptive ecology. *Adv. Ecol.*, **1**, 35-68.
— and McVEAN, D. N.	1957	A new approach to Scottish mountain vegetation. *J. Ecol.*, **45**, 401-439.
SAMUELSSON, G.	1910	Scottish Peat Mosses. A contribution to the knowledge of the late-quaternary vegetation and climate of North-Western Europe. *Bull. Geol. Inst. Univ. Uppsala*, **10**, 197-260.
SMITH, R.	1898	Plant associations of the Tay Basin. *Proc. Perth Soc. Nat. Sci.* **2**, 200-217.
	1899	On the study of plant associations. *Nat. Sci.*, **14**, 109-120.
	1900a	Botanical Survey of Scotland. I. Edinburgh District. *Scot. geogr. Mag.*, **16**, 385-416.
		— II. North Perthshire. *Scot. geogr. Mag.*, **16**, 441-467.
and SMITH, W. G.	1904	— III and IV. Forfar and Fife. *Scot. geogr. Mag.*, **20**, 617-628.
	1905	— III and IV. Forfar and Fife. *Scot. geogr. Mag.*, **21**, 4-23; 57-83; 117-126.
SMITH, W. G.	1911	In, *Types of British Vegetation*, ed. A. G. Tansley, Cambridge.
	1912	Anthelia: an arctic-alpine plant association. *Scot. Bot. Rev.*, **1**, 81-89.
and CRAMPTON, C. B.	1914	Grassland in Britain. *J. Agric. Sci.*, **6**, 1-17.
SPENCE, D. H. N.	1960	Studies on the vegetation of Shetland. III. Scrub in Shetland and South Uist, Outer Hebrides. *J. Ecol.*, **48**, 73-95.
TANSLEY, A. G. (ed.)	1911	*Types of British Vegetation.* Cambridge.
	1949	*The British Islands and their vegetation.* Cambridge.
WATT, A. S.	1931	Preliminary observations on Scottish beechwoods. *J. Ecol.*, **19**, 137-157.
WATT, A S. and JONES, E. W.	1948	The ecology of the Cairngorms. I. The environment and the altitudinal zonation of the vegetation. *J. Ecol.*, **36**, 283-304.
WEST, G.	1905	A comparative study of the dominant phanerogamic and higher cryptogamic flora of aquatic habit in three lake areas of Scotland. *Proc. Roy. Soc. Edinb.*, **25**, 967-1023.
	1910a	A further contribution to a comparative study of the dominant phenerogamic and higher cryptogamic flora of aquatic habit in Scottish lakes. *Proc. Roy. Soc. Edinb.*, **30**, 65-181.
	1910b	An epitome of a comparative study of the dominant phenerogamic and higher cryptogamic flora of aquatic habit, in seven lake areas in Scotland. In, Murray, J. and Pullar, L., *Bathymetrical Survey of the Scottish Freshwater lochs*. Vol. I, 156-260. Edinburgh.

PART I

THE PHYSICAL BACKGROUND

CHAPTER 2

THE CLIMATE OF SCOTLAND

F. H. W. GREEN

The term interpretive climatology has been used (Frisby and Green, 1949) to denote climatic studies tailored to the needs of a particular group of users. More is known about the kind of climatic information sought by botanists than is readily available; much of the raw data is there, but not all, and it has been only partially "interpreted" as yet. Thus a chapter on Climate in a book such as this must inevitably be a compromise between a hackneyed extract for Scotland of standard tables or maps of the conventional meteorological factors, with explanatory text, and a review of the climate of the country in terms of those parameters which are of the greatest significance to the vegetation.

This chapter will attempt three things. First, an attempt will be made to discuss what kind of information an ecologist would like to have about the climatic environments in Scotland, if it were indeed possible to give it to him in the form he would like. This will be followed by a, more or less, conventional presentation of the variations within Scotland of the conventional climatic parameters, because this kind of data is readily available. Finally, an attempt will be made to discuss what is known of those parameters which seem much more use to ecologists than the conventional meteorological factors.

Vegetation, like humans and other animals, experiences weather *as a whole*. It does not experience such things as dry bulb temperature, wind speed, or hailstorms, separately. Plant physiologists and meteorologists need to get together to see where they can meet each other half way. That they do not always meet each other half way can be illustrated by the example of transpiration. Meteorologists know a good deal about the evaporative power of the atmosphere (or, more strictly, of available energy for evaporative processes) and about available water; plant physiologists know more than a little about the function of water in, and of transpiration by, plants. But, just as the former cannot readily discover, from botanical literature, precisely how plants are able to respond to the hydrological environment, so botanists cannot readily discover what are the variations from place to place in water availability and evaporative potential. There is not yet a real meeting point half way and so, for instance, no one knows enough about how much of the water vapour in the air has transpired through plants (or animals) and how much was directly evaporated.

Climate, past or present, enters into almost every feature of plant environment. Some features are, however, a function of climate only indirectly. The underlying rocks are partly a function of the palaeoclimate, and the soil is a function of both present climate and, through the geological bedrock, of the palaeoclimate. It is not possible to be concerned here with the more indirect climatic effects, but only with the direct effects, and to some extent with the less indirect effects, such as the relation of the *present* climate to topography and soils.

It seems that, in considering the direct effects of climate, botanists are concerned mainly with what may be called "climatic productivity potential". Ultimately this is dependent on incoming solar radiation, which can come *direct*, after filtering by the atmosphere, or by *reflection*. There is also an advective factor which, if some over-simplification is allowed, can be identified as wind: to give a simple example, the effect of a strong, dry wind flowing from over a desert towards an area of lush vegetation is to transport some available radiative energy from the former to the latter.

This energy can be used in several ways, but most of it is used either to increase temperatures or to evaporate water. The proportion used in these two ways (more strictly, the Bowen ratio, which is the ratio between energy used for evaporation and sensible heat exchanged between a land or water surface and the atmosphere) is not constant. The ratio is nearly constant in any particular locality, but it shows variations with altitude which, although relatively small, are significant. There is thus some evidence to suggest that at higher altitudes in Great Britain, a somewhat smaller proportion of the incoming energy is used to maintain high air temperatures.

The radiative energy can be expressed in calories per square centimetre, but it is neither, in fact, directly measured at many places, nor is the advective factor taken into account adequately. Consequently it is probably more satisfactory, by invoking the Bowen ratio, to express the energy in terms of air (and/or soil) temperature, or in terms of potential evaporation. The temperature has for a long time been commonly expressed as "accumulated temperature" in day-degrees, above a certain threshold usually taken as 6°C. (*c.* 43°F.). It can be claimed that this provides a not unsatisfactory general index of "climatic productivity potential". It will be seen however, from consideration of the Bowen ratio, that potential evaporation, i.e. the amount of evaporation which would take place if there were always water available for evaporation, is nearly proportional to accumulated temperature. Values of potential evaporation are not so readily available as temperature, and so less use has so far been made of them. But they do have the great advantage of being expressible in the same units as rainfall. It is, therefore, suggested that potential evaporation is the most valuable single parameter by which to assess the whole climatic environment.

This last suggestion is made in spite of the fact that it is obvious that availability of water is also essential for plant growth. Where rainfall is insufficient, water can always, in theory, be made available. Nevertheless, in practice, especially in respect of natural vegetation as distinct from irrigable crops, rainfall must be considered. Ideally then, the climate of Scotland could best be expressed in terms of potential evaporation and rainfall, both recorded, as a natural, in the same units.

Potential evaporation is a parameter which can be computed with an accuracy, sufficient for many purposes, from meteorological factors which are already fairly generally measured, but it can also be measured more or less directly (Green, 1960) and an embryonic, although quite insufficient, network of observations of potential evaporation now exists in Scotland (cf. Green, 1962.) The fact that it can be computed from other factors is a reminder that in some localities one single factor has such extreme values that, to all intents and purposes, it can conveniently be considered alone. Thus on Scottish Atlantic islands, wind, although it operates by increasing evaporation, is the limiting factor for tree growth. It will break twigs and stems and fell trees even if these have survived the strains of excessive transpiration. The effect of snow is analogous. Freezing and thawing, snowfall and rainfall, are related to temperature, but localities where snow lies long are also a function of wind, which sweeps snow off exposed places and piles it up in more sheltered sites. The extent and duration of snow cover can be of paramount importance, for instance, in determinining the distribution of *Nardus* communities in the Highlands. These special cases do not, however, invalidate the thesis that potential evaporation is the most convenient single index of growth potential.

It will be as well to introduce here two terms, which will be referred to again at the end of this chapter. These are *potential water surplus* and *potential water deficit*. These parameters result from subtracting potential evaporation from rainfall, or *vice versa*. The amount of water surplus is less important to the ecologist than to the hydrologist, but, as will be indicated later, variations in the value of potential water deficit are of great ecological significance.

TEMPERATURE

The most widespread network of thermometers is for air temperature about 1·5 m. (4-5 ft.) above the ground, where thermometers are by convention exposed in a white-coloured, louvred screen over a sward of grass or similar low herbage. The merit of this "standard" exposure lies in that it enables one locality to be compared with another, free, as far as possible, from the wide variations experienced close to the ground, or between the stems and leaves of plants. These wide micro-meteorological variations are, it must be remembered, related to the temperatures of the ambient air more closely than to anything else; they thus provide a datum on which to tie individual micro-climatic observations.

The first thing to be looked for is some measure of the total temperature, above certain thresholds, which is experienced in the course of an average year. This is called *accumulated temperature*, and is usually expressed in day-degrees above the specified threshold. Two thresholds will be considered here, 0°C. (32°F) (freezing point) and 6°C. (42·8°F.). The first of these thresholds is critical for life and death in some species

B

at all, or certain, periods in their growth cycle. It is conveniently shown by maps giving the average dates of the first and last air frosts (Figs. 1 and 2). From this it will be seen that the most favoured localities in Scotland, e.g. the southern Outer Hebrides, can

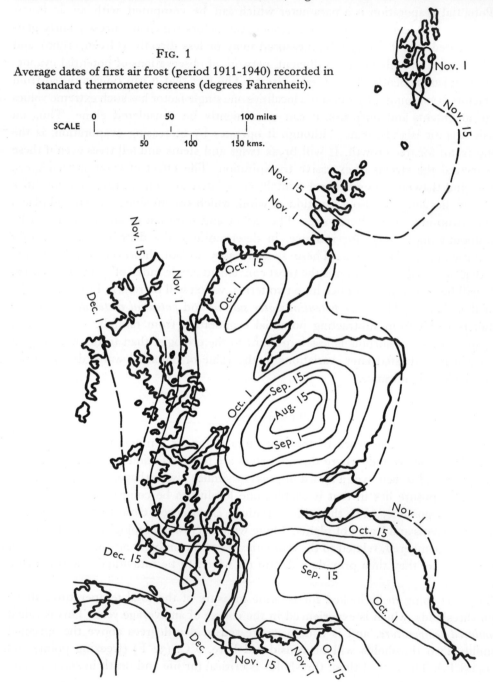

Fig. 1

Average dates of first air frost (period 1911-1940) recorded in standard thermometer screens (degrees Fahrenheit).

SCALE

usually expect, on low ground, an air-frost-free period from just before the beginning of April to just after the beginning of December. The least favoured, e.g. the glens in the eastern Highlands, again considering low ground, can expect such a period to last only from mid-June to mid-August. On the hills, in the central and eastern Highlands, air frosts are likely to be experienced in any month of the year.

FIG. 2

Average dates of last air frost (period 1911–1940) recorded in standard thermometer screens (degrees Fahrenheit). (Figures 1 and 2 after the *Climatological Atlas of the British Isles*.)

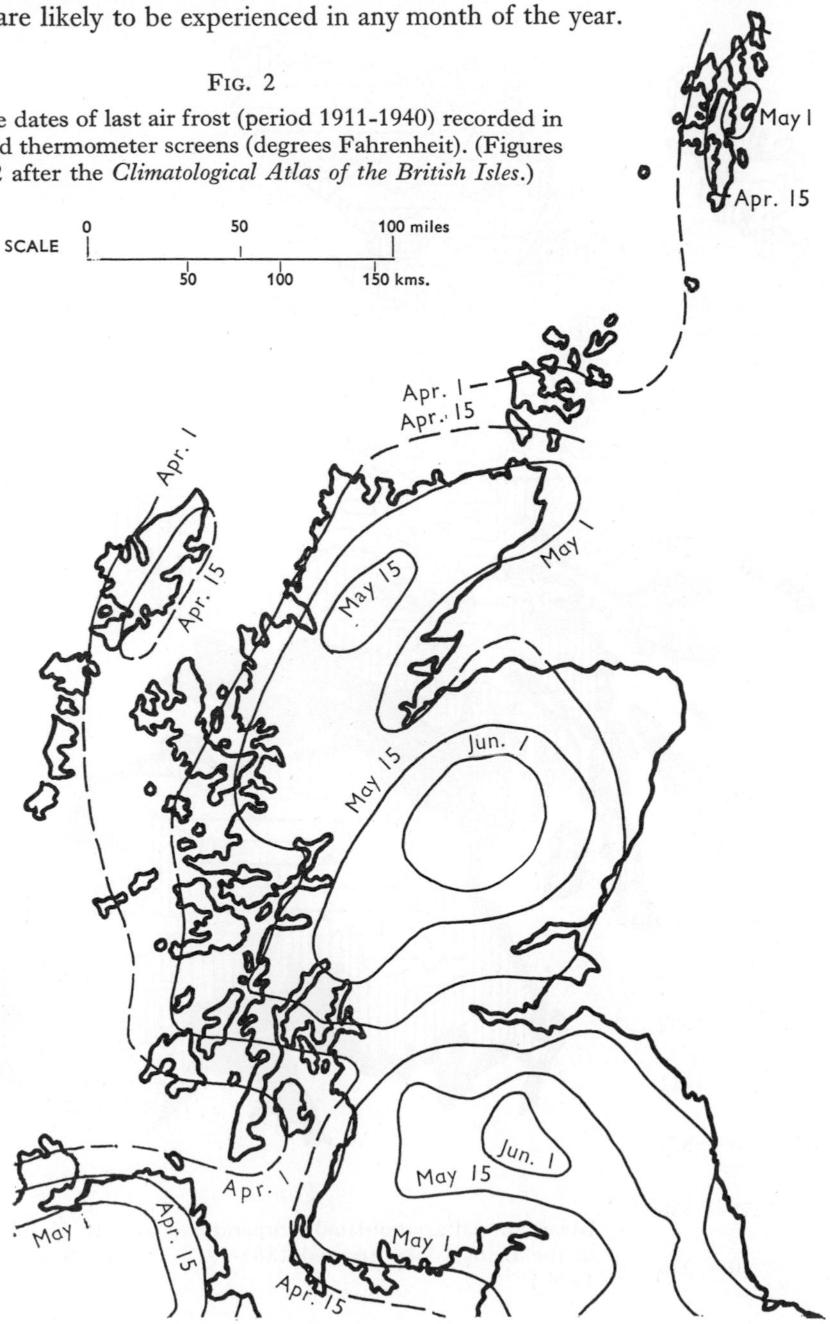

The 6°C. (42·8°F.) threshold is not critical in the same sense, i.e. life or death, as the 0°C. threshold, but it is generally accepted as the point below which vegetative growth in most plants is insignificant. It is more conveniently expressed as accumulated temperature, and is shown on Fig. 3. From this it will be seen that the variation in

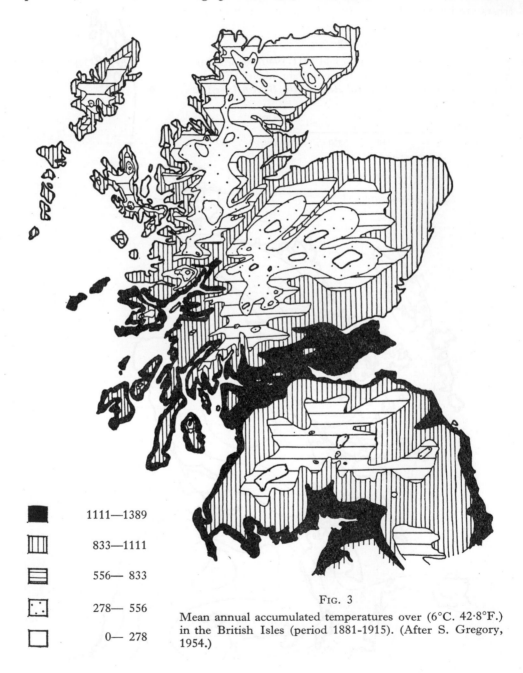

■	1111—1389
▥	833—1111
⊟	556— 833
⸬	278— 556
□	0— 278

FIG. 3

Mean annual accumulated temperatures over (6°C. 42·8°F.) in the British Isles (period 1881-1915). (After S. Gregory, 1954.)

Scotland is from almost nil to 1400 day-degrees C. (*c.* 2500 day-degrees F.); in contrast, the most favoured parts of the south of England have just over 1900 day-degrees C. (*c.* 3500 day-degrees F.). Thus while no part of Scotland receives the "total warmth" of some parts of England, there is no part of the British Isles which has a significantly longer frost-free period than the Outer Hebrides, except for the Scilly Isles and Channel Islands, where the advantage lies in freedom from frosts in early spring rather than from frosts in early winter.

Fig. 4

Range of average monthly temperatures in degrees Fahrenheit. In degrees Centigrade 15°F. is approximately 8°C., and 20°F. is approximately 11°C. (After the *Climatological Atlas of the British Isles*.)

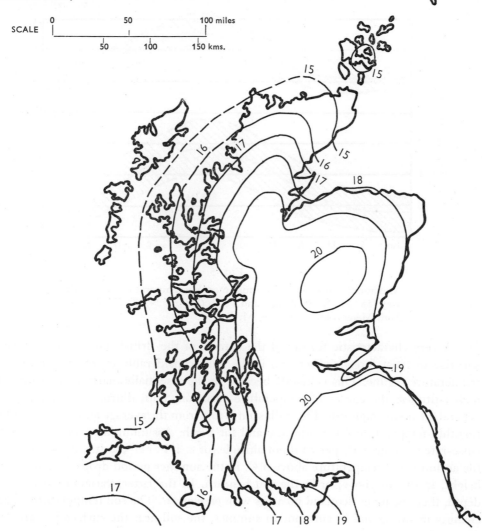

Average monthly and diurnal ranges of temperature are again of considerable, if not always vital, significance to plant life. Average monthly temperature ranges (i.e. the range between the month with the highest and the month with the lowest mean temperature), on low ground, in Scotland, vary from a little under 8·3°C. (15°F.) in the Outer Hebrides, Orkney and Shetland to somewhat over 11·1°C (20°F.) in the southern parts of the Eastern Highlands (Fig. 4). The average diurnal ranges vary from a little over 3·9°C. (7°F.) in the western and northern islands, in the winter months, to somewhat over 10°C. (18°F.) in the southern and eastern Highlands in June. There is a difference, however, in the distribution of the ranges over Scotland, the "monthly" range on the mainland showing primarily an increase from west to east, and the "daily" range an increase from the coast inland.

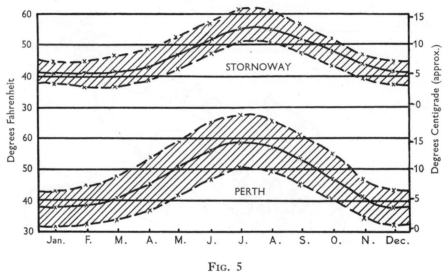

FIG. 5

Maximum, Mean and Minimum monthly temperatures for Stornoway (58° 11′ N., 6° 2′ W.) and Perth (56° 24′ N., 3° 27′ W.). Data from Meteorological Office, M. O. 407.

A very characteristic feature of the climate of the British Isles, which comes as a surprise to most foreign observers, is the very considerable effect of altitude on the temperature regime. This is mainly because in the essentially maritime climate in these high latitudes, the curves of temperature variation, both diurnal and annual, are, in general, of small amplitude. Fig. 5 illustrates this from the average annual curves of mean monthly temperature for Stornoway and for Perth. Assuming an average temperature lapse-rate of about 1°C. per 50 m. of altitude (or *c.* 1°F. per 300 ft.), it can be seen how the accumulated temperature above 6°C. in the summer period drops very rapidly with height, in the air above, or in the soil beneath. In the latter, variations decrease with depth, there being in Scotland no areas with *permafrost*. The soil temperature lapse-rate changes in spring and in autumn. In summer, the soil near the surface is warmer than further down, while in winter the reverse is the case; this has, among other things, an important effect on the movement of water vapour in the soil, since this tends to follow the temperature gradient and, in the spring and autumn transition periods, the tendency is, for a time, subject to frequent short periodic reversal. The crossing of the soil temperature threshold between freezing and thawing is important in relation to soli-fluction, which, as can be seen in most of the Scottish hills, is greatest at the levels where this threshold is crossed most frequently. Very generally speaking, these levels increase across country from west to east, and there is a general correspondence with the levels at which vegetation ceases to cover more than half the surface (Galloway, 1961).

RAINFALL AND SNOWFALL

It must be stressed, to recall the remarks made at the beginning of this chapter, that for most ecological purposes rainfall must always be considered in relation to evaporation. Even when considering rainfall itself, it must be noted that the water which descends, in one way or another out of the atmosphere, must originally have got into it by evapora-tion. But it is most important to remember the scale of the atmospheric evaporation/ precipitation cycle. This is essentially a gigantic transfer of water from ocean to land via the atmosphere, and failure to appreciate the large scale of this process leads to various fallacies about the effect of lakes and green vegetation—including trees—on rainfall. Essentially, and with caveats only for micro-climates (e.g. concerning rainfall on the ground under a vegetational canopy), rainfall affects plants, but the plants do not affect rainfall. In contrast to this, the vegetation cover can, under certain conditions which apply seasonally in the British Isles, affect evaporation from the land.

In attempting to discuss rainfall as an individual factor in the climate of Scotland, it is natural to consider first total annual averages. These are portrayed on so many widely reproduced maps that it is unnecessary to include such a map in this book. It can be observed that the annual average varies from about 560 mm. (22 in.) in a few places on the lowland shores of the Moray Firth to somewhat over 3800 mm. (150 in.) in the Lochaber mountains in Inverness-shire. Apart from these extremes there is a clear decrease in total fall on low ground from 1140 mm. (45 in.) in the west to about 760 mm. (30 in.) in the east; on relatively extensive areas (i.e. excluding exposed isolated peaks) at about 1000 m. (c. 3000 ft.), the comparable decrease is from about 3000 mm. (120 in.) in, for example, the Isle of Mull, to about 1500 mm. (60 in.) on, for example, Lochnagar. The proportionate increase of rainfall with altitude is greater in the west than the east. The rainfall on the open coastline is almost invariably less than it is a little distance inland, and this must be ascribed mainly to the disturbance in air flow due to changes in relief. Thus the wettest parts of the country lie in a band some miles inland from the west coast of the mainland, from Ross-shire to Argyll.

The total rainfall is made up of rain caused by several factors, acting simultaneously or in conjunction; frontal activity, instability in the air mass, and orography, all of which have in common that they cause air to rise upwards. The orographic effect has been illustrated above, while frontal activity accounts for the west being wetter; the majority of fronts are associated with depressions moving from west to east. Instability, illustrated by summer storms over the land, produces a considerable part of the rain in the east, and especially in summer (see below).

Still considering total annual rainfall, another aspect of "wetness" is the duration of rainfall. This is commonly expressed by the number of *wet days* or of *rain days* (the former is defined as days with 1 mm. (·04 in.) of rain or more, and the latter as days with more than 0·2 mm. (·01 in.) of rain). Very generally speaking, the *average* rate of rainfall is the same over the whole of the British Isles. So a map of rain days or of wet days looks like a "smoothed out" map of total annual rainfall, with variations from an average, in the case of rain days, of less than 175 in East Fife to well over 250 in parts of the west. The distribution of rain days has been found (McVean and Ratcliffe, 1962) to coincide better with the distribution of certain plants than any other readily accessible index of "wetness".

The seasonal distribution of rain is every bit as important as the total amount. In the open ocean to the west of Scotland there is a marked rainfall minimum in spring and a maximum in winter, while in north central Europe there is a distinct major maximum in summer. On the west coasts of Scotland the distribution of rainfall is of the almost purely oceanic type; the east approaches the continental type, but not to the extent of a *single* maximum in summer. The most characteristic distribution in the east is a gradual rise from January to December, with slight maxima in late summer and in early winter, the latter being almost always rather more pronounced than the former. In other words, the great excess of rainfall in the west as compared with the east is mainly a winter contribution. The east would, however, have a much smaller rainfall in the summer if it were not for the convectional storms in unstable air referred to previously. Characteristic of these storms are their heavy falls in short periods which not only cause floods and do other damage but, because of rapid run-off, make the rainfall less effective for plant absorption and transpiration. A satisfactory map showing the proportions of rainfall falling in the winter, and in the summer half-years is not readily available, but Figs. 6 and 7 (Mill and Salter, 1915) give some idea of this. It can be illustrated by the fact that whereas Aberdeen has about 75 mm. (3 in.) in each of the months July and December, Stornoway has about 75 mm. (3 in.) in July and nearly 150 mm. (6 in.) in December.

The "reliability" of rainfall is another aspect to note. Taking the year as a whole, the mean deviation (as a percentage of average) increases on the whole from the coast inland; spring and autumn, however, show no very striking pattern, while midsummer and midwinter show a pattern of general increase in deviation from west to east, especially in January. In winter this could be described as primarily a "rain-shadow" effect and in summer as a reflection of the "random distribution" of convectional rain. Both are, in fact, associated with the east coming periodically under the influence of continental anticyclones, with warm air giving rain in summer and cold stable air "staving off" rain in winter, while the west continues to be under the oceanic cyclonic influences nearly all the time. In spring and autumn the continental anticyclone is not usually well developed.

Snowfall is, of course, a special case of "rainfall" but snowfall has one profoundly different characteristic from rainfalls it does not obey the laws of gravity in the same way. It not only remains on the ground until it melts, but it drifts, both at the time of falling and afterwards. There is a time-lag in run-off or of percolation into the soil also; although rain drifts to some extent in high wind, snow shows this characteristic very much more. This causes it to lie in sheltered places and to leave exposed areas uncovered. Ecologically this has two main effects: (i) it "shelters" dormant vegetation where it lies, and (ii) it moistens the ground on which it lies and on to which its melt water runs when it thaws. Meanwhile the drift-free places are more subject to temperature variations and are ecologically much drier. The combination of high winds and snowfall, and also of frequent alternation of freezing and melting, make the climate of the Scottish Highlands much more severe for plants than, for example, the Norwegian fells, and thus much poorer in plant species and in vegetation cover generally. In summer, the usual winter snowbeds can be distinguished easily by the entirely different vegetation cover from their surroundings.

The above considerations show that maps of such things as the average number of days of snowfall, or of snow lying, can be very misleading, especially in hilly country. In respect of low ground they are however of some interest. In the case of "snow falling", the increase in the average number of days per annum is from south-west to east, from about 10 in southern Galloway to about 40 in Shetland, or, excluding these extreme situations, from about 12 in Islay to about 36 in Buchan. In the case of "snow lying", the very general distribution is somewhat similar, but with a pronounced increase in number of days inland from the coast. Thus a place like Stranraer will have only about 5 days annually of "snow-lying", while Braemar has nearly 70, but Stranraer has more days of snow *fall* than of snow *lying*. The reverse is the case in many inland places in the north-east.

HUMIDITY: FOG AND CLOUD

Botanists, recognising that amounts of rainfall are an inadequate index of the wetness of plant environment, have sought to find additional indices. They have made much use of saturation deficit as an index, but it is not to be recommended, because its reliability as an index depends on the temperature of the air being the same as that of the evaporating surface, a condition that rarely exists. The relative humidity of the air, or an analogous parameter to express the relative wetness of the soil, has some value in describing the plant environment. The relative humidity of the air is subject to great diurnal variation, and may be regarded as being as much an effect as a cause of differences in plant transpiration. In the particular cases when the relative humidity rises to 100 per cent. and dew or mist results, there is a very significant effect on vegetation. This can be important in rainless areas, or rainless periods, since, whether or not plants can absorb water through the leaves (as distinct from, more normally, transpiring it from them), dew or mist inhibit transpiration, and therefore reduce "water need". Such things as dew (including hoar frost) and fog drip (including rime) are sometimes known as "occult" precipitation, because their amounts are not readily measured, and evade collection in rain-gauges. It remains to be said that, in general, the diurnal variation in air humidity increases with distance from the coast, especially from the west coast, and especially in summer.

Fog and mist (and cloud reaching the ground surface in the hills is the same thing) are not only features of the "humidity environment"; they reduce temperature, and also, like cloud, reduce light intensity. Thick fog at low levels is most frequent in areas of greatest smoke pollution, and thus in Scotland is most frequent and most persistent in

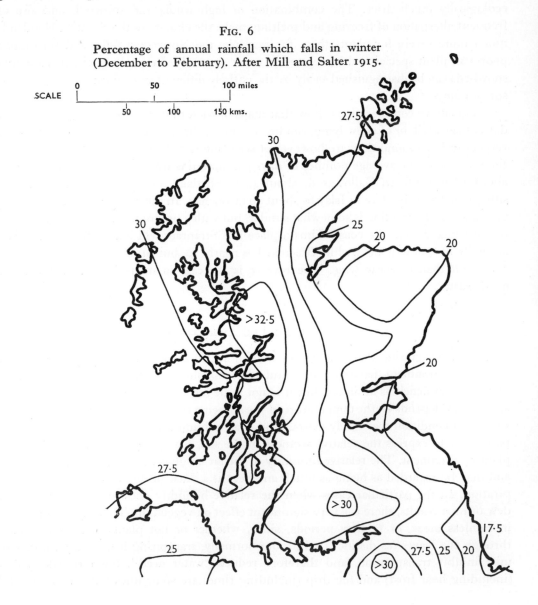

FIG. 6

Percentage of annual rainfall which falls in winter (December to February). After Mill and Salter 1915.

the industrial areas of Clydeside and other parts of the central lowlands, but mist is also
a feature of the east coast (where it is known as haar) especially in spring and early
summer. Here it is due to differences in temperature between sea and air and thus it
forms over the sea and drifts inland with easterly winds. The height of the cloud base
tends of course to be low in northern latitudes, and so "Scotch mist" is a feature of all
the hills, the frequency of occurrence being roughly proportional to the height of the hills.
It should however be remembered that, in not infrequently occurring conditions, fog or
cloud forms in valleys especially at night and when it persists into the day it will cause the
valleys to receive less sunshine than the hills. Haze, which is usually considered as the

FIG. 7

Percentage of annual rainfall which falls in summer
(June to August). After Mill and Salter 1915.

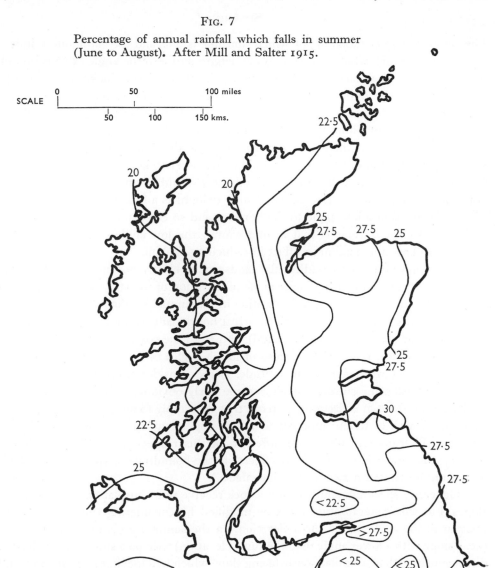

poor visibility due to dry aerosols, and not to water vapour or hygroscopic particles, is sometimes thick enough to reduce sunlight significantly in otherwise fine weather, but it is only a minor cause of variations in amount of sunshine.

Amount of cloud, other than as mentioned above, can be considered as the inverse of amount of sunshine. It is also important, as a factor in night temperatures, and its absence at night leads to the formation of dew or hoar frost. Stratiform cloud has a different effect on insolation from cumulus cloud; the grey monotony of the underside of stratus cloud is clearly different from the dazzling whiteness of piles of cumulus.

SUNSHINE

The amount of solar radiation, of which sunshine is one, and the commonest, index, is a function of latitude, which determines day length and also the angle of elevation of the sun. The angle of elevation acts to determine, in turn (a) the thickness of atmosphere through which the radiation passes and (b) the shadowing effect of hills. The total annual duration of *possible* sunshine (i.e. assuming a flat landscape and no cloud) is very nearly the same throughout the range of latitude of the British Isles; it averages just over 12 hours per day, but there is a very considerable difference in seasonal distribution. Whereas in the south of Galloway it would be just over 17 hours in June and a little over 7 hours in December, in the north of Shetland it would be about 19 hours in June and not much over 6 hours in December. A long twilight is a feature of northern latitudes, where the sun is at a low angle to the horizon, and so Shetland in mid-summer has no real darkness; the obverse is that in mid-winter, the low angle causes any kind of air pollution to have the maximum effect in reducing sunshine.

The assumption of a cloudless flat landscape is clearly not applicable to Scotland. The net result of cloud, of the lower angle of elevation of the sun, and hazy air, in more northerly latitudes, is to cause a diminution in the annual average of daily "bright sunshine" amounts from south to north (nearly 4 hours daily average in the south down to not much over 2·5 hours in N. Shetland), and from the coast inland.

Topographical relief, also because of lower angles of elevation of the sun, has an increasing effect with increase in latitude. Some considerations of three-dimensional geometry reveal some subtle, as well as some fairly obvious, incidences of hill shadow. In discussing these, it is desirable to recall that they apply to temperature, to frost and to snow-lie, as well as to sunshine *per se*: all are dependent upon amounts of direct solar radiation. Plateaux and plains are different, in this respect, from "heavily dissected" country; the former have only "edge effects" at the bounding escarpments, but the latter has an uninterrupted network of "edge effects".

Generally speaking, south-facing slopes receive more insolation than north-facing slopes, but this generalisation must be modified by considering the angle of slope in relation to the angle of the sun's elevation. In the summer a gentle north-facing slope (i.e. a slope with a lower angle than the sun's elevation) will, on a sunny day, receive more direct sunshine than a similar south-facing slope which will inevitably be shadowed, for a greater or larger period, at the beginning and end of the day. On the other hand, a steep north-facing slope may receive no sunshine at all in the winter and even be steep enough to receive only relatively weak morning and evening sunshine in summer; the steep south-facing slope will miss only the latter. Highland corries, with their long snow-cover, owe their greater abundance of snow on north-facing slopes to this very fact.

In long straight Alpine valleys, in Central Europe, this effect is so well known as to have led to special words, such as *ubac* and *adret*, to describe the conditions on opposite valley sides. This matter is very well described and discussed by Garnett (1937), and it deserves a good deal more attention in the Scottish Highlands than it has received. The serious effects of its neglect are well illustrated by the siting of the industrial settlement of Kinlochleven in a very sunless location, to the harm of those obliged to live there.

The subtle effects of other environmental factors with the geometry of slopes and sun angles are infinite in their variety. Some of these are illustrated and discussed by McCormack and MacHattie (1961).

WIND

The British Isles are windy. The general effect of the roughness and unyielding surface of the land as compared with the sea is to damp down wind speeds. So, as would be expected, the windiest places are the most oceanic islands. Only in the Outer Hebrides does the average annual wind speed, at the standard elevation of 10 m. (33 ft.) above the ground, exceed 32 k.p.h. (18 miles per hour), and only in the Outer Hebrides and Shetland does the annual average number of days with gale-force winds much exceed 30. Winds of all speeds tend to decrease gradually from the coast inland, and, since winds over Britain are mainly westerly, this effect is more striking from the west coast inland than from the east coast inland. Winds of higher speeds show this feature, on the average, rather more markedly. The exposure of hill summits is comparable to that of open coasts, and the shelter of valleys is comparable to that of distance from the ocean.

Wind affects vegetation in various ways, which can be roughly classified according to how much effect is direct and how much it is indirect. Its direct effect is seen in physical, i.e. "mechanical", damage. Plants cannot grow at all if wind prevents the accumulation of any medium for them to take root in. Bare rock or constantly drifting sand are almost without vegetation; the bare rock is characteristic of hill summits, and shifting sand-dunes of the coast, especially of low coast. Once vegetation has managed to take root (and man can artificially aid it in doing so), survival depends primarily upon the strength and elasticity of the plant. Woody vegetation, especially tall trees, is more inhibited than low springy vegetation, because the stems are broken off; trees are thus virtually absent from the Outer Hebrides, Orkney and Shetland, as well as from exposed peninsulas of the other islands and the mainland. The direct effects of wind are also inhibiting at high levels.

The indirect effects of wind, which are in fact more important, are *desiccating* effects. They increase evapo-transpiration and lower temperatures. Inland, in the hills a visible effect of this is a general stunting of vegetation with increase in altitude; on the coast the stunting is often one-sided, owing partly to the wind being stronger on-shore than off-shore and partly to the suspension of salt, which itself is desiccating.

Trees and other woody vegetation sometimes adapt themselves to constant high winds by assuming a low-bushy, or prostrate growth, such as can frequently be seen in the outer islands. Occasional gales, i.e. high winds of limited duration, do not have the same effect. Growth is not inhibited until the gale occurs, and only then does it cause severe damage or death by uprooting. Thus north-east Scotland still has highly productive forest plantations, even although occasional gales, such as in 1953, sometimes do immense damage.

Wind affects snow cover, as has already been discussed, and to a lesser extent affects rainfall distribution; thus in areas most subject to high winds, the highest rainfall is not so much on the summits as slightly to leeward of them. This is well illustrated by recent observations made by the Nature Conservancy in the relatively small but rugged Isle of Rhum. Here the west coast has a much lower rainfall than the east coast, and the highest rainfalls are on the eastern slopes of the hills.

Wind affects temperatures and evapo-transpiration in various ways, but a special effect is that due to diurnal changes in wind speed and direction. There is a tendency everywhere for a change in direction between day and night, although this tendency is often completely masked on individual days of generally high winds from a persistent direction, or absent in some other conditions. It clearly shows on tables of averages. There is characteristically, a major maximum during the middle of the day and a minor maximum at night, with minimum wind speeds near dawn and dusk, associated with the tendency to change in direction. Diurnal on- and off-shore winds are the best known examples; these have important effects, operating mainly through temperature, on vegetation near the coasts.

MISCELLANEOUS WEATHER PHENOMENA

In many parts of the earth, certain phenomena associated with storms of one kind or another become significant ecologically. Lightning is one such factor; it is characteristic that with increasing latitude the incidence of lightning discharges changes. The total number of days with thunder and lightning decreases, and becomes much less pronounced. In Britain, the annual figures show a greater number of days in the south, and a greater number inland. When winter alone is considered, the relatively small number of such days is markedly greater in the western and northern seaboards, Shetland and Orkney having the greatest winter average of thunderstorms, but the mean, even there, is not more than two each winter. For the year as a whole, the number averages somewhat over ten in the Southern Uplands. The other feature of high latitudes is that the proportion of cloud-to-earth discharges, as compared with cloud-to-cloud discharges, considerably increases. Since, however, the total number of electrical storms is so small and not particularly concentrated in the driest periods of the year, the chief menace of lightning, namely fire, is in present times almost a negligible ecological factor in Scotland. This is, incidentally, not to say that fire caused by human agency is a negligible factor, and it is not to say that lightning fires were not at one time as important as they now are in parts of North America (cf. comment on charcoal layers, pp. 564, 565).

Hail storms do much damage to vegetation in many parts of the world, but again, the amount of damage done in Scotland is relatively very small, and can scarcely be considered as a factor in determining the distribution of vegetation communities.

POTENTIAL EVAPORATION AND POTENTIAL WATER DEFICIT

We may now attempt to review the climate of Scotland in terms of the evaporation and precipitation balance of Britain and the surrounding sea. Annual evaporation at the ocean weather ships I and J, in the Atlantic, to the west of Britain, has been estimated as well over 1000 mm. (40 in.) (Shellard, 1962), the rainfall probably being about the same value at the northern ship station, and about 650-750 mm. (25-30 in.) at the southern one. Over almost the whole of the land of Britain, annual rainfall greatly exceeds annual evaporation. The rain comes from air that has taken up water from the ocean, and Britain tends to get most rain from cold, northern air which has passed in a loop across the relatively warm waters of the Atlantic. The net result on the map is that, topographic complications apart, rainfall increases over the British Isles from east (650 mm.—25 in.) to west (1300 mm.—50 in.) while potential evaporation increases from north-north-east to south-south-west.

Following Penman's formula (Penman, 1948), potential evaporation (PE) increases from an annual average of 360 mm. (14 in.) in Shetland to 560 mm. (23 in.) in the Scillies. It is doubtful if these actual figures are reliable; they are almost certainly underestimates. We can, however, use them to draw a map showing the way in which potential water deficit varies across Scotland, provided we do not take the absolute values too seriously. Fig. 8 is an attempt to draw such a map based on the monthly PE figures given in "Irrigation" (Ministry of Agriculture, Fisheries and Food, 1962), and the average monthly rainfall figures from about a hundred stations. Since the calculation was made in time divisions of calendar months the potential water deficit (PWD) is underestimated because significant dry spells can occur within a month, but these are hidden if the total month's rainfall exceeds the PE. Bearing in mind the two main sources of error, i.e. (a) the probable underestimate of PE and (b) the use of calendar months instead of shorter periods, the map can, nevertheless, be used to sum up some features of paramount importance to Scottish ecology.

First, it can be seen that there is a large area in the west where there is no significant PWD. In most years there are short dry spells which would prevent the PWD from dropping to nil, but the values in many places would still be so small that only unattainably perfect drainage would allow the soil to dry. This would still be true even if the PE is underestimated because the average rainfall would still, in the heart of this area, exceed PE in every month, even if the PE were doubled. This area of insignificant PE is

FIG. 8

Average annual potential water deficit in inches;
(approximate millimetre equivalents in brackets).

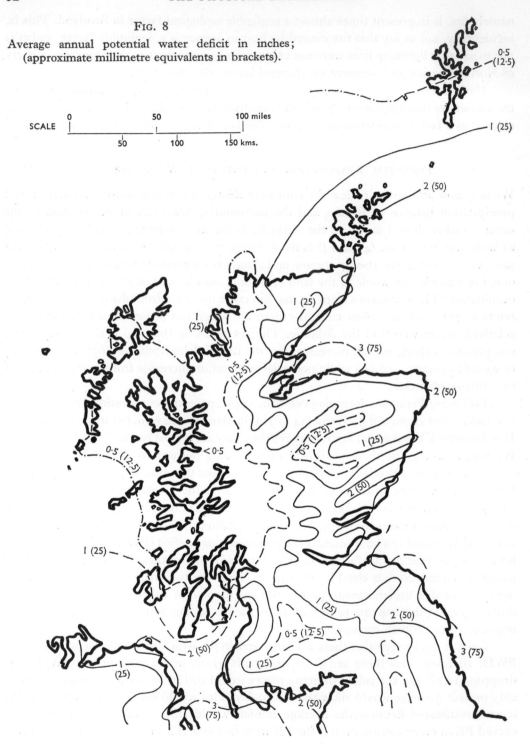

the area of climatic bog, and is virtually incapable of being cultivated. The pockets within it which are, in fact, cultivated merely draw attention to the fact that the map shows a larger area than it would do, if the sources of error discussed above had been eliminated.

PWD increases where either the rainfall is low or PE high, or both. On the east coast lowlands, rainfall is low. Thus the inner shores of the Moray Firth and the lowlands of East Lothian and Berwickshire show the highest values of PE; a slightly higher rainfall in the latter two places is compensated for by rather higher PE. A considerably higher PE allows nearly as high a PWD in the south-west, even though the rainfall is almost twice as great.

As soon as one considers these figures in relation to soil, it is clear that a PWD of 7·5 cm. (3 in.) will only rarely signify a serious shortage of water to any plant in any ordinary soil. Yet of course, in fact, some obvious shortage of water occurs in almost every year in parts of Scotland. Indeed, it is arguable that few seed-bearing field crops would mature if this were not so, for some water tension is usually necessary for maturation. So it must be emphasised that, although the *pattern of distribution* shown on the map is, almost certainly, substantially correct, the actual values are not realistic. PWDs of 38 cm. (15 in.) annually are not uncommon; these of course do not occur in one long "drought" but there is usually a dry spell of sufficient length for soil moisture to be so drawn on that wilting is reached by many species. In 1955 there was even the rare spectacle of wilting-point being reached, here and there, by mature trees. Potential water deficit must, therefore, be considered in relation to soil and plant before conclusions are reached about *actual* water deficit.

There is no doubt that the boundary between the areas with, and without, significant annual PWD is an extremely important phytogeographical dividing-line. Although one would expect the distribution of plant communities to reflect this difference in climate more clearly than individual species, yet the B.S.B.I., *Atlas of the British Flora* (1962) shows that such plants as *Drosera anglica*, *D. intermedia*, *Hymenophyllum* spp. (*wilsonii* and *tunbridgense*), or *Osmunda regalis* are almost confined to the area of insignificant PWD and others, such as *Silene alba*, *Verbascum thapsus*, *Viola tricolor*, or *V. arvensis* almost completely avoid it. Exceptions are explained by the necessary generalisation of the isopleths; for instance, the interdigitation of land and sea, mountain and glen, in Argyll, allows of more variety than the map can show.

In general, the boundary between areas with, and without, significant annual PWD is at sea-level in the west but climbs steadily towards the east. It is almost absent from the Cairngorms and Lochnagar, and very likely the area of insignificant PWD would disappear if these mountains extended any further to the east. In mountainous southern Norway, PWD begins to increase again towards the east because the rainfall is less, especially in spring, and the spring and summer PE is rather higher. The distribution of blanket bog on the hills has thus an eastern limit. The diagram given by Knut Faegri in *Maps of Distribution of Norwegian Vascular Plants*, Vol. I (1960), is simplified and, in part, replaceable by a diagram such as in Fig. 9, which uses only one simple

C

parameter, average annual PWD, instead of three. This diagram helps to make it clear that we have in Scotland an almost unique climatic habitat.

It is of course impossible to study adequately the distribution of the present flora without considering climatic change. This vast subject cannot be embarked on in this chapter; it is, however, discussed generally in Chapter 16 on "Vegetational History". There is one particular point which is, nevertheless, worth making at the end of the

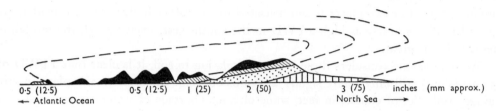

0·5 (12·5)   0·5 (12·5)   1 (25)   2 (50)   3 (75)   inches   (mm approx.)
◄— Atlantic Ocean   North Sea ——►

FIG. 9

Diagrammatic section across Scotland from the Western Isles to near Aberdeen. The isolines are for Potential Water Deficit, as on the map (Fig. 8).

present chapter. It needs comparatively little change in the atmospheric circulation pattern to alter the average seasonal distribution of rainfall in relation to PE, and thus the values of PWD. It is clear, for example, that the size and shape of the area of insignificant PWD shown on Fig. 9 has fluctuated sufficiently to explain the alternate development and decay of climatic bog near the boundaries of this area, for instance in the Outer Hebrides on the one hand, and high up on Lochnagar on the other. Reflection on the small change in circulation needed to induce this ecological change helps to reconcile the sometimes conflicting views of meteorologists and ecologists.

REFERENCES

BOTANICAL SOCIETY OF   1962   *Atlas of the British Flora.* London.
THE BRITISH ISLES

FAEGRI, K.   1960   *Maps of Distribution of Norwegian Vascular Plants:* I *The Distribution of Coast Plants.* Oslo.

FRISBY, E. M. and   1949   Further notes on comparative regional climatology. *Publ. Inst.*
GREEN, F. H. W.   *Brit. Geogr.,* **15**, 143-151.

GALLOWAY, R. W.   1961   Solifluction in Scotland. *Scot. geogr. Mag.,* **77**, 75-87.

GARNETT, A.   1937   Insolation and Relief. *Publ. Inst. Brit. Geogr.,* **5**, 1-8.

GREEN, F. H. W.   1960   A technique for measuring potential evaporation and some of its applications. *Wat. & Wat. Engng.,* **64**, 558-563.

GREEN, F. H. W.   1962   *British Rainfall,* 1958, Part III, 10-14.

GREGORY, S.   1954   Accumulated temperature maps of the British Isles. *Publ. Inst. Brit. Geogr.,* **20**, 59-73.

McCormack, R. J. and   1961   Forest microclimate: a topographical study in Ontario. *J. Ecol.*,
MacHattie, L. B.   **49**, 301-323.

McVean, D. N. and   1962   *Plant Communities of the Scottish Highlands*. H.M.S.O.,
Ratcliffe, D. A.   London.

Mill, H. R. and   1915   Isomeric Rainfall Maps of the British Isles. *Q.J. Roy. Met. Soc.*,
Salter, C.   **41**, 1-44.

Ministry of Agricul-   1962   Irrigation. *Bulletin No. 138*. H.M.S.O., London.
ture, Fisheries &
Food

Penman, H. L.   1948   Natural evaporation from open water, bare soil, and grass.
                                Proc. Roy. Soc. **A193**, 120-145.

Shellard, H. C.   1962   Some calculations of terms in the energy balance for monthly
                                periods at the Ocean Weather Stations I and J in the North
                                Atlantic. *Meteorological Office Scientific Paper No. 11*. H.M.S.O.
                                London.

Various publications of the Meteorological Office, Air Ministry, including especially the *Climatological Atlas of the British Isles* (1952) have been extensively used in the preparation of this chapter.

CHAPTER 3

THE SOILS OF SCOTLAND

E. A. FITZPATRICK

The soil mantle of Scotland as seen today represents the
sequence of evolution which, for simplicity, may be consid
with the glacial epoch. However, the pre-glacial landscape
is still dominant and to a very great extent controls the soil moistu
the other factors of soil formation.

From the evidence at present available (Nairn, 1961) it s
Tertiary period Scotland carried a markedly different flora associ
ditions and possibly a deep soil cover produced by chemical proces
With the advent of Pleistocene glaciations, the movement of ice
periglacial processes removed most of the existing soils and in n
rocks bare of their weathered mantle and even eroded the under l
As the glacial periods waned and the ice melted, varying thickne
deposited over most of the country and formed the parent materia
soils. Melting ice also liberated large volumes of water, giving r i
alluvial deposits which also contributed largely to the parent
deposits have been derived from a heterogeneous variety of rock
evaluation of the parent materials very difficult. Frequently at t l
only occasionally at lower elevations, it is possible to find soils
the *in situ* rock and then they are usually shallow.

The change from glacial to the present post-glacial conditio
gradual, passing through a period when tundra-like conditio
period the glacial drifts and rocks in many parts of the country
periglacial processes. With further amelioration of the climate—
rainfall—the vegetation and soils gradually changed and deve
today. Variations that have occurred in the climate between
present undoubtedly produced changes in the vegetation, but
not been so clearly demonstrated (Durno, 1957).

The wide diversity in the factors of soil formation in
differentiation of many different kinds of soils arranged in a m
pattern. Muir and Fraser (1939-40) state: "Of the various pedo

McCORMACK, R. J. and   1961   Forest microclimate: a topographical study in Ontario. *J. Ecol.*,
MACHATTIE, L. B.   **49**, 301-323.

McVEAN, D. N. and   1962   *Plant Communities of the Scottish Highlands.* H.M.S.O.,
RATCLIFFE, D. A.   London.

MILL, H. R. and   1915   Isomeric Rainfall Maps of the British Isles. *Q. J. Roy. Met. Soc.*,
SALTER, C.   **41**, 1-44.

MINISTRY OF AGRICUL-   1962   Irrigation. *Bulletin No. 138.* H.M.S.O., London.
TURE, FISHERIES &
FOOD

PENMAN, H. L.   1948   Natural evaporation from open water, bare soil, and grass.
                                 Proc. Roy. Soc. **A193**, 120-145.

SHELLARD, H. C.   1962   Some calculations of terms in the energy balance for monthly
                                 periods at the Ocean Weather Stations I and J in the North
                                 Atlantic. *Meteorological Office Scientific Paper No. 11.* H.M.S.O.
                                 London.

Various publications of the Meteorological Office, Air Ministry, including especially the *Climatological Atlas of the British Isles* (1952) have been extensively used in the preparation of this chapter.

CHAPTER 3

THE SOILS OF SCOTLAND

E. A. FITZPATRICK

The soil mantle of Scotland as seen today represents the present stage in the sequence of evolution which, for simplicity, may be considered as having started with the glacial epoch. However, the pre-glacial landscape or geomorphic pattern is still dominant and to a very great extent controls the soil moisture regime and some of the other factors of soil formation.

From the evidence at present available (Nairn, 1961) it seems that during the Tertiary period Scotland carried a markedly different flora associated with warmer conditions and possibly a deep soil cover produced by chemical processes (FitzPatrick, 1963). With the advent of Pleistocene glaciations, the movement of ice and the accompanying periglacial processes removed most of the existing soils and in many cases scraped the rocks bare of their weathered mantle and even eroded the underlying rocks themselves. As the glacial periods waned and the ice melted, varying thicknesses of glacial drift were deposited over most of the country and formed the parent material of many of the present soils. Melting ice also liberated large volumes of water, giving rise to glacio-fluvial and alluvial deposits which also contributed largely to the parent materials. These drift deposits have been derived from a heterogeneous variety of rock types which makes the evaluation of the parent materials very difficult. Frequently at the higher altitudes, and only occasionally at lower elevations, it is possible to find soils developed entirely from the *in situ* rock and then they are usually shallow.

The change from glacial to the present post-glacial conditions must have been very gradual, passing through a period when tundra-like conditions existed. During this period the glacial drifts and rocks in many parts of the country were further affected by periglacial processes. With further amelioration of the climate—higher temperatures and rainfall—the vegetation and soils gradually changed and developed into what is seen today. Variations that have occurred in the climate between the tundra era and the present undoubtedly produced changes in the vegetation, but the effects on soils have not been so clearly demonstrated (Durno, 1957).

The wide diversity in the factors of soil formation in Scotland has lead to the differentiation of many different kinds of soils arranged in a most intricate and complex pattern. Muir and Fraser (1939-40) state: "Of the various pedogenic factors it is difficult to single out any one as being of primary importance when considering the soils as a whole. Each factor plays its part and it is only in relation to given sites that it is possible to particularise." This statement, made in connection with the study of a relatively small part of the country, is nevertheless true for the whole country. However, the soil pattern is dominated by a limited number of major soil types which include mountain tundra soils, rankers, podsols, semi-podsols, thin iron pan soils, brown earths, gleys and peat. In each of these it is usual to see an evolutionary sequence from de-glaciation to the present and, in some, the sequence can be traced back to the pre-glacial soil mantle (FitzPatrick, 1963). This may form the parent material of the present soil or it may have been disseminated in the drift deposits.

More recently man has adapted many of these soils for agriculture and forestry but, in most cases, they have not been sufficiently changed to prevent the recognition of most of the characteristics formed during their evolution. Although this chapter is intended primarily to deal with the natural and semi-natural soils, most of the lowland agricultural soils find a place.

GEOLOGY AND GEOMORPHOLOGY

The geology and geomorphology of Scotland have been determined largely by crustal movements of both ancient and recent dates and consist in the main of three major areas: the Highlands; the Midland Valley; and the Southern Uplands. It will be most convenient to consider first the pre-glacial geology of these areas separately, and then to deal with the glaciation of the whole country.

Pre-glacial geology

Highlands. This is by far the largest of the three areas and includes the whole of the country north of a line from Stonehaven on the east to the island of Arran on the west. This southern boundary is sharply marked by a great fault, the Highland boundary fault, which is one of many in this area.

The Highlands were once an uplifted peneplain having its main slope from north-west to south-east, but the old peneplain plateau surface has now been largely destroyed by denudation leaving mountains to just over 1200 metres and narrow steep-sided valleys. One of the most striking features of the Highland region is the contrast between the east and west coasts, due partly to geologic structure and partly to erosion. The west coast is skirted by innumerable islands and indented by lochs, many of which are fjords. The east coast has a few off-lying islands derived from ancient volcanic necks, but extends mostly in unbroken stretches with a trend from north-north-east to south-south-west, the Moray Firth being the only important break in the coastline. There is a general slope eastward and hence the eastern Highlands are bordered by a wide plain in the north east.

This area is, in the main, a block of pre-Palaeozoic schists and gneisses overlain in places by younger sediments and having intrusions of many ages. These rocks comprise five main members.

The Lewisian system is made up of coarse gneisses and forms the lowest member of north-west Scotland, and therefore the oldest rocks in the country. Their composition ranges from ultrabasic rocks such as banded amphiboles, pyroxenes and peridotes to muscovite-biotite gneiss.

The Moinian system is typically a flaggy granulitic gneiss, consisting mainly of quartz and alkali felspars of equal size. They occupy a large stretch of country from the Pentland Firth nearly to the southern edge of the Highlands and from the great thrust plane of the west to the Tay Valley and Banffshire on the east.

The Dalradian system is composed of a complex series of schists, quartzites, gneisses and crystalline limestone, extending across the country in a broad belt from Banff, Aberdeenshire and Kincardineshire on the east, to Argyll and the Firth of Clyde on the west. These rocks are invaded by masses of granite, diorites, quartz porphyries, etc., and contain bands of hornblende schist due to foliation of igneous rocks, but the Dalradian system as a whole consists of altered sediments.

The Lennoxian system occurs as a narrow band of shales and grits from Stonehaven to Arran.

The Torridonian system consists of thick red sandstones, conglomerates and shales extending in a strip about 32 km. wide along the north-west coast for a length of 185 km. from Cape Wrath to Skye.

The only Cambrian rocks in Scotland are found in a band in the north-west between the Lewisian gneiss and the eastern gneisses. The rocks themselves are limestones (Durness limestone), mudstones, quartzites and grits (Fucoid beds and Serpulite grits).

Also within the Highlands there is a large group of igneous intrusions which may be assigned to an epoch slightly earlier than that of the lowest Old Red Sandstone. These rocks are known by the name of the Newer Granites, but they are not all of acid composition. The largest masses occur in the neighbourhood of the Dee Valley, but others are found farther north in Sutherland and Caithness, and to the west through the county of Inverness. They are largely biotite and hornblende granites and quartz diorites, but there are also more acid as well as ultrabasic rocks.

There are extensive deposits of Old Red Sandstone in the northern valleys of the Grampians, along the shores of the Moray Firth, Caithness and in the neighbouring portion of Sutherland, the Orkneys and the Shetlands.

The only other rocks in the Highlands which occupy large areas are the Tertiary olivine basalts and dykes in the west, including the Inner Hebrides and some small patches of New Red Sandstone and Jurassic rocks.

Midland Valley. This valley lying to the south of the Highland boundary fault has been formed by a great trough fault. To the east its coastal limits are from Stonehaven to Dunbar, and on the west from the mouth of the Clyde to near Girvan. The southern extremity is marked by the "Southern boundary fault" which is made up of a series of parallel step faults and is, therefore, less conspicuous than that to the north. No pre-Palaeozoic rocks are found within this area, the main formations are Upper Palaeozoic rocks chiefly Old Red Sandstone, Carboniferous and Permian deposits. The floor of the midland valley is hilly for it includes moorlands of Old Red Sandstone, and ranges of Silurian sediments and Devonian igneous rocks. From Renfrewshire to Stirling is a series of Lower Carboniferous volcanic plateaux—the Renfrewshire Hills, the Kilpatrick Hills, the Campsie Fells and the Fintry Hills.

The Old Red Sandstone is composed mainly of sandstones, conglomerates and shales, but within the Lower Old Red Sandstone are a number of volcanic rocks and intrusions. The lavas are mainly basic pyroxene-andesite grading into olivine basalt, while the dominant types of plutonic rocks vary between hornblendic granites and quartz diorites and are similar to those of an earlier epoch.

The Carboniferous strata include sandstones, limestones and volcanics which are predominantly basalts and trachytes. They form two belts, the larger in the valley itself, and the other along its southern boundary.

Southern Uplands. Geographically this is the simplest division of Scotland, covering the area from the Southern boundary fault to the English border. It has a distinct structure being composed mainly of Lower Palaeozoic rocks of Ordovician and Silurian age. The rocks, although intensely folded, have a predominant dip to the southeast, the oldest rocks occurring along the northern edge. These older rocks are capped in places by sheets of Old and New Red Sandstone and Carboniferous rocks and have been invaded by masses of Devonian Granite. However, the differences between the Upper Palaeozoic rocks of the Midland Valley and the Lower Palaeozoics of the Southern Uplands are less marked than those between the Highlands and the Midland Valley, hence there are less striking geographical differences between the two southern areas which are usually grouped together as the "Lowlands".

The succession of Ordovician rocks in the northern belt and in the Girvan area begin with a volcanic series of diabase and spinel lavas and tuffs, followed by mudstones and cherts. In the central belt there are thin shales, mudstones and volcanic rocks. In the northern belt some of the shales pass into grits and grey-wackes, here also there are calcareous conglomerates, graptolites and volcanics.

Silurian rocks occupy extensive areas in the southern uplands and consist of dark shales, mudstones, conglomerates, flags and grits.

Finally, in the south-west, there is the set of Galloway granites or Newer granites.

The distribution of the rocks is given on the map in Fig. 10, while further details may be obtained from the *Memoirs of the Geological Survey of Scotland*, from which the foregoing was largely obtained.

Glaciation

A satisfactory glacial chronology of Scotland has not yet been produced, so that it is not possible to give details with certainty. This period was marked by active glacial erosion and deposition which affected the whole country. Although there may have been

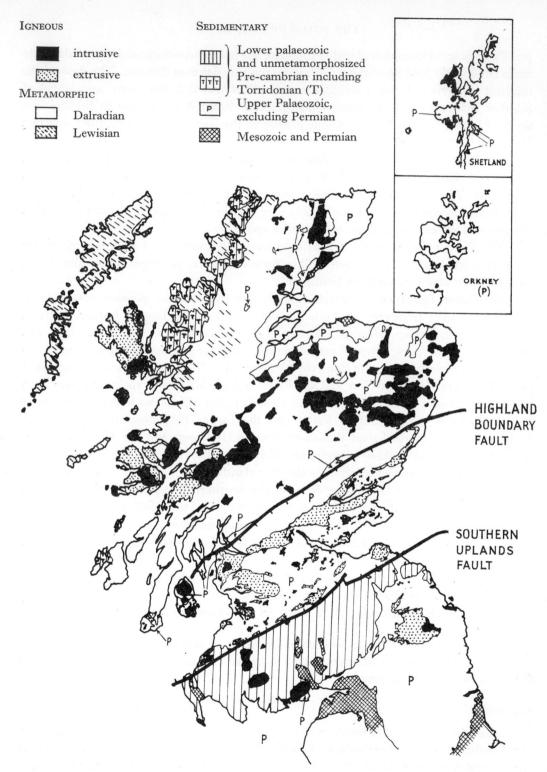

IGNEOUS

██ intrusive

▒▒ extrusive

METAMORPHIC

□ Dalradian

▨ Lewisian

SEDIMENTARY

▥ Lower palaeozoic and unmetamorphosized
⊤⊤⊤ Pre-cambrian including Torridonian (T)
P Upper Palaeozoic, excluding Permian

⬚ Mesozoic and Permian

SHETLAND

ORKNEY (P)

HIGHLAND BOUNDARY FAULT

SOUTHERN UPLANDS FAULT

FIG. 10 Geological map of Scotland to show the principal rock formations and geological features (based on a map by Oxford University Press).

several glaciations, only the last two appear to be important in so far as the soils are concerned (Synge, 1956), yet, even so, there is some doubt whether the ice of the last period covered the whole country.

In general, the ice accumulated on the high ground and glaciers radiated out from these centres of accumulation. They flowed down to the sea along most of the coast, cutting deep fjords in the pre-glacial valleys of the west, but there are no fjords in the east. In many cases two or more glaciers impinged on each other, causing one to deflect the other. Particularly good examples of this action are shown by the tills of the east where glaciers from the land were deflected to the north and south by ice coming from Scandinavia.

Glacial striae and roches moutonnées clearly mark the direction of ice movement while sheets of till, moraines and outwash plains are evidence of glacial deposition. In fact, a considerable part of the country is covered by varying thicknesses of glacial debris. The rock fragments contained in the tills also indicate the direction of ice movement, but in general the tills contain a predominance of locally derived material, although far-travelled erratics are not uncommon. The details of the rock composition of the drift deposits are even more complex than those of the solid geology and since these drift deposits constitute the greater part of the soil parent materials, some idea can be obtained of the complexity of the latter. The only two generalisations that can be made about the parent materials are that (1) they are mainly acid and (2) that they show little evidence of chemical weathering since their deposition; for the particle size distribution shows a predominance of the coarser separates and stones except where deposition took place in water, or where the source material itself contained a high percentage of fine particles such as from argillaceous or shaley rocks.

The waning of the glacial period saw marked periglacial activity (FitzPatrick, 1958) which further helped to mould some of the features of the landscape. The intense mass movement that took place during these times caused a redistribution of some of the glacial debris. Evidence of this is best seen in the top metre or so of the soils on slopes where the stones have been re-orientated, so that their long axes lie at right angles to the contour and parallel to the slope. In a number of cases the rocks themselves were attacked by frost action, so that the present soil is dominated by angular rock fragments which may lie almost *in situ* in areas of flat or gently sloping ground.

The landscape during this period must have resembled parts of the present-day arctic with its stone circles, stone stripes, mud polygons, etc. Permafrost would also have been found (FitzPatrick, 1956) and the soils would have been similar to those described for Spitsbergen by Smith (1956).

Although such tundra conditions have long since disappeared from the low ground they still exist at higher altitudes, where soils have developed in association with montane floras.

The Soils

The soil pattern of Scotland is so complex that it must suffice to give generalised descriptions of each of the major soils, together with some of their more important properties. Further information can be obtained from the *Memoirs of the Soil Survey of Great Britain*, for those areas which have been surveyed. Later in this chapter an attempt is made to give some of the temporal and spatial relationships which exist among these soils.

A Synoptic Classification of the Soils of Scotland

I. Incipient Soils
- 1. Ramblas
- 2. Paternias
- 3. Syrosems

II. Rankers
- 4. Protorankers
- 5. Dystrophic rankers
- 6. Mull rankers
- 7. Podsol rankers

III. Podsols
- A. Semi-podsols
  - 8. Cryptopodsolic braunerden (Slightly podsolised soils)
  - 9. Eupodsolic braunerden (Moderately podsolised soils)
- B. Podsols
  - 10. Iron humus podsols
  - 11. Iron podsols
  - 12. Dwarf podsols
  - 13. Gley podsols
  - 14. Podsolic gleys

IV. Thin Iron Pan Soils
- 15. Thin Iron Pan Soils

V. Brown Earths
- 16. Oligotrophic braunerden (Sols bruns acides)
- 17. Eutrophic braunerden
- 18. Mesotrophic braunerden

VI. Parabraunerden (Sols lessivés)
- 19. Parabraunerden (Sols bruns lessivés)

VII. Gley Soils
- A. Ground Water Gleys
  - 20. Moder gleys
  - 21. Mull gleys
  - 22. Brown gleys
  - 23. Humic gleys
- B. Surface Water Gleys (Wetness due to low permeability)
  - 24. Pseudogleys
  - 25. Marbled braunerden
  - 26. Stagnogleys
  - 27. Pseudogley parabraunerden
  - 28. Marbled parabraunerden

VIII. Peat
- 29. Topogenic peat
- 30. Blanket peat

IX. Mountain Tundra Soils
- 31. Patterned mountain tundra soils
- 32. Hamada mountain tundra soils

X. Rendzinas
- 33. Rendzinas

XI. Sub-aqueous Soils

Several attempts were made to employ systems of soil classification that were already in use and that had some measure of acceptance. However, it was found impossible to use any one system, since either it did not include all the soils found in Scotland, or the principles on which the system was based were not sound. In an endeavour to reduce ambiguities and the multiplication of terms, an effort was made to use the terms currently used by the Soil Survey of Great Britain. Here again this was not possible, because of inconsistencies and, in some cases, their unacceptable approach to soil taxonomy.

Ultimately the simple classification listed below, was adopted using terms drawn from other European workers, namely, Kubiëna (1953), Mückenhausen (1959), Duchaufour (1960), Aubert (1938) and Tavernier (1952).

The soils are arranged in classes designated by roman numerals. The classes are divided into types but, where necessary, into sub-classes and then types. The sub-classes are designated by capital letters and the types by arabic numerals.

The nomenclature and definition of the soil horizons is that given in the *Soil Survey Manual* (1951), except where stated otherwise.

Incipient soils

These soils show little differentiation of horizons or weathering of the parent material, since they began to form. They are, therefore, the starting-point of an evolutionary sequence. However, the incipient soils in Scotland today will pass through very different stages from those formed at the end of the glacial and periglacial periods, so that they should not be regarded as the precursors of the well-differentiated soils.

Ramblas. These soils are developed in recent alluvium that has been colonised by plants such as grasses, mosses and sedges, but do not show any marked signs of horizon differentiation. Typically, they consist of an **A** horizon with little sign of decomposition of the thin cover of organic matter (raw soil humus) some of which may be crudely incorporated into the mineral surface; below this is the relatively unaltered stratified alluvium. Since these areas are subject to periodic flooding with the consequent deposition of more sediments several buried **A** horizons may be seen. Where slight gleying may be seen, these soils are *slightly gleyed ramblas*. These soils usually have a high sand content and are of widespread but localised distribution but, as they are found only in association with rivers, their total area is small.

Paternias. These young soils are developed in alluvium and show little chemical weathering, but they have a well-developed humus horizon of either mull or mull-like moder. Thus they have an **A/C** sequence of horizons. They are usually fairly rich in exchangeable cations and have moderately acid reaction. In some cases where slight gleying or browning of the sediments has taken place they are in transition towards gleys or brown earths and are known respectively as *"gleyed paternias"* or *"slightly browned paternias"*. Where flooding and the deposition of material takes place fairly regularly several buried **A** horizons may be found.

Syrosems. Around the coast of Scotland there are numerous areas of sand dunes which show little horizon differentiation and are, therefore, *silicate syrosems*. The uppermost horizon may contain a large number of roots and some crudely incorporated organic matter, but there is no definite humus horizon. Below this is the unaltered material. In cases where sand dunes have been stabilised for some time horizon differentiation may have taken place, and more usually a podsol has formed.

Rankers

These soils are characterised by well-developed humus horizons which rest directly on the parent material. In Scotland the four types of this class have been recognised.

Protorankers are poorly developed ranker formations of moder humus consisting of an incoherent mixture of mineral and organic constituents. They are 3-5 cm. in thickness, of black or greyish-black colour and rest directly on hard siliceous rocks colonised by mosses, lichens and grasses. These are found in areas of frequent rock outcrop and in positions where erosion, periodically destroys the humus layer so that a fully developed ranker formation is seldom attained.

Dystrophic rankers are fully developed ranker formations occurring in areas similar to the above but in moist situations and not exposed to severe erosion. They consist of a dystrophic thick A_0 horizon of 10-15 cm. in thickness with low mineral content and peaty appearance. This may either be a raw humus or dystrophic moder formation. Frequently at the boundary with the parent material a black transition horizon is found which may have a high stone content particularly in areas affected by frost action. These soils are colonised by mosses, *Calluna*, *Erica* spp. and *Vaccinium* spp.

Mull rankers. Throughout Scotland there are scattered, small areas of superficial deposits of glacial, or early post-glacial, age in which only an **A** horizon has fully developed. This is particularly true of some heavier textured parent materials and thin till over basic rock where a mull humus has developed and thus formed *mull rankers* or sometimes *brown rankers*.

Podsol rankers. These have the same features as the upper part of podsols finishing at the A_2 horizon and resting on the underlying rock. In some cases where the rock is fissured the position occupied by the **B** horizon has brown staining on the faces of the rock fragments. (See podsol, page 45, for further details.)

Podsols

Semi-podsols

This sub-class of soils has characteristics of both brown earths and podsols, but are either stable formations or are changing very slowly and are therefore classified separately.

Cryptopodsolic braunerden. (Slightly podsolised soils) Generally these soils have the following characteristics:

L	5 cm. >	Loose, undecomposed plant litter sharply defined from:
F	5 cm. >	Dark brown, or black, partially humified, plant material sharply defined from:
H	2·5 cm. >	Black, humified plant material, often discontinuous or absent. Sharply defined from:
A_1	25 cm. >	Dark, or medium brown mixture of organic and mineral material. Many bleached sand grains, weak crumb structure. Clearly defined from:

B_1 25 cm. > Bright yellowish-brown with weak crumb, or sub-angular blocky structure. Clearly defined from, or merges into:

B_2 30 cm. > Less brightly coloured than the above and may be indurated. Clearly defined from:

C Relatively unaltered parent material which may be till, fluvioglacial deposit, alluvium or congeliturbate and may be indurated.

These soils are of frequent occurrence in the east, north-east and southern parts of the country, while in the south-east Ragg (1960) has shown that they are important soils. Elsewhere they occupy relatively small areas. Many of the soils, known as "brown forest soils of low base status" by the Soil Survey of Great Britain, belong to this type (Muir, 1955).

The exchangeable cations, dominated by calcium, are medium to low in the surface horizons and decrease steadily with depth, or reach a minimum in the **B** horizon. The same trend is shown by exchangeable acidity. The percentage base cation saturation is usually low and tends to increase downwards, although it may reach a minimum in the **B** horizon (Ragg, 1960). In many of these soils which are being used for agriculture the present distribution of base cations is different from that found under relatively undisturbed conditions. This may account for the minimum in exchangeable cations and exchange capacity found in the **B** horizon. The percentage of carbon and of nitrogen decreases downwards and so does the carbon:nitrogen ratio. In Scotland there is a much stronger tendency for the formation of moder and even raw humus in these soils than at lower latitudes. The silica:sesquioxide ratios of the clay fraction show slight to moderate translocation of sesquioxides.

Eupodsolic braunerden. (Moderately podsolised soils) In these soils podsolisation is more pronounced. There is commonly a well-developed moder humus in which all of the sand grains are strongly bleached. Beneath this are flecks, and thin discontinuous seams, of a bleached horizon, while the morphology of the **B** horizon clearly indicates the translocation of sesquioxides and sometimes considerable amounts of humus. Many of the chemical and physical analytical data closely resemble those of the iron podsol and for this reason are included with the latter by the Soil Survey of Great Britain. They are of frequent occurrence.

Podsols

Iron podsols and iron humus podsols are the two main types of this class which occur in Scotland. The latter is the dominant formation and is found throughout the country, while the former is confined to some of the drier sites particularly in the north-east.

Iron humus podsols. An example of these soils is shown in Plate 2, and below is a generalised description:

L 5 cm. > Undecomposed plant material, clearly defined from:

F   15 cm. >   Dark brown or dark reddish brown fibrous partially humified, organic matter; a few sand grains and some small isolated areas of completely decomposed organic matter may be present. Profuse ramification of roots. Sharply defined from:

H   10 cm. >   Dark brown, or black, humified organic matter, amorphous and plastic containing a few bleached sand grains. Sharply defined from:

A$_1$ 15 cm. >   Dark grey, sandy loam or loamy sand, a mixture of black humus and bleached sand grains, usually having a speckled appearance. Sharply or clearly defined from:

A$_2$ 15 cm. >   Grey, or greyish-brown, sandy loam or loamy sand with marked bleaching of the larger separates. Clearly or sharply defined from:

B$_1$ 30 cm. >   Dark brown, or black, with slightly heavier texture than the above due to the enrichment with organic matter, sesquioxides and sometimes clay. There may also be a blotchy pattern of ochreous yellow, brown and black in this horizon. A thin, soft, discontinuous iron pan may be present at the base of the horizon. Clearly defined from or merging into:

B$_2$ 60 cm. >   Yellowish brown, enriched with sesquioxides: may be cemented or indurated. Usually merges into:

C   Light yellowish brown or grey glacial, periglacial or fluvioglacial material which may be strongly indurated.

These soils are similar in most of their characteristics to iron humus podsols found elsewhere in Europe.

The chemical and physical properties displayed by the various horizons show marked differences and trends which closely parallel the morphology. The organic carbon content has two maxima, one at the surface and the second in the **B** horizon, the greater being in the surface. The silica:sesquioxide ratios of the clay fractions clearly demonstrate a translocation of iron and aluminium from the **A** horizon and its deposition in the **B** horizon. This is sometimes accompanied by a slight increase in clay content in the **B$_1$** horizon.

The pH values increase from 3·5 to 4·0 in the surface horizons, to 5·5 to 6·0 in the **C** horizon. There is generally a very low degree of base cation saturation with calcium dominant. Most of the base cations occur in the surface horizon and the amounts decrease steadily downwards, but occasionally there is a slight increase in the **B$_1$** horizon associated with the accumulation of clay, sesquioxides and organic matter which together give a higher exchange capacity.

Iron podsols are differentiated from the iron humus podsols mainly on the basis of the nature of the **B$_1$** horizon. In this case they show strong translocation and accumulation of iron and aluminium with but little or no visible signs of humus. Many podsols in Scotland have only a small amount of visibly deposited humus in the **B$_1$** horizon, but it

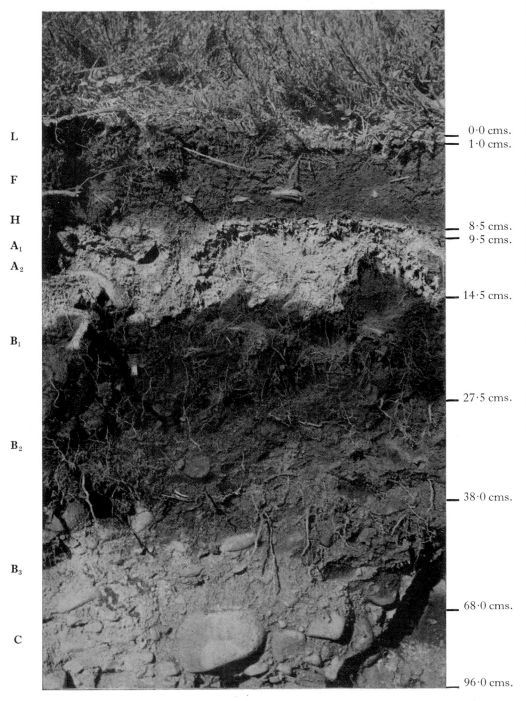

L   0·0 cms.
            1·0 cms.

F

H   8·5 cms.

A_1 9·5 cms.

A_2

            14·5 cms.

B_1

            27·5 cms.

B_2

            38·0 cms.

B_3

            68·0 cms.

C

            96·0 cms.

PLATE 2. An Iron Humus Podsol. Compartment 2:
Dalliefour wood, Alltcailleach Forest, Ballater, Aberdeenshire
(*cf.* description, p. 45).

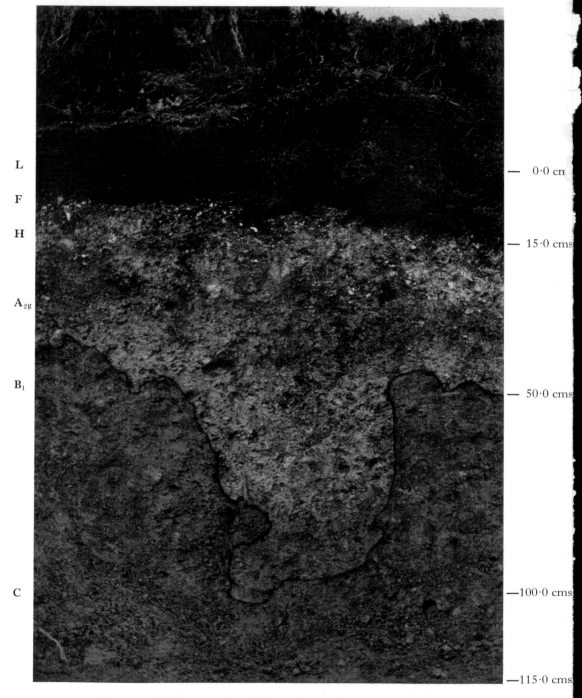

L

F

H

A₂g

B₁

C

— 0·0 cm

— 15·0 cms

— 50·0 cms

—100·0 cms

—115·0 cms

PLATE 3. A thin Iron Pan Soil. Cairn O'Mount, Kincardin-
shire (*cf*. description, p. 47).

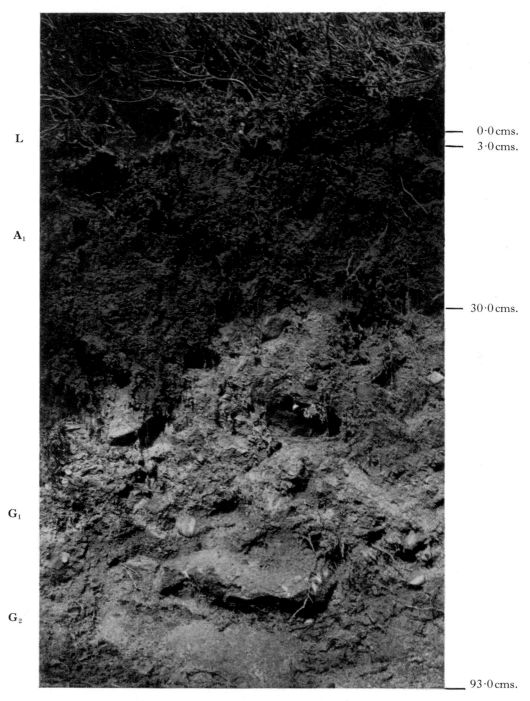

L

A₁

0·0 cms.
3·0 cms.

30·0 cms.

G₁

G₂

93·0 cms.

PLATE 4. A Moder Gley Soil. Compartment 37: Alltcailleach Forest, Corrie Burn Basin, Ballater, Aberdeenshire (*cf.* description, p. 49).

would seem more appropriate to classify these as iron humus podsols, rather than as iron podsols as is sometimes done by the Soil Survey of Great Britain. The H and A_1 horizons which are always present to a greater or lesser extent in the iron humus podsols are thin and may be absent in these soils, so that the F horizon may rest on the strongly bleached A_2 horizon. Apart from the second maximum of organic carbon in the B_1 horizon the chemical and physical properties of these two soils are similar.

Dwarf podsols. In a number of instances the complete sequence of horizons of the iron humus podsol can be found developed within a thickness of fifteen to twenty centimetres. These formations, so far as is known, are restricted to stabilised sand dunes.

Gley podsols. Occasionally iron humus podsols are encountered that have olive-grey, gleyed A_2 horizons. These are found more particularly on flat or gently sloping sites where the surface becomes temporarily waterlogged following deforestation.

Podsolic gleys. These soils show in their upper part the characteristic features of podsols below which are gleyed horizons. The podsol characteristics are usually those of an iron humus podsol, often considerably modified by the presence of the underlying, waterlogged layers. This is seen particularly in the B horizon which may be dark brown or black in colour and sometimes hardened to rock like consistency.

These soils are infrequent, but where they do occur they are found on very gentle slopes in a transition position between podsols and gleys.

Thin iron pan soils

Thin iron pan soils. A characteristic and widespread soil found in Scotland is one that resembles a podsol but which has, beneath the apparently leached horizon, a thin hard continuous iron pan and, very often, a thick accumulation of organic matter at the surface. These soils have been called, "Peaty Gleyed Podsols with thin iron pan", by the Soil Survey of Great Britain. An example is shown in Plate 3 while the following is a generalised description:

L	10 cm. >	Undecomposed plant litter. Clearly defined from:
F	35 cm. >	Dark brown, or black, partially humified, plant material with profuse root growth. Clearly defined from:
H	5 cm. >	Dark brown, or black, humified organic matter containing some bleached sand grains. Sharply defined from:
A_1	15 cm. >	Dark grey, mixture of black humus and bleached sand grains, usually having a speckled appearance. Clearly defined from:
A_2 $(A_{2(g)})$	45 cm. >	Pale grey sandy loam, or loamy sand, very often showing gley features. Very sharply defined from:
B_1	1 cm. >	Dark reddish brown, thin iron pan having maximum enrichment of sesquioxides. Very often a root mat develops above this pan. The pan is often continuous through stones and boulders. Very irregular outline and very sharply defined from:

B_2 25 cm. >	Ochreous-yellow to rusty-brown, often with some cementation or induration. Merges into:
B_2 25 cm. >	Similar to the above, but not as brightly coloured, may be absent. Merges into:
C	Glacial, periglacial or fluvioglacial material, very often strongly indurated.

Although the characteristics given above are the more usual there are some departures worthy of note, especially when considering the genesis of these soils. Sometimes the outline of the pan is so irregular that small pockets of **B**, and even the **C**, horizon occur above the pan as is shown in Plate 3. The presence of the pan causes the accumulation of moisture in the upper part of the soil which may lead to the development of intense gley features such as ochreous mottling; even blueing of the material may take place under more humid conditions such as are found in the Shetland Islands. Commonly the accumulation of moisture leads to the formation of peat at the surface. When the original mineral soil becomes buried at some depth below thick blanket peat the surface soil is then a peat and is classified as such.

Transition types to the humus iron podsols are frequently found in which a pan is found beneath the humus-iron **B** horizon.

The genesis of these soils is still somewhat obscure. Muir (1934), who first conducted detailed investigations on them, suggested two possible mechanisms for their formation. These were later considered and amplified by Crompton (1952, 1956).

Brown earths

The cool maritime climate of Scotland leads more normally to the formation of oligotrophic braunerden than to eutrophic braunerden. However, the latter do occur in restricted areas particularly on the very base rich parent materials.

Oligotrophic braunerden (Sols bruns acides). A few of the group of soils classified as brown forest soils of low base status by the Soil Survey of Great Britain fall within this type. They are characterised by a thin mull humus which merges into the yellowish brown (**B**) horizon (Laatsch, 1938) which may be indurated at the base. This in turn merges into the **C** horizon. These soils are moderately acid and have a medium to low degree of base cation saturation, but show no translocation of sesquioxides or clay.

Although these are the most common brown earths in Scotland they are relatively infrequent and somewhat restricted to parent materials of fairly high base status, such as superficial deposits derived from basic or ultra basic rocks.

Eutrophic braunerden. The type of soils known as brown forest soils of high base status fall within this group. They are striking in appearance, having a deep, dark brown, mull humus of excellent crumb structure which grades into the dark brown (**B**) horizon. This, in turn, grades into the dark-coloured parent material since these soils are usually developed on the most basic parent materials such as serpentine initially weathered physically by frost action. Where these soils are shallow and stony they could be classified as *brown rankers*.

In these soils weathering of the primary minerals keeps pace with leaching so that the percentage base cation saturation remains high. The dominant cation is usually calcium, but in some cases where there is a high content of ferromagnesium minerals, magnesium may attain high proportions.

There is no movement of clay, and because of the very active soil fauna, the content of carbon and nitrogen is low and decreases with depth. The carbon:nitrogen ratio is also low throughout the whole soil.

Between the oligotrophic braunerden and eutrophic braunerden is the transition form *mesotrophic braunerden*.

Parabraunerden (Sols brns lessivés)

Parabraunerden (Sols brns lessivés). These are similar in most of their properties to the oligotrophic braunerden and appear to have been derived from them by progressive leaching during which clay was removed from the **A** horizon and deposited lower down to form a **B** horizon. However these soils are not as well developed in Scotland as further to the south. From them there are a number of transitions to cryptopodsolic braunerden, oligotrophic braunerden, and to pseudogley parabraunerden.

Gley soils

Ground water gleys

High rainfall and high humidity in Scotland combine to encourage widespread formation of high water-tables and, consequently, varying degrees of gley phenomena in many soils throughout the country. Even in the drier eastern part of the country gley soils are ubiquitous on gentle slopes and in depressions. Under more humid conditions they occur on elevated plateau surfaces particularly in the south and west (Mitchell and Jarvis, 1956).

Moder gleys. These are the commonest type of gley soils. An example is shown in Plate 4 and below is a generalised description:

L	5 cm. >	Undecomposed plant litter, sharply defined from:
F	10 cm. >	Dark brown, or black, partially humified plant material, sharply defined from:
H	2 cm. >	Black, completely humified organic material, sharply defined from:
A$_g$	25 cm. >	Grey to dark grey mixture of organic and mineral material usually with a speckled appearance; colour varies with organic matter content. Weak crumb to granular structure with ochreous mottling associated with the roots. Usually clearly defined from:

D

G_1 25 cm. >   Gleying of parent material with grey coatings on peds where there is well developed structure. Marked ochreous mottling. Clearly defined from or merging into:

G_2 Olive grey, or bluish-grey, massive or structureless, often with well defined iron tubes around roots. Complete absence of parent material colours.

The chemical and physical properties of these soils are somewhat variable. There is usually a slightly higher content of clay in the surface mineral horizon A_g which, together with the higher content of organic matter, has the highest amount of exchangeable base cations. Sometimes a high degree of base cation saturation is found which always increases markedly with depth, very often attaining complete saturation of the exchange complex in the lower horizons. In these soils, exchangeable magnesium is sometimes high and may equal, or exceed, the amount of exchangeable calcium which is normally the dominant cation. Usually the pH value is 3·5-4·0 in the surface and increases to 6·5-7·0 in the lower horizons.

Mull gleys. These soils differ from the above in a few features only. They have a mull humus form particularly in soils with high clay content. They also have higher pH values in the surface and a higher base cation saturation especially when developed in calcareous parent material.

Brown gleys. As the name implies, these soils have marked signs of gleying and a weakly developed (**B**) horizon. The humus form is more usually mull, or mull-like moder, but dystrophic moder is very often found.

Humic gleys. These soils are characterised by their thick dark grey, or black, mineral rich humus horizon which has a peat-like consistency and which passes fairly quickly into the strongly gleyed lower horizons. These may be grey, bluish-grey, or olive grey in colour and commonly have flecks of iron oxide staining or iron tubes around old roots. These soils are usually fairly rich in nutrients with moderate to strong acid reaction.

They include the ground water humic gleys of Mitchell and Jarvis (1956) and the peaty gley soils of Glentworth (1954).

Surface water gleys (Wetness due to low permeability)

Pseudogleys. In many places, heavy textured parent materials or the presence of an indurated layer may impede the free vertical movement of moisture through the soil. It therefore accumulates within the soil itself and gives rise to their characteristic morphology. A generalised description of these soils is as follows:

L   5 cm. >   Undecomposed plant litter. Sharply defined from:

F   10 cm. >   Dark brown, or black, partially humified plant material. Sharply defined from:

H	5 cm. >	Black, amorphous, humified plant material containing a few bleached sand grains. Thin and often absent. Sharply defined from:
A_1	15 cm. >	Dark grey or greyish-black mixture of organic and mineral material speckled with bleached sand grains. Clearly defined from:
G_1	60 cm. >	Grey, brownish grey, or olive-grey, with ochreous mottling, sometimes the mottling may be very strong and dominate the colour of the horizon. Prismatic or subangular blocky structure. Clearly defined from, or merges into:
G_2	30 cm. >	Similar to the above but with marked decrease in gleying and mottling. Clearly defined from:
C		Angular blocky, prismatic or massive glacial, fluvioglacial or lacustrine material.

The predominant variation in the morphology of these soils is in the intensity of gleying. When it is small there is usually only a thin mottled, or marbled, horizon.

In some of these soils streaks of veins of the **G** horizon extend downwards into the parent material. The morphology of these soils is particularly striking when the parent material is highly coloured, such as Old Red Sandstone drift. They are particularly wide spread in the southern belt of the country.

Stagnogleys. This soil may be regarded as a further stage in the development of the pseudogley in which the surface soil is sufficiently wet for the formation of a thick peat-like humus.

Pseudogley parabraunerden. The accumulation of water in the soil sometimes seems to take place above a horizon of clay accumulation such as is found in the parabraunerden. Thus these soils have properties of both pseudogleys and parabraunerden. They occur in the south and south-west of the country (Ragg, 1960). When the degree of gleying is small the soils are called *marbled parabraunerden.*

Peat

Peat can be defined as organic remains, chiefly of plants, which have accumulated under anaerobic conditions. There are, broadly speaking, three sets of conditions in Scotland which bring about such accumulations. Firstly, there are the gently sloping and depression areas where water can accumulate in the soil as well as at the surface, thereby producing the necessary anaerobic conditions. This type of peat is known as Topogenic, Basin or Soligenous peat. Secondly, under conditions of high humidity and rainfall, the soil surface is continuously wet and organic matter will accumulate everywhere except on the steepest, well-drained slopes. This type of peat, due entirely to climatic conditions, is "Climatic peat" or "Blanket peat" (Fraser, 1954). Thirdly, soil horizons may develop and impede the vertical movement of water to such an extent that the surface soil becomes wet enough for peat formation. This is often the final stage in soil development after the formation of a thin iron pan, as in the thin iron pan soils, and is classified as Blanket peat.

Topogenic peat. These formations are found throughout the whole country but have their maximum development in the west and north. They vary considerably in thickness from a few centimetres up to ten metres or more, but they are only considered to be "true" peat by the Soil Survey of Great Britain if thicker than 40 cm. When thinner than this they are referred to as peaty soils of one sort or another.

Generally these formations reflect the nature of the vegetation from which they are derived and consequently show considerable variation in structure, both between deposits as well as within deposits. On the one hand the peat may be a dark brown or black amorphous mass formed from sedge, grass or moss vegetation, while at the other end of the scale it may contain a predominance of woody material from a previous tree cover. There is usually a greater or lesser amount of mineral material, depending upon the amount of natural or induced erosion that has taken place on the adjacent ground, and whether streams flowed into the area during the period of accumulation. It is difficult to make any generalisations about their structure or mineral content but usually they are strongly acid with pH values of about 3·5, sometimes less. If the water entering the depression comes from, or passes over, basic rock, the peat will have high base cation saturation and high pH values but this is unusual in Scotland. In a number of cases where there are lime-rich rocks, calcareous marl is found inter-stratified in peat formations. This is a reflection of the variation in climatic conditions during post-glacial times.

The final phase in the development of topogenic peat is raised bog.

Blanket peat. These formations are extensively developed in the west and north of Scotland, including the islands. In the east and south they are more usually found at higher elevations on broad, rounded hill tops. These soils vary considerably from place to place, and even within the same locality, depending on such factors as age and the nature of the vegetation making up the deposit. However, it is the latter which exerts the strongest influence on their composition. Sedges, grasses and mosses impart amorphous and plastic properties while woody species, like heather, make the deposit fibrous. In the west the vegetation is dominated by *Trichophorum cespitosum*, *Sphagnum* spp. and *Eriophorum* spp.; with an increase in elevation, other species, such as *Rhacomitrium lanuginosum*, become important members of the community. In the east and north there is a greater abundance of *Calluna vulgaris*.

Blanket peat is most often found lying on a previously formed mineral soil and seems to have started to form in Boreal times. Generally such peats are acid or very acid, low in exchangeable cations and show progressive decomposition with depth, i.e. the older layers are more decomposed than the younger ones. The whole mass has a high water-holding capacity which is greatest in the lower layers which shrink considerably when they dry.

Mountain tundra soils

These soils are characterised by very poorly developed horizons resulting from either weak chemical, or biological, processes or both, but they do show many unique features resulting from the very cold conditions under which they are formed. In Scotland two subdivisions of this group have been recognised.

Patterned mountain tundra soils. These are high mountain soils characterised by a strong alternation of freezing and thawing and frost splitting of the rocks. The surface is distinguished by the presence of numerous tundra structures, such as stone circles, polygons or stripes. In Scotland small solifluction terraces with their faces bound by vegetation are the most common phenomenon.

The soil is composed of angular fragments of rock from which the fine material has either been blown or washed away and no horizons can be distinguished. Plant life under these conditions is poorly developed occurring only as small patches. However, where plants do occur a thin poorly developed **A** horizon is visible.

Hamada mountain tundra soils. These soils have little or no development of tundra phenomena, instead their surfaces are covered with a continuous layer of angular stones and boulders which plants only colonise with difficulty. Beneath the stones there is usually a considerable amount of gravel and coarse sand. These soils cover extensive areas in the Highlands at the highest elevations and correspond to those described for Europe by Kubiëna. However, they have been little studied in Scotland.

Rendzinas

Rendzinas. Under this heading are included all the soils developed from highly calcareous parent material which have Rendzina-like features, but are not necessarily true Rendzinas. These soils are very rare in Scotland because of the infrequent and widely scattered occurrences of calcareous rocks. They are usually shallow, black, dark brown or reddish brown soils of almost neutral reaction and containing free calcium carbonate. They have only been given limited attention, particularly by ecologists who find them interesting through the plant communities which they support (McVean and Ratcliffe, 1962; Ferreira, 1959).

Sub-aqueous soils

Up to the present very little work has been conducted on these soils in Scotland, therefore it is not possible to give any details (but cf. Chapter 9). Preliminary observations have shown that there are extensive areas of these soils which appear to be similar to these described for Europe by Kubiëna (1953).

CLAY MINERALOGY

The clay minerals found in Scottish soils are those commonly found in soils (Mitchell, 1955). They are illite, kaolin, montmorillonite and vermiculite. Only a small degree of correlation exists between these minerals and the various soils, but it is more pronounced with the parent materials. Soils derived from parent materials containing a

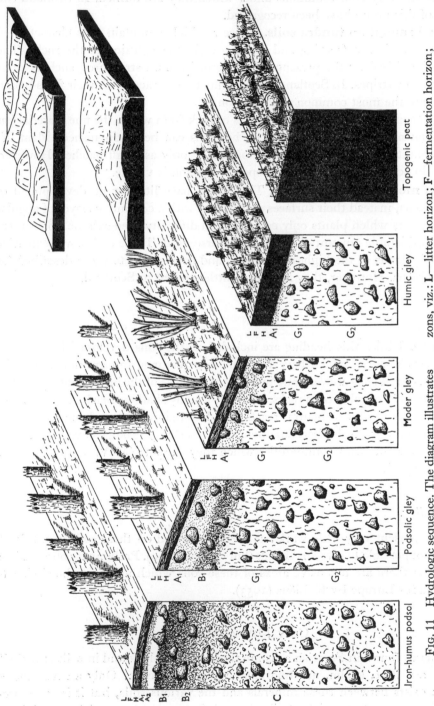

Fig. 11 Hydrologic sequence. The diagram illustrates the soil sequence in relation to drainage as affected by slope on acid parent material. The two block diagrams represent the types of landscape on which this sequence occurs. An indication is given of the associated vegetation types. Symbols represent the different soil horizons, viz.: **L**—litter horizon; **F**—fermentation horizon; **H**—humified horizon; A_1—organic/mineral upper horizon of zone of eluviation; A_2—strongly leached horizon; B_1, B_2—horizons of accumulation; G_1, G_2—gleyed horizons; **C**—relatively unaltered parent material.

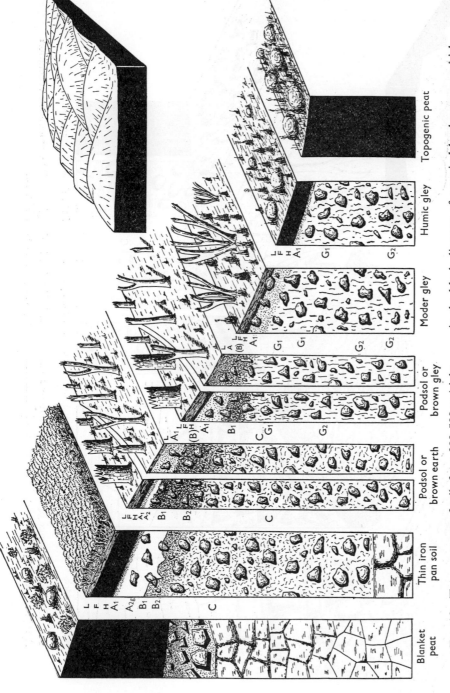

FIG. 12 Toposequence of soils from 300-500 m (right-hand side) down to sea-level (left-hand side). With increasing altitude there is an increase in rainfall, hence the formation of thin iron-pan soils and blanket peat. This is aided by the domed shape of the hills illustrated in the block diagram of a typical landscape on which such a sequence occurs. An indication is given of the associated vegetation types. Symbols as in Fig. 11; in addition, A_{2g}—gleyed A_2 horizon; (B)—horizon of simultaneous weathering and deposition.

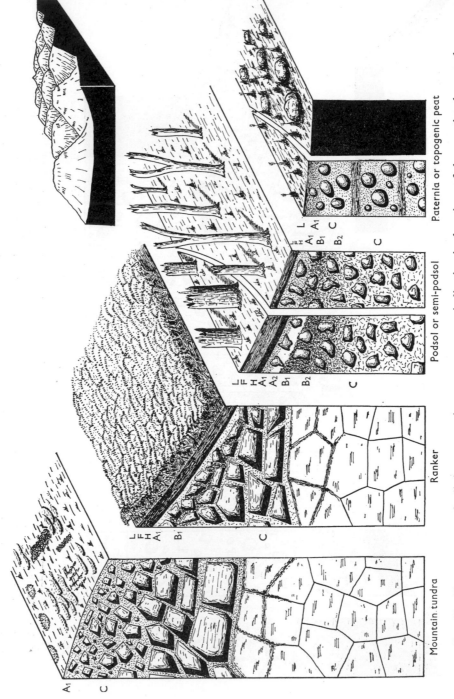

Paternia or topogenic peat

Podsol or semi-podsol

Ranker

Mountain tundra

FIG. 13   Toposequence of soils in a mountainous area.
A typical landscape is shown in the block diagram and
an indication is also given of the associated vegetation
types. Symbols as in Fig. 12.

high percentage of ferro-magnesian minerals have their clay fraction dominated by vermiculite and montmorillonite, with the latter increasing in amount with increasing soil wetness. Thus the brown earths formed in these parent materials contain these two minerals with an increased amount of montmorillonite in their associated gleys.

Soils formed in other parent materials contain kaolin and illite with some vermiculite and seem to be much less affected by changes in soil moisture status. However, there is a tendency for kaolin to increase in amount towards the surface of the freely drained soils.

Appreciable amounts of chlorite occur in the clay fraction of soils developed on Silurian shales which contain macroscopic chlorite.

SOIL RELATIONSHIPS

The previous discussion of the soils has treated each as a separate entity, but under natural conditions they are usually found to bear certain specific relationships to one another. It will only be possible to mention some of the more important relations which occur. These will also give some indication of the complexities of the pedology of Scotland.

The moisture regime is usually a major factor in determining many of the soil relationships found in Scotland. The variation in soil moisture status on uniform parent material resulting from differences in topography is known as an *Hydrologic sequence*. This concept was first developed in Canada by Ellis (1932) and later applied to certain Scottish soils by Glentworth and his colleagues (1949). A common relationship of soils in such a sequence on acid parent material is shown in Fig. 11. At the top of the slope a podsol soil is developed under free drainage, while on the sides which receive some run-off and where the ground water-table is higher, a podsolic gley is found. Towards the bottom, gleys and then peat are formed. Although the slope is shown as having discrete soils this is seldom found in nature, instead there is usually a gradual change from one soil to the other unless there is a sharp break in slope.

The physical and chemical properties of the soil in such a sequence (Glentworth, 1958) show many marked differences and trends which correspond to changes in moisture status.

Over a much wider range of topography, where the altitude may be 150 m., or more, a slightly different sequence is encountered, particularly when the slope is steep. The water draining off the higher ground and through the soils of the middle slope causes an enrichment of the cation content and the formation of oligotrophic braunerden or crypto-podsolic braunerden. Further down the slope the sequence is the same as above.

The cooler and more humid conditions associated with the higher elevations lead to the formation of thin iron pan soils and blanket peat in the kind of sequence illustrated in Fig. 12. In such a sequence, oligotrophic braunerden or cryptopodsolic braunerden may, or may not, occur depending upon the steepness of the slope. On the more gentle slopes, with little lateral movement of moisture, podsols are found.

In the mountainous areas yet another sequence is encountered as is shown in Fig. 13.

The mountain tops have mountain tundra soils or ranker soils while rankers predominate on the upper slopes. The soils on the middle and lower slopes vary considerably depending upon the angle of the slope; when steep, hamada mountain tundra soils are found, while on the less steep slopes, semi-podsols and podsols are formed. At the base of the mountains there is usually a sharp break to alluvium in which ramblas, paternias, or gleys have developed or there may be a covering of peat. Departures from this sequence are common where the valleys have many terraces or moraines.

The effect of aspect is sometimes very pronounced and influences the distribution of the soils. South-facing slopes being warmer are colonised particularly by deciduous species. These two factors tend to retard podsolisation which may be marked on the north-facing slope colonised by conifers or ericaceous species.

The general climatic trend in Scotland shows a steady increase in the amount of rainfall from east to west (cf. Chapter 2). This is clearly reflected in the distribution of the soils, particularly peat. In the west there is much more widespread development of blanket peat which even extends to sea-level in many places. Where the slope is not very steep the peat covers large stretches of the countryside. Further, Mitchell and Jarvis (1956) have clearly demonstrated the increased frequency of gley soils corresponding to an increase in the amount of rainfall.

In addition to relationships resulting from differences in altitude, slope and climate, the nature of the parent material may strongly influence the soil which is formed. Podsols and thin iron pan soils are more usually developed in coarse textured, parent materials while finer textures give rise to semi-podsols, brown earths or pseudogleys. In the few cases where the parent material is very rich in bases, eutrophic braunerden develop. Since the range of parent materials in Scotland is extremely varied only two attempts have been made to show the soil-parent material relationship. These are given in Figs. 14 and 15 and show how difficult it is to delimit many of the criteria differentiating the various soils since, so often, there is a continuum in the various chemical, physical and biological properties. This variation extends through both time and space; the time aspect will be considered next.

SOIL EVOLUTION

Soils are naturally occurring phenomena whose properties are largely governed by the factors of their environment. Thus if the intensity of any one factor changes there will be a manifestation of this in the soil properties. Between the Pleistocene and the present there have been marked changes in the climate and vegetation of Scotland which have induced changes in the soils. This concept of soil evolution has steadily gathered support and is now widely accepted as a factor in soil formation.

One of the conspicuous features of many Scottish soils is the extent to which they have been influenced by late Pleistocene periglacial processes, whence the similarity of the landscape at that time to many parts of the present-day arctic (FitzPatrick, 1958). With the gradual amelioration of the climate the soils have changed and developed from

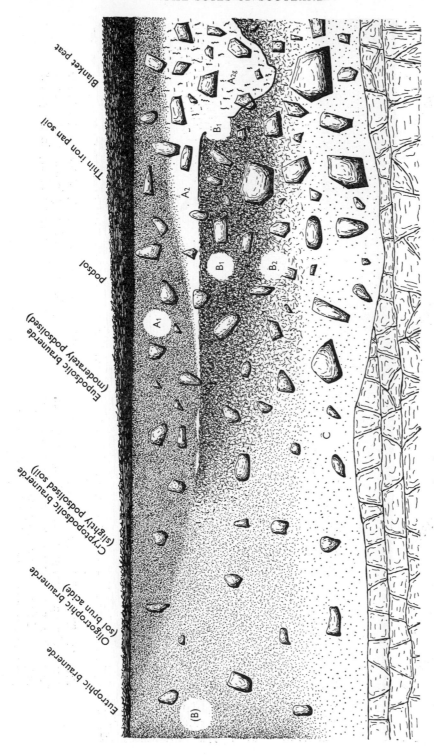

Fig. 14 Idealized diagram showing the continuous variation in soils with continuous change in parent material. This is becoming more acid from left to right and is symbolized by the increasing frequency of stones in the profiles. Symbols as in Fig. 12.

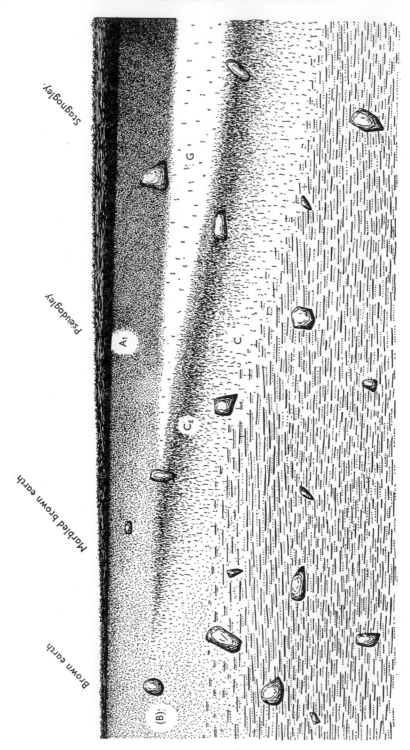

Fig. 15 The relationship between brown earth, marbled brown earth, pseudogley and stagnogley soils. The soils may occur in one locality as the result of the influence of topography or they may form on similar parent materials in different localities in similar topographic situations, as a result of increased rainfall. They may, in addition, develop in the same locality as a result of increasing amounts of clay in the parent material.

Tundra soils through Rankers into what is seen today. Further the presence of large amounts of lake marl in some places is ample evidence of the amount of leaching that has taken place in the soils of the surrounding areas.

At the end of the Pleistocene period there would have been little peat on the landscape. The peat has steadily increased in amount and distribution, particularly during the last six thousand years since the Boreal period (Durno, 1957). It seems, too, that gleying has also become more widespread and the gley soils have undergone an evolutionary sequence. Under arctic conditions gleying would be limited to a small amount above the permafrost, but later it increased considerably in amount and intensity.

The thin iron pan soils show one of the most interesting series of evolutionary changes. Before the iron pan formed it seems most likely that these soils were podsols but with the formation of the pan, vertical movement of soil moisture ceased and it accumulated in the upper horizons to induce gley processes. The intensity of gleying is very variable being conditioned by the amount of moisture retained which, in turn, is determined by slope and rainfall. At the final stage in the evolutionary sequence, when blanket peat forms the surface cover, these soils should be regarded as buried soils. This is an example of the deflection of soil formation along new lines after the full development of a specific soil property. However, the formation of blanket peat is not restricted to the thin iron pan soils for it can be found covering podsols, gleys, rankers, etc. The widespread formation of blanket peat seems to be due to the climatic change of the Atlantic period when conditions became more moist (cf. Chapter 16).

SOIL EROSION

Any discussion of Scottish soils would be incomplete without some mention of the actual, and potential, soil erosion in the country. It is frequently stated that there is very little soil erosion in Britain. Although this may be true compared with some other countries, it is nevertheless misleading. Erosion of an insidious nature has taken place for centuries and is at present taking place to a considerable extent. This is particularly well shown on the more steeply sloping agricultural fields where ploughing is still carried on up and down the slope. It is common to find soil piled high on the up-slope side of dykes* which follow the contour.

In some areas the soil is particularly prone to erosion. Such an area is found just south of Fochabers where deep gullies have been cut into the deeply weathered Old Red Sandstone.

Cloud-bursts are a major contributory factor to the more spectacular gully erosion found in the hilly and mountainous regions, particularly in the west and on some of the islands off the west coast. Winds of high velocity are frequent in Scotland, but only cause damage when they follow a period of drought. Although such conditions are relatively infrequent, occurrences of this sort have been known to have transported sufficient soil to block the roads west of Forres.

* Dyke is the Scottish term for a dry stone wall which surrounds fields, etc.

The rotational burning of heather is another factor which contributes to the move-ment of soil down the slopes. Although no instances of large-scale erosion following burning are known, it is common to find alternating layers of humus and mineral material in the surface horizons of many heath and moorland soils.

Induced erosion due to overgrazing by sheep is widespread, particularly in the more remote parts of the west and north of the country. The burrowing of rabbits into the hillside is yet another factor contributing to soil erosion (cf. Plate 29, Chapter 6).

Finally, peat-hagging, whether natural or induced, is further evidence of erosion currently taking place.

ACKNOWLEDGEMENTS

I thank Dr. J. Tinsley for his encouragement and helpful discussions, and also Dr. R. Glentworth for reading the manuscript and making a number of pertinent criticisms.

REFERENCES

AUBERT, G.   1938   In "*La Dynamique du Sol*" (A. Demolon, ed.) 2nd ed. Dunod, Paris.

CROMPTON, E.   1952   Some morphological features associated with poor drainage. *J. Soil Sci.*, **3**, 277-289.

         1956   The environmental and pedological relationships of peaty gleyed podsols. *Report of the Sixth Congress of the International Society of Soil Science, Paris, Commission V,* 155-161.

DUCHAUFOUR, P.   1960   *Précis de Pédologie.* Paris.

DURNO, S. E.   1957   Certain aspects of Vegetational History in North-east Scotland. *Scot. geogr. Mag.*, **73**, 176-184.

ELLIS, J. H.   1932   A field classification of soils for use in soil survey. *Sci. Agric.*, **12**, 338-345.

FERREIRA, R. E. C.   1959   Scottish mountain vegetation in relation to geology. *Trans. bot. Soc. Edinb.*, **37**, 229-250.

FITZPATRICK, E. A.   1956   An indurated soil horizon formed by permafrost. *J. Soil Sci.*, **7**, 248-254.

         1958   An introduction to the periglacial geomorphology of Scotland. *Scot. geogr. Mag.*, **74**, 28-36.

         1963   Deeply weathered rock in Scotland: its occurrence age and contribution to the soils. *J. Soil Sci.*, **14**, 33-43.

FRASER, G. K.   1954   Classification and nomenclature of Peat and Peat Deposits. *Inter. Peat Symposium, Dublin, Section* **B 2**, 1-8.

GLENTWORTH, R.   1954   The soils of the country round Banff, Huntly and Turriff. *Memoirs of the Soil Survey of Great Britain: Scotland.*

         1958   The geography and soils of north-east Scotland. *Agric. Progress*, **33**, 58-64.

GLENTWORTH, R. and DION, H. G.	1949	The association or hydrologic sequence in certain soils of the podsolic zone of north-east Scotland. *J. Soil Sci.*, **1**, 35-49.
KUBIËNA, W. L.	1953	*The Soils of Europe.* Madrid & London.
LAATSCH, W.	1938	*Dynamik der deutschen Acker—und Waldböden Steinkopff.* Dresden und Leipzig.
McVEAN, D. N. and RATCLIFFE, D. A.	1962	*Plant communities of the Scottish Highlands.* H.M.S.O., London.
MITCHELL, B. D. and JARVIS, R. A.	1956	The soils of the country round Kilmarnock. *Memoirs of the Soil Survey of Great Britain: Scotland.*
MITCHELL, W. A.	1955	A review of the mineralogy of Scottish soil clays. *J. Soil Sci.*, **6**, 94-98.
MÜCKENHAUSEN, E.	1959	*Die wichtigsten Böden der Bundesrepublik Deutschland.* Verlag Kommentator, Gmbh.
MUIR, A. and FRASER, G. K.	1939–40	The soils and vegetation of the Bin and Clashindarroch forest. *Trans. Royal Soc. Edinb.*, **60**, 233-241.
MUIR, A.	1934	The soils of the Teindland state forest. *Forestry*, **8**, 25-55.
MUIR, J. W.	1955	The Effect of Soil-Forming Factors over an area in the South of Scotland. *J. Soil Sci.*, **6**, 84-93.
	1956	The soils of the country round Jedburgh &] Morebattle. *Memoirs of the Soil Survey of Great Britain: Scotland.*
NAIRN, A. E. M. (Ed.)	1961	*Descriptive Palaeoclimatology.* London.
RAGG, J. M.	1960	The soils of the country round Kelso and Lauder. *Memoirs of the Soil Survey of Great Britain: Scotland.*
SMITH, J.	1956	Some moving soils in Spitsbergen. *J. Soil Sci.*, **7**, 10-21.
SYNGE, F. M.	1956	The Glaciation of North-East Scotland. *Scot. geogr. Mag.*, **72**, 129-143.
TAVERNIER, R.	1952	*Discussion on Soil Classification Meeting in Europe*, 50 pp. Mimeo. Geol. Inst., Ghent.

PART II

THE VEGETATION

THE MARITIME ZONE

CHAPTER 4

MARITIME AND SUB-MARITIME COMMUNITIES

C. H. GIMINGHAM

Much of the diverse coastline of Scotland and its island archipelagoes is of almost unrivalled beauty. Its charm springs largely from the endless variety and harmony between vegetation and habitat in the landscape (Plates 5 and 6). The highly dissected west coast with sea lochs, like small fjords, and bays of white shell sand contrasts strongly with the more regular outline of the east, made up in part of cliffs and in part of miles of dune-fringed beaches. Cutting deeply into the hinterland are the big Firths or river estuaries of the Clyde and Solway to the south-west, and of the Tay and Forth to the east. The coastal features of the many islands lying off the west of Scotland and of the Inner and Outer Hebrides are akin to those of the west mainland, while the gentle contours of most of the islands of Orkney contrast with the sheer cliffs of more distant Shetland (Plate 5). Even more remote are certain isolated rocky islands such as the St. Kilda group, lying in the Atlantic 64 km. (40 miles) west of the Outer Hebrides, and Rockall, a lonely granitic cone 298 km. (185 miles) from the nearest land.

While the coast of east Scotland has much in common with that of north-east England, the west resembles a less rugged version of the Norwegian coast, sharing not only its configuration but also many geological features. Similar characteristics appear in north and north-west Ireland. Orkney has affinities with the north-east of Scotland, but Shetland on the other hand is more related to the highland region.

These relationships can be traced not only in geology and outline, but also in climate. Scottish maritime and sub-maritime communities are all subject to a more or less oceanic type of climatic regime, but those on the west are under the influence of hyper-oceanic conditions. Here the annual rainfall is high, 1270-1525 mm. or more (50-60 in.), and winters are mild. Besides a general moderating effect of the sea upon temperature variation, a warming influence from the North Atlantic Drift is felt on the west coasts of Scotland. Calculation of an Index of Oceanicity (Kotilainen, see Poore and McVean, 1957) for a series of localities in this region, gives a range from 267 to 467, similar to, but rising a little higher than, the range 200-417 for the W. Norwegian coast. In contrast, rainfall on the east coast of Scotland is about 635-990 mm. (25-35 in.) per year, temperatures fall lower in winter and the Indices of Oceanicity lie between 127 and 173. Passing northwards, temperature conditions become increasingly unfavourable, so that in Shetland Spence (1960) describes the climate at sea level as "sub-montane oceanic" and points out that mean monthly temperatures here are equivalent to those at an altitude of 359 m. in central Scotland.

However, the generally moderate climatic regime throughout much of the Scottish coastline is in places to some extent outweighed by the effects of exposure to high winds. Since the prevailing winds are westerly, the west coast is particularly affected by this factor, and where exposed to the full force of Atlantic gales environmental conditions may be severe. Elsewhere, north-facing coastlines, such as those of the north mainland of Scotland and of the southern margin of the Moray Firth (particularly in the counties of Banff and part of Aberdeen), are among the most exposed to high winds. On the other hand, east-coast bays lined by cliffs clearly show the beneficial effects of shelter on the plant communities.

The geological formations exposed at the coast represent another aspect of habitat showing great variety. Except in the case of sand and alluvial deposits, the nature of the rock in coastal areas directly affects the composition of plant communities since these depend upon fissures, rock debris, recently weathered material or skeletal soils, for their establishment. In Scotland siliceous rocks account for the greater part of the coastline, notably the Lewisian gneiss of Hebridean as well as mainland shores and the Torridonian sandstone in the north-west; the Dalradian and Moine schists in the north, east and parts of the west; and the Old Red Sandstones along several stretches of the east. Granite and other igneous rocks are exposed in various places, while the southernmost portions of the coast on both sides of the country are formed of strata of Ordovician and Silurian age. Basic and calcareous rocks, however, play a relatively minor role in coast formation: gabbro and serpentine and other basic igneous rocks, including lavas, occur in certain places, e.g. Skye, Shetland; hornblende schist and Dalradian limestones in localised areas of north and west; and carboniferous limestone surrounding the Firth of Forth. Other lime-rich habitats occur where beach sand is largely composed of finely divided shell fragments, particularly in the north-west highland area. Here highly calcareous dunes are formed, and sand overblowing the peaty hinterland gives rise to the characteristic enriched "machair" habitats (p. 98). Elsewhere the beach and dune sand is mainly siliceous and low in calcium content, although not necessarily bearing any close relationship to the regional geology.

Most maritime substrata, however, even those derived from materials of very low base status, are to some extent enriched with nutrient ions contributed by rainfall from clouds brought in across the sea. In particular, sodium and chloride ions are incorporated from this source, as well as from droplets of sea spray which may, at least temporarily, produce relatively high concentrations of these ions in the rooting medium. The influence of sea spray is clearly strongest along coasts exposed to high winds. Salt-marsh, shingle and foreshore communities are subject to occasional or regular submergence in sea water.

Scotland's coasts are in general unspoilt by human interference, and hence provide a territory of exceptional interest and importance for the study of largely natural plant communities, their relationships with the various aspects of the environment, and the dynamic processes occurring in them. They are subject only to a limited extent to the effects of fire, which has played such a large part in moulding certain types of inland vegetation, but the attentions of grazing animals, particularly rabbits and sheep, extend to all but the steepest or most inaccessible situations. A further biotic factor, in the form of dense populations of nesting sea-birds, has a profound influence on the vegetation in certain localities (p. 79).

Owing to the fundamentally different nature of the substratum and other aspects of environment, it is convenient for the purpose of discussing maritime plant communities to divide coastal habitats into the following main groups: cliffs, shingle, sandy foreshore, dunes and salt marshes. Such a grouping omits certain habitats occurring quite frequently along the coasts, such as the narrow rocky ravines cut by streams on their way to the sea, but it attempts to include those in which maritime influences are most evident in the plant communities and on which floristic and ecological interest has centred.

GENERAL ASPECTS OF THE MARITIME FLORA

Of the habitats listed above as characteristic of the maritime regions of Scotland, only those of salt-marsh, foreshore, and cliffs or rocks reached by sea spray are subject to high salinities in the rooting medium for any length of time, and may justifiably be described as "halophytic". Others such as dunes, dune slacks, sheltered cliff tops and slopes standing back from the sea are not strongly halophytic. Consequently only a relatively small proportion of the Scottish maritime flora may be ranked as halophytes, in the sense of Chapman's (1942) use of this term to describe plants which can tolerate prolonged exposure to concentrations of 0·5 per cent. or more NaCl in the soil. Among these are the few "submersed halophytes" (Stocker, 1928) such as *Zostera* spp., certain salt marsh species including *Salicornia* spp., *Glaux maritima* and *Suaeda maritima* which are subject to frequent submergence in sea water, and other species said to show better growth on saline soils than elsewhere, e.g. *Scirpus maritimus* and *Juncus gerardii* (see Chapman, 1960). Many species of maritime regions, however, while including halophytic habitats in their ecological amplitude, grow as well or better elsewhere. Some are common species such as *Agrostis stolonifera* and *Festuca rubra* ranging continuously from saline to non-saline and from coastal to inland habitats, others including *Plantago maritima*, *Armeria maritima* and *Silene maritima* have discontinuous inland stations often far from their maritime areas (e.g. p. 524).

The plant communities of the habitats less influenced by salinity, however, also include a number of species showing characteristically maritime patterns of distribution, being absent or less frequent elsewhere. Some of these are best represented near the sea, probably merely because suitable habitats or substrata occur chiefly at the coast: examples are *Carex arenaria*, *Gentianella amarella* subspp. and *Plantago coronopus*, which have scattered inland stations where appropriate conditions occur. A few, such as *Scilla verna*, belong exclusively to coastal situations, but whether this represents a special relationship with one or more factors of the maritime environment, or more rigorous competition in inland communities, or has any other explanation, remains an open question.

The contrast between the west and east coasts of Scotland, already discussed, is reflected in the distribution of certain components of the maritime flora. Some are mainly western, for example *Umbilicus rupestris*,* which occurs on rocky coasts in S.W. Scotland and some of the Inner Hebrides, e.g. Great Cumbrae (Fletcher and Martin, 1960), Arran, Bute; others, such as *Astragalus danicus* which belongs to dune grassland, are predominantly eastern. More conspicuous, however, are the "northern" and "southern"

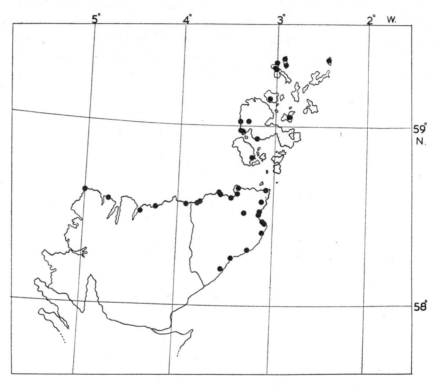

FIG. 16   Map of North of Scotland showing distribution of *Primula scotica* (closed circles). (From Ritchie (1954), *J. Ecol.*, **42**, 624).

elements in the maritime flora. In Scotland, besides the plants widely spread from north to south of western Europe, a number of species of boreal and arctic distribution approaching their southern limits overlap with others of Mediterranean or southern European affinities approaching their northern limits. This is true of coastal plants as it is of the flora as a whole.

Examples of coastal species ranging mainly northwards from Scotland are *Carex maritima*, *Juncus balticus*, *Ligusticum scoticum* and *Mertensia maritima*. A small group of considerable interest is composed of arctic-alpine species, present in the mountains of

* An isolated eastern locality in Kincardineshire has been reported (Sommerville, 1959).

Scotland, which become maritime in the extreme north, or on other exposed coasts, where perhaps the climate is sub-montane in character. These include *Sedum rosea*, quite widespread around northern coasts, and *Saxifraga hypnoides*, *S. oppositifolia*, *Saussurea alpina*, *Oxytropis halleri*, *Silene acaulis* and *Dryas octopetala* which are more restricted.

Among the southern element may be mentioned *Eryngium maritimum*, *Trifolium scabrum*, *T. striatum*, *Silene nutans*. Some species very characteristic of certain maritime habitats in England reach only the southernmost coasts of Scotland, e.g. *Glaucium flavum*, *Crambe maritima*, *Limonium vulgare* and *L. humile*. Others, widespread in England both in coastal and inland habitats, become increasingly restricted to maritime areas on passing northwards into Scotland: examples are *Dianthus deltoides* and *Saxifraga granulata*, while even *Primula veris* occurs more frequently on the coast than elsewhere in the north of Scotland.

Finally, at least one well-known species endemic to Scotland is largely a coastal plant. This is *Primula scotica*, occurring around the coasts of Caithness, Sutherland and Orkney (Fig. 16; cf. Ritchie, 1954).

CLIFFS

A number of regional floristic surveys, accounts of the flora of particular islands, etc., have given lists of species occurring on sea cliffs but there have been few comprehensive sociological or ecological studies of cliff communities. However, enough information is now available to build up a summary of the chief types occurring in Scotland, although much important detail is lacking. Mention will be made first of the simplest groupings of species characteristic of the most exacting habitats, such as for example the seaward slopes of the most exposed rocky coastlines and islands, and the lowermost belts of sea-washed cliffs frequently subject to splash or spray. This will be followed by reference to the several types of closed community of varying complexity, some influenced by the salinity factor but others consisting of relatively rich assemblages of species not themselves especially associated with maritime areas.

Communities much influenced by sea spray

Even above the direct influence of tidal submergence, sea-washed boulders, rocky stacks and cliffs are repeatedly wetted at their lower levels by splash and spray. On sheltered coastlines these influences are felt only in a narrow belt, but with increasing exposure to wind and wave action their effects extend considerably higher. The first two types of stand to be described under this heading are composed mainly of lichens; in the remainder, flowering plants become increasingly important.

Verrucaria—Cyanophyta stands. In sheltered areas this type of community is restricted to the inter-tidal region. It is regarded by Lewis (1957, 1961) as belonging to the upper part of the littoral zone and by Stephenson (1949) to a "supralittoral fringe", rather than to maritime terrestrial vegetation. However, on exposed coasts it may occupy a broad belt above tidal limits, and therefore is briefly mentioned here. It appears as a black zone owing to the predominance of species of *Verrucaria*, of which the commonest is probably *V. maura*, often growing alone or with scattered algae and other lichens. The height of the zone varies with exposure. On the most severely exposed of all sea rocks in the British Isles, Rockall, a black zone extending about 3 m (10 ft) above the effective high-water mark is occupied by *V. microspora* with species of Cyanophyta (*Pleurocapsa kerneri*, *Plectonema battersii*, *Phormidium fragile* and *Calothrix scopulorum*), accompanied by the small green algae *Blidingia minima* and *Prasiola stipata*. Above this, however, the algae give rise to dense patches, constituting a "green zone", but the *Verrucaria* also extends another 12-13·8 m. (40-50 ft.) to the top of the rock (Powell and Chamberlain, in Fisher, 1956).

Xanthoria—Lecanora stands. In contrast to the absence of lichens other than *Verrucaria* throughout the full vertical extent of Rockall, societies containing *Xanthoria parietina*, *Lecanora* spp. and other lichens may descend to within 0·5-1 m. (2-3 ft.) of mean high-water mark on more sheltered coasts, forming a zone characterised by the mixture of bright orange and grey patches. Some of the species concerned are given below:

AILSA CRAIG, boulders (Vevers, 1936)

Lichens

Buellia aethelia	*Pseudophyscia fusca*
B. hochstetteri	*Ramalina curnowii*
Lecanora sp.	*R. scopulorum*
Parmelia saxatilis	*Rhizocarpon reductum*
Pertusaria sp.	*R. geographicum*
	Xanthoria parietina

Bryophytes

Rhacomitrium lanuginosum

ST. CYRUS, Kincardineshire, cliffs and stacks
(Robertson, 1951)

Lichens

Caloplaca citrina	*Physcia leptalea*
Diploicia canescens	*Pseudophyscia fusca*
Lecanora atra	*Ramalina scopulorum*
	Xanthoria parietina

Although not listed in the above examples, a limited number of moss species enter this type of community. These include *Grimmia maritima*, *Ulota phyllantha*, *Tortella flavovirens* etc.

This is the lowest of the strictly maritime, rather than littoral community-types, being regarded by Stephenson (1949) as part of a "supralittoral zone".

***Armeria—Cochlearia* stands.** On the east coast of Scotland flowering plants colonise sea cliffs and rocks from about 1·4 m. (4 ft. 6 in.) above tidal limits, while on the more exposed shores this boundary is displaced upwards. They are confined at first to crevices and ledges, while the rock surface supports only a lichen cover similar to that of the lower zones. Species with a penetrating tap root such as *Armeria maritima* or dense, binding fibrous root system such as *Koeleria cristata* often extend furthest towards the sea. A few feet above they are joined by other species tolerant of a halophytic habitat, in particular *Cochlearia officinalis*, *Tripleurospermum maritimum*, *Plantago maritima*, *P. coronopus*, *Silene maritima* and *Sedum anglicum*. Although not invariably present, *Ligusticum scoticum* is also a characteristic component of this community in Scotland. Other species are included in Table 8 (p. 128): as to be expected the majority are perennials, although the annual, *Cerastium atrovirens*, occurs in some examples.

An interesting component of some of these stands, frequent (though not constant) especially in the west and north, is *Sedum rosea*. It is perhaps restricted rather more to the higher crevices and ledges than some of the other species, but is regularly associated with this characteristic group of mainly halophytic plants. A very similar assemblage occurs in W. Norway, as for example on the island Utsire, where Nordhagen (1921) names it "Rhodioletum roseae". However, this appears to be an instance of an arctic-alpine species becoming a component of northern examples of a widespread coastal community-type, and it is paralleled by the presence of *Silene acaulis* in the same community on base-rich cliffs on Canna (Asprey, 1947).

A number of bryophytes and a few lichens also occur but never seem to have been fully listed. At St. Cyrus, Kincardineshire, on rocky stacks (Robertson, 1951) *Porella thuja*, *Metzgeria furcata* and *Peltigera canina* are present as well as *Grimmia maritima* and *Camptothecium sericeum*, which occur in many examples of these communities. *Bryum alpinum* is mentioned along with *Armeria maritima*, *Cochlearia officinalis* and *Senecio jacobaea* for Ailsa Craig (Vevers, 1936).

Records from St. Cyrus stacks suggest that the arrival of sodium chloride in spray in the zone occupied by this community-type is greatest in the period December to May, resulting in the highest concentrations in the soil solution between April and July as drying out proceeds. The pH of the debris (weathered rock fragments, humus, etc.) in the crevices varies here between about 7·0 and 8·0.

***Plantago* swards.** Closely related to the foregoing and, like them, situated where sea-spray is a prominent environmental factor (Plate 7), are the *Plantago*-swards (Table 8). These are slightly more complex communities than the *Armeria—Cochlearia* ones, with a longer species list. They occur locally near the sea on all Scottish coasts where a thin layer of detritus or weathered rock fragments sparsely clothes the bare rock surface. This may be over rock dipping at angles of anything up to about 45°, when a partially open community forms in which the plants gather small terraces of debris and help to stabilise the slope, or on ledges and flat surfaces when a more or less closed "turf" develops. The chief species are always *Plantago maritima*, *P. coronopus* and *Armeria maritima*, while *Festuca rubra* and sometimes *Koeleria cristata* may contribute significantly. In the more open communities a few annuals may be very abundant, such as *Cerastium atrovirens* and *Bromus mollis*, and here also mosses including *Bryum capillare*, *Ceratodon purpureus*, *Hypnum cupressiforme*, and lichens such as *Cladonia rangiformis*, *C. pyxidata* var. *pocillum* and *Candelariella vitellina* play a part. (See also Table 8.)

Such stands, which are tolerant of much exposure to wind as well as to variable salinities and the direct deposition of droplets of spray on the foliage, were described by Tansley (1949), but only Irish examples were then available for discussion (Praeger, 1934). A related *Armeria* sward (Table 8) lacking *Plantago maritima* occurs in the St. Kilda group and on the island of North Rona, particularly where the soil has a greater mineral content including particles of shell sand (McVean, 1961). Both of these types are undoubtedly closely related to members of the salt-marsh series of communities as developed on the west coast (pp. 112-115), the distinction resting largely on the absence of certain characteristic salt-marsh plants and, on the other hand, the occurrence of *Plantago coronopus* and sometimes other species.

Few data are available on habitat factors: soil samples from *Plantago* swards have shown pH values between 6·5 and 7·9 (St. Cyrus) and chloride contents in July of 321 mg. Cl./100 g. soil (Hirta, St. Kilda—McVean, 1961), while one from an *Armeria* sward (North Rona—McVean, 1961) gave 423 mg. Cl./100 g. soil.

Communities less strongly influenced by spray

In spite of the floristic wealth of many cliff communities few comprehensive lists have been published and little is known of the environmental conditions which obtain. Only a very generalised account can, therefore, be given, with few examples, of a series of communities occupying a considerable range of habitats. Fine spray and spume will reach all of them from time to time but, at one end of the series, temporary subjection to fairly high soil salinities will still be a factor of importance responsible for the presence of several species belonging to the lower zones while, at the other end, this will play only a small part. These latter cliff grasslands and related communities have few maritime features and resemble the inland groups of species typical of rough slopes, neglected pastures, hedgebanks and scrub. The floristic composition frequently reflects the geological structure of the cliff, and the simplicity or complexity of the community structure depends upon slope, the nature of the rock surface and the degree of soil accumulation.

Rock faces. Where steep, bare rock faces are in evidence many of the lichens and bryophytes already mentioned are present. On dry rock, however, cushion-forming species also occur such as *Zygodon* "*stirtoni*" and *Barbula tophacea*, sometimes with *Phascum cuspidatum* var. *piliferum* and *Bryum argenteum*. These may provide the anchorage for mat-formers such as *Camptothecium sericeum* and *Hypnum cupressiforme* var. *tectorum*, which also establish and spread from crevices and roughnesses of the rock.

Alternatively, on many of the slightly more sheltered Scottish cliffs *Hedera helix* clothes the rock face, spreading from a ledge or crevice, where its expanding stems and roots may cause chunks of rock to split away from the surface and add to the talus below. On damper surfaces, particularly at the foot of shaded cliffs standing back from the sea, and in caves, *Conocephalum conicum* dominates large areas, sometimes accompanied by ferns such as *Asplenium marinum* (as on the Isle of May, Watson, 1953) or *Cystopteris fragilis*, *Athyrium filix-femina*, and *C. dickieana* (Kincardineshire) or *Phyllitis scolopendrium*. Where water rich in dissolved minerals seeps or trickles over the surface, dense masses of *Cratoneuron commutatum*, sometimes with *C. filicinum*, are conspicuous.

Clefts and ledges. Initial accumulation of fine particles permits colonisation by additional species of mosses, including *Tortula subulata*—especially on sandstone cliffs— and *Pohlia albicans*, as well as *Hypnum cupressiforme* and others already mentioned. Further elaboration of the community depends on the amount of fine material accumulated, and may be seral in character, as on the rocky stacks of St. Cyrus. Here, the clefts and ledges are at first occupied by an *Armeria*—*Cochlearia* community similar to that of lower levels, but additional lichens take part such as *Cladonia cervicornis* var. *subcervicornis*, *C. rangiformis* and *Peltigera canina*, while *Festuca rubra* soon becomes prominent, equalling or surpassing *Armeria maritima* and *Sedum acre* which are the chief initial colonisers. A later stage seems to be based on the entry and spread of *Thymus drucei*. *Koeleria cristata* also contributes, but there is some evidence that in this rather unstable habitat patches of vegetation periodically disrupt and the sequence starts again, following a cyclical pattern. *Silene maritima* also appears in these situations.

In places where a greater accumulation of debris leads to a richer species list, *S. maritima* is one of the few constant species in a series of rather various stands of rock ledges. As well as species such as *Cochlearia officinalis*, *Sedum anglicum*, etc., groups of ferns figure in several lists (e.g. Petch, 1933, St. Kilda: *Athyrium filix-femina*, *Dryopteris dilatata* and *Polypodium vulgare*; Asprey, 1947, Canna and Sanday: *Athyrium filix-femina* and *Blechnum spicant*). In both localities *Angelica sylvestris* and *Lonicera periclymenum* are present, with *Luzula sylvatica* in addition on Canna, and *Rumex acetosa* on St. Kilda. These species form a group which reappears with a wider set of associates on the boulder fringe and peaty flank of islands in the freshwater lochs of Shetland and S. Uist, and in the scrub communities on rock ledges of inland cliffs in the same areas (Spence, 1960). The relationship between these rock ledge communities and those of sea cliffs is further demonstrated by the following species which have been recorded in examples of both:

Rosa spp.	*Sedum rosea*
Digitalis purpurea	*Solidago virgaurea*
Scilla verna	*Succisa pratensis*
Jasione montana	*Thymus drucei*
Primula vulgaris	

The remaining species in the maritime rock-ledge assemblage differ very much from place to place. For example, on Ailsa Craig in the Firth of Clyde *Lavatera arborea* occurs on cliffs beyond the range of grazing goats (Vevers, 1936), and among other species are *Rhaphanus maritimus* and *Umbilicus rupestris*, the latter occurring also in similar situations in other localities of the same region, e.g. Arran, Great Cumbrae, etc. At St. Cyrus, Kincardineshire, the easily weathered, base-rich, andesitic lavas of the cliffs are probably responsible for the addition of a number of calcicolous species, some of them with southern distributional affinities, e.g. *Geranium sanguineum*, *Echium vulgare*, *Silene nutans*, *Anthyllis vulneraria*, etc. There is an appreciable depth of skeletal soil here, the pH of which varies between 6·3 and 7·7, and in such sites there is seldom any very marked increase in salinity.

Talus slopes. It is impossible to generalise about the flora colonising talus slopes, since so much depends upon the geological nature of the rock, the size of the fragments and the extent of accumulation of fine particles between them. The crevices between boulders may be occupied by large herbaceous perennials, often spreading by means of rhizomes, as for example the following which occur in such situations at St. Cyrus:

Pteridium aquilinum	*Myosotis arvensis*
Brachypodium sylvaticum	*M. ramosissima*
Dactylis glomerata	*Primula vulgaris*
Arctium minus agg.	*Teucrium scorodonia*
Campanula glomerata	*Urtica dioica*
Heracleum sphondylium	*Veronica chamaedrys*

Slopes consisting mainly of smaller rock fragments, forming a less deeply dissected substratum, may become more or less stable and support an almost closed community similar to that of adjacent soil-covered areas. At St. Cyrus, species such as *Origanum vulgare*, *Rubus fruticosus* and *Vicia sylvatica* are included here as well as in the grassy communities.

Only three of the species listed above occur also in the flora of talus slopes on Ailsa Craig (Vevers, 1936) where an acid, peaty humus of pH 5·2 has accumulated between granite blocks:

Sambucus nigra	r.	*Galium saxatile*	f.
Pteridium aquilinum	f.	*Senecio jacobaea*	f.
Holcus mollis	a.	*Silene dioica*	a.
Poa annua	a.	*Teucrium scorodonia*	dom.
Anchusa arvensis	o.	*Umbilicus rupestris*	f.
Cardamine hirsuta	va.	*Urtica dioica*	va.
Carduus acanthoides	f.	*Urtica urens*	o.
Erodium cicutarium	r.		

In the absence of disturbance, such a community might pass in time to scrub, and similar indications are found at St. Cyrus and elsewhere.

Festuca—Plantago **grasslands.** Table 8, containing a column compiled from the higher parts of certain cliffs on Fair Isle (kindly supplied by Miss U. K. Duncan), shows that in these rather exposed situations there is a community fundamentally similar to the *Plantago* swards, but incorporating a higher proportion of *Festuca ovina* and *Poa pratensis*. In one of these, on a drier rocky bank, an element of heath species is represented (cf. p. 129).

Festuca rubra **and** *Festuca—Holcus* **cliff grasslands, and related stands.** Where slopes are such that surface stability is readily achieved, a closed community develops. Often this takes the form of a herb-rich grassland, frequently fairly closely grazed by rabbits. *Festuca rubra*, *Festuca ovina* and *Holcus lanatus* are among the commonest dominants, with a variety of other species, depending upon the degree of exposure. There is, in fact, so much variation in the nature of the habitats available, the composition of the rock and the general and local climatic conditions that very few unifying features of community composition can be detected, and so no comprehensive floristic table is given.

Once again, stability and the depth of soil overlying rock seem to be the main factors governing the composition of the communities, both being to some extent dependent upon angle of slope. Considering first the less stable and more exposed situations, a *Festuca rubra* grassland is among the communities listed for North Rona and St. Kilda by McVean (1961), and a related richer type dominated by *F. rubra*, *Agrostis tenuis* and *Anthoxanthum odoratum* occurs in St. Kilda (Table 9, p. 130). A very different set of species, however, is listed by Anthony (1959) as among those of steep grassy slopes at Bettyhill on the N. Coast of Scotland:

Dactylis glomerata	*Parnassia palustris*
Holcus lanatus	*Plantago maritima*
Angelica sylvestris	*Prunella vulgaris*
Anthyllis vulneraria	*Rumex acetosella*
Cochlearia officinalis	*Urtica dioica*

On drier sites in the neighbourhood, *Vicia sylvatica* is prominent, and similar grassy communities on the cliff tops provide a habitat for *Primula scotica*. This assemblage of species seems to have features transitional between certain communities of the spray zone, and the richer *Festuca—Holcus* stands to be described next.

Among the more exposed of these is one described by Ferreira and Roger (1957) from north-facing scree slopes in the parish of Gamrie, Banffshire, an isolated coastal habitat for *Saxifraga hypnoides*. The stand extends from near the foot of the cliffs to about 15·5 m. (50 ft.) above, the scree being formed from Dalradian slates, with a thin covering of humic soil of pH 5·0-5·1. The following species are listed:

Pteridium aquilinum	r.	*Hypochoeris radicata*	o.
Festuca ovina	f.	*Ranunculus acris*	o.
Holcus lanatus	f.	*Rumex acetosa*	o.
Bellis perennis	o.	*Saxifraga hypnoides*	f.
Geranium robertianum	o.	*Solidago virgaurea*	o.
Hypericum pulchrum	o.	*Succisa pratensis*	o.
Dicranum scoparium	o.	*R. triquetrus*	f.
Hypnum cupressiforme	f.	*Frullania tamarisci*	f.
Pleurozium schreberi	f.	*Lophozia atlantica*	r.
Pseudoscleropodium purum	f.	*Cladonia pyxidata*	o.
Rhytidiadelphus squarrosus	f.	*Peltigera canina*	f.

An example of the floristic diversity of *Festuca—Holcus* cliff communities in the more sheltered situations and on soils of higher base status is taken from St. Cyrus, on a steep and somewhat unstable soil-covered slope where the pH varies between 6·6 and 7·5:

Ulex europaeus	*Cochlearia officinalis*
	Galium verum
Brachypodium sylvaticum*	*Heracleum sphondylium*
Dactylis glomerata*	*Hyoscyamus niger*
Festuca ovina*	*Campanula glomerata**
F. rubra	*Hypericum hirsutum*
Helictotrichon pratense	*Myosotis arvensis*
Holcus lanatus*	*Plantago lanceolata**
Koeleria cristata	*P. major*
Poa pratensis	*Rumex acetosa*
	R. crispus
Agrimonia eupatoria	*Senecio vulgaris*
Armeria maritima*	*Silene maritima*
Achillea millefolium	*Sonchus asper*
Bellis perennis	*Trifolium scabrum*
Carlina vulgaris	*Veronica serpyllifolia*

* These species, together with *Arrhenatherum elatius, Festuca pratensis, Campanula rotundifolia Centaurea nigra, Anchusa arvensis, Tragopogon pratensis,* etc., make up a short grass community on the cliff tops, much grazed by rabbits.

In certain parts of the cliffs, minor landslides have taken place in areas occupied by communities of this type, and a feature of the unstable substratum exposed is the development of large colonies of *Hyoscyamus niger* which may for several years remain virtually the only species present.

More sheltered sectors of cliffs with moderately deep soil, and those standing well back from the beach, are frequently dominated by *Arrhenatherum elatius*. These stands have seldom been examined and complete lists are not available, but in spite of much variation there seem to be few important differences from the richer *Festuca—Holcus* communities, beyond changes in the proportions in which certain species are represented. These are normally tall stands in which large herbs such as *Heracleum sphondylium* are prominent, as well as the grasses.

Where cliffs stand back from a sandy sea-beach, there is a tendency for sand, driven by on-shore winds, to be piled up against at least the lower slopes of the cliffs. Here *Ammophila arenaria* and *Carex arenaria* become regular members of the flora, and this habitat seems to favour the development of *Helianthemum chaemaecistus* which, however, also grows on other cliff soils of moderate to high base status. At Bettyhill, strong winds from the north have piled sand up against the cliffs throughout their height, and it is here that the arctic-alpine species *Dryas octopetala* becomes a maritime plant, growing into cushions and hummocks in which the sand is held amongst the intertwined stems with their dense foliage. The full composition of the community in such sites is shown in Table 10, column 1 (p. 132).

Stands containing *Empetrum nigrum*. On the smoother upper slopes of the sand-covered cliffs at Bettyhill (lying immediately above the *Dryas* hummocks just described) and on the cliff tops where blown sand spills out over the surrounding acid soils, a low dense *Dryas—Empetrum* sward develops, accompanied by a number of species characteristic of "machair" grasslands (Table 10, column 2; cf. p. 99). Elsewhere, *Empetrum nigrum* is commonly a component of cliff communities, mainly where the substratum is on the acid side. It becomes increasingly prominent along the more northern coasts and in Orkney and Shetland, where the communities frequently show many of the features of the *Festuca—Holcus* grasslands and represent only a slight variant of these, probably produced by a shift of soil conditions favourable for the entry of ericaceous species (which, besides *E. nigrum*, may include *Calluna vulgaris*, *Erica cinerea* and *E. tetralix*) and their associates. An example from Caithness (Ritchie, 1954) is given in Table 10, col. 3. Barkley (1953) mentions *Empetrum nigrum* occurring in association with *Festuca ovina*, *Holcus lanatus*, *Deschampsia flexuosa* and *Salix repens* on Soay cliff tops.

Pure stands of *Luzula sylvatica*. Cliff communities particularly those of acid, heathy character, are frequently interrupted by large patches in which *Luzula sylvatica* is dominant, almost to the exclusion of all other species. In such situations, this species finds a refuge from the effects of fire and grazing to which it is very susceptible, but the factors which determine its occurrence are largely unknown.

"Bird cliffs." Although the cliffs of many Scottish islands and numerous mainland localities are occupied in the breeding season by vast populations of sea birds, there are few accounts which refer to their influence upon the plant communities. Frequently the bird colonies occupy ledges on sheer cliffs where, in any case, only *Armeria—Cochlearia* communities and species of the higher clefts and ledges occur. Vevers, however, drew attention to the accumulation of guano below, having a pH of 7, and colonised on Ailsa Craig by *Urtica dioica*, *Silene dioica* and *Poa annua*.

Where, however, cliff slopes or tops supporting grassy communities are occupied by puffins (*Fratercula arctica grabae* (Brehm)) the vegetation is profoundly affected both by manuring and by the burrowing habits of the birds. Petch (1933) gives the following list from the island of Dun (St. Kilda group):

*Festuca (rubra)**	f.	*Montia fontana*	r.
*Holcus (lanatus)**	dom.	*Potentilla anserina*	f.
Poa annua	a.	*Ranunculus acris*	f.
Angelica sylvestris	o.	*Rumex acetosa*	a.
Cerastium holosteoides	f.	*Stellaria media*	a.

* These species were listed as *F. ovina* and *H. mollis*, but Poore and Robertson (1949) indicate that their proper identity is that given.

The area was one which might have been expected to support a community including heath species, but in fact it bears a modified *Festuca—Holcus* community, in which the two plants most directly associated with the puffin burrows are *Stellaria media* and *Poa annua*. These observations were repeated in the same area by Poore and Robertson (1949), who mention the additional observations in 1948 of *Tripleurospermum maritimum* (which "appears to be able to stand a greater proportion of bird guano than any of the other plants") and *Agrostis tenuis*, while dominance had passed from *Holcus lanatus* to *Rumex acetosa*. Attention is drawn to the absence of *Urtica dioica* here.

SHINGLE BEACHES

Several important investigations have been carried out on the ecology of shingle beach vegetation in England, but only scattered observations have been published relating to Scottish examples. However, studies of several areas have now been made by Scott (1960) and much of the following account is based on his unpublished records. Small shingle beaches are frequent on Scottish coasts, and more extensive ones occur, for example, on the Isle of Arran, and along the southern margin of the Moray Firth.

The species present on shingle depend very largely on the formation of the beach, the size of the boulders or pebbles and the nature of the matrix lying between them. The commonest type is the *fringing beach*, consisting of a narrow fringe of shingle composed of pebbles carried along the shore by wave action. Such a fringing beach may be extended as a *shingle spit*, projecting away from the coastline, if the latter changes direction, e.g. near Nairn at the western end of the Culbin sands (p. 106). (Between such a spit and the coastline there is protection from wave action, and as silting proceeds a salt marsh community may result.) Where fringing beaches have been thrown up in series, one upon another, a wide area of shingle known as an *apposition beach* may result, as on parts of the shores of Arran.

In a few places, the shore consists of very large boulders, lacking any interstitial matrix high enough to be colonised by plants. The boulders may have been derived either from adjacent cliffs or from glacial drift, as at the Struey Rocks, Arran, where they are mainly composed of porphyry or similar rock and rest on horizontal Triassic sand-stone slabs. Here the habitat is in many respects similar to that of the lowest part of the spray zone of cliffs and, correspondingly, plant colonisation is restricted to lichens (cf. p. 71). A black belt of *Verrucaria* sp. may occur, while *Xanthoria parietina* and *Pseudophyscia fusca* are perhaps the most conspicuous on the boulders.

Elsewhere the boulders, pebbles or gravel-sized stones of which the beach is built are set in a matrix which consists usually of varying proportions of sand and "wrack" (i.e. the remains of marine algae thrown up as tide-drift), or in some instances silt or mud. The nature of this matrix may be of greater importance than the pebbles in determining the composition of the vegetation and distribution of species. A distinction must also be drawn between shingle as a plant habitat when it lies in the foreshore zone, and when it extends inland well behind the foreshore, as on apposition beaches. For the present purpose the foreshore may be taken as extending a certain distance above high-water mark of spring tides at least as far as the *storm crest* which is a common feature of fringing beaches. Consideration will first be given to plant colonisation of shingle in the foreshore zone.

Foreshore

Atriplex glabriuscula—Silene maritima—Tripleurospermum maritimum stands on pebble beaches with a matrix of "wrack" and sand. The most frequent shingle habitat in Scotland seems to be the fringing beach composed of pebbles (2-10 cm. diameter) set in a sandy matrix with an admixture of algal debris. Although there is considerable variation in the assemblages of species found in such habitats, lists from widely separated localities show a recognisable floristic pattern (Table 11, p. 133). A num-ber of species show high degrees of constancy, in particular *Tripleurospermum maritimum*, *Silene maritima*, *Atriplex glabriuscula*, *Rumex crispus* (usually the var. *trigranulatus*) and *Galium aparine*. Other species rather characteristic of this habitat include *Rumex acetosa* and *Festuca rubra*. Although less regular, *Potentilla anserina*, *Honkenya peploides* and *Sonchus arvensis* may, in certain localities, be very conspicuous, covering extensive patches. A further species particularly characteristic of "pebble-wrack-sand" beaches on the north and west coasts of Scotland is *Mertensia maritima*, although its constancy is over-estimated in Table 11 owing to the choice of some of the stands as examples of sites in which it is well represented. The geographical range of this species has contracted north-wards in a striking fashion, especially on the east side of the country, during the past 50 years or more (Fig. 17, p. 82).

Mertensia maritima is a "northern element" in the Scottish shingle flora. By contrast, communities of this type in Arran and elsewhere towards the southernmost coastlines of Scotland include *Glaucium flavum*, and there are also scattered localities for *Crambe maritima* both on the west and east. These species constitute a "southern element", being very characteristic of shingle habitats in England where, however, the com-munities to which they belong tend to differ from those in Scotland. (The only British

F

species apparently exclusive to maritime shingle, *Suaeda fruticosa*, does not reach Scotland.)

Where shingle is subject to frequent disturbance by wave action it is quite bare of vegetation. Zones where shingle movement is largely restricted to winter are open to colonisation by annuals such as *Atriplex* spp. and *Galium aparine*, which are capable of a prostrate growth habit. Some of the perennials can establish and persist for a period in situations reached perhaps only once in three or four years by destructive waves. But the surface shingle in these habitats is probably disturbed more often than this, and certain of these plants

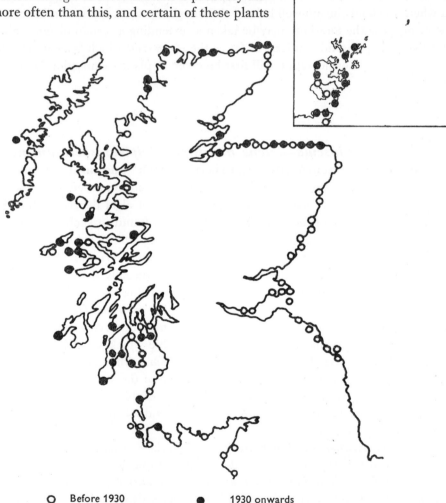

○ Before 1930   ● 1930 onwards

FIG. 17   The Scottish distribution of *Mertensia maritima*. (From *Atlas of the British Flora*, 1962, p. 216).

such as *Mertensia maritima*, *Rumex crispus*, etc., have stout woody rootstocks, while their aerial parts are often in the form of a more or less compact rosette. Other shingle species also exhibit a rosette, cushion or mat form during the greater part of the year, as for example *Tripleurospermum maritimum*, *Potentilla anserina*, *Sonchus arvensis*, *Silene maritima*, *Armeria maritima*. Those belonging to the more stable parts frequently spread rapidly by vegetative means, e.g. stolons in *Sonchus arvensis*, *Tripleurospermum maritimum* or surface runners in *Potentilla anserina*.

Owing to the mobility of shingle in storms and the redistribution of finer particles and organic debris by waves, conditions suitable for seed germination and the establishment of young plants may obtain only intermittently. As Salisbury (1942) has shown, species with high reproductive capacity are often best equipped to take advantage of favourable periods, and his estimate of 29,000 potential offspring per plant for *Rumex crispus* var. *trigranulatus* may be quoted as an illustration. Seeds may be distributed by the waves and this, together with local differences in the habitat, leads to extensive variation in the composition of the vegetation.

Although as a result of this instability the vegetation does not become closed, some species possess means of rapid vegetative spread and hence may occur in almost pure stands or patches of considerable area. This again leads to quantitative variation in the composition of the vegetation in different stands. Sometimes, for example, as on a small shingle beach near St. Cyrus, the vegetation may be based on patches of *Silene maritima*, developing into a sward with *Armeria maritima*, *Cochlearia officinalis*, *Plantago coronopus* and *Festuca rubra*, in which the other species typical of this assemblage become established (cf. "*Armeria* sward", p. 74). Elsewhere, large patches of *Potentilla anserina* or *Sonchus arvensis* are observed (e.g. Crovie, Banffshire) and particularly characteristic of Scottish beaches of this type are extensive colonies of *Galium aparine*, in which the tangled stems of many plants grow in a prostrate mat over the pebbles.

Owing to this variability, the assemblage of species shown in Table 11 can hardly be properly described as a community-type. None the less, there is a certain floristic conformity, and similar groupings have been incorporated in schemes of classification. Braun-Blanquet and Tüxen (1952) describe, for example, an *Atriplex glabriuscula*— *Polygonum raii* association which occurs in Ireland and bears some relation to the Scottish examples considered here, especially certain stands from Arran.

Scott (1960) points out that the most important source of mineral ions, and in particular calcium, is the fine fraction of the substratum, constituting the matrix between the pebbles. On two beaches in Arran, the pH of this material was 8·3 and 8·7. However, analyses of this fraction are difficult to interpret in view of the rapid passage of ions in solution through the substratum. A further source of supply, particularly of sodium and chloride, is clearly sea water, arriving either in spray or during occasional inundation, while an additional source of certain ions may be rain water. Decomposition of drift and humus may contribute to the supply of potassium, phosphate and, especially, nitrogen which may often be present only in very low concentrations. Some shingle beaches are relatively iodine-rich, and at least one species, *Mertensia maritima*, has been shown to be tolerant of higher than normal concentrations of iodine in its tissues (Scott, 1960).

On most shingle beaches the plants are above the reach of the water table, and hence rain water is the most important moisture supply. Most of the plants concerned are to a considerable degree drought-resistant, but the structure of the substratum tends to conserve moisture in the fine fraction, which is relatively protected from evaporation. Scott showed, for example, that during a week's fine weather at Kilmory variations in temperature and humidity at 30·5 cm. (12 in.) below the surface were imperceptible to a recording hygro-thermograph. There was some diurnal fluctuation at 15·3 cm. (6 in.), but for most of the time relative humidity was about 90 per cent. In sunny weather the surface pebbles showed temperatures of 26°C. when the air temperature was 21°C.

Foreshore plants are subject to rapid fluctuations in salinity which may rise following inundation or spray deposition and subsequent evaporation, or fall as a result of rainfall or leaching.

Colonisation may sometimes be restricted to annual species, if the shingle is subject to considerable movement each winter and the algal deposits are of an annual nature. Thus, on a pebble-wrack beach at Kilmory, Arran, *Atriplex glabriuscula* is the only regular species, associated sometimes with other species of *Atriplex* and some weeds such as *Polygonum aviculare*, *Spergula arvensis* and *Poa pratensis*. Equally restricted, but in different directions, is the flora of beaches composed of larger boulders. On parts of the Struey Rocks there is a deep, poorly drained wrack bank thrown up among the boulders just above the summer mean high-water mark. Here only *Tripleurospermum maritimum* and *Rumex crispus* occur. Gillham (1957) mentions boulder-strewn shores of sea-lochs on the west coast of Mull where belts of *Potentilla anserina* a few metres wide occupy the strip of beach between the high-water marks of ordinary and spring tides. Locally this mingles with or is replaced by *Polygonum hydropiper* or *Rumex crispus*. Where there is a matrix of sand as well as wrack deposits, a rather longer list of species is obtained.

On the other hand, where the stones are smaller and the matrix more sandy, other changes are apparent. Parts of the foreshore at Longniddry, East Lothian, described by Hulme (1957) may be referred to as "gravel-wrack-sand" beaches, having a flora composed mainly of *Atriplex glabriuscula* with *A. laciniata*, *A. littoralis*, *Rumex crispus* and *Honkenya peploides*. As the proportion of sand increases so does the quantity of *Honkenya peploides*, and the accompanying flora becomes that of a sandy foreshore (see p. 86).

Apposition banks

Arrhenatherum elatius stands on apposition banks to landward of the foreshore. On stable shingle beyond the influence even of the strongest storms, development of the vegetation is influenced by the habitats lying immediately to landward, and by neighbouring floras. The community quickly becomes closed, with the addition of *Arrhenatherum elatius* and other species of maritime grassland communities. Examples of communities of this kind are given in Table 11, some of which probably receive drainage water from inland. Scott (1960) points out that this vegetation is in some respects similar to the "Tangwälle" of Norway (Nordhagen, 1940). The most vigorous invader may be *Arrhenatherum*, but other species in this category may be *Pteridium aquilinum*, *Agropyron repens* or even *Carex arenaria*, any of which may, at least temporarily, become dominant.

The flora of some of these sites begins to approximate to that of maritime cliffs (p. 77). Thus *Geranium robertianum* is prominent in several examples, while *Vicia sylvatica* and *Prunus spinosa* have high frequencies in certain lists. In other cases, especially on the west coast where the hinterland is marshy, species such as *Iris pseudacorus* and *Filipendula ulmaria* may give rise to dense stands, e.g. in Mull (Gillham, 1957).

Heath communities on apposition banks. A series of low shingle ridges, separated by flat areas of pebbles with sand, lies near the mouth of the river Lossie, Morayshire on the south-west side. Here the ridges are occupied by *Ulex europaeus* and *Sarothamnus scoparius*, while the flat areas contain an open community with low bushes of *Calluna vulgaris*. The individual plants are separate from one another, but sufficiently numerous to give a patchy heath-like vegetation, in which *Erica cinerea* and *Lotus corniculatus* are numerous, with *Campanula rotundifolia* and *Carex arenaria*. The community is rich in lichens, which colonise the open spaces between the dwarf-shrubs.

Shingle salt marsh communities

Where a high proportion of silt occurs among the pebbles and salinity is maintained by percolation of sea water through the storm crest, fragments of communities similar to those of salt marsh develop. These are also seen, here and there, where narrow shelving beaches of shingle have accumulated in the bays and sea lochs of the west coast. Asprey (1947) lists the following species from the harbour at Canna:

Festuca rubra var. *glaucescens*	o.	*Cochlearia officinalis*	o.
Puccinellia maritima	co.d.	*Glaux maritima*	f.
Juncus gerardii	l.f.	*Plantago coronopus*	o.
Triglochin maritima	o.	*P. marina*	a.
Armeria maritima	co-d.	*Spergularia marginata*	o.
Atriplex hastata	o.	*Suaeda maritima*	o.

The tufts of *Puccinellia* and rosettes of *Armeria* and *Plantago maritima* form an intermittent, eroded turf on the stable shingle. Gillham (1957) also refers to low-lying islands of halophytic vegetation on the dissected pebble flats along the margins of sea-lochs in Mull. Here *Plantago maritima*, *Armeria maritima*, *Glaux maritima* and *Juncus gerardii* are the chief species at first, with later development of a closed community containing in addition *Juncus maritimus*, *Aster tripolium* and *Triglochin maritima*.

Across a narrow transition zone, characterised by *Leontodon autumnalis*, *Agrostis stolonifera*, *Carex flacca* and *C. demissa*, this merges into peat-communities.

The Sandy Foreshore

Although frequently included under the heading of Sand Dunes as the first seral stage in the dune succession, the sandy foreshore is here given separate treatment since it may occur quite independently of any dune development and is subject to very different environmental influences. During the summer months the upper portions of sandy beaches are frequently colonised by a belt, or sometimes two or more parallel belts, mainly of annual plants. The small assemblage of species concerned is very much the same wherever suitable sandy beaches occur around the Scottish coastline, consisting of plants generally regarded as halophytes and characterised by succulence, mealiness, or both (Table 1).

Table 1

Composition and Percentage Presence of Species in Foreshore
and *Agropyron junceiforme* ("embryonic dune") Stands

Localities	Foreshore Bay of Luce, Wigtownshire; Luskentyre, Outer Hebrides; St. Cyrus, Kincardineshire; Tentsmuir, Fife; Longniddry, E.Lothian	*Agropyron junceiforme* stands Bay of Luce, Wigtownshire; Luskentyre, Outer Hebrides; St. Cyrus, Kincardineshire
No. of Stands	5	3
Agropyron junceiforme . .	60	100
Ammophila arenaria . . .	40	100
Elymus arenarius . . .	20	33
Festuca rubra	...	67
Atriplex glabriuscula . . .	80*	67
A. laciniata	80	33
A. littoralis	40	...
A. patula	20	...
Cakile maritima . . .	100	67
Cerastium atrovirens . .	...	67
Cirsium arvense . . .	20	33
Honkenya peploides . .	100	100
Rumex crispus	40	33
Salsola kali	60	33
Additional species recorded in one stand only . . .	*Plantago maritima*	*Agrostis* sp. *Potentilla anserina* *Taraxacum* sp.

* Hulme (Longniddry) refers throughout to *A. hastata* s.l. but probably most of the foreshore populations are referable to *A. glabriuscula*. Data are included from Hulme (1957), Gimingham *et al.* (1949), Gimingham (1951), Smith & Smith (1904-5).

With the exception of one or two species listed from a few localities only, representation of the few plants which constitute the flora of the foreshore is on the whole very regular. Their relative abundance varies widely, but in Scotland it would be meaningless to attempt any subdivision of this often-repeated grouping. Its exact relationship with the several associations of the alliances "Salsola-Minuartion peploidis" (*Minuartia peploides = Honkenya peploides*) and "Atriplicion littoralis" in the "Cakiletalia maritimae" of the Braun-Blanquet system has not been determined.

Among the more constant species, only *Honkenya peploides* is a perennial. This has the effect that, on certain highly exposed beaches, it is the only representative of this group of species, as at Bettyhill, Sutherland, a north-facing beach on the north coast of Scotland. Here the surface sand is so unstable under the influence of high winds throughout the year that colonisation by annuals is presumably prevented. Even in less exposed situations, instability of the surface together with variations in tidal submergence and wave action, renders conditions on the foreshore very variable from year to year, while the influences governing seed dispersal may also change irregularly. This probably accounts for the great fluctuations in the numerical proportions of the several species. So, at St. Cyrus, Kincardineshire, in 1947 when foreshore colonisation was rather restricted in extent, *Salsola kali*, *Atriplex glabriuscula* and *Cakile maritima* were approximately equal in abundance. In the two subsequent years, however, a much longer strip of beach was occupied and *Salsola kali* became the most common with first *Atriplex* and later *Cakile* decreasing. More recently *Cakile* has again been numerous in this area (Gimingham, 1951). Similarly, at Longniddry, Hulme (1957) reports that in addition to numerous *Atriplex hastata** and some *A. laciniata* there were also in 1953, *A. littoralis* and a few plants of *A. patula* and *Cakile maritima*. In 1954, however, the first two were absent while *Cakile* was much more frequent. These fluctuations serve to emphasise the changing and unstable conditions.

Foreshore plants seldom, if ever, occur in sufficient density to produce a closed community, hence competition between the species is unlikely to be severe. This may provide an additional reason for their marked fluctuations in numbers. However, it is often noticeable that individuals of a particular species may occur in rather dense groups. The reason for this has not been determined, but some doubt has been cast on the suggestion that whole fruiting inflorescences become buried in sand, the contained seeds germinating *in situ* next year. There is evidence for considerable redistribution of surface sand each winter, and it is perhaps more probable that some degree of sorting of particles thrown up in tide drift leads to the aggregation of seeds. Many observers have mentioned the regular association of the roots of foreshore plants with tide drift (Gimingham *et al.*, 1949; Gimingham, 1951; Hulme, 1957): this, however, could be explained either by the seeds being contained in the drift, or by the presence of drift making conditions locally favourable for germination and establishment.

Most of the foreshore species have root systems which are both deep and extensive (Table 2). The tap roots may reach layers of sand which, even on the foreshore, remain moist throughout much of the year, while the most extensive laterals, being situated only

---

* Hulme refers throughout to *A. hasta* s.l., incorporating *A. glabriuscula*, to which many of the foreshore plants may be referable.

6·3-7·6 cm. (2½-3 in.) below the surface can obtain moisture even from light showers which wet the surface only temporarily.

TABLE 2

Measurements of Root Systems of Foreshore Species (cm.)

(Means refer to 10 measurements, except where otherwise stated)

	Luskentyre, Isle of Harris, Outer Hebrides		St. Cyrus, Kincardineshire						
	Depth of longest root		Depth of longest root		Length of longest lateral		Position of longest lateral below surface		
	Mean.	Max.	Mean.	Max.	Mean.	Max.	Mean.	Min.	Max.
Atriplex glabriuscula .	...	...	24·1	34·3	22·1	40·1	6·9	5·1	8·9
A. sabulosa . . .	15·2†	20·3	17·0	21·6	8·4	10·2	6·1	5·1	7·6
Cakile maritima . .	17·8	22·7	...	...	...	...	...	...	...
Salsola kali . . .	...	...	22·4	36·8	20·3	33·0	7·1	3·8	11·4
Agropyron junceiforme .	...	...	20·8	25·4	16·0	31·8	3·8	2·5	5·1
Honkenya peploides . .	47·0*	68·6	...	...	...	...	...	...	...

† 7 measurements   * 4 measurements

Data from Gimingham, Gemmell and Greig-Smith (1949) and Gimingham (1951)

Foreshore plants, especially when occurring in rather dense groups of individuals, accumulate low hummocks of blown sand around their lower branches. These are normally rapidly dispersed in autumn but they sometimes provide a niche for the entry of more permanent colonists, in particular, the perennial grasses *Agropyron junceiforme* and *Ammophila arenaria*. Both species will also establish independently in the foreshore, and hence must be included in any list of the foreshore flora (as in Table 1). In view, however, of their dune-building properties they are best considered in more detail in the next section.

Seedlings do not appear on the foreshore until rather later than in many other habitats, generally at the end of April or early May. Hulme (1957) points out that many authors have too readily assumed that the zone of the beach occupied by foreshore plants is that above the reach of the tides, or perhaps just reached by the highest spring tides. In fact, the regular examination of permanent transects on the beach at Longniddry showed that this was far from the truth. The first-established plants may be along the line of drift thrown up by the highest spring tides, but as the season advances through May and June germination takes place at successively lower levels, not disturbed by tides at this time of year (Fig. 18), e.g. young plants were seen on 16th June just above high-water mark, then at its lowest level in the summer. Such plants must have been

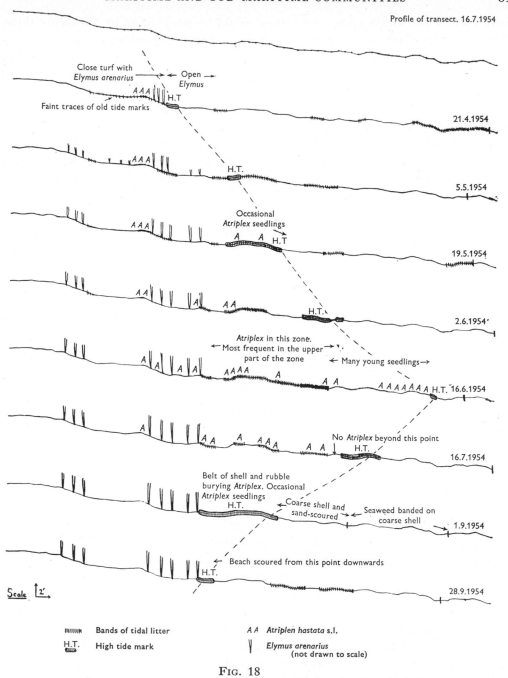

Profile of transect. 16.7.1954

Close turf with
Elymus arenarius — ← Open → *Elymus*

A A A H.T

Faint traces of old tide marks

21.4.1954

A A A H.T.

5.5.1954

Occasional
Atriplex seedlings

A A A *A A* H.T

19.5.1954

A A *A A*

H.T.

2.6.1954·

Atriplex in this zone.
← Most frequent in the upper →
part of the zone   ← Many young seedlings →

A A A A *A* *A A* *A A A A A A A* H.T. 16.6.1954

A *A A* *A* *A A A* *A A* No *Atriplex* beyond this point
H.T.

16.7.1954

Belt of shell and rubble
burying *Atriplex*. Occasional
Atriplex seedlings
H.T.

← Coarse shell and → ← Seaweed banded on
sand-scoured   coarse shell

1.9.1954

← Beach scoured from this point downwards

H.T.

28.9.1954

Scale ↕2′

IIIIIIK   Bands of tidal litter   *A A*   *Atriplen hastata* s.l.

H.T.   High tide mark   Y   *Elymus arenarius*
                                          (not drawn to scale)

Fig. 18

A permanent transect across the foreshore at Longniddry, East Lothian,
charted at intervals throughout the summer. Note the downward extension
of colonization by *Atriplex*, as the zone free from tidal scour (to left of
dotted line) increases during the early part of the summer. (From Hulme,
1957.)

short-lived since, within a few weeks, they would be swept away by advancing tides. Further up the beach, however, plants remain undisturbed for long enough to flower before the advancing tides of late summer and early autumn scour the beach. It may be, however, that only those in the highest belts, undisturbed until well into September, set ripe seed.

The sand in the foreshore zone is freely-drained, lacking any appreciable quantity of organic matter except in the vicinity of tide-drift. Its surface dries out rapidly, but moisture draining to lower levels may be conserved. As in the case of shingle, the plants are generally situated above the level of a water-table and hence the roots are not normally bathed by sea water. The habitat is, at least from time to time, halophytic as a result of spray deposition. Quantities of salt in the sand vary (0·001 per cent., 0·009 per cent, Mull and Iona, Gillham, 1957; 0·04 per cent, St. Cyrus, Gimingham, 1951—all as g. NaCl/100 g. dry soil), but its influence on plants depends upon its concentration in the water contained in the sand. If it is assumed that all the salt present is in solution, which may not be the case, strengths reaching that of sea water have been recorded (1·7 and 3·2 per cent., Gillham, 1957), but it is very unlikely that plants would be subjected for long to concentrations of this order.

The mineral composition of the sand varies greatly from the highly calcareous shell sands of some west coast beaches with over 60 per cent. calcium carbonate, to the siliceous sands with 2 per cent. or less. In the foreshore, however, pH is generally above 7, ranging usually from about 7·2 to 8·4. An analysis of the chief minerals in the surface sand of the foreshore at St. Cyrus gave the following:

P_2O_5	K_2O	MgO	MnO
as mg. per 100 g. sand			
0·7	5·5	25	1·5

Sand Dunes

Sandy beaches backed by dunes, large and small, constitute a characteristic feature of Scotland's maritime scenery. Continuous stretches of sand dune up to 19 km. (12 miles) in length occur along the smoother outlines of the east coast as well as smaller arcs lining many of the bays. Extensive systems of great interest to the ecologist occur on both sides of the Tay estuary—the Tentsmuir Sands and Sands of Barry—while further north the Forvie and Culbin sands are famous for the way in which their "wandering dunes" have overblown on to adjacent land. Large systems are also a feature of the bays facing the Solway Firth, such as the Bay of Luce, and innumerable smaller dunes have developed in the indentations of the north and west, and of the island shores. Here too, the long-continued blowing of sand on to nearby cliffs and peat land has produced the fertile and characteristic "machair" pastures.

Sand dunes have for many years been recognised as dynamic systems depending upon supplies of wind-blown sand, which is arrested and partially stabilised by vegetation composed of species whose growth can keep pace with sand accretion. The relatively rapid changes in the habitat are associated with further vegetational changes in the direction of increasing stability. Many of the aspects of this succession have been well documented and investigated on Scottish dunes, but research in this part of the world has also drawn attention to properties of sand dune systems additional to the processes belonging to the primary succession. These include the potential instability of dunes, the occurrence of blow-outs, the formation of "wandering dunes" and their subsequent stabilisation, as well as the vegetational developments accompanying wind erosion, in particular, erosion to levels fixed by a ground water table.

The earlier stages in the development of sand dunes take place under environmental conditions which are relatively exacting as far as the establishment of vegetation is concerned. Hence the flora is restricted to a small number of rather specialised species. However, as the process of dune building proceeds, a considerable degree of shelter and protection is created, affecting particularly the habitats of the later stages of plant succession, the dune heaths, dune pastures, and the damp hollows or dune slacks which often occur behind the main ridges. The communities in these situations are often much richer in the variety of species represented, few of which are exclusive to dunes. Many are plants typical of mesophytic or moist habitats, demonstrating by their presence considerable amelioration of environmental conditions. Even in the later, more stable phases, however, the habitats evidently possess certain distinctive properties, as indicated both by the characteristic composition of the communities and by the evidence for ecotypic differentiation in the dune populations of certain species.

Landwards of the main dune ridges, especially where dunes have formed in the more sheltered bays or inlets, climatic conditions may locally be milder than in the surrounding district. It is here that species belonging to the southern elements of our flora enter the communities: for example *Saxifraga granulata*, *Dianthus deltoides*, *Campanula glomerata*, *Carlina vulgaris*, *Filago germanica*. By contrast, a northern montane element is represented in highly exposed situations, especially in the far north, including *Dryas octopetala*, *Oxytropis halleri*, *Festuca vivipara*, *Draba incana*, *Carex maritima*, *Trollius europaeus*, *Saxifraga hypnoides*. Floristic differences between dunes of the east and west coast include the prevalance of *Astragalus danicus* on the east, and the abundance on the west, especially in dune pastures, slacks and machairs, of numerous orchids, including *Dactylorchis maculata* ssp. *ericetorum*, *D. purpurella*, *D. fuchsii*, *Orchis mascula*, *Coeloglossum viride*, *Gymnadenia conopsea*, *Listera ovata*, *Epipactis atrorubens*.

More striking, however, than the differences correlated with climatic variation are those related to the origin and composition of the sand. Even where the sand is largely siliceous, containing only 2 per cent. calcium carbonate or less, the communities frequently include a number of more or less "basiphilous" species such as *Galium verum*, *Thymus drucei*, *Campanula rotundifolia*, *Lotus corniculatus*, *Achillea millefolium*, etc. The sand may, however, be of a much higher "base status", particularly where it is composed largely of finely divided shell fragments, as in a number of examples on the west mainland and island coasts. Here, where the calcium carbonate content may rise to nearly 70 per cent. (Gimingham *et al.*, 1949; Vose *et al.*, 1957), the flora is considerably enriched with numerous species normally regarded as to some extent calcicolous, e.g. *Anthyllis vulneraria*, *Arabis hirsuta*, *Carlina vulgaris*, *Daucus carota*, *Helictotrichon pratense*, *H. pubescens*, *Origanum vulgare*, *Pimpinella saxifraga*, *Solidago virgaurea*, *Camptothecium lutescens*, *Ditrichum flexicaule*, etc.

General aspects of dune development

In localities where active forward colonisation and dune development are taking place, the pattern of dynamic changes in vegetation and habitat in Scotland resembles that in England and elsewhere. The first signs of permanent establishment of dune-forming species appears when *Agropyron junceiforme* invades the foreshore communities already described (p. 86), usually at and above the high-water mark of spring tides. The establishment of clones and colonies of this plant leads to the formation of low "embryonic" dunes, on which *Ammophila arenaria* becomes established. On some very exposed beaches, e.g. on the west coast of the Outer Hebrides, at Bettyhill on the N. Sutherland coast and on the island of Barra (MacLeod, 1949), *Agropyron* although present in the area, does not initiate dune formation, and this process is carried out directly by *Ammophila*. The main phase of dune building springs from the development of dominance by *Ammophila*, sometimes preceded or accompanied by *Elymus arenarius*. At first the sand surface between the groups of leafy shoots of these species is bare and mobile ("mobile dunes", "yellow dunes"), but as the rate of sand accretion decreases the first signs of surface fixation by rosette plants such as *Senecio jacobaea*, *Taraxacum* sp., and mosses, are apparent. At about the same stage additional species of grasses enter, the first usually being *Festuca rubra* var. *arenaria*. As fixation proceeds the number of species participating rises steeply, and the community becomes closed. A turf composed of various grasses, legumes and mosses results. Its formation coincides with the beginning of degeneration of *Ammophila*, which however, persists for a considerable time in the form of residual tussocks in the subsequent stages.

Further development depends both upon the nature of the sand and upon the intensity of grazing, particularly by rabbits. A dune pasture develops naturally on the calcareous substrata, and also on the more acid sands if grazing prevents the entry of ericaceous dwarf shrubs. During the course of succession on the siliceous sands, with the incorporation of humus and other changes, pH usually falls well below 7 and here, if grazing is not excessive, dune heath becomes established (pp. 255 & 264). On either type of community, shrubs and trees may invade, but outside agencies in almost all cases prevent further successional change.

In addition to the straightforward sequence of changes concerned in the formation and fixation of dunes, outlined above, other series of communities may be represented. In regular dune systems, as one dune ridge ceases to build, another may form parallel and to seaward of the first. Scottish dunes are seldom so simple in construction, but this pattern is approached in parts of Tentsmuir, and at Balnakiel, Durness. In the hollows enclosed between the ridges ground water-tables may stand at, or near, the sand surface, and a sequence of stages in the development of dune slack communities can be followed. These are also present in erosion hollows and other depressions in more complex systems. All dunes are subject to blow-outs and secondary recolonization successions occur on eroded surfaces. The sand released, together with additional supplies of wind-blown sand is in certain areas aggregated into "wandering dunes" which frequently take the form of a U, the bow advancing in the direction of the prevailing wind and the "arms" trailing behind. Stages in the gradual colonisation and stabilisation of these "wandering dunes" have also been worked out as well as the vegetational sequences concerned, as the territory over which they have passed is exposed by wind erosion, frequently removing sand down to the level of a permanent water-table.

Some of the communities taking part in these processes will now be considered in more detail.

Agropyron junceiforme stands: "embryonic dunes". *Agropyron junceiforme* normally colonises most readily where clusters of foreshore species (see p. 88) have accumulated low mounds of sand around and above high-water mark of spring tides. Hence, the foreshore community often represents the first stage in the succession leading to dune formation, and *A. junceiforme* is the chief species of the second stage. However, this species may also establish in open sand, acting as a pioneer colonist. The first leaves and tillers form a small rosette, closely pressed against the surface (Plate 8). Even at this stage small accumulations of sand may appear in the lee of the plants and when, with the development of horizontally extending rhizomes, a colony of overlapping shoots is formed a low dune begins to grow (Fig. 19). The tillers later tend to adopt an erect habit of growth and the rate of sand accumulation increases. Embryonic dunes may take the form of more or less distinct, rather flat domes, but where *Agropyron* is vigorous, as for example in an actively colonising system fringing an uninterrupted dune ridge, these distinct mounds may coalesce as a "fore-dune" or undulating forward extension of the main ridge, on which the stand of *Agropyron* becomes largely continuous. In such a community, *Agropyron junceiforme* may have few associates, these being limited to some relicts of the foreshore species and a few invading individuals of *Ammophila arenaria*, *Festuca rubra*, etc. (Plate 9: Table 1). The community here corresponds to the "Agropyretum boreoatlanticum"="Minuartio*—Agropyryetum juncei" of Continental authors.

A detailed investigation of the autecology of *Agropyron junceiforme* carried out at St. Cyrus by I. A. Nicholson (1952) showed that establishment may take place either from "seed" or from broken portions of rhizome, but that "seed" production is limited, possibly varying from year to year. In a series of samples only about 3·5 per cent. of shoots bore an inflorescence, and the number of seeds produced per spike was 6. With an average percentage germination of 30, this represents a production of only 7 viable seeds per hundred vegetative shoots, or less than 3 per 9·3 sq. dm. (1 sq. ft.) within the community. Germination may commence within 2-4 days of deposition if the sand is

* Referring to *Minuartia* (=*Honkenya*) *peploides*.

moist, but is completely inhibited by sea water, and reduced in amount and rate by any concentration of sodium chloride exceeding 0·5 per cent. Hence, except in eroded areas moistened by an underlying freshwater table, germination presumably occurs only when the sand is kept moist by rain water, or among moist tide-drift if the latter has previously been leached by rain water. However, only a limited series of tests has been carried out, and there is evidence to suggest that the factors controlling germination and establishment of *A. junceiforme* are complex and would repay further investigation.

The single primary root quickly extends to a depth of about 15 cm. (6 in.) where a level of moisture content rather higher than that of surface layers is often maintained.

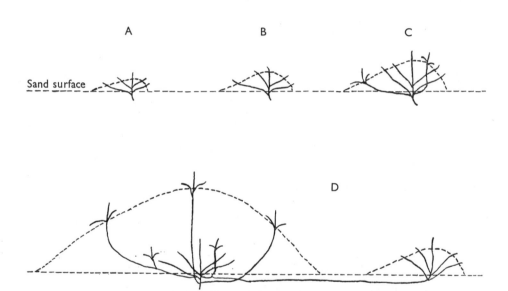

Fig. 19 Stages in colony development and formation of "embryonic dunes" by *Agropyron junceiforme*. The upper broken line represents the surface of the dune. (From Nicholson, 1952.)

The first formed lateral roots, however, extend horizontally closely below the sand surface. After a rosette of tillers has been established, short rhizomes are formed extending obliquely for distances of between 5 and 30 cm. (2 and 12 in.) from the original plant, giving rise to new groups of tillers (Fig. 19, A, B and C). This type of growth may continue for two seasons, but in time long horizontal rhizomes are produced, greatly increasing the vegetative spread of the plant (Fig. 19 D). Their tips normally turn upwards in autumn, just breaking the surface, ready to produce a new group of shoots in spring. Development may continue indefinitely in this way if sand accumulation is only slight, for elongation of the shoots can bring them to the surface through layers not exceeding about 23 cm. (9 in.) in depth. Where, however, burial is more rapid, shoots are killed and rhizomes instead of extending laterally assume a vertical direction until the new surface is reached, when again tillering takes place. This sympodial development may keep pace with repeated sand deposition, often up to heights of 1·8 m. and sometimes considerably more. Hence, by its lateral extension *Agropyron* may stabilise the foreshore region and initiate the process of arresting blown sand and, provided accumulation is not too rapid, it may act as a dune builder. This is the case for example at Balinoe, Tiree, where *Ammophila* is locally absent (Vose *et al.*, 1957).

Active roots of *Agropyron* are seldom found more than two feet below the surface and hence are well beyond the influence of the underlying water-table which is at least 1·2 m. (4 ft.) deep and often more. While for much of the time salinity in the rooting region is low, *Agropyron* is tolerant of occasional tidal submergence with accompanying increases in salinity.

Ammophila arenaria stands: "mobile" and "fixed" dunes. The pattern of behaviour of *Ammophila arenaria* is broadly similar to that of *Agropyron junceiforme* and hence, as already mentioned, it can act as a pioneer colonist and embryo-dune former. However, it is not as tolerant of submergence in sea water and does not colonise as far forward, normally entering among the colonies of *Agropyron* which have already built up low dunes out of reach of normal tidal influence (Plate 9). Detailed studies of *Ammophila* on a dune system on the west coast of Harris, Outer Hebrides (Gemmell *et al.*, 1953), have shown that it too may establish either as seedlings (Fig. 20A) or from portions of broken rhizome. The reproductive capacity is probably much greater than that of *Agropyron*. (Salisbury (1942) mentions a figure of 36,650 "seeds" produced from a "young" isolated clump of *Ammophila*.) There is evidence (Greig-Smith, 1961) that seedlings are very much more abundant in some years than others, also that some degree of pattern or aggregation occurs, presumably due to local variations in habitat conditions. Sometimes a whole inflorescence falls before the "seeds" are shed and a dense cluster of seedlings results.

On certain dune systems, particularly those in exposed situations where *Agropyron* plays little part in initial stabilisation, e.g. Harris, W. Ross, etc., *Ammophila* spreads laterally with vigorous horizontal rhizomes from which groups of leafy shoots are produced. These begin to accumulate blown sand and initiate dune formation. However, this phase of growth is superseded by that in which the rhizomes are directed upwards as sand gathers, producing groups of tillers at the new sand surface as in the case of *Agropyron*. This, as demonstrated in sections of dunes exposed by blow-outs, is the principal method of growth of *Ammophila*. When colonising embryonic or fore-dunes already built by *Agropyron* the plant probably develops in this way from the start and horizontally spreading rhizomes are then rarely produced (Fig 20 B, C). The taller, more rigid persistent shoots and leaves of *Ammophila* cause more rapid accumulation of sand than that produced by *Agropyron*. This may be one of the factors leading to the reduction and eventual elimination of the latter, which may be progressively weakened by the vertical growth consequent upon repeated burial. Not only is vertical extension in *Ammophila* very vigorous, but the groups of tillers themselves remain aggregated in a pattern retained from that of the original establishment. These aggregates develop into

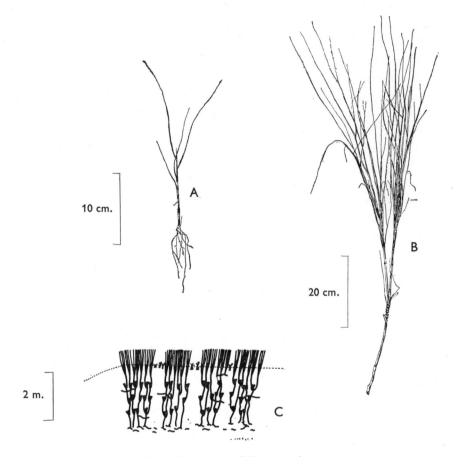

FIG. 20.   *Ammophila arenaria*

A. Drawing of seedling showing erect habit of growth in the young plant.

B. Drawing of top of a vertical rhizome from an actively growing dune, showing vigorous leaf production at the tips of the branches.

C. Diagram of sympodial renewal growth with repeated burial by sand.

(A and B from Gemmell, Greig-Smith and Gimingham, 1953).

large tussocks eventually forming a more or less continuous stand, and the dunes, hitherto discontinuous, merge into a continuous ridge which builds to its maximum height.

PLATE 5
Scottish sea-cliff scenery:
Shetland (east coast).

PLATE 6
Cliff and dune on the north
coast of Scotland: Bettyhill,
Sutherland.

PLATE 7
Crovie, Banffshire, on the
coast of the Moray Firth.
Shingle beach in the foreground. Immediately to the
left of the most distant house
is a slope colonized by an
excellent example of a "*Plantago* sward".

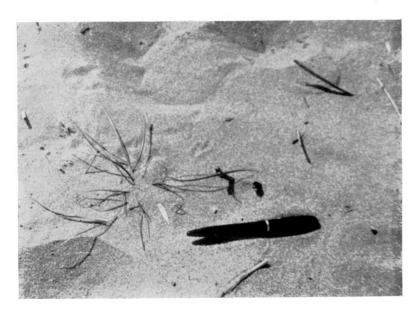

PLATE 8. Young plant of *Agropyron junceiforme* colonizing in the foreshore zone. The tillers adopt a position almost adpressed to the sand surface.

PLATE 9. Colony of *Agropyron junceiforme* forming a low "embryonic dune". Plants of *Salsola kali* occur nearby. At top left, and right of centre, are shoots of colonizing *Ammophila arenaria*.

PLATE 10. Root profile in machair vegetation, Hebrides. Heavily grazed by rabbits.

Photo I. A. Nicholson

A frequent associate of *Ammophila* is *Elymus arenarius*, which has some of the same dune-building properties. However, this species may be altogether lacking and, even where present, it may occur only as scattered clumps or patches amongst *Ammophila* when its ecological role is negligible. Its varying status presents a problem, since on certain systems as at St. Andrews, Tentsmuir, Aberdeen and elsewhere it becomes dominant in a zone in advance of the main dunes and gives rise to low dunes, later being superseded by *Ammophila*. There is evidence that in some of these localities, e.g. St. Andrews, it was planted as a stabilising agent. However, like *Ammophila* it shows high fidelity to the communities concerned, which have consequently been named "Elymo-Ammophiletum" by followers of the Braun-Blanquet school.

The communities covered by this title show in fact considerable variation since they are seral in nature and represent progressive development from the "mobile dune" stage to "fixed dune", with stabilisation of the surface sand and formation of a turf. They fall conveniently into four categories:

  (i) Pure stands of *Elymus arenarius*.
  (ii) Stands of *Ammophila arenaria*, pure or with scattered *Elymus*.
  (iii) Early, and (iv) Later stages of surface fixation.

The floristic composition of communities in (iii) and (iv) demand more detailed discussion:

Early stages of surface fixation

At first *Ammophila* and *Elymus* may be the only species present, but even while the rate of sand accretion is rapid, scattered individuals of some other species enter (Table 12, p. 134). *Festuca rubra* (mainly the var. *arenaria*) is the most important; others regularly occurring include *Cirsium arvense*, *Lotus corniculatus*, *Plantago lanceolata*, *Senecio jacobaea*, *Sonchus asper*, *Taraxacum* sp., *Trifolium repens*, and sometimes *Tussilago farfara* and *Carex arenaria*. Most of these are plants with a compact rosette of leaves at the sand surface, while rhizomes, runners and other organs of rapid vegetative spread are characteristic and play an additional part in binding the surface layers of sand. Contributing also to this process are mosses, at first the erect, short-turf forming species. The pioneers are frequently *Bryum pendulum* and *Ceratodon purpureus*, usually with *Tortula ruraliformis* following abundantly a little later. However, D. H. N. Spence (unpublished) has pointed out that it is chiefly on the less exposed dune systems (e.g. at St. Cyrus and Tentsmuir, both on the east coast) that these three species are prominent as agents of fixation. In more windswept areas such as Luskentyre (Outer Hebrides) and Quendale (Shetland) *Trifolium repens* seems to be particularly prominent in this capacity. The earliest colonists are often followed by the more spreading mosses such as *Brachythecium albicans*, *Rhytidiadelphus squarrosus* and *Camptothecium lutescens* (the latter mainly on calcareous sands). The efficacy of mosses as agents of surface sand fixation is

G

illustrated by the following figures, from Bettyhill, of the weight of sand held when a sample 10 × 20 cm. is cut and raised from a pure stand of the species listed:

Tortula ruraliformis . . . . 179·7 g.
Camptothecium lutescens . . . . 448·9 g.
Rhytidiadelphus triquetrus (from a later stage of
fixation) . . . . 335·9 g.

Later stages of surface fixation

These are usually recognised by a rapid increase in the number of species present (Table 12), and the closure of vegetational cover so that bare sand is no longer visible except on disturbed spots (Plate 11). Besides *Ammophila*, which retains dominance although flowering less freely, the following species are among those most regularly represented: *Achillea millefolium, Bellis perennis, Carex arenaria, Cerastium atrovirens, Euphrasia* spp., *Festuca rubra, Galium verum, Lotus corniculatus, Plantago lanceolata, Poa pratensis, Taraxacum* sp., *Trifolium repens.* There is considerable variation in the community composition from place to place, with different species of grass and legume taking part (*Ononis repens,* for example, is very abundant on some dunes): normally the more calcareous dunes yield the richest species lists. Perhaps the most important development at this stage is the spread of leguminous species with consequent enrichment of the soil in nitrogen, and this is no doubt associated with the increase in number of grassland plants. Of the mosses, *Tortula ruraliformis* and *Rhytidiadelphus squarrosus* remain important, but characteristic of this stage is the entry into the turf of mat-forming species such as *Hypnum cupressiforme,* robust types including *Rhytidiadelphus triquetrus, Hylocomium splendens, Mnium undulatum,* and others indicative of increasing moisture retention at the surface, e.g. *Lophocolea bidentata.* In some areas different facies of the community have been recognised, mainly in terms of the chief moss species, e.g. *Festuca—Mnium undulatum* facies, *Rhytiliadelphus squarrosus* facies and *R. triquetrus* facies (D. H. N. Spence, Quendale, Shetland).

Dune pastures and Machairs. These communities are not fundamentally very distinct from those of the later stages of fixation of *Ammophila* dunes, except that *Ammophila arenaria* is greatly reduced in vigour, occurring as scattered degenerating groups of shoots in the turf. Dune pastures may develop on very old dune ridges which have to some extent settled and contracted, and are frequent on the smoother areas where wind-blown sand has spread inland of the main ridges. In sheltered places there is little renewed deposition of blown sand but on exposed coasts, as at Quendale, Shetland, (D. H. N. Spence) sand is deposited continually in the dune pasture area, sometimes being blown 1300 m. and more inland. This is no doubt correlated with the greater frequency of *Ammophila* in the community here as compared with many other dune pasture.

There are certain floristic differences between pastures developed on siliceous and on "base rich" sands (Table 12), while those on the extremely lime-rich shell sands, particularly in the west and north of Scotland and in the Hebrides, are the richest in species and are usually termed "machairs". Here the percentage of calcium carbonate by weight may vary from 40 to 58 (Harris; Gimingham *et al.*, 1949: Tiree; Vose *et al.*, 1957), these figures usually being slightly below those for the earlier stages in the dune sequence, probably as a result of leaching and the incorporation of organic matter. However, at this level such differences amount to little change in the composition of the soil, and the pH remains between 6·8 and 7·8. Machair communities also extend into areas where shell sand has blown over on to adjacent cliffs, slopes or peat-covered land and these regions often provide the most fertile grazing or cultivated land of the district (Plate 10).

The basis of the communities throughout this range of habitats is a grassland composed mainly of *Festuca rubra*, *Poa pratensis*, *Trifolium repens* and *Lotus corniculatus*, with *Achillea millefolium*, *Galium verum*, and numerous other species, the extent of diversity depending upon the nature of the soil. Among the bryophytes, *Rhytidiadelphus squarrosus* is probably the most widespread and important.

On the more acid substrata, *Agrostis tenuis* and *Holcus lanatus* play important parts, but the list of associated species is relatively restricted. Among these may be mentioned *Carex arenaria*, *Campanula rotundifolia*, *Galium saxatile*, *Rumex acetosa*, *R. acetosella* and among the mosses and lichens, several species characteristic of heaths: *Hylocomium splendens*, *Pleurozium schreberi*, *Cladonia* spp. and *Peltigera canina*. A grass-lichen heath (or "grey dune") occurs in some places (e.g. at Forvie), in which *Carex arenaria* is often dominant or co-dominant with species of *Cladonia*, *Cetraria aculeata*, etc.

Much longer lists of species (including many so-called calcicoles) can be obtained where the mineral ion status of the soil is higher, even although the calcium carbonate level is not high (e.g. little over 1 per cent. at St. Cyrus, 1-4 per cent. at Bettyhill). Where grazing is relatively light a *Carex arenaria*-grassland community often results, but heavy grazing produces a short turf in which grasses are dominant. Among the species which contribute to the character of communities in this type of habitat are *Anthyllis vulneraria*, *Botrychium lunaria*, *Bellis perennis*, *Centaurea nigra*, *Ceologlossum viride*, *Daucus carota*, *Erodium cicutarium*, *Euphrasia* spp., *Plantago lanceolata*, *Pimpinella saxifraga*, *Primula vulgaris*, *P. veris*, *Prunella vulgaris*, *Ranunculus acris* and *Thymus drucei*, with the addition in the unusual examples at Bettyhill of arctic-alpine species such as *Oxytropis halleri* and *Dryas octopetala*.

There is little in the basic composition and structure of machair communities to separate them from those just described, except the wealth of interesting and beautiful plants which confer a special interest upon these areas. It is impossible to comment fully on the species concerned, which include localised plants such as *Gentianella amarella* ssp. *septentrionalis*, *Antennaria dioica*, *Trollius europaeus* (often in profusion). In addition to all the species mentioned above for the richer dune pastures, *Trifolium medium* is rather characteristic and numerous Cyperaceae are represented. Perhaps, however, the most distinctive feature of the machairs is the profusion of orchids, which may include, besides *Coeloglossum viride* already mentioned, *Epipactis atrorubens*, *Gymnadenia conopsea, Listera ovata, Dactylorchis fuchsii* and ssp. *hebridensis, D. purpurella* and *D. mascula.*

Effects of fire. Pure stands of vigorous *Ammophila* in the earlier stages of dune development regenerate rapidly after fire, with little permanent effect upon the community. However, accidental fires are also rather frequent in areas representing the later stages of fixation or dune pasture and here there is only a partial regeneration of *Ammophila.* A lichen-rich community with numerous annuals and other dwarf species results, in which the following are typical in addition to a number of the more usual dune pasture plants:

Aira caryophyllea	*Plantago coronopus*
Aira praecox	*Sagina* spp.
Phleum arenarium	*Sedum acre*
Arenaria serpyllifolia	*Rumex acetosella*
Cerastium atrovirens	*Cladonia cervicornis* var. *subcervicornis*
C. semidecandrum	*Cl. fimbriata*
Erodium cicutarium	*Cl. foliacea*
Erophila verna	*Cl. rangiformis*
Filago minima	*Peltigera canina*
Hieracium pilosella	

Salix repens dunes. Although not figuring prominently in Table 12, *Salix repens* is often an important component of the community on the flat or smoothly sloping areas of blown sand behind dune systems, particularly in the oceanic climate of the west. In regions still subject to considerable sand deposition, although some distance inland, *Salix repens* may in fact build low dunes firmly bound by the extensive creeping, intertwined rhizome systems. One such rhizome excavated from a machair at Bettyhill measured nearly 7 m. In parts of the west coast where blow-outs and wind erosion have occurred (e.g. Red Point, south of Gair Loch) relics of *Salix repens* dunes occur as sheer-sided platforms standing 1-1·5 m. higher than the level of the new sand surface, recently fixed by recolonisation.

Dune heaths. On siliceous sands, low in $CaCO_3$ content, the later stages of fixation may be invaded by *Calluna vulgaris* and *Erica cinerea*, with the development of dune heath. Accounts of the communities so formed are given in Chapter 7 on pp. 254-256, while in parts of certain dune systems on the east coast of Scotland *Empetrum*-rich communities, as described on pp. 264-265, occur.

Dune scrub. The occasional presence of species of *Rosa* (including *R. pimpinellifolia*), *Acer pseudoplatanus, Crataegus monogyna, Rubus fruticosus, R. idaeus, Ulex europaeus*, etc., in dune pastures indicates the probable lines of successional development should the habitats become free of rabbit grazing and other influences. At Tentsmuir, and at the Sands of Barry, *Hippophaë rhamnoides*, although presumably not native in Scotland, has locally formed dense thickets with an understorey of *Urtica dioica*. On the acid sands from Tain northwards, *Juniperus communis* appears in the dune heath (cf. p. 254 *et seq.*) and historical records suggest that it may have been present on the sands at Culbin prior to the period of extensive sand movement. Occasional seedlings of *Betula* spp. on dunes suggest that a birch-juniper scrub might have been a natural development in these areas. Types of scrub developing in dune slacks are mentioned below.

Dune "slacks" and "winter lochs". In the communities so far considered, only a very few species have sufficiently deep roots to reach a permanent water-table beneath the dunes. One such is *Ononis repens* whose tap root (as measured at St. Cyrus) descends often for more than 2 m. For the majority the rooting region is seldom if ever moistened by ground-water. However, nearly all dune systems except the simplest include a number of low-lying areas in which a water-table lies near the sand surface at least in winter. These may be the "valleys" separating one dune ridge from the next, where successive ridges have been formed at intervals as seaward colonisation has advanced. Similar hollows are generally found also among and behind the dunes in more complex systems. Wind erosion may excavate hollows down to a water-table, beyond which, as the sand is moist, there can be no further removal (cf. p. 112). As is to be expected, there is much variation in the hydrology of dune slacks, only a few Scottish examples having been investigated in detail (Landsberg, 1955; Birse, 1958). Low-lying areas very close to the beach may be subject to marine influence as at Tentsmuir, Culbin, etc., where communities akin to those of the more sandy salt-marsh substrata occur, including particularly *Glaux maritima* (often dominant), *Armeria maritima Aster tripolium, Sagina maritima, Triglochin maritima, Juncus gerardii, Juncus balticus.* This type of habitat will not be further considered here. Elsewhere the underlying water-table is not saline, and conditions range from those in which the surface is dry throughout much of the year and moistened only in winter, to those in which the water level is at, or above, the surface in winter and the sand normally remains moist throughout the year. The term *slack* is usually applied to these moister habitats, while those in which sizeable areas of standing water regularly gather each winter are often described as *winter lochs* (e.g. Forvie, Culbin, etc.).

It is scarcely surprising, therefore, that while there are certain floristic features demonstrating affinity between the communities in such habitats, there is a very considerable range in their composition. This is further complicated by the fact that the sites are usually valley or basin-shaped, with accompanying gradients in habitat conditions and associated vegetational zonation. The chemical composition of the sand also, as usual, has its influence upon the flora.

In the drier dune slacks, not normally submerged at any time of the year, the community most frequently includes components of the dune pasture and, if acid, dune heath, mixed with species characteristic of marsh and swamp (Chapters 9 and 10). A small number of species, mentioned below, while not exclusive to these habitats, are here particularly prominent and may be regarded as characteristic of the communities. In the wetter habitats there is a greater preponderance of species of swamp or bog, while in certain instances *Salix* and *Alnus* scrub develops (particularly at Tentsmuir). Table 13

(p. 139) displays the chief features of community composition normally associated with "typical" slacks, including those at the drier end of the sequence as well as those submerged in winter at least in certain years (e.g. Foveran, Aberdeenshire: Plates 11, 12, 13). The vegetation is invariably very low (except for the scattered tussocks of *Juncus effusus*, etc.) and includes a number of species of very small stature, e.g. *Radiola linoides*, while most of the rest grow in a dwarf or procumbent form, e.g. *Epilobium palustre*, *Juncus articulatus*, *Plantago coronopus*, sometimes *Ophioglossum vulgatum*.

On the more calcareous sands the aspect of the community is predominantly grassy, with *Festuca rubra* dominant and *Bellis perennis*, *Carex arenaria*, *Euphrasia* spp., *Lotus corniculatus*, *Linum catharticum*, *Plantago lanceolata*, *Prunella vulgaris*, and *Trifolium repens* regularly represented, all species typical of dune pastures. More or less constantly associated with these, however, are *Agrostis stolonifera*, *Carex flacca*, *Filipendula ulmaria*, *Hydrocotyle vulgaris*, *Juncus articulatus*, *Rhytidiadelphus squarrosus* and *Parnassia palustris*. The latter species is perhaps particularly characteristic of this type of dune slack as are the following, although their occurrence is less regular: *Ophioglossum vulgatum*, *Selaginella selaginoides*, *Corallorhiza trifida*. Dune slacks are usually very rich in bryophytes, often including a number of rare or unusual species such as *Moerckia flotoviana* (Sands of Barry, etc.). *Haplomitrium hookeri* (Foveran), *Riccia glauca*, *Blasia pusilla*, etc. To the south of Scotland, as at the Bay of Luce and elsewhere, *Leontodon taraxacoides*, so prominent in similar habitats in England, figures in the drier, grassy slack communities; to the north on the shell sands *Gentianella amarella* ssp. *septentrionalis* and *Primula scotica* are among the species which give special interest to these habitats.

On the more acid sands, the calcicolous and basiphilous species are reduced or lacking and while the general composition of the flora is similar, dominance is normally exerted by other species. Most widespread as a dominant is *Salix repens*. Often this species is present mainly in its prostrate form, very frequently associated with *Climacium dendroides*, but where vigorous it may adopt a more erect habit, and will then catch any sand blowing back off the dunes and give rise to low hummocks of bound sand scattered over the slack ("gegenwälle", see p. 110). Where *Salix repens* is dominant, *Juncus articulatus*, *Hydrocotyle vulgaris*, etc., are again abundant, but species of acid habitats play a bigger part, for example, *Erica tetralix*, *Empetrum nigrum*, *Ranunculus flammula*, *Juncus squarrosus*, *Bryum pseudotriquetrum*.

Dynamic stages in the development of the above communities are often observed, as in the saucer-shaped hollows behind the parabola dunes at Forvie (see also p. 110). Here an early stage in the colonisation of moist sand is represented by an open community in which such species as *Juncus articulatus*, *Carex arenaria*, *Festuca rubra*, *Agrostis tenuis* and sometimes *Equisetum arvense* are pioneer colonists, along with some species from the drier dune flora. Following this comes a stage in which the typical slack community develops, including *Cardamine pratensis*, *Carex demissa*, *Carex nigra*, *Carex serotina*, *Hydrocotyle vulgaris*, *Juncus bufonius*, *J. bulbosus*, *J. effusus*, *J. squarrosus*, *Ranunculus flammula*, *Viola palustris*, very dwarf species such as *Isolepis setacea*, numerous bryophytes, e.g., *Acrocladium cuspidatum*, *Blasia pusilla*, *Pellia* spp., *Preissia quadrata*,

Riccardia spp., and various hepatics. A further stage is marked by the entry of *Salix repens, Erica tetralix, Empetrum nigrum, Climacium dendroides* and damp heath species (including, here, *Lycopodium clavatum*). A dune slack or hollow may exhibit any one of these phases of colonisation, while those in which the floor of the depression is at a late stage show a zonation outwards passing through communities akin to those of the earlier stages. Zonation in these saucer or horseshoe-shaped depressions, however, is a complex phenomenon which cannot be discussed in full here.

In the more marshy areas, especially those furthest from the shore, a great variety of communities may occur, including stands dominated by *Iris pseudacorus, Phragmites communis, Potentilla palustris, Juncus effusus* or *J. conglomeratus*. Later these are invaded by bushes of *Salix* spp. and *Alnus glutinosa*. Detailed consideration cannot be given here of all the types represented. Reference must be made, however, to the communities of mainly dwarf species developed in the winter lochs. These are perhaps best known from the Sands of Forvie and Culbin, but occur elsewhere. Again the vegetation is usually markedly zoned, but the relationships of the various communities have never been fully investigated. Dense stands of *Littorella uniflora* (cf. pp. 110-112) are frequently developed in these sites, with low-growing species some of which have already been mentioned as characteristic of slacks, including *Eleocharis palustris, Radiola linoides, Juncus bufonius, Juncus articulatus, Ranunculus flammula*, etc. Where the vegetation is less dense, such sites sometimes provide a habitat for one or more species of very localised distribution such as *Peplis portula* (Tentsmuir, Forvie, Culbin), *Lycopodium inundatum* (Culbin) (cf. p. 112).

Development and Modification of the Habitats in Scottish Dune Systems

Along with the development of vegetation as outlined in the preceding pages goes a series of changes in the nature of the habitat, particularly in the soil conditions. These are best reviewed by reference to a few specific examples.

Rate of forward colonisation by sand dunes: St. Andrews and Tentsmuir

Graham (1938) reports that *Elymus arenarius* was introduced on to the sands at St. Andrews in 1847, following which forward colonisation and dune formation took place, representing a seaward advance of 340 m. in 91 years. There is also clear evidence of the forward colonisation by dune-building plants at Tentsmuir, where a datum is provided by the seaward limit of tree-planting in 1924 which, at the time, marked the front edge of the dunes. In the succeeding 38 years this margin has advanced by 0·8 km. (½ mile). However, such spectacular evidence of forward colonisation is exceptional, and in many localities on the east coast the seaward edge of the dunes shows signs of erosion. That this may be temporary is indicated in some places by the subsequent development of a new series of embryonic dunes, as at St. Cyrus and near Aberdeen.

Dune-building succession on a non-calcareous sand: St. Cyrus

Although the sand at St. Cyrus is relatively rich in mineral ions, the percentage of calcium carbonate is low (Table 3). As the process of dune-building and stabilization proceeds, the concentration of calcium carbonate falls from 2·7 per cent. in the foreshore sand to 1·0 per cent. in the dune pasture. This represents a certain degree of leaching by rainfall, together with the effect of incorporation into the soil of humic materials derived from the dead parts of plants. The latter is shown by a rise in the figure for loss on ignition particularly in the later stages of the sequence, while the pH, initially above 7, falls slightly to about 6 at the surface in the dune pasture. This tendency towards greater acidity is often more marked than at St. Cyrus, as for example in parts of Tentsmuir and Forvie (Table 3), where the vegetation develops towards dune heath.

Sodium chloride is present in appreciable quantities only in the upper sand layers in the foreshore zone and from time to time in the embryonic dunes (normally the *Agropyron junceiforme* zone). Elsewhere spray is presumably deposited periodically during storms but as a result of subsequent leaching its effect is short-lived. The moisture content in the relatively open habitats prior to complete surface fixation fluctuates widely but is seldom high for any length of time in the earlier stages as a result of rapid downward drainage and surface evaporation. Once a closed vegetation is established, the moisture conditions become rather more stable. At the surface in the later stages of fixation the range of water content normally lies between 7 per cent. and 32 per cent. of the dry weight of soil, while in dune heath it seldom falls below 15 per cent. The dense turf of a dune pasture and the closed canopy of a heath maintain a still, humid air layer at ground level in which relative humidity seldom falls below 85 per cent., in contrast to the fluctuations in the earlier stages where it may often fall to 50 per cent.

Dune-building succession on a calcareous sand: Luskentyre, Harris, etc.

In this example the sand is composed largely of shell fragments, yielding about 60-70 per cent. calcium carbonate at the foreshore. At these high levels leaching has little effect upon the concentration, which scarcely changes throughout the sequence except at the surface in the dune pasture, where there is considerable accumulation of organic matter.

Furthermore, the whole system (with the partial exception of the dune pasture) is subject to high winds and periodic deposition of additional blown sand. Correspondingly, the pH remains between 7·2 and 7·6 throughout, heath plants do not enter the vegetation and the dune pasture is rich in calcicolous species.

For comparison, very similar conditions obtain on dunes at Quendale, Shetland (D. H. N. Spence), and at Tiree (Vose, *et al.*, 1957) (Table 3). From the latter locality figures are available also along transects passing into machair areas. In two out of three of these, pH remained above 7 throughout, although there is a slight overall decline, but in the third it fell very slightly below. With greatly increasing quantities of organic matter, however, the percentage, by weight, of calcium carbonate drops.

TABLE 3

Changes in pH, Loss on Ignition, and Calcium Carbonate Content of Sand in Dune Systems

(Samples from upper 15 cm. (6 in.) of sand)

	pH								Loss on Ignition (% dry wt.)		CaCO$_3$ (% dry wt.)*		
	Tentsmuir, Fife	Forvie, Aberdeenshire	St. Cyrus, Kincardineshire	Tiree,† Hebrides Series: 1	2	3	Quendale, Shetland	Luskentyre, Outer Hebrides	St. Cyrus	Tiree†	St. Cyrus	Tiree†	Luskentyre
Foreshore	7·5	6·8	7·5	8·2	7·5	7·7	8·5		0·1	...	2·7	...	63·3
Mobile dunes: *Ammophila*	6·8	6·7	7·8	...	...	...	8·2		0·2	...	1·6	66·0	55·0
Fixed dune: early stage	...	5·1	7·8	..	..	7·5	8·2	7·2–7·6 throughout	0·1	2·1	1·5	56·8	58·0
Fixed dune: later stage	6·3	...	7·9	8·1	7·5	..	...		1·0	3·5	1·7	...	58·4
Dune pasture or "young machair"	...	4·8	6·4	7·8 7·8 7·5 7·1	7·7 7·5 7·7 7·5	7·4 7·5 7·5 7·4	7·7		3·4	4·4 11·5	1·0	58·0 56·6	58·2
Mature and old machair	...	...	...	7·0 6·9 7·0 6·8 6·8 6·8	7·5 7·4 7·6 7·7 7·5 7·4	7·4 7·5 7·7 7·5 7·4 7·5	...	...	...	10·8 21·9 19·3 14·1	...	55·9 45·9 47·4 38·7	...
Dune heath	4·4	4·3	...	...	...	...	...	...	Dune heath at Balmedie, Aberdeenshire 4·1–4·4	12·1–18·0	...	...	...

* As determined either by Collins' calcimeter, or approximate titration method (Piper, 1950).

† Samples were taken in order along transects passing inland from the shore and the readings are quoted in sequence according to the position of the samples.

Data incorporated from Webley *et al.* (1952), Gimingham (1951), Vose *et al.* (1957), Gimingham *et al.* (1949) and D. H. N. Spence (unpublished).

Changing habitat in a sequence of dune slacks: Tentsmuir

At Tentsmuir a series of dune slacks occurs at successive intervals landward of the main dune system, separated by low dune ridges. In Table 4 the results of analyses by

TABLE 4

Soil Properties in a Series of Dune Slacks, at Tentsmuir, Fife

	I	II	III	IV	V
Dominant species . . .	*Salix repens*	*Juncus balticus* and *S. repens*	*Alnus glutinosa, Dactylis glomerata*	*Betula* sp. or *Erica tetralix*	*Salix aurita, Filipendula ulmaria* or *Carex nigra*
Depth of litter (cm.) . . .	0·6	0·6	1·2	2·5	2·5
Depth of humus (cm.) . .	2	2	2·5	3-4	4
Approx. % cover of vegetation:					
Shrub stratum . . .	...	5	100	25	10
Field stratum	75	100	100	100	100
Soil pH	6·9	6·6	6·9	5·8-5·3	6·1-5·9
Conductivity of 1 : 2 soil extract:					
μ ohms	130	160	197	89	105
Conductivity of saturation extract					
of soil : μ ohms . . .	...	1258	1555	390	363
Moisture content % oven dry soil					
(June 1960)	5·5	9·1	6·9	15·0	15·6
% metal ion saturation . .	...	50·0	76·6	66·6	70·6

Unpublished data supplied by D. H. N. Spence.

D. H. N. Spence of certain aspects of the soil habitat are given, and although no simple developmental sequence can be detected without further investigation, certain points emerge. The sand here is not calcium-rich, but none the less there is a tendency for the water supplying the slacks to become enriched with mineral ions, the soil extracts having characteristically high values for conductivity. It is possible that high conductivity in certain of the forward slacks, where *Juncus balticus* occurs together with *Salix repens*, etc., is due to the influence of sodium chloride, but this is unlikely to be the case further back where a rich slack flora is associated with a scrub of *Alnus glutinosa*. Here it may be presumed that the ground-water supply has some flushing effect upon the habitat. A rather different condition exists in slack No. IV where the pH drops to below 6 and the conductivity of soil extracts is lower than before, while the vegetation is rich in *Erica tetralix* or has passed to *Betula* scrub with species such as *Pyrola minor* and *Corallorhiza trifida*. The moisture content of the sand is higher here, and this remains true of the most landward of the series of slacks (No. V) where conditions approximate to those of an inland swamp dominated by *Salix* spp. and *Filipendula ulmaria* (cf. p. 352).

"Wandering dunes": Culbin and Forvie

The two areas in Scotland most noteworthy for the extensive movement of dunes are Culbin in Nairn and Morayshire and Forvie in Aberdeenshire. Both are situated close to the mouth of a river where blown sand has been able to accumulate for long periods of time over rather extensive raised beaches. In the case of Culbin what is known of the history of sand movement has been summarised by Patton and Stewart (1917). A story of catastrophic overblowing of sand in the autumn of 1694 has been handed down, with details of the resulting burial of a large estate including house, farm, crofts and fields. It may be in fact, as Patton and Stewart point out, that encroachment was gradual over a period of years, but it is certain that a considerable acreage of land was engulfed by sand. There is some evidence to suggest that the sand was blown out during storms from existing, partially stabilised, dunes after damage or destruction of *Ammophila arenaria* and other species for thatching purposes; a practice thereafter discouraged by an Act of the Scottish Parliament in 1695:

> "Considering that many Lands, Meadowes and Pasturages lying on sea coasts have been ruined and overspread in many places in this kingdom by Sand driven from adjacent Sand Hills . . . His Majesty does strictly prohibit and discharge the pulling of Bent, Broom or Juniper off the Sand Hills for hereafter."

The sand so liberated was probably gathered into bare wandering dunes, moving eastwards in the direction of the prevailing winds and adopting a parabola or U-shape. Sand, derived by erosion from the rear, or windward, side, was blown across the dome-shaped top and spilled over a slip-face to leeward. Such dunes, with slip-faces at about 34° to the horizontal, were still moving in the Maviston sandhills region of Culbin until 1922 (when stabilisation by afforestation began in earnest) and actually advanced through belts of trees planted to arrest their progress, killing the trees as they went. Both as an attempt to halt this advance and as an experiment in the profitable use of such areas, the greater part of the Culbin Sands has now been planted, largely with Corsican Pine (*Pinus nigra* ssp. *laricio*), but also with *P. sylvestris* in the frost hollows and *P. contorta* in the wet shingle beds between dunes, at first by private individuals and, since 1922, by the Forestry Commission. Initially, *Ammophila arenaria* was planted to stabilise the surface, but a more rapid method proved to be a system of thatching with brushwood, amongst which the young trees are planted. In the growing forests species typical of coniferous woodland have become established, including some which are scarce in Scotland such as *Orthilia secunda* and *Moneses uniflora*.

In a fascinating study of the Sands of Forvie, Landsberg (1955) has reconstructed the history of the area since prehistoric times. While part of the area is bounded along the coast by an irregular dune ridge parallel to the shore and another following approximately the line of the bank of the river Ythan, the dune system has never been one based on parallel ridges of dunes built of sand brought in by on-shore winds. Instead, large accumulations of sand have gathered at the southernmost tip of the area. It has been shown that in this area the direction in which sand is most frequently and effectively moved (i.e. by winds exceeding about 16 km./hr. (10 miles/hr.) in velocity) is in general *along* the coast, from the south northwards. Hence the accumulations of sand have been formed into parabola dunes, moving northwards across the roughly triangular area,

expanding as they went. The outcome of this process at the present
day is a series of seven "waves" of
sand arranged as shown in Fig. 21.
By skilful correlation with archaeological and historical evidence,
Landsberg has been able to give
approximate dates to the passage of
sand across the area (Fig. 22). Thus
while some earlier dwellings had
been found at site A, near the south
of the area, situated directly on
raised-beach material, Landsberg
discovered some fine stone circles
and other remains probably of early
iron age (Kirk, 1953) at site B, a
little further north, built on several
feet of sand (Plate 18). This suggests
that the first "wave" of sand had
reached or passed this site by about
0 B.C. ± 100 years.

Next it appears that a thriving
village community existed in the
region of site C from about A.D. 700
until shortly after 1400. Document-
ary evidence is available, as well as
the remains of the walls of a small
Chapel built directly upon the
underlying clay. Hence it may be
presumed that during this mediaeval
period sand had not reached this

FIG. 23

Sands of Forvie: Communities of the
Dunes. In passing from south to north
Forvie, a change can be seen from grass
to heath-dominated communities. This
is more noticeable in the flanks than the
bows, since greater sand movement on
the bows prevents the invasion of heath
plants in large numbers. The type of
vegetation is closely correlated with the
dune phase. (From Landsberg, 1955.)

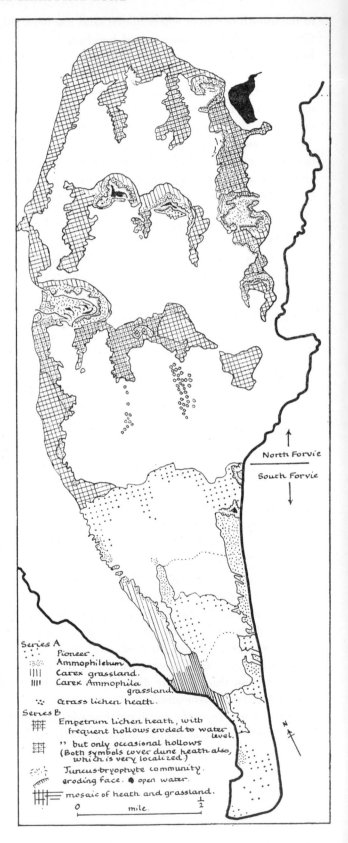

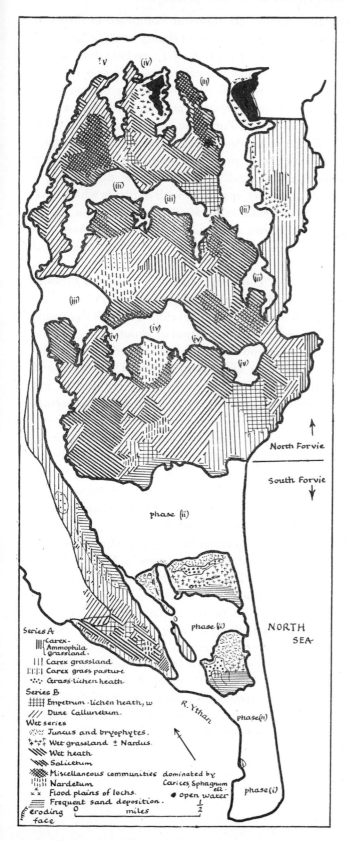

part. However, according to local legend a catastrophic movement of sand, similar to that at Culbin over 200 years later, took place in 1413, completely obliterating the village. Again it may be that the process was in fact more gradual, but it probably occurred about this time. Over much of the area to the north of this site mediaeval plough ridges have been detected, representing probably the arable land of the village, which was later also overblown by sand. From these and other sources, together with a series of maps dating from 1782 onwards, the progress of at least the first "wave" of sand has been followed, until it reached its present position in about 1782. This was followed at later stages by "waves" 2, 3 and 4, while a second advance, probably mainly in the sixteenth and seventeenth centuries, led to the movement of "waves" 5 and 6 to their present position, and a seventh dune lies at the southernmost tip. There has probably been little major change in the past 170 years. In some years, however, the shallow forward lapping of sand may be as much as 9 m. (30 ft.), while in others no perceptible advance occurs.

Fig. 24

Sands of Forvie: Communities of the Plains. In passing from south to north Forvie a change can be seen in the vegetation of the plains, from grass-dominated to heath-dominated communities. This is accompanied by a change from phase (i) and (ii) to phase (iii) and (iv) dunes. (From Landsberg, 1955.)

Proceeding from south to north, the "waves" are therefore composed of dunes of increasing age and stability. Correspondingly, there is a marked change in dune form and vegetation (Figs. 22 and 23). At the south, "wave" 7 consists of a parabola dune with a slip-face along its northern margin, largely devoid of vegetation apart from a ridge of *Ammophila* on the crest probably derived from an artificial planting near the mouth of the river (phase i, Plate 14). However, this phase of greatest dune mobility with a slip-face along the leading edge is not well represented at Forvie (in contrast to Culbin prior to 1922), and "waves" 6, 5 and 4 are in the phase described by Landsberg as "lapping dunes" (phase ii). Here the U-shape becomes more pronounced and the distinguishing feature is the forward lapping movement of the sand locally along the dune front, a shallow deposit being spread out and recolonised by upward growth of plants which have been completely or partially buried, e.g. *Ammophila arenaria, Potentilla anserina, Carex arenaria* and species typical of deposits of blown sand such as *Senecio jacobaea* and *Cirsium arvense* (Plate 15). The crest of the dune is more irregular and is partly occupied by *Ammophila* hummocks.

A third phase (iii) in the sequence is the "knife-edge dune", represented to some extent in "wave" 3, particularly characteristic of "wave" 2 and present also in "wave" 1. Here the most conspicuous feature is the sharp crest which develops between the windward and leeward slopes, both of which may have an inclination of about 32°-34° to the horizontal. The dune is increasingly hollowed out on the windward face, emphasising the U-shape with trailing "arms". The windward slope of the dune is bare of vegetation and becomes progressively eroded; forward movement is by now greatly reduced or has ceased and the leeward slope becomes fully colonised by a *Carex arenaria-Ammophila* grassland community.

The final phase (iv) at Forvie, represented in "wave" 1 but also occurring in 3, is the stable phase, where there is almost complete vegetation cover of both windward and leeward slopes, although local hollows may be eroded out in both bow and flanks, the latter often showing many small circular erosion hollows. Sand movement is almost absent except around these hollows, and the community consists of the various facies of dune heath and *Empetrum*—lichen heath, or in some cases, dune pasture.

Along with this evolution of dune form and vegetation there is a gradual change in the soil, with an overall fall in pH and rise in organic matter as shown in Table 5. In the later stages a considerable degree of podsolisation is visible in the profile under heath communities, while under grassland a leached brown earth develops.

In between each of the "waves" deflation plains occur, in parts of which erosion down to the level of the water-table has occurred (Fig. 24; Table 14, p. 141). These are often traversed by small *Ammophila*—covered dune ridges termed "gegenwälle", formed at intervals by sand blown *back* off the bare dune slope by winds from the north (see p. 102 and Plate 16). The moist deflation plains between the mobile parabola dunes 6, 5 and 4 show a range of plant communities from *Juncus articulatus* with *Carex arenaria, Carex maritima* and incomplete bryophyte cover, to a closed damp grassland similar to that of a grassy dune slack (p. 102). In these regions Landsberg found only one small plant of

TABLE 5

Percentage Cover of Species, pH and Loss on Ignition of Sand on Dunes of Increasing Age and Stability: Forvie, Aberdeenshire

(Samples taken on the lee slope of the dune, % cover calculated from 100 point samples taken at 15-yard intervals)

Dune phase	(i) Parabola dune with slip face	(ii) Lapping dunes			(iii) Knife-edge dunes						(iv) Stable phase				
Reference letter of dune	a	b	c	d	l	e	j	o	k	i	n	m	f	g	h
Bare sand	99	88	78	75	72	56	40	38	31	28	7	13	12	22	9
Ammophila arenaria	1	11	14	17	18	22	39	14	27	25	7	3	7	3	3
Poa pratensis	...	1	1	1	...	3	2	17	11	12	14	11	2	...	...
Festuca rubra	...	...	1	...	1	...	1	1	2	1	3	1	1	...	...
Carex arenaria	...	...	1	2	1	7	5	11	6	10	2	4	8	3	6
Cirsium arvense	...	...	3	1	...	...	1	...	2	2	...	...	...	...	...
Senecio jacobaea	...	...	2	4	...	9	2	1	2	3	...	...	1	...	...
Agrostis spp.	...				3	...	3	8	3	2	4	2	3	1	1
Festuca ovina	...				2	...	1	1	2	1	3	1	1	...	...
Holcus lanatus	...				1	...	1	1	1	2	1	...	1	...	...
Salix repens	...				...	...	1	...	...	...	8	9	7	...	2
Juncus spp.	...				...	...	...	...	...	...	2	1	1	...	...
Empetrum nigrum	...				...	...	...	...	...	3	16	14	17	36	52
Calluna vulgaris	...				...	...	...	...	...	...	10	22	14	11	13
Other phanerogam spp.	...				2	...	1	1	4	1	6	4	1	...	1
Total Mosses	...				...	2	3	3	2	3	2	4	6	...	...
Total Lichens	...				...	1	...	3	...	7	15	13	18	25	13
pH (mean of 5 determinations)	...	6·5	6·1	6·2	5·9	5·7	5·6	5·8	5·5	5·6	5·3	5·4	5·3	5·1	4·9
Loss on ignition (% d.w.) (mean of 2 determinations)	...	0·2	0·3	0·2	0·3	0·8	3·0	2·0	3·6	3·1	2·5	5·6	4·3	5·3	11·8
Approx. depth of sand accretion/annum (cm.)	...	...	58	25	33	8	<0·5	1	0·5	<0·5	Nil	Nil	Nil	Nil	Nil

Data from Landsberg (1955).

Salix repens and a single patch of *Empetrum nigrum*. However, in the deflation plains behind the knife-edge parabola dunes, *Salix repens*, *Calluna vulgaris*, *Erica tetralix* or *Empetrum nigrum* may be among the dominants according to the position of the water-table in relation to the sand surface. In the rather extensive stable wet deflation plains, wet heath occurs in which *Calluna*, *Empetrum nigrum*, *Nardus stricta*, *Erica tetralix*, *Salix repens* and *Agrostis tenuis* are prominent, with a variety of species of *Carex* and *Juncus*. In one situation just behind "wave" 1, *Salix pentandra* forms an almost closed scrub.

In the hollows of the parabola bows of the northern dune "waves" 1-3, the water table is relatively high, and here winter lochs occur with flat flood plains round their margins (Plate 17), where stands of *Peplis portula*, *Littorella uniflora* and *Apium inundatum* occur (cf. Culbin, p. 107). In other hollows behind these dunes the dune slack communities discussed on pp. 101, 103 occur, while restricted hollows in the dune flanks a few yards in diameter may erode down to the water-table. Those which have become fully colonised show a distinct zonation from *Salix repens* with tufts of *Juncus effusus* in the centre, through a belt of *Erica tetralix* to a rim occupied by *Calluna* and *Empetrum nigrum*, passing outwards to the open *Ammophila* of the dune where *Carex arenaria* and *Teesdalia nudicaulis* characteristically occur and bryophytes including *Pohlia annotina*.

Although not studied in detail, parabola dunes are also a feature of the extensive dune system at the Sands of Barry and the lesser ones at Burghead, Balmedie (Aberdeenshire), etc.

SALT MARSHES

The Scottish coastline contains some fine examples of salt marshes, particularly along the northern shores of the Solway Firth (as, for example, in Wigtown Bay). To a somewhat lesser extent the tidal reaches of the Firth of Forth and Firth of Tay are fringed with marshes, as are the Montrose Basin, Findhorn Bay, the Beauly, Cromarty and Dornoch Firths and the smaller river mouths and estuaries such as those of the North Esk at St. Cyrus, the Ythan at Newburgh, the Lossie, etc. Salt marsh has also developed behind off-shore "bars" at Heckie's Hole, East Lothian, and near the Culbin Sands (counties of Moray and Nairn) and small marshes are a very typical feature of the upper reaches of the numerous sea lochs and inlets of the west coast and islands. A short survey of Scottish salt marshes is given by Chapman (1960) in his *Salt Marshes and Salt Deserts of the World*.

The flora of British salt-marshes consists of a rather distinct and restricted group of species, which is further limited in Scotland by the absence or scarcity of some of those whose distributional affinities are southern. Thus, *Spartina townsendii* has never spread on Scottish salt marshes in spite of scattered plantings, while a number of species very characteristic of English marshes extend northwards only as far as the Scottish shores of the Solway Firth and sometimes those of the Firth of Forth, where they play a relatively minor role. Among these are *Limonium vulgare*, *L. humile*, *L. binervosum* and *Halimione*

PLATE 14. Sands of Forvie, Aberdeenshire. Youngest wandering,
dune (No. 7, map, Fig. 21) from the south: bare, unstabilized
dome-shaped outline. In the foreground the River Ythan flows
to its mouth to right of edge of photo.

PLATE 15. Sands of Forvie, Aberdeenshire. Overblow of sand
(from right to left) on the north edge of wave No. 5 (map, Fig. 21).
Colonization of the new surface by *Cirsium arvense* and *Senecio
jacobaea*.

PLATE 16

Sands of Forvie, Aberdeenshire. U-shaped dune from south (wave No. 2, map, Fig. 21). Erosion of windward face, with tufts of *Ammophila arenaria* slipping down. The trailing "arms" of the dune enclose a hollow, eroded down to the level of the water-table. The damp hollow, crossed by "gegenwälle" dunes, is occupied by *Juncus*—bryophyte communities, and low mounds formed by *Salix repens*.

PLATE 17

Sands of Forvie, Aberdeenshire. Area of "winter loch" or damp hollow behind stabilized dune (wave No. 1, map, Fig. 21). Colonization by *Juncus effusus* and (in distance) *Salix* spp. Communities dominated by *Calluna vulgaris* and *Empetrum nigrum* occur even on the windward slope of the dune.

PLATE 18

Sands of Forvie, Aberdeenshire. Early iron age circle built on sand, photographed in 1954. Since that date the area has become colonized by *Ammophila arenaria*, etc.

PLATE 19
Triglochin maritima, St. Cyrus salt
marsh. Dome-shaped young plant.

PLATE 20
Triglochin maritima: older plant
showing beginning of degeneration
in centre with entry of other species
(*Atriplex glabriuscula*). St. Cyrus
salt marsh.

PLATE 21
Triglochin maritima: old plant in the
form of a ring, the centre of which
is now occupied by *Agrostis stolonifera*, *Cochlearia officinalis*, etc. St.
Cyrus salt marsh.

portulacoides. Scottish marshes have few distinctive floristic features apart from the diversity of rather strange forms or "ecads" of fucoid algae which characterise those of the west coast.

The chief communities of Scottish salt marshes can be briefly surveyed as follows.

Algal communities

Algal mats on bare mud. A patchy film of green algae may colonise bare mud ahead of any flowering plants, but this mat is not always represented. In general, the species are the same as those occurring in the lower zones of the salt marsh, among the most regular being species of *Vaucheria, Rhizoclonium, Cladophora,* and sometimes *Enteromorpha* (Loch Creran; Chapman, 1960: St. Cyrus; Gimingham, 1953). At Findhorn Bay (Chapman, 1960) the species concerned are *Enteromorpha intestinalis* var. *microphylla, Vaucheria sphaerospora* var. *dioica* and *Cladophora fracta* var. *marina.*

Purely algal communities, composed of Chlorophyta and Cyanophyta, occur also on the walls of creeks and the floor of pans in the marsh. The following examples are given by Chapman:

	Heckie's Hole Marsh Creek-walls	Findhorn Bay pans
Aphanocapsa marina		+
Calothrix scopulorum		+
Chroococcus turgidus var. *maximus* . .		+
Cladophora sericea	+	
Enteromorpha nana (*E. minima*) . . .	+	
E. torta	+	
E. percursa	+	+
E. prolifera f. *capillaris*	+	
Lola implexa	+	+
Lyngbya aestuarii		+
Microcoleus chthonoplastes		+
Phaeococcus adnatus		+
Phormidium corium		+
Ulva lactuca	+	
Vaucheria sphaerospora var. *dioica* . .		+

Mention is also made of a community of *Bostrychia scorpioides* on certain creek edges of Heckie's Hole.

Plant communities of the salt marshes

In spite of the limitation and relative uniformity of the flora a number of rather distinctive communities are formed, and the interest attaching to salt-marsh vegetation lies in the representation of these and their spatial and dynamic relationships. Further, on any particular marsh there is often a clear zonation of communities according to

H

gradients in habitat factors such as the duration of tidal exposure and submergence, salinity, etc. Where active silting occurs there may be evidence of a dynamic system in which the zonation reflects the order in which the communities replace one another in the course of succession. Where zonation is present it is usually visible as a series of areas dominated by different species, often with rather narrow belts of transition between them. There is normally also a change in the associated species, although this is often more gradual and may be shown by increasing or decreasing quantity rather than by presence or absence. Similarly the progress of succession, where evident, may be observed most readily by the invasion and gradual replacement of one dominant by another.

Owing partly to the fact that, in most salt marshes, the communities are either zoned or seral or both, they are most simply and effectively characterised by their dominants. While this may not apply to some other types of vegetation, it has often been found convenient for salt marshes and produces, in fact, a result closely parallel with classifications following the principles of the Braun-Blanquet school (Tüxen, 1955; Chapman, 1960). Perhaps this is because competition will be more severe between potential dominants than among the remaining species when a restricted flora is associated with rather steep gradients in habitat factors, and hence the dominants may be more exclusive to particular sectors of the range in habitat conditions than the other species. They are, therefore, appropriately chosen as "characteristic" of the several communities. However, as might be expected, at least one of the common dominants, *Puccinellia maritima*, ranges rather more widely and it becomes necessary to recognise more than one community-type in which this species may be dominant.

Zostera **stands.** All three British species of *Zostera* occur in Scotland. *Z. marina* is found as far north as Orkney and *Z. noltii* reaches Dornoch, but *Z. angustifolia* is probably now restricted to the extreme south-east. There is little information on their present status: formerly there were extensive beds on the mud flats below many of the Scottish salt marshes, for example at Aberlady Bay, Burntisland, Montrose, St. Cyrus, Fort George, Beauly Firth, and Deer Sound in Orkney, Bute, the coast of Ayrshire and elsewhere. Throughout the British Isles populations of *Zostera* were greatly reduced by disease in the years following 1930, and in some of the localities mentioned, as in the estuary of the North Esk at St. Cyrus, there is no longer any trace of the plants. In some, however, it has survived, but no recent survey has been made.

Salicornia **stands.** In some salt-marsh localities the first colonists of the mud flats, apart from algae, are annual species of *Salicornia*, initially as widely separated bushy individuals and, higher up, in denser stands. Few critical studies of the species concerned have been made, but at Wigtown the chief one in the zone of primary colonisation is *S. dolichostachya*, with *S. ramosissima* entering a little later and playing a considerable part in subsequent communities. *S. dolichostachya* is mentioned by Chapman (1960) as present at Dingwall. *Suaeda maritima* sometimes becomes prominent in the higher parts of the *Salicornia* zone, and may become dominant locally, e.g. Heckie's Hole (Chapman, 1960). The green algae already mentioned as colonists of mud flats are frequently present amongst *Salicornia*, and at Heckie's Hole *Pelvetia canaliculata* is present in its peculiar unattached form, the ecad *libera* (Chapman, 1960). At St. Cyrus, *Salicornia* was known from the lower levels of the salt marsh until about 1935, but has disappeared. It also seems to have decreased in other places along the north-east coast, possibly as a result of increasing proportions of sand in the deposits (Gimingham, 1953).

Pioneer *Puccinellia maritima* stands. Where a *Salicornia* zone is present, *Puccinellia maritima* may begin to colonise its higher levels; otherwise the latter may be the primary colonist. A continuous stand is soon formed, building a more or less uninterrupted turf. Besides species of *Salicornia* and *Suaeda maritima* which may have become established in advance of *Puccinellia*, a few additional plants now enter, particularly *Aster tripolium* and *Triglochin maritima* (Table 6).

TABLE 6

Composition and Percentage Presence of Species in Stands of certain Salt Marsh Community-types containing *Puccinellia maritima*

	Pioneer *Puccinellia maritima* stands	Stands of *Puccinellia maritima* with *Plantago maritima*	Stands of *Puccinellia maritima* with *Armeria* and/or *Glaux*
Localities . . .	Wigtown Bay; Mull, Inner Hebrides; Findhorn, Moray; St. Cyrus and Montrose, Kincardineshire; Aberlady Bay, E. Lothian	Wigtown Bay; Dingwall; Loch Creran	Wigtown Bay; St. Cyrus, Kincardineshire; Loch Creran
No. of Stands . . .	6	5	6
Agrostis stolonifera . .	...	...	33
Festuca rubra . . .	...	...	50
Puccinellia maritima . .	100	100	100
Juncus gerardii . . .	...	...	17
Triglochin maritima . .	50	20	17
Armeria maritima . .		60	83
Aster tripolium . . .	67	100	83
Atriplex glabriuscula . .	17	...	...
Cochlearia anglica . .	...	20	...
C. officinalis . . .	...	...	17
Glaux maritima . . .	...	60	83
Plantago maritima . .	17	100	67
Salicornia spp. . .	67	60*	17†
Spergularia media . .	17	40	67‡
Suaeda maritima . .	50	20	...

* *S. ramosissima* and *S. dolichostachya* both occur in lists.
† *S. ramosissima.*
‡ *S. media* and *S. marina* both occur in lists.

Additional species recorded in one stand only of column 3 :*Carex extensa, Hypochoeris radicata, Lotus corniculatus, Plantago coronopus.*

Data are included from: Chapman (1960), Gillham (1957), Gimingham (1953).

The bare mud between the shoots and rosettes is frequently colonised by algae, including *Bostrychia scorpioides, Catenella repens, Vaucheria sphaerospora, Enteromorpha clathrata, E. intestinalis* var. *tubulosa, E. percursa,* and *Lola implexa* (Chapman, 1960).

Stands containing *Puccinellia maritima* and *Plantago maritima*, domin-ance exerted by either, or shared. The first associate of *Puccinellia* to become really prominent in the sward is often *Plantago maritima*. The quantitative balance between these two species varies, presumably according to variations in the habitat which have not yet been investigated. Dominance is often retained by *Puccinellia* but, as for example in parts of the Wigtown marshes, it may appear to be shared, or *Plantago* may be the leading species as in many of the west coast marshes. Most of the species of the pioneer *Puccinellia* communities retain a position, sometimes in reduced numbers, while *Aster tripolium* may become particularly important here, as at Creetown, where it is co-dominant with *Plantago*. Other plants normally present, although in a subordinate position, are *Armeria maritima, Glaux maritima* and *Spergularia* spp. (Table 6). An algal flora similar to that of the preceding community type may be present on the mud.

Stands containing *Puccinellia maritima, Armeria maritima* and *Glaux maritima*; any of which may be dominant. In parts of most marshes there are communities still very frequently dominated by *Puccinellia maritima* and floristically rather similar to those of the preceding group, but in which either, or both, of *Armeria maritima* and *Glaux maritima* are prominent and *Plantago maritima* reduced. There are certain other differences including the absence or reduction of some of the pioneer species, and the entry in some examples of species characteristic of the higher levels of the marsh. Thus *Suaeda maritima* is generally lacking, *Salicornia* spp. restricted to gaps or depressions and *Aster* reduced while some stands include *Juncus gerardii, Festuca rubra* and *Agrostis stolonifera. Cochlearia officinalis* occurs irregularly but is sometimes numerous in this type of community; elsewhere, however, it tends to be restricted to the margins of creeks and channels. The contribution of *Armeria maritima* varies; there appear to be certain conditions under which it will equal or exceed *Puccinellia* although, on the whole, this tendency is less pronounced than it is at equivalent levels in some English marshes. On the west coast of Scotland there seems to be a tendency for *Armeria* to be well represented at rather lower levels, extending vigorously into the preceding community-type or even behaving almost as a pioneer. Conversely it is much more restricted on the north-east coast; at St. Cyrus, for example, it is confined to a narrow belt at the upper levels of the marsh where it borders on to sand dunes (p. 119).

In certain areas *Glaux maritima* may be dominant. These often prove to be sites containing a high proportion of sand in the substratum, where *Glaux* adopts a prostrate habit of growth and may be associated with abundant *Plantago coronopus*, while *Puccinella maritima* is reduced.

Although detailed surveys in Scotland are lacking, communities of this type seem, on the whole, to occupy slightly higher levels than those in which *Plantago maritima* is more prominent, and this is borne out in some examples by the associated flora.

Besides green algae, these communities may include salt-marsh forms of several fucoids. At Aberlady, for example, forms of *Fucus spiralis* and *F. vesiculosus* (ecad *muscoides*) occur, while this feature of the flora is particularly characteristic of the west coast marshes where in addition to the above species forms of *Ascophyllum nodosum*, e.g. *Ascophyllum nodosum* ecad *mackaii* (turf form) and *A. nodosum* var. *minor* (Gibb, 1957), and *Fucus ceranoides* occur.

The two preceding community types were not differentiated by earlier workers (e.g. Oliver *in* Tansley, 1911) but were described under the heading of "General Salt Marsh", in which any of four or five species might be dominant or co-dominant in various combinations.

This may have resulted from the rather wide habitat ranges of *Puccinellia maritima* and its chief associated species, such that differences in the communities may be partly of a quantitative rather than a qualitative nature, and minor fluctuations in the level of the marsh may cause confusing intermingling of types. The differences have been obscured by the fact that so often in the past records have taken the form of mere lists without even the most general quantitative assessment. Grazing is frequently an additional factor modifying the composition and arrangement of the communities.

Although Tansley (1949) commented that more recent work had often resulted in the separation of types within this aggregate, the title "General Salt Marsh" is retained by Chapman (1960) and applied to Scottish examples. This is perhaps unfortunate since it constitutes a group which does not balance with others generally recognized in the classification of salt marsh vegetation and, rather than helping to clarify relationships which are as yet poorly understood, may have the effect of obscuring them. As far as Scotland is concerned, interpretation becomes particularly difficult since in England the term "Lower General Salt Marsh" is usually equated with parts of the marsh in which *Limonium* spp. are among the leading components, and "Upper General Salt Marsh" with those in which *Armeria maritima* is often in this role. In Scotland, *Limonium* spp. are never at this level of abundance, and in a number of examples this can also be said of *Armeria*.

Stands dominated by *Festuca rubra*. *Festuca rubra* is a common component of the upper *Puccinellia* communities and on many marshes, particularly on the east coasts of Scotland, is dominant over extensive areas. *Puccinellia* is here rather rapidly reduced or eliminated but most of the other species remain as associates of *Festuca*, e.g. *Cochlearia officinalis*, *Plantago maritima*, *Glaux maritima*, *Spergularia marina* and, to a lesser extent, *Aster tripolium*, e.g. St. Cyrus (Gimingham, 1953).

Stands dominated by *Juncus gerardii*. *Juncus gerardii* occurs in many Scottish salt marshes, often colonising well forward in the *Puccinellia* zones, forming at first scattered patches or rings. These under suitable conditions extend and coalesce and the plant comes to dominate quite extensive areas. A compact, dense stand is formed from a system of intertwined rhizomes 20 cm. (8 in.) or more below the surface, resulting in the reduction or exclusion of associated species.

Stands dominated by *Juncus maritimus*. Occurring sometimes in conjunction with *Juncus gerardii* (as at Creetown) and sometimes as sole dominant, *J. maritimus* is rather more local in its occurrence than *J. gerardii*. It is a component both of east coast marshes (e.g. Findhorn Bay) and of those on the west coast, including the Solway Firth. According to Gillham (1957), it may precede *J. gerardii* in the upshore zonation on the margins of sea lochs in the Island of Mull.

Stands dominated by *Scirpus maritimus*. *Scirpus maritimus* also occurs in dense stands on many Scottish marshes. Chapman suggests that it is indicative of the influence of fresh water, which may account in part for its appearance at rather diverse levels on different marshes. At Dingwall, for example, it dominates the lower marsh; at Creetown it occurs in a belt above *Juncus maritimus* and *J. gerardii*, while at St. Cyrus there is a large patch at the upper end of the marsh with several smaller ones actively colonising in or beside channels in the lower parts (Fig. 28). In the latter station it seems to mark poorly-drained habitats where the substratum is submerged or saturated for long periods even when the tide is out. In active colonies the density of shoots may exceed 60-100 per 93 sq. dm. (1 sq. ft.) and here there are few associated species. Where density is less, other species characteristic of the wetter parts of salt marshes may be present including *Aster tripolium*, *Atriplex glabriuscula*, *Cochlearia officinalis* and even *Glaux maritima* in a tall, straggling form. *Vaucheria* sp. spreads over the mud and basal parts of the shoots of *Scirpus*.

Stands dominated by *Agrostis stolonifera*. To some extent this species may also indicate the influence of fresh water, or at least occupies the less saline parts of the marsh. It may occur as a component of the *Festuca rubra* communities, but in certain cases becomes extensively dominant, e.g. St. Cyrus, where it occupies a waterlogged but not highly saline area at the upper reaches of the marsh and extends downwards along the more or less permanently wet channel margins. By the sea lochs of the west coast, where *Festuca rubra* is not important, *Agrostis* may border on to *Plantago maritima* and *Juncus gerardii* areas, in the region in which salinity decreases rather steeply (Gillham, 1957).

Communities characteristic of transitional belts between salt marsh and adjacent vegetation

Transition to non-saline swamp. The commonest dominant in this type of situation is *Phragmites communis*, which frequently extends a considerable distance into communities characteristic of the salt marsh. In the sheltered bays of the sea lochs on the west coast, e.g. Mull (Gillham, 1957), Loch Eriboll, etc., the true salt marsh grades, at the upper levels, into a rather characteristic community of *Juncus articulatus* with *Carex demissa*, *Carex flacca*, and sometimes *Blysmus rufus*, *Leontodon autumnalis*, etc. Where the fresh-water influence is pronounced it is very common for this type of community to give place in turn to dense stands of *Iris pseudacorus*, sometimes with *Filipendula ulmaria*; alternatively it may pass over to acid peat with *Eriophorum angustifolium* and *Molinia caerulea*.

Transition to sand dune. The zonation at the edge of the salt marsh at St. Cyrus where it is fringed by sand dunes is illustrated in Fig. 25. In this example *Armeria maritima* which plays no part in the main salt-marsh communities forms a belt at this higher level where, in addition, the proportion of sand in the substratum is increased. Above it occurs a zone of dense *Honkenya peploides*, in which *Agropyron pungens* is established. At the extremity of the salt marsh, where it passes into an area of scattered

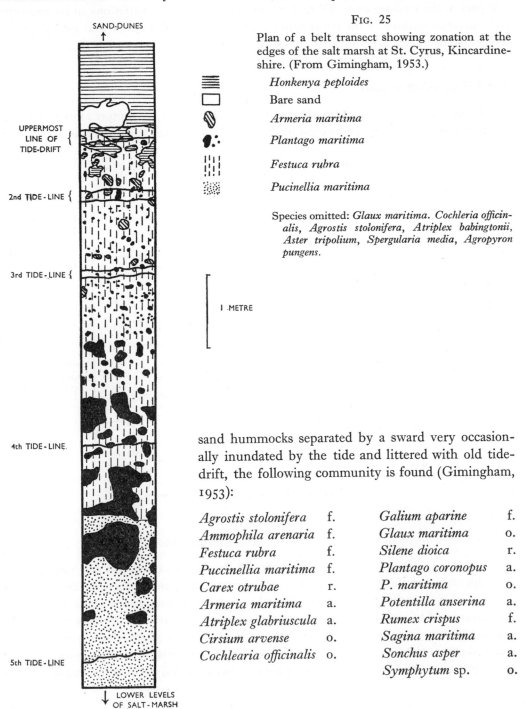

Fig. 25

Plan of a belt transect showing zonation at the edges of the salt marsh at St. Cyrus, Kincardine-shire. (From Gimingham, 1953.)

Honkenya peploides

Bare sand

Armeria maritima

Plantago maritima

Festuca rubra

Pucinellia maritima

Species omitted: *Glaux maritima. Cochleria officin-alis, Agrostis stolonifera, Atriplex babingtonii, Aster tripolium, Spergularia media, Agropyron pungens.*

1 .METRE

sand hummocks separated by a sward very occasion-ally inundated by the tide and littered with old tide-drift, the following community is found (Gimingham, 1953):

Agrostis stolonifera	f.	*Galium aparine*	f.
Ammophila arenaria	f.	*Glaux maritima*	o.
Festuca rubra	f.	*Silene dioica*	r.
Puccinellia maritima	f.	*Plantago coronopus*	a.
Carex otrubae	r.	*P. maritima*	o.
Armeria maritima	a.	*Potentilla anserina*	a.
Atriplex glabriuscula	a.	*Rumex crispus*	f.
Cirsium arvense	o.	*Sagina maritima*	a.
Cochlearia officinalis	o.	*Sonchus asper*	a.
		Symphytum sp.	o.

REGIONAL VARIATION IN SALT-MARSH VEGETATION

While the main species of the Scottish salt-marsh vegetation do not vary greatly from one part of the country to another, there are marked regional variations in composition and interrelationships of the communities. These are briefly summarised by Chapman, whose arrangement, appropriately, distinguishes the following Scottish types:

The Solway Firth marshes

Some areas on the northern shores of the Solway Firth are unique among Scottish salt marshes in the width and extent of the flats, across which the level falls very gently

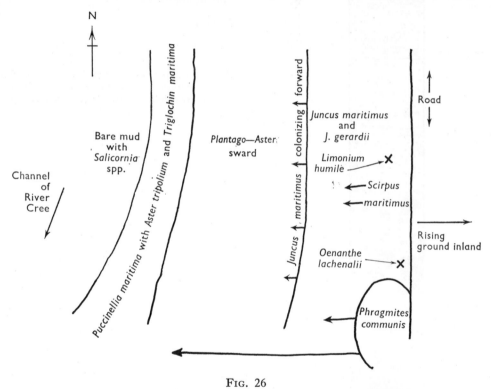

FIG. 26

Sketch-map of salt marsh zonation near Creetown, Kirkcudbrightshire.

except along an occasional terrace or beside the drainage channels. In this respect they resemble some of the English marshes rather more than most others in Scotland. In addition they are often extensively grazed, as at Wigtown, which leads to floristic uniformity and to certain ecological variations becoming obscured. Perhaps because the Cumberland coast opposite has been more visited by ecologists, these marshes have received scant attention, as can be seen from the absence of any separate account of them in Chapman (1960). Chapman and other authors have pointed out that the marshes of the north-west of Britain have developed on a coastline which has been rising in relatively recent times. The terraces to be observed on the Solway Firth marshes may be a result of this, and it may also be reflected in the rather characteristic extension of non-halophytic species such as *Phragmites communis*, *Juncus articulatus*, etc., towards the salt marsh proper. A typical zonation is that seen at Creetown (Fig. 26). Marshes on the north shore of the Solway Firth are closely similar to those on the south, and agree with other marshes on the north-west English coasts in the widespread dominance of *Puccinellia maritima*, the importance of *Aster tripolium*, the presence of certain species such as *Oenanthe lachenalii*, and the general lack of salt-marsh fucoids. They differ, however, in the virtual absence of *Halimione portulacoides* and the restriction of *Limonium* spp. to scattered individuals in the upper levels of the marsh.

The marshes of the sea lochs of north-west and north Scotland

The majority of these are rather narrow belts of marsh fringing bays and sea lochs in a high-rainfall area. The rate of silting is relatively low and the substratum has a high proportion of sand. This appears to be associated with a reduction in the role of *Salicornia* as a primary colonist, and the substitution in this position of *Puccinellia maritima*. *Aster* is no longer important, but *Plantago maritima* is frequently widely dominant. A further feature is the abundance of non-halophytes in the upper parts of the marshes. Some of these seem to be species occupying a habitat in which saline water has raised the pH to almost neutral (Gillham, 1957), e.g. *Leontodon autumnalis*, *Plantago coronopus*, *Potentilla anserina*, *Rumex crispus*, *Trifolium repens*, *Carex demissa*, *C. flacca*, *Juncus articulatus*. Most of these, like *Agrostis stolonifera* and *Festuca rubra*, occur in other maritime habitats and are tolerant of fluctuating salinities, reaching relatively high levels for varying periods. Others extend from the adjacent, acid peat substrata into these transitional habitats and hence also show some tolerance of rising salinity, e.g. *Molinia caerulea*, *Eriophorum angustifolium*, *Myrica gale*, etc. A further characteristic feature of these north-west coast salt marshes is the variety of salt-marsh forms of fucoid algae (see p. 117).

Salinity conditions have not been measured in many examples of Scottish marshes. However, besides the ranges quoted by Gillham for Mull, Gibb (1957) gives a graph, of variation in salinity throughout one tidal cycle at a sample site between tide marks in Loch Riddon. Salinity is highest at high tide, when it approaches that of the open water (here about 3·4 per cent.), falling as the tide recedes, so that the last water to drain off is only of medium salinity (about 2 per cent.). As the tide advances, the first water to rise above ground-level shows even lower concentrations, but there is a rapid rise as the water flows directly over the site.

If heavy rain falls on an exposed shore, or during the advance of the tide, it may cause a general reduction in salinity, so that maximum values are not reached even at high water. On the other hand in dry weather, particularly at the higher parts of a marsh not submerged during periods of neap tides, concentrations temporarily in excess of those of sea water may be produced in the soil solution by evaporation (cf. data from St. Cyrus, Table 7).

Marshes of the south-east coast

The marshes of Midlothian and East Lothian have been little studied, but seem more closely related to the English east-coast marshes than to those further north in Scotland. However, as with the Solway marshes, *Halimione* and *Limonium* play no significant part, and *Puccinellia maritima* is widely dominant. The upper levels of the marsh frequently provide appropriate habitats for *Scirpus maritimus* to become dominant. At Aberlady the following species are associated with *Scirpus maritimus*: *Schoenoplectus*

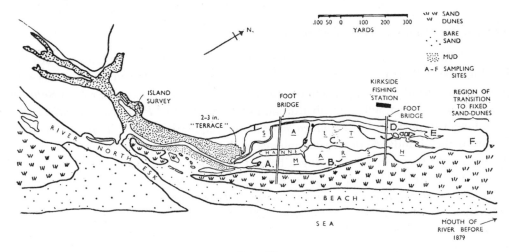

FIG. 27

Map of St. Cyrus salt marsh, 1951. (From Gimingham, 1953.)

tabernaemontani, *Blysmus compressus*, *Cochlearia anglica* and *Equisetum palustre*. A further feature is the abundance of certain salt-marsh fucoids, particularly at Aberlady.

Marshes of the east and north-east coast

Most of these are rather small marshes in river estuaries or other enclosed situations. Like those on the north-west, the silt is often mixed with a considerable proportion of sand. The vegetational sequence is also more akin to that of the west-coast marshes, since *Puccinellia maritima* is the pioneer rather than *Salicornia* spp., while *Festuca rubra* and *Agrostis stolonifera* may be important dominants at higher levels. Salt-marsh fucoids are, however, very little in evidence.

A good example is furnished by the small marsh at St. Cyrus, Kincardineshire. This is a narrow area of marsh, covering about 32 ha. ($\frac{1}{8}$ sq. mile), in a depression surrounded by sand dunes and opening at one end into the estuary of the river North

Esk, from where the tide fills the marsh. The marsh occupies a part of the old course of the river which before 1879 reached the sea a short distance to the north of the present upper extremity of the marsh. In that year abnormal conditions caused the river to break out at the bend where it turned northwards, while its original mouth was closed by blown sand. This left a land-locked basin, filled and emptied at each tide from the point of junction with the new channel, and now occupied by a salt marsh which is therefore of no great age (Fig. 27).

Since the sea water is already diluted to some extent by river water before entering the marsh, which also receives some fresh water draining from landward, the salinity of the soil moisture is not generally as high as in some other salt-marshes (Table 7). The

TABLE 7

pH and Salinity of Rooting Medium, St. Cyrus Salt Marsh

(Means of weekly analyses during 12 months)

		pH	Salinity, expressed as % NaCl in soil water
A	Near outlet of marsh to river estuary .	7·2	1·6
B	Margin of marsh, *ca.* half-way along its length	6·7	1·2
C	Centre of marsh	6·8	0·9
D	Margin of marsh towards upper end .	6·9	1·2
E	Near upper extremity of marsh .	6·8	0·7
F		6·8	0·6

Data from Gimingham (1953).

lower levels of the marsh yield the higher figures, being submerged more frequently and for longer periods than the rest. Lower values tend to be found not only at the upper extremity but also in the centre of the marsh. This portion is somewhat convex, rising between the two main drainage channels, and hence is submerged for shorter periods than some of the surrounding zones.

These conditions are reflected in the distribution of the chief species and their dynamic relationships. *Puccinellia* is the pioneer species and dominant at the lower end and parts of the marginal regions but is rapidly invaded by *Festuca rubra*, which is strongly represented in the central part of the marsh (Fig. 28). At the upper end there are areas dominated by *Juncus gerardii*, but in the wetter parts *Agrostis stolonifera* is the most important species and there is a large colony of *Scirpus maritimus* (which is also represented in, and beside, the channels in the lower regions).

Some of the species associated with *Puccinellia* in the forward parts of the marsh, such as *Aster tripolium*, *Triglochin maritima* and *Atriplex glabriuscula* decrease on passing upwards except along the margins of channels (Fig. 29) and in badly drained areas which, while generally less saline than the lower levels, are rather continuously wet. Here these species are associated with dominant *Agrostis stolonifera*, and they also occupy sites marginal to or overlapping with the dense stands of *Scirpus maritimus*. *Cochlearia officinalis* and *Plantago maritima* are numerous throughout the marsh, particularly in its central portion with *Festuca rubra*. *Plantago*, however, does not reach the lowest levels

124

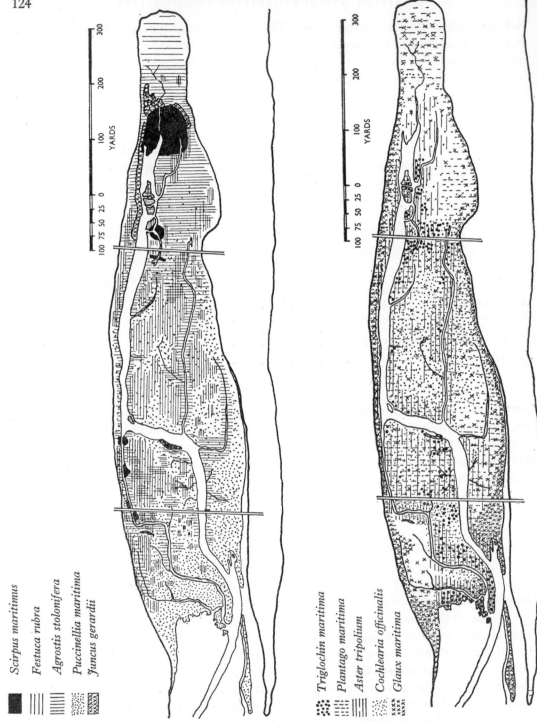

FIG. 28. Approximate distribution of *Scirpus maritimus*, *Festuca rubra*, *Agrostis stolonifera*, *Puccinellia maritima* and *Juncus gerardii* on St. Cyrus salt marsh, 1951. (From Gimingham, 1953.)

FIG. 29. Approximate distribution of *Triglochin maritima*, *Plantago maritima*, *Aster tripolium*, *Cochlearia officinalis* and *Glaux maritima* on St. Cyrus salt marsh, 1951. (From Gimingham, 1953.)

in any numbers and increases towards the sandy margins of the marsh where it is prominent in a zone just below that occupied by *Armeria maritima* (p. 118). *Glaux maritima* is similarly widespread, without being particularly numerous, except in the less wet, more freely-drained, sandy situations at the sides of the lower part of the marsh. *Spergularia media* occurs at the lower end and around the margins but is apparently largely replaced by *S. marina* among the taller and denser vegetation of the centre.

Along drainage channels in the upper part of the marsh the following mosses have been found by A. C. Crundwell: *Amblystegium serpens, Bryum inclinatum,* and *Lepto-dictyum riparium.*

Dynamic relationships

Schemes in which the community-types on a particular marsh, or throughout a given region, are linked by arrows suggesting their relationships, tend to be conjectural. While the zonation in some instances doubtless reflects a succession it is difficult to obtain objective evidence for this, and no Scottish examples have been studied in sufficient detail to assess fully the ecological and dynamic relationships of the various communities. Some isolated observations are, however, available from St. Cyrus. Patches of *Festuca rubra* established in the lower *Puccinellia* areas have been shown to be expand-ing at rates of up to 61 cm. (2 ft.) in a year, whereas a larger colony of *Scirpus maritimus* could not be proved to have spread during a period of three years. Individual plants of *Triglochin maritima* expand slowly in a circular fashion but later degenerate and die away in the centre. The gap so formed is colonised first by *Puccinellia maritima* and other species of the surrounding community (Plates 19, 20, 21). In rare instances, a new individual of *Triglochin* is established within the ring formed by an old one, demonstrat-ing a potential cycle of change. However, *Triglochin* is not here sufficiently numerous for the rings to coalesce and the plant to become dominant.

REFERENCES

ANTHONY, J.	1959	Contribution to the flora of Sutherland. Bettyhill region. *Trans. bot. Soc. Edinb.,* **38**, 7-15.
ASPREY, G. F.	1947	The vegetation of the islands of Canna and Sanday, Inverness-shire. *J. Ecol.,* **34**, 182-93.
BARKLEY, S. Y.,	1953	The vegetation of the island of Soay, Inner Hebrides. *Trans. bot. Soc. Edinb.,* **36**, 119-31.
BARKMAN, J. J.	1955	*Brachythecium erythrorhizum* Br. et Schimp. New to Great Britain. *Trans. Brit. Bryol. Soc.,* **2**, 568-70.
BIRSE, E. M.	1958	Ecological studies on growth-form in Bryophytes. III. The relationship between the growth-form of mosses and ground-water supply. *J. Ecol.* **46** 9-27.

BRAUN-BLANQUET, J. and TÜXEN, R.   1952   Irische Pflanzengesellschaften *in* Lüdi, W. (ed.): Die Pflanzenwelt Irlands. V*eröff. Geobot. Inst. Rübel*, **25**, 224-420.

CHAPMAN, V. J.   1942   The new perspective in the Halophytes. *Quart. Rev. Biol.*, **17**, 291-311.

   1960   *Salt marshes and salt deserts of the world.* London.

FERREIRA, R. E. C. and ROGER, J. GRANT   1957   *Saxifraga hypnoides* L. on the coast of Banffshire. *Trans. bot. Soc. Edinb.*, **37**, 133-6.

FLETCHER, W. W. and MARTIN, D. J.   1960   The flora of Great Cumbrae Island (Firth of Clyde). *Trans. bot. Soc. Edinb.*, **39**, 46-61.

GEMMELL, A. R., GREIG-SMITH, P. and GIMINGHAM, C. H.   1953   A note on the behaviour of *Ammophila arenaria* (L.) Link in relation to sand-dune formation. *Trans. bot. Soc. Edinb.*, **36**, 132-6.

GIBB, D. C.   1957   The free-living forms of *Ascophyllum nodosum* (L.) LeJol. *J. Ecol.*, **45**, 49-83.

GILLHAM, M. E.   1957   Coastal vegetation of Mull and Iona in relation to salinity and soil reaction. *J. Ecol.*, **45**, 757-78.

GIMINGHAM, C. H.   1951   Contributions to the maritime ecology of St. Cyrus, Kincardineshire. II. The sand-dunes. *Trans. bot. Soc. Edinb.*, **35**, 387-414.

   1953   III. The salt-marsh. *Trans. bot. Soc. Edinb.*, **36**, 137-64.

GIMINGHAM, C. H., GEMMELL, A. R., and GREIG-SMITH, P.   1949   The vegetation of a sand-dune system in the Outer Hebrides. *Trans. bot. Soc. Edinb.*, **35**, 82-96.

GRAHAM, R. J. D.   1938   The development of *Elymus arenarius* Linn. on the West Sands, St. Andrews. *Trans. bot. Soc. Edinb.*, **32**, 409-10.

GREIG-SMITH, P.   1961   Data on pattern within plant communities. II. *Ammophila arenaria* (L.) Link. *J. Ecol.*, **49**, 703-8.

HULME, B. A.   1957   *Studies on some British species of* Atriplex L. Ph.D. Thesis, University of Edinburgh.

KIRK, W.   1953   Prehistoric sites at the Sands of Forvie, Aberdeenshire. *Aberdeen Univ. Rev.*, **35**, 150-71.

LANDSBERG, S. Y.   1955   *The Morphology and Vegetation of the Sands of Forvie.* Ph.D. Thesis, University of Aberdeen.

LEWIS, J. R.   1957   Intertidal communities of the northern and western coasts of Scotland. *Trans. Roy. Soc. Edinb.*, **63**, 185-220.

   1961   The littoral zone on rocky shores—a biological or physical entity? *Oikos*, **12**, 280-301.

MacLEOD, A. M.   1949   Some aspects of the plant ecology of the Island of Barra. *Trans. bot. Soc. Edinb.*, **35**, 67-81.

McVEAN, D. N   1961   Flora and vegetation of the islands of St. Kilda and North Rona in 1958. *J. Ecol.*, **49**, 39-54.

NICHOLSON, I. A.   1952   *A study of* Agropyron junceum (Beauv.) *in relation to the stabilization of coastal sand and the development of sand dunes.* M.Sc. Thesis, King's College, Newcastle, in the University of Durham.

NORDHAGEN, R.   1921   Vegetationstudien auf der Insel Utsire im westlichen Norwegen. *Bergens Mus. Aarb.*, Nat. raekke, **1**, 1-149.

	1940	Studien über die maritime Vegetation Norwegens. 1. Die Pflanzengesellschaften der Tangwälle. *Bergens Mus. Aarb.* (1939-40), 1-123.
PATTON, D. and STEWART, E. J. A.	1917	The flora of the Culbin Sands. *Trans. bot. Soc. Edinb.*, **26**, 345-74.
PETCH, C. P.	1933	The vegetation of St. Kilda. *J. Ecol.*, **21**, 92-100.
PIPER, C. S.	1950	*Soil and Plant Analysis.* Adelaide.
POORE, M. E. D. and McVEAN, D. N.	1957	A new approach to Scottish mountain vegetation. *J. Ecol.*, **45**, 401-39.
POORE, M. E. D. and ROBERTSON, V. C.	1949	The vegetation of St. Kilda in 1948. *J. Ecol.*, **38**, 82-99.
POWELL, H. T. and CHAMBERLAIN, Y. M.	1956	Plant Life on Rockall *in* Fisher, J. *Rockall.* London.
PRAEGER, R. L.	1934	*The Botanist in Ireland.* Dublin.
PRITCHARD, N. M.	1957	*Taxonomic and Ecological Studies on the Genus* Gentianella. D.Phil. Thesis, University of Oxford.
RITCHIE, J. C.	1954	*Primula scotica* Hook. Account for Biological Flora of the British Isles, *J. Ecol.*, **42**, 623-8.
ROBERTSON, E. T.	1951	Contributions to the maritime ecology of St. Cyrus, Kincardineshire. I. The Cliffs. *Trans. bot. Soc. Edinb.*, **35**, 370-87.
SALISBURY, E. J.	1942	*The Reproductive Capacity of Plants.* London.
SCOTT, G. A. M.	1960	*The biology of shingle beach plants with special reference to the ecology of selected species.* Ph.D. Thesis, University College of North Wales, Bangor.
SMITH, R. and SMITH, W. G.	1905	Botanical survey of Scotland. III. and IV. Forfar and Fife. *Scot. geogr. Mag.*, **20**, 617-628; **21**, 4-23, 57-83 & 117-126.
SOMMERVILLE, A. H.	1959	*Umbilicus rupestris* (Salisb.) Dandy. (*in* Notes on the Scottish Flora). *Trans. bot. Soc. Edinb.*, **37**, 287.
SPENCE, D. H. N.	1960	Studies on the vegetation of Shetland. III. Scrub in Shetland and in South Uist, Outer Hebrides. *J. Ecol.*, **48**, 73-95.
STEPHENSON, T. A. and ANNE	1949	The universal features of zonation between tide-marks on rocky coasts. *J. Ecol.*, **37**, 289-305.
STEWART, E. J. A., and PATTON, D.	1927	Additional notes on the flora of the Culbin Sands. *Trans. bot. Soc. Edinb.*, **29**, 27-40.
STOCKER, O.	1928	Das Halophytenproblem. *Ergebnissse der Biologie*, Bd. **3**, 265-354.
TANSLEY, A. G.	1911	*Types of British Vegetation.* Cambridge.
TANSLEY, A. G.	1949	*The British Islands and their Vegetation.* Cambridge.
TÜXEN, R.	1955	Das System der nordwestdeutschen Pflanzengesellschaften. *Mitt. Flor.-Soz. Arbeitsgem. in Niedersachsen*, N.F, **5**, 155-76.
VEVERS, H. G.	1936	The land vegetation of Ailsa Craig. *J. Ecol.*, **24**, 424-45.
VOSE, P. B., POWELL, H. G. and SPENCE, J. B.	1957	Machair grazings of Tiree. *Trans. bot. Soc. Edinb.*, **37**, 89-110.
WATSON, E. V.	1953	Observations on the bryophyte flora of the Isle of May. *Trans. bot. Soc. Edinb.*, **36**, 165-80.
WEBLEY, D. M., EASTWOOD, D. J. and GIMINGHAM, C. H.	1952	Development of a soil microflora in relation to plant succession on sand-dunes, including the 'rhizosphere' flora associated with colonizing species. *J. Ecol.*, **40**, 168-78.

TABLE 8

Composition and Percentage Presence of Species in Stands of certain Cliff Community-types
(Figures in brackets denote mean Cover-Abundance value (Domin scale),
where available)

	Armeria—Cochlearia stands	Armeria "swards"	Plantago "swards"	Festuca—Plantago grassland
Localities	Ailsa Craig, Canna and Sanday— Inner Hebrides; St. Kilda; St. Cyrus, Kincardineshire	North Rona, St. Kilda Group	St. Kilda; Canna, Sanday and Soay —Inner Hebrides; Crovie, Banffshire	Fair Isle
No. of Stands	5	2	9	3
Asplenium marinum	40			
Aira praecox			11	33
Festuca ovina	} 20 {	+ + (7)	} 89 (4) {	100
F. rubra				
Holcus lanatus			33 (2)	
Koeleria cristata	40		22	
Poa pratensis				67
Carex panicea			22 (2)	
Armeria maritima	100	+ + (8)	67 (3)	100
Cerastium atrovirens	40		11	
C. holosteoides			33 (2)	
Cochlearia officinalis	100	+ + (2)	11	
Euphrasia sp.			22 (2)	
Glaux maritima		+ + (4)		
Leontodon autumnalis			44 (2)	
Ligusticum scoticum	40			
Plantago coronopus	60	+ + (3)	100 (4)	
P. lanceolata			78	100
P. maritima	60		89 (7)	100
Sagina procumbens			22 (2)	
Sedum anglicum	60		22	
S. rosea	40			
Silene maritima	60		11	
Sonchus asper			11	
Tripleurospermum maritimum	60		11	

Note: + + = recorded in both stands listed.

Additional species recorded in one stand only:

Armeria—Cochlearia stands	Armeria "swards"	Plantago "swards"	Festuca—Plantago grassland
Juniperus communis ssp. nana	Atriplex sp.	Agrostis sp.	Calluna vulgaris
Brachypodium sylvaticum		Anthoxanthum odoratum	Luzula multiflora
Atriplex glabriuscula		Bromus mollis	Scilla verna
Sagina maritima		Carex echinata	Galium saxatile
Sedum acre		Juncus kochii	Jasione montana
Senecio jacobaea		Anagallis tenella	Thymus drucei
		Anthyllis vulneraria	
		Campanula rotundifolia	
		Hypochoeris radicata	
		Thymus drucei	
		Trifolium repens	

Data are included from Anthony (1959), Asprey (1947), McVean (1961), Barkley (1953), Petch (1933), Poore and Robertson (1949), Robertson (1951), Vevers (1936) and from information kindly supplied by Miss U. K. Duncan. The following Bryophytes are listed by McVean (1961) in *Plantago* "swards", St. Kilda:

Eurhynchium praelongum	75 (2)	Single records of:	
Hypnum cupressiforme	50 (4)	Acrocladium cuspidatum	
Mnium hornum	50 (2)	Plagiothecium undulatum	
Aneura latifrons	50 (2)	Sphagnum plumulosum	
		Cephalozia bifida	
		Lophozia ventricosa	
		Pellia sp.	
		Scapania dentata	

At Crovie, Banffshire, the following occur in "*Plantago* swards": *Bryum capillare, Ceratodon purpureus, Hypnum cupressiforme*.

I

Table 9

Composition of *Festuca rubra* Cliff Grasslands on N. Rona and Hirta (St. Kilda)

(+ + = present in 2 stands; + = present in one stand; (*) = species with high cover values)

	Festuca rubra grassland		*Festuca—Agrostis— Anthoxanthum* grassland
	North Rona	Hirta	Hirta
No. of Stands	2	1	2
Calluna vulgaris			+
Ophioglossum vulgatum	+		
Selaginella selaginoides			+
Agrostis tenuis	+	+	+ + (*)
Anthoxanthum odoratum			+ + (*)
Festuca rubra	+ + (*)	+ (*)	+ + (*)
Holcus lanatus	+		+ +
Nardus stricta			+ +
Poa pratensis	+ +		
Poa trivialis	+		
Sieglingia decumbens			+
Carex nigra			+
C. panicea			+ +
C. pilulifera			+
C. pulicaris			+ +
Luzula campestris			+ +
L. multiflora			+
Ajuga reptans			+
Anagallis tenella			+
Armeria maritima	+	+	
Atriplex glabriuscula		+	
Cerastium holosteoides			+
Euphrasia sp.			+ +
Glaux maritima	+		
Leontodon autumnalis	+		
Montia lamprosperma	+ +		
Plantago coronopus		+	
Plantago lanceolata			+
P. maritima		+	+
Potentilla erecta			+ +
Primula vulgaris			+
Senecio jacobaea			+
Stellaria media	+	+	
Ranunculus flammula	+		
Rumex acetosa	+		
Sagina procumbens	+		
Taraxacum officinale agg.			+
Trifolium repens	+		+ +
Tripleurosopermum maritimum		+	
Viola riviniana			+ +
Dicranum scoparium			+
Drepanocladus uncinatus			+

	Festuca rubra grassland		*Festuca—Agrostis—Anthoxanthum* grassland
	North Rona	Hirta	Hirta
Eurhynchium praelongum . .			+
Frullania germana . . .			+
Hylocomium splendens . . .			+
Hypnum cupressiforme . . .			+ +
Pseudoscleropodium purum . .			+ +
Rhytidiadelphus squarrosus . .			+ +
Peltigera canina			+

Data from McVean (1961)

TABLE 10

Composition of Communities containing *Dryas octopetala* and *Empetrum nigrum*
on Cliffs on the N. Coast of Scotland

(+ + =present in both stands; + =present in one stand)

	Dryas "hummocks"	*Dryas—Empetrum* "sward"	*Empetrum* grassland
Localities . . .	Bettyhill, Sutherland: wind-blown sand deposited on N. and N.E.-facing cliff slopes	Bettyhill, Sutherland: gently sloping cliff top exposed to N.E.	Caithness (Ritchie, 1954)
No. of Stands . . .	2	1	1
Empetrum nigrum . .	+ +	+	+
Salix repens . . .	+	+	
Festuca ovina . . .		+	+
Koeleria cristata . .		+	+
Carex flacca . . .	+ +	+	+
Bellis perennis . . .	+	+	+
Cerastium holosteoides .	+	+	
Dryas octopetala . .	+ +	+	
Euphrasia sp. . . .		+	+
Galium verum . . .	+	+	
Linum catharticum . .	+	+	+
Plantago lanceolata . .		+	+
Polygala sp. . . .	+ +	+	
Thymus drucei . . .	+ +	+	
Bryum sp. . . .	+ +		+ (*B. pallens*)
Climacium dendroides . .	+	+	
Ditrichum flexicaule . .	+	+	
Hylocomium splendens .	+		+
Pseudoscleropodium purum .	+	+	
Plagiochila asplenioides . .	+	+	
Peltigera sp. . . .	+		+

Additional species occurring in one
only of the above communities:

Salix aurita	*Selaginella selaginoides*	*Calluna vulgaris*
Dactylis glomerata	*Agrostis tenuis*	*Erica tetralix*
Festuca rubra	*Antennaria dioica*	*Cynosurus cristatus*
Cirsium arvense	*Campanula rotundifolia*	*Holcus mollis*
*Brachythecium erythrorhizum**	*Oxytropis halleri*	*Sieglingia decumbens*
Camptothecium lutescens	*Polygonum viviparum*	*Carex pauciflora*
Rhytidiadelphus triquetrus	*Viola* sp.	*Juncus articulatus*
	Rhytidiadelphus squarrosus	*J. squarrosus*
	Thuidium tamariscinum	*Angelica sylvestris*
		Parnassia palustris
		Pinguicula vulgaris
		Plantago maritima
		Potentilla erecta
		Primula scotica
		Trifolium pratense
		Campylium stellatum
		Hypnum cupressiforme
		Rhacomitrium canescens
		Cladonia rangiferina

* The only known British locality for this species, first discovered in 1948 by Barkman (1955).

TABLE 11

Composition and Percentage Presence of Species in Shingle Beach Community-types

	Foreshore: *Atriplex glabriuscula—Silene maritima —Tripleurospermum maritimum* stands	Landward areas of apposition banks: *Arrhenatherum elatius* stands
Localities	Isle of Arran; St. Cyrus, Kincardineshire; Coulport, Loch Long	Isle of Arran
No. of stands	11	5
Prunus spinosa		40
Agrostis spp.*	18	
Agropyron spp.†	9	20
Arrhenatherum elatius	55	100
Festuca rubra	73	40
Atriplex glabriuscula	82	
Cardamine flexuosa		40
Cerastium holosteoides . . .	18	
Galium aparine	64	60
Geranium robertianum . . .	9	80
Mertensia maritima	64‡	
Polygonum raii	18	
Potentilla anserina . . .	45	
Rumex acetosa	55	40
R. crispus	82	40
Senecio jacobaea	18	
Silene maritima	73	
Stellaria media	9	20
Tripleurospermum maritimum . .	82	
Urtica dioica	9	40
Viola riviniana	9	40
Vicia sylvatica		40

Additional species recorded in one stand only:

Dactylis glomerata	*Rubus fruticosus*
Phragmites communis	*Pteridium aquilinum*
Scirpus maritimus	*Iris pseudacorus*
Armeria maritima	*Calystegia sepium*
Cirsium vulgare	*Cirsium arvense*
Cochlearia officinalis	*Heracleum sphondylium*
Glaucium flavum	*Hypochoeris radicata*
Honkenya peploides	*Lythrum salicaria*
Plantago coronopus	*Oenanthe crocata*
Polygonum persicaria	*Plantago lanceolata*
Sedum acre	*Silene dioica*
Sonchus arvensis	
Senecio vulgaris	

* *A. stolonifera* occurs in some lists, but other species may also be present.
† *A. repens* in landward areas. *A. pungens* may be present on foreshore shingle.
‡ An inflated figure due to selection of stands including this species, during a special investigation.

Data incorporated from Scott (1960)

TABLE 12

Synoptic Table showing Composition of Seral and Relatively Stable Dune Communities

(Figures in these columns show % presence of each species in the stands examined)

Localities	Mobile dunes and early stages of fixation: Wigtownshire, Harris, Tiree, Sutherland, Shetland, Caithness, Kincardineshire, Fife	Fixed dunes: Wigtownshire, Harris, Barra, Shetland, Sutherland, Kincardineshire	Dune grassland (acid): Stands in one locality only: Sands of Forvie, Aberdeenshire	Dune grassland (calcareous): Harris, Lewis, W. Ross, Sutherland, Shetland, Caithness	Machair: Barra, Lewis, Tiree, Shetland, Sutherland
No. of Stands	9	9	17	12	11
Salix repens					18
Botrychium lunaria				17	18
Equisetum arvense				17	9
Selaginella selaginoides					18
Aira praecox	11	11		17	
Agrostis tenuis	78	33	100	25	27
Agropyron junceiforme	89				
Ammophila arenaria		100	71	100	18
Anthoxanthum odoratum			47	25	18
Arrhenatherum elatius		22		17	
Cynosurus cristatus				8	27
Dactylis glomerata	11	11		25	
Elymus arenarius	33				
Festuca ovina			88	8	
F. rubra	67	100	47	100	100
Helictotrichon pubescens				17	
Holcus lanatus	33	33	88	50	27
Koeleria cristata		11	24	8	46
Lolium perenne		11		8	18
Poa annua					
P. pratensis	33	78	100	25	55
Carex arenaria	55	78	100	50	18
C. flacca				33	36
Coeloglossum viride				8	18
Dactylorchis fuchsii				8	9
Listera ovata					18
Luzula campestris		22	77	25	46

	1	2	3	4	5
Angelica sylvestris	8				33
Anthyllis vulneraria	25				22
Arctium minus agg.					
Astragalus danicus	8			22	22
Atriplex glabriuscula					11
Bellis perennis	91	67		78	11
Campanula rotundifolia	9	25	53	11	22
Centaurea nigra	46	17	29	22	
Cerastium atrovirens				78	11
C. semidecandrum		33		22	
C. holosteoides	27	25	18	11	
Cirsium arvense		25	18	44	67
C. vulgare		8		22	44
Crepis capillaris	9	17		22	
Daucus carota	64	25		11	
Erodium cicutarium	27	8		11	
Euphrasia sp.	91	83		44	
Galium saxatile			88		
G. verum	91	67	71	78	22
Gentianella amarella ssp. *septentrionalis*	18	75		11	11
G. campestris	27			22	22
Heracleum sphondylium	36	8		33	44
Hieracium pilosella	18	17		44	
Honkenya peploides				22	44
Hypochoeris radicata	18	8		11	11
Leontodon autumnalis	9	25	6	22	
Linum catharticum	36	50	82		22
Lotus corniculatus	73	67	18	78	
Myosotis arvensis		17		11	
M. ramosissima					
Ononis repens	18				
Oxytropis halleri	18				
Pimpinella saxifraga	18	8		55	
Plantago lanceolata	91	92		78	55
P. maritima	46	58		33	55
Polygala vulgaris	46	33		33	
Polygonum viviparum	18				
Potentilla anserina		8		44	
Primula veris	9	17			
P. vulgaris	18	17			11
Prunella vulgaris		58		33	
Ranunculus acris	55	42		22	22
R. bulbosus	55	8		22	22
R. repens		33	29	22	22
Rhinanthus minor agg.	55*	25		22	22

* Here recorded as *R. minor* ssp. *stenophyllus*, to which many of the other records of *R. minor* incorporated in this Table can probably be referred.

	Mobile dunes and early stages of fixation	Fixed dunes	Dune grassland (acid)	Dune grassland (calcareous)	Machair
Rumex acetosella . .	22	11	47	8	
R. crispus . .	55	11		8	
Sagina procumbens .			35	8	
Sedum acre . .	22				9
Senecio jacobaea .	55	55		33	55
Solidago virgaurea .		11	6	8	
Sonchus asper .	55	22		8	
Stellaria media .			41	8	
Symphytum sp. .		22			
Taraxacum sp. .	67	67		17	55
Thalictrum minus agg. .	22	44		33	55
Thymus drucei .		22		58	64
Trifolium medium .					46
T. pratense .	55	78	59	42	27
T. repens .		22		58	82
Veronica arvensis .		11	41		
V. officinalis .				8	
Vicia cracca .	11			8	18
V. lathyroides .		22			
Viola canina .				25	9
V. riviniana .		22	41	17	
†V. tricolor agg. .	11	11		8	27
Acrocladium cuspidatum .		33		8	9
Brachythecium albicans .	22	22		8	
B. rutabulum .		22		17	
Bryum argenteum .		11	24	25	
B. pendulum .	44	33		8	
Camptothecium lutescens .	11	33	82	8	18
Ceratodon purpureus .	22	11		8	
Climacium dendroides .				8	
Dicranum scoparium .		11	35	8	
Hylocomium splendens .	11	33	71	17	18
Hypnum cupressiforme .		33	47	17	18
Mnium spp. .		33		17	
Mnium undulatum .			41	25	
Plagiothecium undulatum .			71		
Pleurozium schreberi .				8	
Pohlia nutans .					18
Pseudoscleropodium purum .		33	35	25	
Rhytidiadelphus squarrosus .	22	55	82	25	36
R. triquetrus .		33	41	33	9

† Mainly the ssp. curtisii.

Tortula ruraliformis . .	33	67	35	25	9
Lophocolea bidentata . .		44	41	33	25
Cetraria aculeata .			41		
Cladonia impexa/sylvatica .					
Peltigera canina . .		22	47	25	

Additional species occurring with low % presence:—

Eryngium maritimum
Tussilago farfara

Phleum arenarium
Arabis hirsuta
Campanula glomerata
Carlina vulgaris
Filago minima
Filipendula ulmaria
Galium aparine
Lathyrus pratensis
Rumex acetosa
Scrophularia nodosa
Senecio vulgaris
Silene dioica
Teucrium scorodonia
Tragopogon pratense
Veronica chamaedrys
Urtica dioica
Barbula fallax
Cratoneuron filicinum
Dichodontium pellucidum
Ditrichum flexicaule

Cirsium palustre
Lathyrus pratensis
Pedicularis sylvatica
Rumex acetosa
Senecio vulgaris
Urtica dioica
Veronica serpyllifolia

Crataegus monogyna
Rosa sp.
Rubus fruticosus agg.
Ulex europaeus
Pteridium aquilinum
Festuca pratensis
Helictotrichon pratense
Phleum nodosum
Poa trivialis
Carex maritima
Arenaria serpyllifolia
Campanula glomerata
Cardamine pratensis
Dianthus deltoides
Endymion non-scriptus
Filago germanica
Filipendula ulmaria
Galium boreale
G. cruciata
Geranium molle
G. pratense
G. sanguineum
Helianthemum chamaecistus
Hypericum hirsutum
H. perforatum
H. pulchrum
Lathyrus pratensis
Medicago lupulina
Myosotis discolor
Origanum vulgare
Plantago coronopus
P. major
Saxifraga granulata
Stellaria graminea
Tanacetum vulgare
Teucrium scorodonia

Aira caryophyllea
Festuca vivipara
Carex nigra
C. ovalis
Epipactis atrorubens
Gymnadenia conopsea
Luzula multiflora
Orchis mascula
Scilla verna
Antennaria dioica
Armeria maritima
Draba incana
Dryas octopetala
Leontodon hispidus
Succisa pratensis
Trollius europaeus
Ctenidium molluscum
Ditrichum flexicaule
Thuidium tamariscinum

Mobile dunes and early stages of fixation	Fixed dunes	Dune grassland (acid)	Dune grassland (calcareous)	Machair
			Tragopogon pratensis	
			Trifolium arvense	
			T. campestre	
			Valeriana officinalis	
			Valerianella locusta	
			Veronica chamaedrys	
			Vicia sepium	
			Viola hirta	
			Entodon orthocarpus	
			Eurhynchium praelongum	
			Polytrichum juniperinum	
			Thuidium delicatulum	
			Cephaloziella byssacea	
			Lepidozia reptans	

Data incorporated from Pritchard (1955), MacLeod (1949), Landsberg (1955), Vose et al. (1957).

TABLE 13
Composition of Damp Dune Slack Communities

Localities: Wigtownshire, Shetland, Sutherland, Caithness, Aberdeenshire, Fife

No. of areas examined: 11 (Bryophytes recorded in 8)

Species	% Presence	Species	% Presence
Erica tetralix	36	Linum catharticum	46
Salix spp.	27	Lotus corniculatus	73
Salix repens	36	Myosotis caespitosa	9
		M. ramosissima	9
Equisetum arvense	18	Ononis repens	9
Ophioglossum vulgatum	18	Parnassia palustris	55
Selaginella selaginoides	18	Pinguicula vulgaris	18
		Plantago lanceolata	36
Agrostis stolonifera	64	P. maritima	36
Aira praecox	9	Polygala sp.	9
Ammophila arenaria	36	Potentilla anserina	36
Festuca rubra	82	Primula scotica	18
Holcus lanatus	46	Prunella vulgaris	91
Poa pratensis	55	Pyrola minor	9
Sieglingia decumbens	9	Radiola linoides	18
		Ranunculus acris	9
Carex arenaria	82	R. flammula	27
C. flacca	55	R. repens	18
C. nigra	55	Rhinanthus minor agg.	9
C. serotina	18	Sagina sp.	27
Corallorhiza trifida	18	Senecio jacobaea	18
J. articulatus	64	Taraxacum sp.	18
Juncus balticus	18	Thymus drucei	27
J. conglomeratus	18	Trifolium repens	82
Luzula campestris	27	Tussilago farfara	9
Scilla verna	9	Veronica serpyllifolia	18
		Viola canina	9
Achillea millefolium	18	V. palustris	18
Anthyllis vulneraria	27	V. tricolor agg.	18
Bellis perennis	36		
Caltha palustris	9	Acrocladium cuspidatum	50
Cardamine pratensis	36	Bryum sp.	13
Centaurea nigra	9	Dicranum scoparium	50
Cerastium holosteoides	55	Ditrichum flexicaule	25
Cirsium arvense	9	Camptothecium lutescens	13
C. vulgare	9	Climacium dendroides	50
Daucus carota	9	Hylocomium splendens	38
Epilobium palustre	18	Hypnum cupressiforme	50
Euphrasia spp.	55	Mnium sp.	38
Filago minima	18	Philonotis fontana	38
Filipendula ulmaria	46	Pleurozium schreberi	38
Galium verum	9	Polytrichum piliferum	13
G. uliginosum	27	Pseudoscleropodium purum	50
Gentianella amarella spp. septentrionalis	36	Rhytidiadelphus squarrosus	88
G. campestris	9	R. triquetrus	63
Heracleum sphondylium	9	Thuidium tamariscinum	13
Hieracium pilosella	9		
Hydrocotyle vulgaris	46	Cetraria aculeata	13
Hypochoeris radicata	9	Cladonia sylvatica	25
Leontodon autumnale	9	Peltigera canina	38

Additional species recorded in slacks at Sands of Forvie, Aberdeenshire (Landsberg, 1955):

Calluna vulgaris
Empetrum nigrum
Lycopodium clavatum
Anthoxanthum odoratum
Festuca ovina
Nardus stricta
Carex demissa
Isolepis setacea
Juncus bufonius
J. bulbosus
J. effusus
J. squarrosus
Chamaenerion angustifolium
Galium saxatile
Rumex acetosella
Potentilla erecta
Veronica officinalis
Viola riviniana

Aulacomnium palustre
Brachythecium albicans
Dicranella varia
Drepanocladus uduncus
Mnium undulatum
Pohlia annotina
P. nutans
Polytrichum commune
P. juniperinum
P. urnigerum
Rhacomitrium canescens

Blasia pusilla
Calypogeia trichomanis
Cephalozia bicuspidata
Gymnocolea inflata
Lophocolea bidentula
Nardia scalaris
Pellia sp.
Ptilidium pulcherrimum
Preissia quadrata
Riccardia pinguis
Scapania irrigua
Usnea comosa

Additional Bryophyte species recorded at Foveran, Aberdeenshire (Birse, 1958):

Barbula cylindrica
Brachythecium albicans
Bryum pseudotriquetrum
Campylium stellatum
Ceratodon purpureus

Fissidens adianthoides
Mnium punctatum
Polytrichum juniperinum
Rhacomitrium canescens
Tortula ruraliformis

Haplomitrium hookeri
Lophocolea cuspidata
Preissia quadrata
Riccardia multifida

TABLE 14

Composition of Wet Communities of Deflation Plains, Forvie, Aberdeenshire

(Figures in these columns show Cover/Abundance (Braun-Blanquet scale))

	Calluna vulgaris community	Erica tetralix community	Nardus stricta community	Salix repens community
June 1950: Min. depth of water-table (cm.) . .	13·8	15·2	12·7	0
June 1950: Max. depth of water-table (cm.) . .	50·8	27·9	58·4	10·2
Calluna vulgaris . . .	4	1		
Empetrum nigrum . . .	3	2		+
Erica tetralix . . .	3	4	+	
Salix repens . . .	1	1	1	5
Agrostis tenuis . . .	+	+	+	
Ammophila arenaria . . .	+		+	
Deschampsia cespitosa . .		+	1	+
D. flexuosa		+		
Festuca ovina . . .	+	+		+
Molinia caerulea . . .			1	
Nardus stricta . . .	+	+	5	
Carex arenaria . . .	+	+	1	
C. dioica		+	+	+
C. echinata	+	+	+	+
C. flacca		+	+	+
C. nigra	+	+	+	1
C. rostrata				+
Eriophorum angustifolium .		+		+
Juncus bufonius . . .			+	+
J. conglomeratus . . .		+	+	+
J. effusus	1	1	2	1
J. squarrosus . . .	1	+	1	+
Luzula campestris . .		+	+	
Trichophorum cespitosum .		+	1	1
Epilobium obscurum . .			+	
E. palustre			+	
Galium palustre . . .	+			+
G. saxatile		+	+	+
Hydrocotyle vulgaris . .		+	1	1
Parnassia palustris . .				+
Pedicularis sylvatica . .		+		+
Polygala serpyllifolia . .		+	1	+
Potentilla erecta . . .	1	1	+	1
P. palustris				+
Ranunculus acris . . .			1	+
R. repens			1	
Viola palustris . . .	+		+	1
Acrocladium cuspidatum .	+			1
Aulacomnium palustre . .		+	1	2
Bryum spp.	+			
Ceratodon purpureus . .	+			
Dicranum bonjeanum . .	+	+	+	1
D. scoparium . . .	+			
Drepanocladus spp. . .		+	+	+
Hylocomium splendens . .	2	+	+	

	Calluna vulgaris community	Erica tetralix community	Nardus stricta community	Salix repens community
Hypnum cupressiforme . .	+	+		
Mnium hornum . . .		+		
M. punctatum . . .	+	+	+	
M. undulatum . . .	+	+		
Pleurozium schreberi . .	1		+	+
Pohlia nutans . . .		+		
Polytrichum commune . .	+	2	1	1
P. formosum . . .		1	+	+
P. juniperinum . . .	+	1	+	
Rhytidiadelphus triquetrus .	1	1	+	
Sphagnum spp. . . .	+	+	+	1
Riccardia spp. . . .	+			+
Cladonia spp. . . .	+	+		+
Peltigera canina . . .	+	1	+	1
Usnea comosa . . .	+	+		+

Data from Landsberg (1955).

THE FOREST ZONE

CHAPTER 5

WOODLAND AND SCRUB

D. N. McVEAN

DISTRIBUTION

The destruction of the original forest cover of Scotland has been taking place since Neolithic times and is now virtually complete while the advent of re-afforestation programmes, both private and national, is tending increasingly to obscure the last evidence of the native forest pattern. A further difficulty exists in that there can be no certainty that the surviving pattern of species segregation into pure pine-wood, oakwood, birchwood and so on represents the original state of the forest cover in this country. In fact, there is some evidence to indicate that such a complete separation is largely a result of land use over the last one thousand years.

While native pine can generally be distinguished with some confidence from self-seeded introductions, the status of many of our oakwoods is more confused. However, if it is assumed that most oak planting would be carried out on the site of former native oakwood where soil and situation would obviously be most favourable for such an enterprise, although there is little if any direct evidence and, if a second assumption is made, that the present distribution of apparently native oak and pine is a guide to the regions where these species were formerly most abundant, there is a basis on which to form a picture of the original forest cover of Scotland. Oak and pine still form a pattern which is closely linked with differences in latitude, topography, climate and geology while other species such as birch and alder have a more general distribution within their altitudinal range.

McVean and Ratcliffe (1962) have produced woodland distribution maps of Scotland with these considerations in mind, the first showing the present pattern of surviving fragments of oak, pine and birch woodland, the second being an attempt to reconstruct the forest pattern as it was during the present climatic period but prior to the onset of large scale forest clearance by man. The reconstruction shows the central and north-east Highlands as pine forest country to an altitude of about 610 m. with dominant oak forest to about 300 m. in southern Scotland, the midland valley, south-west Argyll, the Great Glen and its tributaries, and all the larger straths and glens which penetrate the Highlands from south and west. Birch dominated woodland and scrub is relegated to the

PLATE 22. Pinewood *Vaccinium*—moss association, Abernethy Forest, Inverness-shire, at 750 ft. A mature, even-aged stand of Scots Pine on a well-drained sandy soil. *Vaccinium myrtillus* and *V. vitis-idaea* are dominant, but in places with an even denser shade their growth becomes sparser and hypnaceous mosses assume dominance.

PLATE 23

Juniper-rich birchwood, Morrone, Braemar, Aberdeenshire, at 1500 ft. The best example of this woodland-scrub combination yet found in Scotland. It lies on a limestone drift soil, and the field layer is species-rich in places.

extreme north and west and to a zone lying above the pine and oak forest. A belt of pine lies between the oak and birch forest on the hill slopes in many places. A very simplified distribution map of the principal forest trees is shown in Fig. 63 (p. 569).

In other words, the Scottish forests are visualised as forming an extreme western phase of the west European transition from temperate deciduous forest through coniferous forest to boreal deciduous forest. The distribution of native pine forest and birch scrub in the northern Highlands, even today, is extremely like the situation in Norwegian and Finnish Lapland in spite of the difference in latitude; the replacement of coniferous forest by birch scrub towards the northern forest limit may be largely the result of human activity in both regions although climatic oceanicity also seems to play its part.

Writing of the vanished forests of Scotland, Tansley (1949) remarks that in ascending the hillsides one evidently passed from oakwood to pine and birch which were, therefore, zoned above the oak both altitudinally and latitudinally. Traces of pine above oak can, in fact, still be seen in many places, the most convincing being at Ardlair on the north side of Loch Maree. The zonation is always traceable to edaphic factors rather than to any climatic effect with increasing altitude, the oak occupying the richer alluvial and colluvial soils in the glens and hollows of the hillsides with pine above on the crags and coarser, stony soils where peat and raw humus formation have taken place. Where free-draining siliceous sands and gravels extend over the low ground in the north-east or where there has been drying out of the deep peat deposits of estuarine bogs, pine reaches almost to the sea. On the other hand, where the underlying rocks or glacial debris consist of calcareous and easily weathered material the pine zone was probably absent and oak passed directly to an upper mixed deciduous zone of birch, rowan, hazel, bird cherry and juniper. Traces of this last zone are few since woodland and scrub have been all but eliminated on these upper base-rich slopes which are now valuable hill grazing. Much the same phenomenon takes place with increase in latitude and many birchwoods in Sutherland have localised patches of an oakwood flora of *Allium ursinum*, *Mercurialis perennis*, *Silene dioica* and other tall herbs.

Evidence of the natural occurrence of birch above pine is even harder to find than that of pine above oak. It does occur in many places as a result of pine felling and birch re-colonisation, but felling is more likely to produce the reverse zonation. A natural pine above birch zonation may occur where steep slopes with brown soil flatten out to a peat-covered plateau above. This is found in Amat Forest west of Bonar Bridge, where the altitude is a little too great to allow the growth of oak on the brown forest soil. The occurrence of birchwood above pine in Crannoch Wood, Perthshire, may be a genuine survival of the original zonation. On the other hand, the highest natural forest limits now remaining in Britain are in the pinewoods of the Cairngorms, with pine passing directly into a narrow zone of juniper scrub.

The lack of relict pine in extreme western and south-western areas, combined with the restricted development of heather moor, make it appear probable that there was a gradual restriction of the pine belt there, even on acid rocks (cf. Map B of McVean and

K

Ratcliffe, 1962). At the present day oak soon gives way to an upper birch zone on the sides of many western sea lochs.

In the south and east of the country the latitudinal transition from oak to pine and birch is first seen on north-facing slopes. In the west and north the replacement takes place readily on the more favourable exposures also. The occurrence of pine on north-facing slopes, with oak on the opposite side of the glen or loch, can still be seen at Loch Maree, Loch Arkaig and Loch Rannoch and in Glen Moriston, a segregation which is primarily geological and only secondarily climatic, since the more lime-rich rocks usually seem to occur on the south-facing slopes.

Another feature of present woodland distribution which seems to be almost entirely natural is the passage of oakwood to hazel scrub as one goes westward on the exposed Tertiary basalt country of Skye, Mull and Morvern. Seral hazel scrub, where oak has been extracted, is more common and quite large areas can be seen on the Lorne plateau east of Oban.

Forest distribution may be summarised by saying that, while a simple climatic zonation of forest types is not found, and was probably never found, in the Highlands, some climatic control is discernible, particularly in latitudinal distribution.

Scottish Woodland Types

Few studies of either the dynamics or phyto-sociology of Scottish woodlands have been made since those of Crampton, Watt and Tansley (Tansley, 1949). In Tansley there is a brief description of oakwoods in the Great Glen, Deeside and the northern Highlands, the planted and sub-spontaneous beechwoods of Aberdeenshire (Watt), the pinewoods of Deeside, Speyside and Loch Maree and the birchwoods of Caithness (Crampton) and Speyside. Steven and Carlisle (1959) give a detailed topographic, historical and floristic account of all surviving fragments of native pine forest while McVean and Ratcliffe (1962) concentrate upon the phyto-sociology of Highland pine, oak and birchwoods with some notes upon forest regeneration and structure. There are no published works on the mixed deciduous woods of the lowland areas. Data for this study are summarised in Table 16. (p. 166).

Pine

The surviving pine forests of the Highlands have been grouped by Steven and Carlisle (1959) as follows:

Deeside: Glentanar, Ballochbuie and Mar.

Speyside: Abernethy, Rothiemurchus, Glenmore, Glen Feshie, Dulnain and Glen Avon.

Rannoch: Black Wood and Meggernie.

Great Glen: Glen Moriston, Glen Loyne, Glengarry, Barisdale, Loch Arkaig and Glen Mallie, Glen Loy, Glen Nevis and Ardgour.

Strath Glass: Glen Affric, Glen Cannich, Strathfarrar, Guisachan and Cougie.

Wester Ross: Loch Maree, Coulin, Achnashellach and Shieldaig.

Northern: Amat, Rhidorroch, Glen Einig and Strath Vaich.

Southern: Black Mount, Glen Orchy, Tyndrum and Glen Falloch.

The largest and best known of these forests are the Deeside group, Abernethy, Rothiemurchus, Black Wood of Rannoch, the Strath Glass group and the Coille na Glas Leitire of Loch Maree.

Vegetation. The vegetation of these forests is relatively uniform but significant differences can be detected between that of the eastern and drier areas and that of the high rainfall west. Two well-defined associations can be recognised.

The **pinewood *Vaccinium*—moss association** is characteristic of moderately dense forest throughout the central and northern Highlands and is also frequently developed in pine plantations (Plate 22). Besides *Pinus sylvestris* the constants of the association are *Calluna vulgaris*, *Vaccinium myrtillus*, *V. vitis-idaea* and *Hylocomium splendens* or *Rhytidiadelphus triquetrus* but *Deschampsia flexuosa* and *Ptilium crista-castrensis* occasionally attain co-dominance. Tall shrubs are almost completely absent although an occasional moribund juniper bush may be found. *Betula pubescens* and *Sorbus aucuparia* may form a small proportion of the tree canopy and their seedlings are frequent in the field and ground layers. *Goodyera repens* is exclusive to the association although it may sometimes also be found on tussocks in the pinewood *Vaccinium*—*Calluna* association (p. 148).

Two facies can be recognised, one dominated by either or both species of *Vaccinium*, the other by *Hylocomium splendens* or *Rhytidiadelphus triquetrus*. The two facies generally occur together, the first under a tree canopy of average density and the second where the canopy is particularly close or has been close in the immediate past. The moss facies may persist for many years after the shade which gave rise to it has been removed and the quantity of *Vaccinium* remaining at this stage determines whether a transition to the *Vaccinium* facies will then take place or whether the more rapidly colonising *Calluna* will assume dominance of the dwarf shrub layer.

The association is found from sea-level to about 500 m., occupying extensive areas of natural forest and plantation in the eastern Highlands but forming only localised patches in the west. Where felled pine has been replaced by natural birch there may be a gradual change to either the second of the birchwood associations described later or to the pinewood *Vaccinium*—*Calluna* association. A change to the other pinewood association can also take place where the pine has been thinned out in the absence of grazing animals.

Soils are invariably well-drained sands and gravels with raw humus and a well-developed podsol profile.

The association can be equated with the "Pineto—Vaccinetum myrtilli" of Braun Blanquet *et al.* (1939, p. 61) and it is widely distributed, with minor floristic variations, throughout north-western Europe. It includes communities 1 and 3-5 of Steven and Carlisle (1959).

The **pinewood *Vaccinium—Calluna* association** is characteristic of more open pine forest, pine-birch mixtures and even pure birchwood where this has recently colonised former pine ground. It corresponds floristically to community 2 of Steven and Carlisle (1959) and differs from the first association in being dominated by a mixture of tall, leggy heather and *Vaccinium myrtillus* with deep *Sphagnum* tussocks and a wide range of other mosses and hepatics. The forest floor is almost always thrown into hummocks due to the presence of boulders and undecayed tree stumps. A greater variety of species may also enter the tree canopy and *Ilex aquifolium* is frequent in the west Highland woods. Juniper is the characteristic tall shrub and it may be abundant in certain areas of the central and eastern Highlands.

There are eight constants (Table 16) while *Calluna vulgaris*, *Vaccinium myrtillus*, *Hylocomium splendens*, *Ptilium crista-castrensis*, and Sphagna of the *Acutifolia* group may each dominate their respective layers. *Ptilium crista-castrensis* is selective for the order "Vaccinio—Piceetalia" to which the association belongs but there are no other characteristic species.

Separate facies have not been distinguished, but further study should make it possible to separate a *Sphagnum*-dominated variant from the wetter localities and districts.

Floristically the association can be distinguished from the *Vaccinium*—moss association by the presence of *Aulacomnium palustre*, *Calypogeia trichomanis* and several other hepatics.

The occurrence of this association is co-extensive with that of native pine forest and it is generally absent from the denser shade of planted forests. It is found from sea-level to over 300 m. in the west and from just under 300 m. to 600 m. in the eastern Highlands, where it tends to replace the previous association with increasing altitude. Sites are again well drained but most stands occur on damp north-facing slopes. The light intensity at ground level is about $\frac{1}{3}$ to $\frac{1}{5}$ full daylight as against $\frac{1}{6}$ full daylight for the *Vaccinium*—moss association.

The pinewood *Vaccinium—Calluna* association also occurs, and can persist indefinitely without a tree canopy, as a result of tree felling especially on north-facing slopes which are normally too moist to be converted to heather moor by rotational burning. It is the only woodland association occurring independently of trees.

Soils are again podsolic with much accumulation of raw humus and the A_2 horizon may attain a thickness of over 1 m.

The closest Continental equivalents of the pinewood *Vaccinium—Calluna* association appear to lie among the spruce forest associations of Central Europe such as the "Mastigobryeto—Piceetum" (Braun-Blanquet *et al.*, 1939, p. 32).

Other types of vegetation such as heather moor and *Molinia* grassland may be found in open pinewoods, apart from various other communities of natural clearings and boggy hollows, but these are usually the result of human interference and cannot be described as forest vegetation (e.g. communities 7 and 10 of Steven and Carlisle, 1959).

Structure and dynamics. Structurally most of the native pine forests consist of a mosaic of segregated age classes arising from localised events such as fires which were followed by a sudden outburst of regeneration. Only rarely can one find small areas on which trees of all ages occur intimately mixed as the result of a long period of relatively constant environment. It is difficult to say which of these structures would have prevailed in the primeval forest before the advent of man but doubtless both had their place. Three main arrangements of the trees are now found:

1. Quasi-even-aged stands generally between 80 and 150 years old but sometimes older. Different crown forms and the occurrence of dominant and suppressed trees may give some appearance of age diversity. Vegetation may belong to either of the two associations described above according to the density of the tree canopy but the *Vaccinium*—moss association is the more common. Pine seedlings in their first and second years are not uncommon, but regeneration is seldom found, due principally to the depth of the undecomposed moss and litter layer which is liable to sudden drying out in springtime. Sapling pines from the *Vaccinium*—moss association in Curr Wood, Dulnain Bridge, proved to be from five to eight years of age although only 10 cm. high. Advance growth, even of this tender age, is exceptional in closed Scottish pinewoods and is found only in the drier eastern districts. A proportion of these saplings could probably commence active growth on the felling of the parent trees.

2. Two-generation stands in which pioneer trees of about 150-200 years of age are embedded in a matrix of straight stemmed, 80-100 year old progeny. The vegetation is a mixture of both pinewood associations and much of it may be in the intermediate stage of development. Regeneration is absent from the older stands which have a closed canopy but may still be taking place if the parent trees were widely spaced.

3. Pine heath in which trees of different ages, but generally 150-200 years, are scattered at wide spacing over the ground and regeneration is absent. The vegetation may belong to the pinewood *Vaccinium*—*Calluna* association but is more often heather moor or *Molinia* bog. Lack of regeneration is most often due to periodic burning but, in the absence of fire, can usually be ascribed to the combination of slow seedling growth among deep moss and vigorous dwarf shrubs with damage caused by browsing deer during winter and early spring. Seedlings and saplings can generally be found in un-burned pine heath, but they are invariably topped by the deer again and again so that they seldom grow beyond a height of 15-20 cm. In the absence of browsing animals it is probable that the small number of trees that became established would just be sufficient to maintain open forest.

The extent to which our pine forests have been dependent upon forest and heath fires for their perpetuation can never be known. Tamm (1950) points out that in Scandinavia edaphic conditions under old pine become unsuitable for regeneration, the surface mor becoming biologically inactive. Fires generally restore this activity and enables regeneration to take place. Handley (1954) considers that this biological stagnation may be the result of human activities through the segregation and encouragement of mor-forming species. He suggests that the original natural communities consisted of mixtures of the mull and mor formers and that coniferous forests should have at least some intermixture of deciduous trees and mull-forming herbs.

All areas of dense natural regeneration in Scotland result from the seeding of heather moor at the correct stage of development after fire or, locally, from the seeding of bared mineral soil. The young trees, after a slow start, grow up vigorously along with the heather and by the time they overtop it are able to tolerate a certain amount of deer damage. The heather eventually becomes killed out by the shade of the young trees and a pine stand of the first type described above is the result. If the amount of seed available is not sufficient to give a close thicket of young trees, open pine heath develops. Unfortunately, the fire which encourages the sudden outburst of regeneration may also produce conditions which make it more difficult for the next generation to become established and perpetuate itself.

Mixed woodland of birch and pine with some rowan and other tree species is much less common than pure woods of either pine or birch. Still fewer of these mixed woods are free from browsing animals so that it is not known if tree regeneration would be any more successful in them than in the pure stands.

Good regeneration occurs locally within a few of the Highland pinewoods. A small area of some twenty acres at the north-west corner of Loch Garten in Abernethy Forest exhibits many of the features of developing mixed-age pine forest. A certain amount of advance growth is taking place in both pinewood associations which in this locality have a considerable shrub layer of juniper, birch and rowan and many mild humus species such as *Viola riviniana* and *Oxalis acetosella* in the field layer. Group regeneration of the pines can be found at all stages, showing the formation of dense thickets in the neighbourhood of parent trees, the self-thinning of these thickets and the eventual death of the parents. Active regeneration is also taking place on clearings containing heather which has not been burned within the life span of the surrounding pines.

Birch and Oak

The birches *Betula pubescens* ssp. *pubescens* and ssp. *odorata* and *B. pendula* are the commonest forest trees of Scotland. Their taxonomic separation is difficult, so that the distribution of the species and sub-species is imperfectly known, but *B. pubescens* ssp. *pubescens* appears to be confined to Argyll, Perthshire and the south while *B. pendula* is abundant only to the east of a line from Garve to Glen Moriston and perhaps in the drier eastern districts of Aberdeenshire, Perthshire and Angus. *B. pubescens* ssp. *odorata* is widespread and may occur as pure populations in all districts (F. J. W. England, personal communication).

The taxonomic situation among the oaks is also slightly confused and past planting of *Quercus robur* in districts and on soils that would naturally carry sessile oak (*Q. petraea*) has led to still greater difficulty. The question of hybridisation between the two species as a possible cause of many of the puzzling forms to be met with in the Highlands is still an open question.

The two forest types, dominated by birch and oak respectively, are considered together since, especially in the Highlands, there is considerable overlap in habitat and floristics. To a certain extent this is also true of pine and birch as has been pointed out above.

Vegetation. The vegetation of most of the Scottish upland birchwoods can be assigned to one or other of two associations which grade into one another to some extent but which cover too wide a range to form separate facies of the one association.

The **Vaccinium-rich birchwood association** has ten constants besides *Betula pubescens* itself (Table 16) and the woodland floor can be dominated by *Vaccinium myrtillus*, *Luzula sylvatica*, *Pteridium aquilinum*, *Hylocomium splendens* or *Thuidium tamariscinum* while *Blechnum spicant*, *Vaccinium vitis-idaea*, *Agrostis tenuis*, *Anthoxanthum odoratum*, *Rhytidiadelphus loreus* and *Ptilium crista-castrensis* may also attain co-dominance.

A tall shrub layer is usually absent, but *Juniperus communis* is occasionally dominant and *Corylus avellana* and *Lonicera periclymenum* may be abundant, the last species being exclusive to the association. Oak can replace birch as the dominant tree up to about 275 m. in the southern and east-central Highlands and 150 m. in the west, with little or no change in the associated field layer, but most of the Highland oakwoods fall rather into the next association. *Sorbus aucuparia* is a common constituent of the tree layer and may be co-dominant or even dominant locally (Anderson, 1950; McVean, 1958).

Numbers of species per stand range from 18 to 39 per 4 sq. m. with an average of 28, and thus tend to be higher than in either of the closely related pinewood associations which can also be separated floristically by the presence of *Goodyera repens* and the absence of *Corylus avellana*, *Lonicera periclymenum*, *Rubus idaeus*, *Endymion non-scriptus*, *Luzula sylvatica* and *Thuidium tamariscinum*.

The **herb-rich birch and oakwood association** has seven constants, all herbs, and mosses, and the possible dominants are *Thelypteris limbosperma*, *Agrostis tenuis*, *Anthoxanthum odoratum*, *Hylocomium splendens* and *Thuidium tamariscinum*. Grasses are often the most prominent plants in the woodland floor, but the association also includes stands in which basiphilous herbs are abundant. It is likely that further study would justify the separation of these two types into distinct associations. Tall shrubs are even less common than in the preceding association, but this is entirely due to the more intense grazing and browsing by wild and domestic animals to which this type of vegetation is subjected throughout the year. Numbers of species range from 24 to 48 per stand of 4 sq. m. with an average of 33.

The association is common to birchwoods and to the poorer stands of oak which typically make up Highland oakwoods. It is distinguished from the *Vaccinium*-rich birchwood association by the virtual absence of *Vaccinium* species and by the appearance of, or increase in, *Holcus lanatus*, *Endymion non-scriptus*, *Anemone nemorosa*, *Conopodium majus*, *Lysimachia nemorum*, *Primula vulgaris*, *Ranunculus ficaria*, *R. repens*, *Viola riviniana*, *Mnium hornum*, *M. undulatum*, *Thuidium tamariscinum* and *Plagiochila asplenioides*. The most herb-rich stands are similar floristically to mixed deciduous wood-land (p. 160). There are no species exclusive to the association, but a few, such as *Anemone nemorosa* and *Conopodium majus*, are selective for it.

The two birchwood associations are found throughout Scotland from sea-level to almost 610 m. Above the tree line, or sometimes well below it, the vegetation of siliceous rock ledges or steep broken ground dominated by *Vaccinium myrtillus* and/or *Luzula sylvatica* can be regarded as a treeless facies of the *Vaccinium*-rich association. On the other hand the vegetation of dense stands of *Pteridium aquilinum* or *Thelypteris limbo-sperma* in dwarf shrub or grass heaths can be said to belong to the herb-rich association, the shade of the ferns acting in much the same way as a tree canopy.

Nordhagen's "*Vaccinium myrtillus*-rich birchwoods" (Nordhagen, 1927-28, p. 112) resembles these first two associations in many ways. There is less resemblance between his grass and herb-rich birch woods (Nordhagen, p. 126) and the second associ-ation although the *Agrostis tenuis*—*Deschampsia flexuosa*-rich birchwoods (Nordhagen, p. 138) resemble certain of our higher Highland woods, lying on or below calcareous rocks, in which *Cirsium heterophyllum*, *Trollius europaeus* and *Polygonum viviparum* occur in the grazed, grassy vegetation of the woodland floor. Ungrazed tall herb communities of this type are rare in the Highlands, but fragments occur locally and are similar to those near High Force in Teesdale, England (cf. Pigott, 1956). Tansley (1949) has pointed out that the vegetation of Highland oakwoods resembles that of English woods of sessile oak on siliceous rocks.

The *Vaccinium*-rich birchwood association has also certain affinities with the "Betuleto—Vaccinietum lapponicum" of Braun-Blanquet *et al.* (1939, p. 57), while both associations, particularly the herb-rich one, tend to transgress the borders of the whole order "Vaccinio—Piceetalia" and show some of the characteristic species of the "Quercetalia roboris".

Soils of these two associations are not so markedly podsolised as the soils of the pinewood associations and the "truncated podsol" or brown podsolic soil is typical. The *Vaccinium*-rich association tends to occur on black, mildly acid humus of good crumb structure lying directly on block scree or on a shallow A_2 horizon. The herb-rich associ-ation, on the other hand, tends to occupy a brown mineral soil with mull humus while the **B** horizon of both is a deep, reddish-brown, sandy and stony loam. Stands rich in basiphilous herbs usually occur on periodically irrigated, fertile brown loams, with pH and calcium status greater than those of the soils of grass-dominated stands.

Several localities are known where the change from one of the pinewood associations to one of the birchwood associations has apparently been brought about within a single generation of birches, following the removal of the pines. All have soil parent materials of intermediate base status so that the balance between mull and mor formation has been delicate. The most convincing demonstration can be seen in Rothiemurchus between Tullochgrue and Achnagoichan, where the two humus and vegetation types are separated by a stone wall so that differential grazing may have played some part in the contrast of soil and vegetation. On the Tullochgrue side of the wall there are twenty-four species including *Anemone nemorosa, Trientalis europaea, Conopodium majus* and *Pyrola media*; on the Achnagoichan side only sixteen species.

On siliceous parent material such as granitic and quartzitic glacial drift the growth of birch apparently fails to convert mor to mull so that felled pinewood which has been recolonised by birch retains vegetation which can only be classified under one or other of the pinewood associations.

Moss communities of birch and oak forest on boulders. Many upland woods in Scotland have a floor consisting of rocks too large to allow the development of a continuous soil layer. The individual boulders remain distinct although overgrown by vegetation in which bryophytes are the chief component. In many western birch and oak woods the bryophyte growth on these block screes is luxuriant, forming an almost continuous, hummocky carpet over hundreds of square metres or even several hectares. The degree of cover depends chiefly on the size of the blocks and the steepness of their sides.

Richards (1938) has shown that in the Killarney oakwoods it is possible to recognise distinct bryophyte communities on both rocks and trees, and similar types have been found in the west Highlands. These bryophyte micro-communities depend chiefly on gravity, and differences in their maturity are to be regarded as the effects of an environmental gradient and not as the results of a varying rate of succession. There may be minor successional and perhaps cyclical changes involving the growth of bryophytes on bare rock but, on the whole, the individual communities are permanently arrested stages of development. The most immature phases are on steep or moist rocks where soil does not accumulate and the various species remain in intimate contact with the rock surface.

There are more mature types in which the cover of bryophytes is dense and complete, with the formation of a loose humus layer, but containing few vascular plants or none. This is distinguished from a still later phase in which hypnaceous mosses are dominant, but grasses and other herbs are abundant, giving an approach to the associations described above, and passing into them where there is a well-developed layer of soil on less rocky ground.

These bryophyte communities are similar in both birch and oakwood but in pinewoods there is more *Sphagnum* and, except where the blocks are large, the vegetation can generally be assigned to one or other of the pinewood associations.

The species lists given for Stack Wood in Sutherland (Table 16) are fairly representative for acidic rocks in birch and oakwoods throughout the west Highlands. *Bazzania trilobata* is a frequent member of such communities but was not found in Stack Wood, while more local species include *Adelanthus decipiens* and *Lepidozia pinnata*. Eastern woodland moss communities of this type differ mainly in the scarcity of these species.

Structure and dynamics. A great many Scottish upland birch and oak woods are open and moribund, and the poor form of many of the birch trees is often due to the damage they have suffered in early life from fire and browsing animals. In birchwoods the absence of seedlings and saplings is invariably attributed to sheep grazing, and this is difficult to confirm or disprove since sheep and other grazing animals have access to practically all the birchwoods. There is some evidence, however, that domestic stock are not always to blame, at least directly. The commonest birchwood structure is a virtually even-aged stand with seedlings of one or two years of age but no older regeneration. The stands may be found at all stages from dense brushwood thickets to aged, open and moribund woodland. A more rare type contains trees of two generations, the mother trees, which are usually of spreading, pioneer form, being set amidst younger growth. In the more recently formed examples of this second structure it is at once apparent that saplings avoid the immediate vicinity of the parent trees, each of which is surrounded by a clear area up to 15 m. in diameter. As the wood matures and natural thinning takes place, this area becomes less obvious.

Since birch saplings can often be found in the dense shade cast by the canopy of other species it is clear that some other effect such as root competition is in operation as well as reduction in light intensity. If this is generally true, then birchwood in which trees are spaced at less than 10-15 m. apart cannot be expected to regenerate even in the absence of grazing. Birch regeneration seldom takes place within birchwood even when the canopy has opened out through the death of the older trees. On the rare occasions when it does so, the vegetation is usually found to be ericaceous rather than grassy.

Over most of the country the birch does not form climax woodland and the species (pine and oak) that once followed in the succession are either not present or are not able for other reasons to take their rightful place. It can be speculated that the edaphic or vegetational conditions following one birch crop are usually unsuitable for the establishment of a second crop although why this should be so is a matter for further investigation. The familiar mosaic pattern of birch regeneration thus emerges. Being a prolific seeder with good powers of local dispersal birch regenerates more freely than any other native tree and extensive areas of colonising birchwood on open moor or grassland may be seen in many places, especially in the eastern Highlands.

Yapp (1953) would extend his concept of non-continuous tree cover in upland Britain to include the pine and oak. He considers the grassy floor and lack of internal regeneration of so many woods to be natural and not due to grazing as hitherto supposed. The occurrence of external regeneration he regards as evidence that woodland is merely a cyclo-climax in which tree cover comes and goes. While this may be true for the pioneer species, it is doubtful if it can be applied to shade tolerating species as well. McVean (1958) has demonstrated that birch regeneration is missing from island woods that are free from sheep while it occurs freely on adjacent unwooded islands. On the other hand the regeneration of rowan (*Sorbus aucuparia*) benefits from the absence of sheep and may take place within the birchwoods to give rise to a low scrub which is kept trimmed back by the red deer which are able to swim out to the islands. Birchwoods fenced against sheep and deer often exhibit an understory of rowan saplings and, in the absence of birch regeneration, it seems likely that these will develop into dominant rowan woods.

Even-aged and two-generation stands are again commonly found in oakwoods, with the entire wood sometimes consisting of coppice-shoot trees. These coppice trees are generally thin, crooked and badly grown so that they give little idea of the potentialities of the oak on any particular site. The oakwoods differ from those of pine and birch already described in that a few seedlings and saplings can usually be found on the floor of even fairly dense stands. Most of the young plants will be found to lack their leading shoot after the first season and further development is obviously prevented by browsing animals. Seedlings are often most abundant in heathwoods with abundant *Vaccinium* where grazing is not so close, mice and voles not so plentiful and where more light penetrates the tree canopy. In the absence of any semi-natural hill oakwoods which are fenced against the grazing animal it is impossible to say how this potential regeneration would develop. Enclosed woodlands are often found in the policies of the larger estates, but the planting of exotics and the presence of the ubiquitous *Rhododendron* almost always rule these out for definitive studies.

Some notable Birch and Oak Woods of the Highlands

It is obviously impossible to give here a complete catalogue of birch and oak woods as Steven and Carlisle have done for pine, but a few of the larger and more interesting examples can be listed:

Birch

Lochinver—Drumbeg area of Assynt: Good examples of northern scrub.

Torridon—Kishorn area: High-level scrub rich in tall herbs.

Lower Glen Affric: Extensive area of well grown trees with *Vaccinium*-rich birch-wood association.

South-east shore of Loch Ness: Some intermixture with oak and ash.

Deeside and Strathspey: Numerous examples, e.g. Dinnet, Kinrara, Craigellachie.

Morrone, Braemar: Herb-rich scrub with juniper understory (Plate 23).

North and south shores of Loch Rannoch: Intermixtures with oak and pine.

Oak

Loch Maree, Letterewe: Most northern of the extensive woods (see below).

Loch Hourne, south slopes Ben Sgriol: Floristically poor, steep topography.

Arisaig: Floristically poor scrub.

Loch Sunart, north shore, particularly Ariundle: Some well grown trees (p. 156).

Deeside, Dinnet: Some interplanting with beech (p. 157).

Port Appin area, Argyll: Mostly now felled and interplanted by Forestry Commission (p. 157).

Clais Dhearg, east of Oban: Probably the most extensive area of oak remaining in Scotland on undulating topography (p. 156).

Loch Lomond, islands and east shore: Complete range from herb-rich to heath floor (p. 158).

Head of Loch Sween, Argyll: Mostly interplanted by Forestry Commission.
Trossachs, east end Loch Katrine: Some pines on crags.
Killiecrankie and Dunkeld: Large areas dominated by bracken.

Ariundle. This 260 ha. woodland was recommended as a National Nature Reserve
in the 1949 report of the Scottish Wild Life Conservation Committee (Cmd. 7814). As
indicated in that report, the wood is only part of a considerable belt of natural oakwood
on the northern shore of Loch Sunart. It occupies a south-west facing slope above the
Strontian River from about 50 to 200 m. above sea-level and the topography is varied a
little by the presence of several shallow gaps in the ridge. The local rock is syenite and the
overlying glacial drift consists largely of this local rock.

The trees are well grown, for a west Highland oakwood, but the age composition is
not a natural one since the oldest ones with semi-pioneer crowns appear to be about 150
years and there are none less than 40 years. Browsed seedlings of birch, holly, rowan and
oak are all present in fair abundance and hazel forms a sparse shrub layer.

Towards the upper limit of the wood at its northern end the trees become more
scattered and the hazel scrub denser with occasional bushes of bird cherry among the
rocks.

Floristic analyses are not available but most of the vegetation can be assigned to the
herb-rich birchwood association (p. 151) in which scattered plants of *Deschampsia
flexuosa*, *Blechnum spicant*, *Potentilla erecta*, *Holcus mollis*, etc., occur throughout the
moss mat. There are considerable areas of bracken and *Molinia* and *Juncus* flushes.
Many species such as *Thelypteris phegopteris*, *Galium odoratum*, *Mercurialis perennis*, and
Sanicula europaea are confined to the gullies cut by tributary streams of the Strontian
River.

Further west along Loch Sunart small areas of the woodland have a more natural
structure than Ariundle with a few very old pioneer trees. In places there is a considerable
development of acid peat with much *Sphagnum* in the woodland floor and little, stunted
oaks.

Clais Dhearg Wood. The triangular area of country bounded by the Taynuilt—
Connel road in the north, the Glen Lonan road in the south and the Black Lochs in the
west includes what is probably the most extensive area of oak scrub remaining in the
west of Scotland, if not in the whole country. A portion of this, lying on either side of the
A85 road east of Stonefield, now constitutes the Fearnoch Forest of the Forestry
Commission and has been planted up with conifers. The rest remains much as shown on
the 1 inch, 7th series, O.S. map (sheet 46) with oak, hazel and some birch scrub covering
undulating country with many enclaves of marsh and grassland in the wood and outliers
of oak and hazel coppice in the surrounding rough grazing.

There can be little doubt that oak is the climax forest of this undulating plateau of
basic Old Red Sandstone lavas lying between Oban and Loch Awe, and that the oak
scrub and hazel thickets are the degraded remnants of the original forest. The terrain is
capable of carrying much better oak forest than it does at present.

Birch is freely colonising the area as it is less sensitive to grazing than either oak or hazel. Patches of young birch are springing up throughout the open grazing land and they also form a fringe to the oak-hazel thickets in places.

The best oaks are only 6-9 m. tall and are either uniformly aged seed trees or have developed from coppice shoots. They do, however, form a close canopy over hundreds of acres and there is relatively little dense bracken or acid peat formation, two features that reduce the interest of many of the surviving fragments of Scottish oakwood.

The vegetation can probably be assigned once again to one or other of the birchwood associations. *Oxalis acetosella*, *Primula vulgaris*, *Holcus mollis* and *Stellaria graminea* are abundant in places.

Dinnet oakwood. This small wood of 70 ha. was recommended as a Nature Reserve by the Scottish Wild Life Conservation Committee, and must rank as one of the more interesting deciduous woods of north-east Scotland.

The wood occupies a strip of level ground by the side of the south Deeside road and the gentle north-facing slope behind this. The trees are generally under 15 m. in height and mostly about 100 years old.

Birch is locally dominant and aspens (*Populus tremula*), rowans, alders and willows (*S. caprea* and *S. cinerea* ssp. *atrocinerea*) are also found. The ground flora is distinguished from that of the woods mentioned so far by the presence of locally abundant *Rubus saxatilis* as well as the more commonplace *R. idaeus*. *Trientalis europaea* is also frequent.

Dense thickets of *Rhododendron ponticum* and bracken are colonising throughout the wood and reducing its floristic interest and its chances of regeneration. Abundant oak seedlings generally appear following a good seed year such as 1956, but rabbits account for most of these. A small part of the wood has been underplanted with beech.

Airds Wood, Appin. The principal area of oakwood still untouched by the encroaching Forestry Commission in 1953 was found to be elliptical in shape, some $2\frac{1}{2}$ km. long by $\frac{1}{2}$ km. broad, and developed on hogsback ridges of graphite schist running approximately north-east to south-west. It consisted mainly of oak and oak-birch intermixtures on the ridges with birch, alder and willow scrub in the intervening troughs. Birch also formed an advancing fringe wherever the wood abutted upon the surrounding wet heath.

Shrubs such as hazel were found to be rare within the closed woodland and the woodland floor was mainly heathy with much *Molinia* and bracken. Here and there were patches of deep mull soil with *Endymion non-scriptus*, *Primula vulgaris*, *Sanicula europaea* and other plants requiring a higher base status. The oaks were found to be in stands of uniform age, reaching 9-12 m. in sheltered sites and forming gnarled 3 m. high scrub on the exposed crests of the ridges. In some places pioneer oaks were surrounded by thickets of young "poles", and seedlings were plentiful everywhere although prevented from developing by rabbit, red deer and cattle grazing.

Woodland of this type seems once to have been widespread throughout Appin and Knapdale and, in 1953, vantage points on the crests of the Airds ridges looking towards

Mull and Lismore still revealed an almost unbroken expanse of birch and oak extending to the west.

Inchcailloch, Loch Lomond. The island of Inchcailloch carries the best example of oakwood of all the Loch Lomond islands. Some felling was carried out during the 1914-18 war, but many of the older oaks were retained so that regeneration is good over most of the island. Subordinate tree species are pine and larch (originally planted and now regenerating freely), ash and alder (locally co-dominant and dominant), gean (*Prunus avium*), bird cherry (*Prunus padus*) and crab apple (*Malus sylvestris*), with hazel, guelder rose (*Viburnum opulus*) hawthorn and blackthorn (*Prunus spinosa*) as shrubs.

The field layer offers a wide range of vegetation from the heathy type (*Vaccinium*-rich birchwood association) with *Vaccinium myrtillus* and *Deschampsia flexuosa* through *Luzula sylvatica* to *Rubus idaeus* and *Dryopteris* spp., *Endymion non-scriptus*, *Holcus* spp. and *Allium ursinum*. This variety may be due in part to the passage of the Highland Boundary Fault through the island with its close juxtaposition of the carbonated serpentine and pillow lavas of the Highland Border Series with Lower Old Red Sandstone conglomerate.

Letterewe Oakwoods. From Ardlair almost to Glen Banasdail, over 400 ha. of mixed oak woodland extends in an intermittent band along the north shore of Loch Maree. Above 150 m. the oak rapidly gives way to birchwood with pine on the crags and patches of pinewood are also found at lower levels on the bedrock as described on p. 145. Ash is co-dominant on one area and is regenerating more successfully than the oak. Elm (*Ulmus glabra*), alder, aspen and a few planted or subspontaneous larches are also found.

Shrubs are rare within the close canopy woodland, but hazel, wild rose, hawthorn, holly, bird cherry and juniper are all present and, just east of Ardlair, the more open woodland on steep rocky ground carries thickets of these species. Regeneration of the oaks benefits from the protection afforded by this rough vegetation against the grazing of sheep, cattle, ponies, red and roe deer and feral goats.

Much of the field vegetation belong to the herb-rich birchwood association which contains a little *Oxalis acetosella*, *Anemone nemorosa* and *Primula vulgaris* but there are local patches of mixed ash-oak with *Brachypodium sylvaticum* (cf. pp. 159-160).

The deep brown soil which is found over much of the area has been developed more or less *in situ* from a wide variety of Lewisian paragneisses, many of which are richly ferruginous. The calc-silicate, actinolite and graphite schists are particularly good soil formers.

Ashwood

Pure ashwoodland is a rarity in Scotland and was first described by McVean and Ratcliffe (1962).

The best example, Rassall Ashwood, occurs at the head of Loch Kishorn in Ross-shire (Plate 24). It is entirely free of birch and oak and the most abundant shrubs are hazel and hawthorn. The ash trees, which are badly cankered, cover an area of about 12 hectares and grow mostly rooted in the crevices of scattered blocks of limestone pavement. Between the pavements the soil is deep and carries a smooth, heavily grazed turf with patches of bracken but, here and there, traces remain of the *Brachypodium sylvaticum*-rich ashwood association described below. Calcicolous species are otherwise few and restricted to the limestone crevices. Scattered ash trees and hazel scrub are found over most of this limestone outcrop to an altitude of about 150 m., but in only one other locality near by do the trees become dense enough to constitute woodland. This is a mixed birch and ashwood occupying a steep south-facing slope of red limestone soil below limestone crags. The instability and steepness of the slope have limited grazing and a floristically rich stand of the *Brachypodium* association has developed.

Tokavaig wood in the Sleat peninsula of Skye is larger (over 40 hectares) and the limestone pavement is only feebly developed. The ash trees are generally larger than those at Kishorn and without canker. They are also more widely scattered and the space between them is occupied by hazel scrub and birches with abundant bird cherry (*Prunus padus*) and hawthorn (*Crataegus monogyna*). Oak is again absent from the limestone itself but is common in an adjacent birchwood which lies on quartzite.

Coille Gaireallach in Strath Suardal shows the retrogression of the ashwood carried one stage further since the trees now consist almost entirely of birch. The wood occurs partly on glacial drift overlying Durness dolomite, where ash trees are absent, and partly on limestone pavement similar to that at Kishorn, where only scattered ashes and a few clumps of hazel remain, but where the composition of the woodland floor bears a strong resemblance to that of Tokavaig wood. There can be little doubt that the dominance of the birches is the result of selective removal of the ash.

Only scattered ash trees are found on the limestone north of Kishorn; to the south the only extensive limestone pavement in Scotland occurs on the island of Lismore where scattered ash trees are abundant but there is no woodland. Local patches of mixed woodland in which ash is a prominent constituent, and in which fragments of the *Brachypodium* association occur, can be found in a few places such as the Kilmartin area of Argyll.

It is quite likely, therefore, that woodland with dominant ash constitutes the climax vegetation on shallow limestone soils and pavements south of Sutherland. Such a habitat has always been restricted in area so that ashwood can never have been widespread, but this northward extension of what must have been a significant element in the forest cover of northern England at one time is of considerable interest.

The **Brachypodium sylvaticum-rich ashwood association** can only be a provisional one in view of the restricted number of stands available for study. There are six constants (Table 16); the tree canopy may be dominated by either *Fraxinus excelsior* or *Betula pubescens* and the woodland floor by *Endymion non-scriptus*, *Circaea intermedia*, *Cirsium heterophyllum*, *Primula vulgaris* or *Brachypodium sylvaticum*.

All the stands listed occur on the Durness dolomite of north-west Scotland and the soil is a deep red loam apparently derived *in situ* from the dolomite.

The status of the association is uncertain. The ground vegetation of a few hazel thickets on the north coast of Sutherland (influenced by shell sand) and on the Tertiary basalt of Ardnamurchan, Morvern and the Inner Hebrides appears to belong to it. Further discussion must wait upon the examination of some of the floristically richer ash-oak woods surviving in the southern Highlands and in the lowlands.

Mixed deciduous woodland

Locally, in the southern and central Highlands, there are patches of a mixed deciduous woodland in which *Quercus* spp., *Betula* spp., *Fraxinus excelsior* and *Ulmus glabra* share dominance and *Corylus avellana*, *Sorbus aucuparia* and *Prunus padus* form an understory. The Keltneyburn wood in Perthshire is a good example with a distinctive *Mercurialis perennis—Allium ursinum* field layer which has been described by Poore (unpublished). Most of the undisturbed stands of this type in the Highlands are small and confined to the steep sides of stream gorges or precipitous hillsides. Due partly to topographic irregularity, the field layer usually tends to be heterogeneous and may include fragments of the *Brachypodium sylvaticum* association. Simple floristic lists have been prepared from two stands, one occupying a gorge at 122 m. altitude on Resipol Burn, Sunart, and the other at 183-305 m. altitude on the steep slopes of Creag Fonvuick, Killiecrankie. The trees and shrubs are those named above and *Ilex aquifolium* is present in the Resipol wood.

These mixed woods with their floristically rich field vegetation are confined to calcareous rocks and the soils are fertile brown loams with mull humus. Similar oak-ash-elm woods are widespread in North Wales and Northern England and some account of these is given in Tansley (1949).

Alder, rowan and holly woodland

McVean (1956) has published three floristic lists for alderwood in Scotland, but there has been no attempt at a phytosociological treatment. In unpublished work Poore (1954) distinguishes a *Lysimachia nemorum—Crepis paludosa* nodum of alder and willow swamps which is obviously present in at least two of McVean's lists.

The alder stands can be divided into alder swamps on level alluvial ground, such as we find in the Urquhart bay of Loch Ness, and the more common hillslope woods which owe their existence to the emergence of springs and surface seepage, such as the floristically rich woodland above Carnoch in Glencoe. The vegetation of the swamp woods comes close to the alder carr of the English fens described in Tansley (1949, and cf. Chapter 9) while that of the hill woods covers a transition from swamp to the wetter examples of the herb-rich birchwood association. Most of the Scottish woods lie within the floristic range of types 1, 2, 3 (*a* and *b*) of McVean's Table B which is reproduced here as Table 15.

PLATE 24. Rassall Ashwood, Loch Kishorn, Ross-shire. The best example of natural ashwood in Scotland. The trees are rooted in the crevices amongst the scattered blocks of limestone pavement which are covered with bryophytes and, in the deep soil between the blocks, heavily grazed turf with patches of bracken occurs.

PLATE 25

Fern-rich Juniper Scrub association, nr. Tomintoul, Banffshire, at 1600 ft.
A dense growth of juniper, with *Thelypteris limbosperma*, *Blechnum spicant*, *Vaccinium myrtillus* and *Luzula sylvatica* passing to *Calluna* heath in open places away from the shelter of the bushes.

TABLE 15

Effect of Soil Water and Base Content on the Subordinate Species of Alder Communities

Increasing water

	1	2	3
a	*Ilex aquifolium*	*Betula pubescens*	*Salix aurita*
	Betula pubescens	*Molinia caerulea*	*Myrica gale*
	Sorbus aucuparia	*Sphagnum* spp.	*Molinia caerulea*
	Agrostis spp.	*Carex binervis*	*Narthecium ossifragum*
	Anthoxanthum odoratum	*Juncus* spp.	*Eriophorum angustifolium*
	Galium saxatile	*Luzula multiflora*	*Sphagnum* spp.
	Dryopteris spp.	*Dryopteris* spp.	*Pinguicula vulgaris*
	Pteridium aquilinum	*Cirsium palustre*	*Potamogeton polygonifolius*
b	*Fraxinus excelsior*	*Fraxinus excelsior*	*Salix* spp.
	Corylus avellana	*Quercus* spp.	*Ligustrum vulgare*
	Prunus spinosa	*Crepis paludosa*	*Hydrocotyle vulgaris*
	Oxalis acetosella	*Chrysosplenium oppositifolium*	*Caltha palustris*
	Prunella vulgaris	*Myosotis scorpioides*	*Filipendula ulmaria*
	Agrostis stolonifera	*Lysimachia nemorum*	*Mentha aquatica*
	Poa trivialis	*Athyrium filix-femina*	*Epilobium hirsutum*
	Deschampsia cespitosa	*Dryopteris* spp.	*Galium palustre*
	Luzula sylvatica	*Carex remota*	
c	*Sambucus nigra*	*Betula pubescens*	*Salix cinerea* ssp. *atrocinerea*
	Hedera helix	*Salix cinerea* ssp. *atrocinerea*	*Carex acutiformis*
	Urtica dioica	*Viburnum opulus*	*Eupatorium cannabinum*
	Galium aparine	*Calamagrostis lanceolata*	*Filipendula ulmaria*
	Ajuga reptans	*Eupatorium cannabinum*	*Phragmites communis*
	Bryonia dioica	*Phragmites communis*	*Solanum dulcamara*
	Glechoma hederacea	*Thelypteris palustris*	*Thelypteris palustris*
	(bare ground)	*Solanum dulcamara*	*Peucedanum palustre*
		Carex acutiformis	
		Lysimachia vulgaris	

Increasing bases

Many of the remarks on the cyclo-climactic nature of birchwoods also apply to alder. Even-aged stands are the rule and the two-generation structure is rare. Regeneration is at its optimum in the open on moist soils with short, not too vigorous, herbaceous vegetation.

Particular interest attaches to the occurrence of moribund, open alderwood at altitudes of 305-547 m. at Loch Treig, Inverness-shire and Loch Coire, Sutherland. The alder does not set good seed above 300 m. altitude at the present day so that these woodlands, which must be the relics of a former climatic fluctuation, are doomed irrespective of any change in land management which would allow the growth of seedlings.

On Eilan Mor of Loch Sionascaig, Inverpolly Forest, there are several acres of pure rowan wood surrounded by an intermixture of birch and rowan, and such a feature is not uncommon throughout the birchwoods of the west Highlands. There are a few reasons for thinking that rowan-dominated woods may have been more widespread at one time. They may, indeed, have replaced oak-dominated woods to some extent on base-rich soils in the north and above the oak limit. Rowan regeneration is potentially more widespread than that of birch, in that more seedlings become established at some distance

L

from the parent trees, but these seedlings are heavily grazed by sheep and deer on account of their palatability. The present tendency for rowan to replace birch in fenced birch woods has already been noted on page 154.

The holly behaves in much the same way as rowan in western districts and there is no doubt that, but for the presence of too many grazing animals, it would be a more prominent constituent of our western woodlands as it is in the south-west of Ireland. McVean (1958) has described a small island in the Fionn Loch, west Ross-shire, which carries a pure holly wood.

Sub-alpine scrub

The transition from forest to the birch, juniper and willow scrub of the sub-alpine zone has been discussed by Poore and McVean (1957), who point out that the scrub birch belt which often occurs above the pine and spruce forest of Scandinavia is fragmentary in Scotland and the picture still further confused by the replacement of pine and oak by secondary birchwoods at lower altitudes.

Only two distinctive associations can be recognised in the vegetation of this zone in Scotland.

Fern-rich juniper scrub association. The Cairngorm juniper scrub at 600 m. first mentioned by Watt and Jones (1948) and again commented upon by Poore and McVean (1957), remains the best example of sub-alpine scrub discovered in this country. It can now be referred to the provisional fern-rich juniper association, stands of which are fairly common in the central Highlands within the forest zone. An insufficient number of lists has been made to allow any discussion of constants but the dominants of the association are *Juniperus communis*, *Vaccinium myrtillus*, *V. vitis-idaea*, *Thelypteris phegopteris*, *T. limbosperma* and various woodland mosses (Table 16 and Plate 25).

The affinities of the association with those of pinewood and birchwood are obvious and it is not at all easy to justify a separation on purely floristic grounds at the present stage. Differential species such as *Lycopodium annotinum* are rare even in the sub-alpine stands.

A similar juniper scrub is widespread in the Norwegian mountains but this may have *Betula nana* as co-dominant, a feature which is missing in Scotland. Nordhagen (1927-1928, p. 50) names it the *Vaccinium myrtillus*-rich *Juniperus nana* scrub in Sylene and in Rondane the corresponding association is the "Hylocomieto-Betuletum nanae juniperetosum" (Dahl, 1956, p. 151).

The soil below juniper scrub is not strongly podsolised and the juniper humus is friable and only mildly acid. A high level of nutrients in the humus can be inferred from the frequent presence of *Urtica dioica* and other demanding species. Patches of this scrub are of common occurrence in damp hollows and north-facing slopes of high level heather moors in the east-central Highlands, where the contrast between the floristics and humus type of the scrub and of the fire climax Callunetum is particularly instructive.

There is a tendency in the north of Scotland for a scrub of *Salix aurita* and S. *cinerea* ssp. *atrocinerea* to develop in damp *Calluna* and grass heaths between successive burnings in much the same way as the juniper scrub. Whether this is a purely secondary development or whether it represents a formerly widespread type of community above the forest limit is not certain, but in any case the stands are mostly too fragmentary to be analysed in the usual way. The most extensive development of this low-level willow scrub occurs at 213 m. on the moors near Edderton in east Ross-shire and the following species list was compiled in a dense thicket of *Salix caprea* 2-3 m. high and measuring 20 by 30 m. in area.

Sorbus aucuparia	*Epilobium montanum*
Prunus padus	*Lysimachia nemorum*
	Rumex acetosella
Blechnum spicant	*Prunella vulgaris*
Dryopteris carthusiana	*Filipendula ulmaria*
D. borreri	*Stellaria graminea*
Thelypteris limbosperma	*Potentilla erecta*
	Trientalis europaea
Deschampsia flexuosa	*Ranunculus acris*
Holcus lanatus	*Oxalis acetosella*
Juncus effusus	*Viola riviniana*
Luzula campestris	
	Thuidium tamariscinum
Cardamine hirsuta	*Mnium undulatum*
Cirsium palustre	*Polytrichum commune*
Galium saxatile	*Sphagnum recurvum*

Spence (1960) has described patches of willow scrub (*Salix aurita* and *S. cinerea* ssp. *atrocinerea*) from islands in the lochs of Shetland and South Uist where they are associated with other low shrub growth (*Rubus fruticosus* agg., *Rosa* spp., *Lonicera periclymenum*) and tall herb communities. These are undoubtedly sub-alpine in their affinities.

The **montane willow scrub association** is the second of the distinctive subalpine scrub associations and is widely distributed in the northern and central Highlands but has a rather eastern bias. Most of the stands are fragmentary and confined to ungrazed crag ledges, and only in the Clova region of Angus do they exceed a few square metres in area.

There are eight constants (Table 16) and the scrub may be dominated by *Salix lanata, S. lapponum, S. myrsinites, S. arbuscula, Luzula sylvatica, Hylocomium splendens* and *Rhytidiadelphus loreus*. In addition *Salix phylicifolia, Alchemilla glabra, Angelica sylvestris, Geum rivale, Saussurea alpina* and *Thuidium tamariscinum* may almost attain co-dominance. *Salix lanata* is exclusive to the association.

This association has obvious affinities with the *Vaccinium* and *Luzula* dominated vegetation mentioned on page 151 as well as with the tall herb association (p. 514). The factors determining whether particular ledges shall be dominated by tall herbs, *Vaccinium—Luzula* or willow, apart from the obvious historical ones of willow distribution, are not clear.

On some of the Breadalbane hills, notably Ben Lui and Meall nan Tarmachan, *Salix arbuscula* is the predominant willow of lime-rich cliff ledges, often to the exclusion of *S. lapponum*.

Soils are wet and stony with much silt accumulation, or peaty muds with silt particles right to the surface, indicating irrigation and instability. The altitudinal range of the stands is from 671 m. to 914 m. and a north to east aspect seems most usual. No information is available about winter snow accumulation on these ledges and banks and, while it must often be considerable, having regard to altitude and aspect, it cannot be particularly reliable. Exposure to winter frosts may indeed be a factor of importance localising the occurrence of the tall willows compared with that of the deciduous tall herbs.

In Norway the "Rumiceto-Salicetum lapponae" of Rondane (Dahl, 1956) closely resembles this association; there are thirty-eight species in common and two of these are constants. The *Salix lapponum* scrubs described by Nordhagen from the Sylene and Sikilsdalen areas of Norway are much richer in tall herbs or in species of moist ground, and are rather to be compared with the tall herb association and the *Carex rostrata—Sphagnum warnstorfianum* mire association of Scotland (p. 537).

Vegetation of this type was probably once extensive on damp, base-rich soils at high levels, within the geographical range of the montane willows. Many of the mesotrophic mires and damp grasslands (cf. Chapters 6 and 10), are likely to have carried a willow shrub layer, and there were probably transitions to the lower level and less base-rich communities of *Salix caprea*, *S. aurita* and *S. cinerea* ssp. *atrocinerea*.

The **Salix myrsinites** scrub of limestone pavement at Inchnadamph, described by Poore and McVean (1957 and Table 16) cannot be included in this association and this lends support to the theory of its secondary origin although it is certainly a subalpine type.

REFERENCES

ANDERSON, M. L.   1950   *The selection of tree species.* Edinburgh.

BRAUN-BLANQUET, J.,   1939   *Produmus der Pflanzengesellschaften* **6**. *Klasse der Vaccinio-*
SISSINGH, G. and   *Piceetea.* Montpellier.
VLIEGER, J.

DAHL, E.   1956   *Rondane: mountain vegetation in south Norway and its relation to the environment.* Oslo.

HANDLEY, W. R. C.   1954   *Mull and mor formation in relation to forest soils.* Bull. For. Comm. (Lond.), **23**.

McVEAN, D. N.   1956   Ecology of *Alnus glutinosa* (L.) Gaertn. V. Notes on some British alder populations. *J. Ecol.*, **44**, 321-330.

                        1958   Island vegetation of some west Highland fresh-water lochs. *Trans. bot. Soc. Edinb.*, **37**, 200-208.

McVEAN, D. N. and RATCLIFFE, D A.   1962   *Plant communities of the Scottish Highlands.* H.M.S.O. London.

NORDHAGEN, R.   1927-28 *Die Vegetation und Flora des Sylenegebeites.* Oslo.

PIGOTT, C. D.   1956   The vegetation of Upper Teesdale in the North Pennines. *J. Ecol.*, **44**, 545-586.

POORE, M. E. D.   1954   *Phytosociology of the Breadalbane district of Perthshire.* Ph.D. Thesis, University of Cambridge.

POORE, M. E. D. and McVEAN, D. N.   1957   A new approach to Scottish mountain vegetation. *J. Ecol.*, **45**, 401-439.

RICHARDS, P. W.   1938   The bryophyte communities of a Killarney oakwood. *Ann. bryol.* (Hague), **11**, 108-130.

SPENCE, D. H. N.   1960   Studies on the vegetation of Shetland. III. Scrub in Shetland and S. Uist, outer Hebrides. *J. Ecol.*, **48**, 73-95.

STEVEN, H. M. and CARLISLE, A.   1959   *The native pinewoods of Scotland.* Edinburgh.

TAMM, O   1950   *Northern coniferous forest soils* Oxford.

TANSLEY, A. G.   1949   *The British Islands and their vegetation.* Cambridge.

WATT, A. S. and JONES, E. W.   1948   The ecology of the Cairngorms. I. The environment and the altitudinal zonation of the vegetation. *J. Ecol.*, **36**, 283-304.

YAPP, W. B.   1953   The high level woodlands of the English Lake District. *Northw. Nat.*, N.S., **1**, 190-207; 370-383.

TABLE 16

Woodland and Scrub

	1	2	3	4	5	6	7	8	9
Average number of species	14	22	28	33	17	36	29	38	18
Number of stands	14	9	11	9	10	5	4	11	5
Plot area (sq. m.)	16	4–16	4	4	1	4	4	4	4–8
Altitude (m.)	0–500	50–400	50–500	0–450	120	0	400–550	660–900	200–270
Aspect (degrees)	Various	Various	Various	Various	45	...	0–180	0–135	180–300
Slope (degrees)	...	0–20	0–45	5–35	25–45	...	0–45	30–45	...
Soil	Podsol	Podsol	Podsol	Brown earth	...	Red loam	Podsol	Brown earth	Brown earth
pH	4	4	5	5–6	...	6–7	4–5·5	6–7	5–6
Cover (%)	100	100	100	100	100	100	100	100	100
Height of vegetation (cm.)	...	...	...	...	...	...	90–120	15–90	15–45
Betula pubescens	... ...	2 +	10 ...	10 ...	10 ...	8 ...	... ...	... ...	... ...
Calluna vulgaris	9 1	10 6	4 1	3 +	1 +	... ...	4 1	1 +	6 +
Corylus avellana	... ...	... ...	3 +	... ...	... ...	4 ...	... ...	... ...	... ...
Fraxinus excelsior	... ...	... ...	... ...	... ...	... ...	8 ...	... ...	... ...	... ...
Juniperus communis	... ...	... ...	1 1	... ...	... ...	... ...	10 7	... ...	... ...
Pinus sylvestris	10 ...	10 ...	... ...	... ...	... ...	... ...	... ...	... ...	... ...
Salix lapponum	... ...	... ...	... ...	... ...	... ...	... ...	... ...	8 6	... ...
S. myrsinites	... ...	... ...	... ...	... ...	... ...	... ...	... ...	2 1	10 7
Sorbus aucuparia	3 +	3 +	9 1	7 1	5 1	10 ...	... ...	... ...	... ...
Vaccinium myrtillus	10 5	10 5	10 5	2 +	2 1	... ...	10 4	8 3	... ...
V. vitis-idaea	10 4	10 3	4 1	... ...	... ...	... ...	10 4	3 1	... ...
Blechnum spicant	3 +	5 +	9 2	10 2	1 +	... ...	7 3	... ...	2 +
Hymenophyllum wilsonii	... ...	... ...	2 +	... ...	6 3	... ...	... ...	... ...	... ...
Pteridium aquilinum	3 +	5 1	6 1	6 2	... ...	2 +	2 1	... ...	... ...
Thelypteris limbosperma	... ...	... ...	1 +	4 2	... ...	2 +	5 1	... ...	... ...
T. phegopteris	... ...	... ...	... ...	1 +	... ...	... ...	... ...	1 +	... ...
Agrostis tenuis	1 +	... ...	7 2	6 2	1 +	10 2	5 1	3 1	8 2
Anthoxanthum odoratum	... ...	... ...	8 2	10 4	5 2	6 1	2 +	2 +	2 1
Brachypodium sylvaticum	... ...	... ...	... ...	... ...	... ...	10 5	... ...	... ...	... ...
Dactylis glomerata	... ...	... ...	... ...	... ...	... ...	10 2	... ...	... ...	... ...
Deschampsia cespitosa	... ...	... ...	1 +	4 1	8 2	9 1	... ...	8 2	... ...
D. flexuosa	7 2	10 2	9 3	4 1	... ...	... ...	2 +	7 2	2 +
Luzula sylvatica	... ...	... ...	4 2	1 +	1 +	... ...	2 +	9 4	... ...

Species	1	2	3	4	5	6	7	8	9
Circaea intermedia	..	..	..	..	..	..	..	..	..
Endymion non-scriptus	..	..	..	..	..	..	..	..	..
Filipendula ulmaria	..	..	..	1 +	1 +	1 +	2 +	2 +	2 +
Galium saxatile	9 2	9 2	10 3	6 2	..	6 1	7 2	6 1	8 2
Geum rivale	..	..	..	..	..	..	..	..	..
Lysimachia nemorum	6 1	..	..	8 2	10 2	..	..	6 2	6 1
Oxalis acetosella	10 3	10 3	10 3	8 1	6 2	10 3	6 2	6 2	10 2
Potentilla erecta	8 2	9 2	5 1	3 1	4 +	5 1	..	..	4 +
Primula vulgaris	1 +	7 1	..	..	8 3	..	..	..	..
Rumex acetosa	..	2 +	2 +	1 +	2 +	8 2	8 2	8 2	4 +
Viola riviniana	5 1	10 2	2 1	..	10 2	2 1	7 1	7 1	10 3
Dicranum majus	7 2	..	7 1	6 1	2 +	7 3	5 1	..	..
D. scoparium	3 1	5 1	1 +	4 1	..	10 5	7 1	..	4 1
Hylocomium splendens	9 4	10 5	8 3	8 3	2 1	7 3	10 6	..	10 5
H. umbratum	2 +	1 +	2 1	8 3	..	..	..	..	..
Plagiothecium undulatum	6 1	4 +	5 +	3 +	..	..	4 1	..	..
Pleurozium schreberi	8 2	7 2	3 +	8 2	..	..	..	..	..
Ptilium crista-castrensis	3 1	3 1	..	1 +	..	..	4 1	..	..
Rhytidiadelphus loreus	5 1	10 3	2 +	10 4	2 +	5 2	9 3	..	2 +
R. triquetrus	7 4	8 2	5 1	..	6 1	5 1	6 2	..	8 2
Sphagnum spp.	2 1	10 5	2 +	3 1	..	7 4	8 2	..	..
Thuidium tamariscinum	9 4	1 +	8 5	9 4	8 2	10 6	8 2	..	6 2
Anastrepta orcadensis	..	1 +	..	..	9 3	..	..	..	..
Scapania gracilis	..	..	..	..	8 2	..	..	..	..

1. Pinewood *Vaccinium*—moss association.
2. Pinewood *Vaccinium*—*Calluna* association.
3. *Vaccinium*-rich birchwood association.
4. Herb-rich birchwood association.
5. Moss dominated vegetation of birch and oakwood on boulders.
6. *Brachypodium sylvaticum*-rich ashwood association.
7. Fern-rich juniper scrub association.
8. Montane willow scrub association.
9. *Salix myrsinites* scrub on limestone pavement.

CHAPTER 6

GRASSLANDS OF THE FOREST AND SUB-ALPINE ZONES

J. KING AND I. A. NICHOLSON

The anthropogenic grasslands of the forest and sub-alpine zones have been derived mainly from deciduous forest and scrub by felling, burning and grazing by domestic animals. The upper limit of the grassland zone is about 610 m. (2000 ft.) and owing to cultivation at lower elevations it does not occur today much below 183 m. (600 ft.).

The influence of man on the original forest probably began in Neolithic times, increasing gradually with each millennium and reaching a considerable magnitude, at least in the lowlands and on the more accessible hills, during the Roman occupation (Steven and Carlisle, 1959). A large population lived in the Southern Uplands at this time, their dwellings tending to be above 305 m. (1000 ft.) where the forest density was no doubt less than at lower levels (cf. Pearsall and Pennington, 1947; Anon., 1956). After the departure of the Romans there were scattered pastoral settlements in existence and by the eleventh or twelfth centuries both the lowlands and the upland areas were grazed by large numbers of sheep and cattle. There is evidence, for example, that the Abbeys of Melrose and Kelso derived a large part of their revenues from sheep and cattle, the former being generally the more numerous (Symon, 1959; Franklin, 1952) and even remote hills may have been grazed in summer under a system of transhumance (Franklin, 1952). Some areas in southern Scotland such as parts of Ettrick and Eskdale were reserved primarily for hunting, but even there restricted grazing and timber rights were exercised (Anon., 1837). Timber was in great demand for building at this time, the felling of trees being further increased to make good the destruction of property in the wars of the period. By the fifteenth century the combined effects of grazing pressure and felling had become clearly apparent and a hundred years later most of the original deciduous forest of the Southern Uplands had disappeared (Steven and Carlisle, 1959). After 1603 conditions in the south of Scotland gradually became more settled and by about 1780 the introduction of improved types of sheep (Trow-Smith, 1957) had formed the basis of a system of sheep ranching, the fore-runner of that existing at the present day. The primary products were wool and mutton and about 20 per cent. of the total stock consisted of wether sheep (castrated male sheep) up to 4 years old (Douglas, 1798) which were confined to the poorest and most inaccessible pastures, those of better quality being reserved for breeding ewes.

By the time that forest clearance was well advanced in the Lowlands and Southern Uplands, the Highlands were still largely covered by forest, and although some destruction had taken place to satisfy timber requirements, and also as a result of deliberate burning, the flocks and herds were small compared with those of the Lowlands (Steven and Carlisle, 1959). Cattle were economically the most important stock although their numbers seem to have been too few for the complete utilisation of the available grazing (Walker, 1812; Symon, 1951). Horses and sheep, the latter being about equal in number to the cattle, were also numerous although kept mainly for domestic rather than for commercial purposes (Walker, 1812; Darling, 1955; Gray, 1957). Transhumance was practised, the cattle being moved to the sheilings* in early June and remaining there for as little as six weeks (Walker, 1812; Gray, 1957; Gaffney, 1959), although by the mid-eighteenth century many sheilings had become occupied and presumably grazed throughout the year (Gaffney, 1959). After 1760 the old Highland economy collapsed and in the following century there was a great increase in the rate of deforestation followed by the introduction of large-scale sheep ranching from the south of Scotland. This was well established in Argyll and Perthshire by 1790, and by 1850 the process was complete throughout the Highland area (Darling, 1955). Although the cattle population declined, the increase in sheep numbers was so great that the overall stocking rate was increased by as much as 40 to 70 per cent. (Symon, 1951). In common with other branches of British agriculture, hill sheep farming enjoyed considerable prosperity in the nineteenth century until a decline began about 1870. This was associated with a change in the emphasis from wool and mutton to the production of store lambs and, by 1914, had resulted in the virtual disappearance of the wether sheep from hill flocks. In the Highlands over a period of about seventy years, beginning in the early 1870's, the total sheep stock was reduced by about 25 per cent. and prior to 1912 many sheep grazings were converted to deer forest or grouse moor. In more recent years the planting of coniferous forest has provided the main alternative to sheep farming (Rep. Comm. Hill Sheep Farm, 1944).

GRAZING ANIMALS AND THEIR HABITS

Ecologists have long recognised the importance of grazing as a factor in the plant's environment and its influence on both the distribution and dynamics of plant communities. As it is rarely possible to attach meaningful quantitative values to the relationships between vegetation and grazing animals without prolonged study of a site, the evaluation of animal influence in practice is frequently confined to an indirect assessment of the intensity of biotic pressure. The full evaluation of grazing, however, requires the characterisation of the separate phenomena of defoliation, defaecation, urination and treading. Stocking rate determines the nature of defoliation by influencing selectivity and severity of grazing, but also reacts upon the vegetation by determining the frequency

* A Scots word for a "summar grazing"

with which the component grazing processes occur on a given area. In controlled grazing
the inherent behaviour pattern and herbage preferences of the animal cannot be fully
expressed, but under natural or free range conditions of animal management, which
normally prevail in the forest zone, these factors are of considerable importance in
determining the intensity of grazing and its seasonal impact on different plant
communities.

The forest zone grasslands are maintained principally by sheep grazing, combined
with burning, although the activities of other animals, namely cattle, deer, hares, rabbits
and voles, must also be considered (Plates 26, 27 and 28).

Sheep and cattle

In 1961 the hill areas supported approximately 2,400,000 breeding ewes and 209,000
breeding cows and heifers, giving a cattle to sheep ratio of about 1:11. It is interesting to
note that since 1949 this ratio had narrowed from 1:23 (calculated from records of subsidy
payment), thus creating a much more desirable balance (Darling, 1955). These figures,
although of considerable interest, require careful interpretation as they include an
unknown proportion of cattle on improved upland pasture. They do show, however, the
trend in recent years. Unfortunately, there are no figures to indicate what proportion of
the sheep (or cattle) are supported by the forest zone grasslands which form one group of
vegetation amongst many, including bogs, mires and dwarf shrub heaths which collectively provide the nutritional basis of animal husbandry. The stocking rate of sheep in
Scotland varies from about 1 ewe per 4 ha. (10 acres) to 1 ewe or more per 0·8 ha. (2
acres), and as the distribution map of stocking rates shows (Fig. 30, and Hunter, 1961),
the highest rates tend to coincide with the "grassy" hills of the Border region, although
in parts of the southern and central Highlands and in more localised areas of the north
and west, intensities are also high.

The grazing behaviour of sheep

Different hill sheep farming systems are practised throughout the Scottish uplands.
The effect of sheep grazing is similar in different regions, but the precise significance of
the sheep in upland ecology can be considered only in relation to the husbandry system
practised in a particular area. In the north and west, where stocking intensities are
generally low, a hill farm may comprise one or more extensive grazing units or, as in
certain localities of the same area, grazings may be held in common. In contrast, on the
more heavily stocked grasslands of the Border region the farming enterprise is based on a
number of much smaller grazing or management units called "hefts", a term which
denotes both the pasture area and the sheep which graze upon it. These grazing units
may be from 60 to 120 ha. (150 to 300 acres) in size and although generally unfenced, the
sheep form self-replenishing flocks which remain within the bounds of the heft throughout the year. Thus the sheep has the opportunity to range over a considerable area, and
as few grazings are homogeneous in their soils and vegetation, they offer the animal a

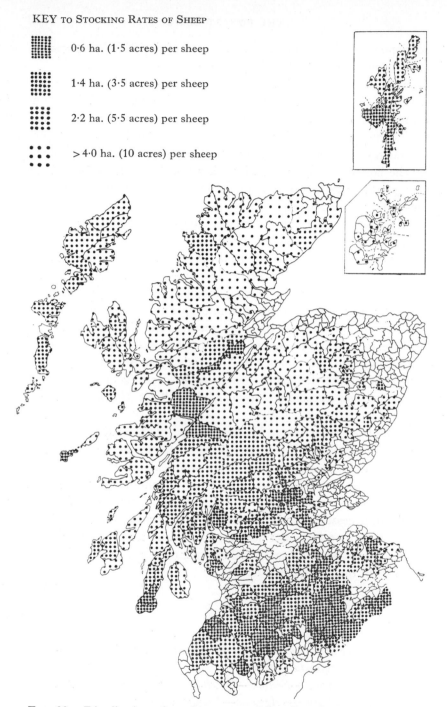

KEY to Stocking Rates of Sheep

0·6 ha. (1·5 acres) per sheep

1·4 ha. (3·5 acres) per sheep

2·2 ha. (5·5 acres) per sheep

> 4·0 ha. (10 acres) per sheep

FIG. 30   Distribution of stocking rates of breeding sheep on Scottish hill grazings, excluding deer forest, calculated from the hill sheep subsidy parish returns 1952. Stippling density is proportional to stocking rate. Highest density equivalent to 0·6 ha. (1·5 acres) per sheep; lowest density equivalent to more than 4·0 ha. (10 acres) per sheep. (Data from Hunter, 1961.)

choice among communities having a wide diversity of floristic characteristics, productivity, palatibility and seasonal availability of grazing.

Recent work has demonstrated that flock behaviour is influenced by both internal and external factors. The internal factors are not clearly understood, but Hunter (1962a, and b) has suggested that a social mechanism induces characteristic individual or group behaviour. The same author shows that groups of sheep tend to have a common grazing range (home range) which is a portion of the total grazing area and, although sometimes overlapping the home ranges occupied by other groups, each range is distinct. Thus, instead of ranging over the entire area, the groups of sheep restrict themselves to home ranges of 32-40 ha. (80-100 acres).

The aspect of sheep behaviour which has received most study is the interaction of the flock with the vegetational mosaic within the grazing unit. Differences in grazing preference both annually and seasonally have long been recognised in practice (Linton, 1918), but Boulet (1939) in Wales made the first attempt at a scientific study. He introduced the concept of comparative grazing intensity which expresses the density of grazing sheep per unit area of plant community. The comparative grazing intensity gives no indication of the actual or potential grazing capacity but expresses the relative grazing pressure to which the communities are exposed. In terms of total annual comparative grazing intensity Boulet in his study area placed the communities, as described in terms of the dominant species, in descending order from *Agrostis* and *Festuca* grassland at one extreme to *Nardus/Molinia*, "wet *Molinia*" and "tall heather" at the other.

Using a more precise technique Hunter (1954, 1962a) made a study of the sheep grazing behaviour and herbage preferences in two localities in the Scottish Border area. To avoid a detailed classification of plant communities and the difficulties of accurate demarcation on a map, Hunter (1954) used the physiognomic dominant to distinguish between communities or "sward types". As Watson and Gregor (1956) point out, however, these are not necessarily the equivalent of the "consociations" of Tansley (1949).

On a study area of 102 ha. (251 acres), managed under the Border hefting system, Hunter (1962a) found the average annual comparative grazing intensity of the major sward types to be in the following order:

		Comparative grazing intensity
Agrostis—Festuca	(*Agrostis—Festuca* types 5 and 9)*	151
Pteridium	(*Pteridium aquilinum* dominant stands of *Festuca—Agrostis* type 5)*	137
Nardus	(*Nardus—Festuca—Deschampsia* types 2 and 3 *Festuca—Agrostis—Nardus* type 6)*	72
Juncus (*effusus/ conglomeratus*)		69
Molinia	(*Molinia—Festuca—Deschampsia* type 1)*	55

* See Tables 19 and 20, pp. 216 & 219.

Those swards represented only by small patches within the pasture studied, for which the estimates were necessarily less accurate, were found to have values as follows:

		Comparative grazing intensity
Deschampsia flexuosa	(*Festuca—Deschampsia* type 3)*	168
D. cespitosa	(*D. cespitosa—Festuca—Agrostis* type 8)*	51
Eriophorum	(Calluneto—Eriophoretum, McVean and Ratcliffe)*	92
Calluna	(Callunetum vulgaris, McVean and Ratcliffe)*	55

* See Tables 19, 20; Chapters 7 and 10 and McVean & Ratcliffe, 1962.

Comparative grazing intensity varied not only between pasture types, but also within types according to the time of year. Thus on the most favoured sward types with high average grazing intensities, the ratio of winter to summer grazing was found to be small, while on the less favoured types (e.g. *Molinia* and *Nardus*) the reverse was the case. The latter tended to be neglected in summer and grazed relatively more in winter when food was scarce.

This seasonal rhythm in the preference for different sward types was first demonstrated by Hunter (1954) and confirmed in another locality (1962a). The seasonal fluctuations in comparative grazing intensity for *Agrostis—Festuca*, *Pteridium*, *Molinia* and *Nardus* are shown in Fig. 31, taken from Hunter (1962a). The principle features are a decline in the comparative grazing intensity for *Agrostis—Festuca* in the period November-March while *Pteridium* shows high values in autumn and again in spring before the fronds emerge. Both *Molinia* and *Nardus* show relatively low values with peaks in the winter period. *Calluna* also was found to receive a relatively high concentration of grazing in winter and again when the current year's shoots appear in July-September before they become lignified and unpalatable.

To facilitate vegetation survey and mapping, Hunter (1962a) gridded the experimental area into 471 complete grid units measuring 30·5 × 60·0 m. (100 × 200 ft.). He classified the various sward types into two categories, the first comprising *Agrostis—Festuca* and *Pteridium* and the second, *Molinia*, *Nardus*, *Juncus*, *Calluna*, *Eriophorum* and *D. cespitosa* sward types. Adopting a mull/mor classification Hunter regarded the first group as tending towards the mull and the second towards the mor type. Although he used the terms "mull" and "mor" respectively in reference to these groups, the terms apparently have relative significance only and should not be too strictly interpreted. The units of the grid were allocated to these two categories according to the sward type by which they were mainly occupied and from these data two histograms were constructed to illustrate the different distributions of grazing intensity associated with the two sward categories (Fig. 32). The figure shows that the "mor" swards are grazed less intensively than the "mull" swards. The contrasting shapes of the two histograms indicate that the distribution of grazing sheep within the "mor" swards more closely resembles a normal

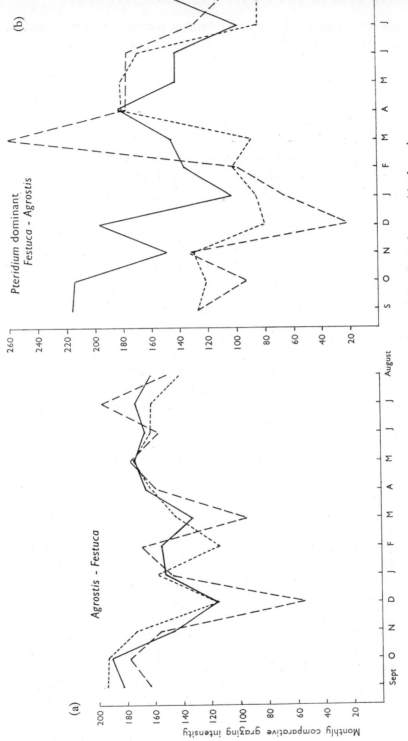

Fig. 31 Seasonal variation in monthly comparative grazing intensity on (a) *Agrostis–Festuca*, (b) *Pteridium*, (c) *Molinia*, (d) *Nardus* for twelve month periods beginning in September

———————1956-57; — — —1957-58; - - - - - -1958-59

(After Hunter, 1962a).

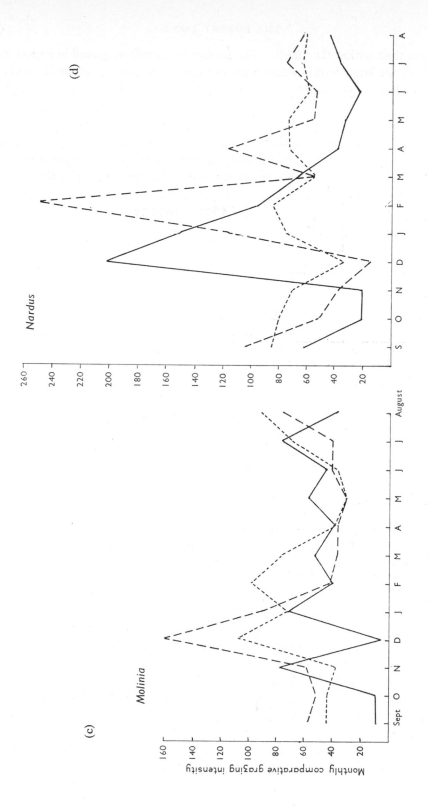

(d)

Nardus

(c)

Molinia

Monthly comparative grazing intensity

distribution than within the "mull". The former is, therefore, grazed in a more random manner than the latter within which a greater degree of grazing selectivity is shown.

In a further analysis of the data the two distributions in Fig. 32, were combined and from the resulting distribution the percentage of grazing sheep in successive 5 per cent. portions of the grid was estimated, moving from the least densely occupied to the most densely occupied 5 per cent. portion. Proceeding in this way it was shown that there were two rates of increase

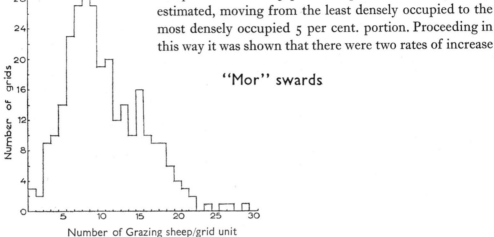

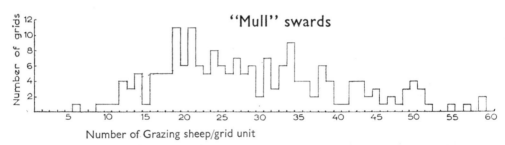

FIG. 32 Frequencies of grid units containing different numbers of grazing sheep for sward types grouped into "mull" and "mor" soil categories. (After Hunter, 1962a.)

in comparative grazing intensity, rates A and B (Fig. 33). Rate A is replaced by rate B passing from the less grazed 80 per cent. of the grid units to the remaining heavily grazed 20 per cent. It is noteworthy that only one grid unit within this 20 per cent. was classified as being occupied by a "mor" sward and it did, in fact, contain a substantial area of "mull". Taken as a whole, the data revealed that the most heavily grazed quarter of the grid units contained 50·5 per cent. of the grazing sheep, the next quarter 25·5 per cent., the third quarter 15·5 per cent., and the least grazed quarter only 8·5 per cent.

The relationship between pasture and animal was further illuminated by a comparison of the comparative grazing intensity values, herbage yield and manurial return.

This is shown in Table 17 for seven patches each 0·4-0·8 ha. (1-2 acres) in extent and belonging to different communities. The values in each column are expressed as a percentage of the highest which is recorded as 100 per cent.

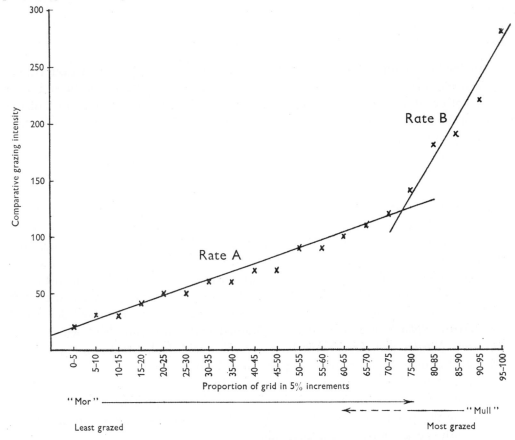

FIG. 33 Rates of increase in comparative grazing intensity from the least grazed 5% portion of the area to the most grazed 5% portion. (After Hunter, 1962a.)

TABLE 17

Relationship between Sward Types and Comparative Grazing Intensity (c.g.i.), Manurial Return and Herbage Yield

(Taken from Hunter, 1962a)

	c.g.i.	Manurial return	Yield of green herbage as dry matter
Agrostis . . .	100	21	100
Pteridium . . .	89	100	39
D. flexuosa . .	68	65	74
Agrostis . . .	60	38	79
Pteridium . . .	59	60	47
Nardus . . .	45	21	63
Nardus . . .	41	30	87

M

These effects are the result of the behaviour pattern already discussed and of the diurnal habits of movement, feeding and defaecation. Together with over- and under-grazing they create an imbalance in the biological system as a whole within the grazing area.

Deer

In mediaeval times both the roe (*Capreolus capreolus*) and the red deer (*Cervus elaphus*) were distributed throughout the upland regions of Scotland. By the end of the seventeenth century both species had virtually disappeared from the Southern Uplands, although the roe returned in later times (Ritchie, 1920) and today the red deer is confined essentially to the south-west of Scotland and to the Highlands and Islands.

Provisional findings of the red deer survey (Report, 1960) suggest that the total spring population is of the order of 155,000 and it is estimated that three-quarters of the deer occur on recognised deer forest ground. The significance of the red deer in the present context is problematical as much of its diet is derived from communities other than grassland, although in the mixed vegetation of the north and north-west they are said to prevent the regeneration of young trees, particularly of birch (Darling, 1937; Crampton, 1911). Darling also suggests that they may depress bracken in areas where it is not too extensive. In Wester Ross the same author pointed out that the bulk of the food supply was derived from the middle slopes between 92 m. and 534 m. (300 and 1750 ft.) which carry various graminaceous and mixed communities. In over-stocked deer forests deer destroy *Sphagnum* and in areas of drained and burnt moorland where *Juncus squarrosus*, *Nardus* and *Eriophorum* have become established, Crampton (1911) found evidence of damage by deer, even the plant roots being eaten.

The roe deer is not a gregarious animal and its influence on vegetation is probably less readily recognised than that of the red deer, but there is apparently little information available on this point. Indeed, in the absence of more critical studies the precise importance of both species must remain uncertain.

Hares and rabbits

The Scottish mountain hare (*Lepus timidus scoticus*), typically associated with heather moorland, occurs generally between 305 m. and 915 m. (1000 and 3000 ft.). It is today most common in north-east Scotland and in the Border area (Flux, 1962), where several introductions were made between 1834 and 1868 (Ritchie, 1925, 1929). To the north and west the mountain hare is rare and introduced populations on the Scottish islands have varied in success (Hewson, 1955).

Flux (1962) carried out population surveys in the north-east of Scotland and recognised a high-density population as being over one hare per 4 ha. (10 acres). Densities were highest in the foothills, falling to below one animal per 400 ha. (1000 acres) westwards towards the main massif of the Grampians. High population densities were typically associated with well managed grouse moors.

On the basis of analyses of stomach contents carried out by W. N. Charles, Hewson (1962) reports that the three main constituents of the food were *Calluna*, *Eriophorum* spp. and grasses (mainly *Deschampsia cespitosa*, *D. flexuosa*, *Festuca rubra* and *Agrostis* spp.) with *Calluna* forming the bulk of the diet throughout the year. In a sample of 47 stomachs the average percentage contents for the winter period (November-March) and the summer period (April-October) were 90 per cent. and 48 per cent. for *Calluna* and 10 per cent. and 17 per cent., respectively, for *Eriophorum* spp. Juniper, gorse and several tree species including rowan, alder and birch also provided a source of food in times of scarcity.

The rabbit (*Oryctolagus cuniculus*) is thought to have been introduced to southern Britain in Norman times (Barrett-Hamilton, 1910-21) but the animal was not abundant in Scotland till the nineteenth century (Thompson and Worden, 1956). In 1810 one author (Robertson, 1810) referring to Kincardineshire, wrote, "I have not seen any wild rabbits in this county." The rise in rabbit numbers in the nineteenth century took place with the extension of cultivation and numbers showed a spectacular rise with the opening of the so-called "Golden Age" of British Agriculture after 1853 (Ritchie, 1920). In the twentieth century the rabbit became a serious pest at the same time as the rabbit-trapping industry developed until 1954 and 1955, when myxomatosis practically eliminated the animal from many areas.

Some indication of the grazing pressure which may be exerted by rabbits is given by the trapping record from an upland farm in Kincardineshire (Nicholson and Robertson, 1958). In the four years before myxomatosis broke out a total of 25,194 rabbits were trapped, an average of over 6000 per annum. Although the farm was over 800 ha. (2000 acres), the area grazed by rabbits was probably no more than a quarter of this. If five rabbits are considered to be the grazing equivalent of one sheep (Hume, 1939), the grazing pressure exerted by the rabbit population was about twice that of the sheep flock on the farm.

The general effects of rabbit grazing on Callunetum were demonstrated in the classic work of Farrow (1916) on Breckland. In the Scottish uplands numerous instances of similar effects occur (Plate 28).

Voles (*Microtus agrestis*)

Voles occur extensively in the forest zone and may be found at any elevation where the vegetation is long and rank (Charles, 1962). The effect of normal vole activity on upland grazing ecology is not clear, but numbers vary cyclically and at times of great population expansion the animals have been known to cause widespread destruction to vegetation (Elton, 1942). The normal range of numbers found by Charles (1962) in the Campsie Fells varied from 12 or less per ha. (5 per acre) to 247 per ha. (100 per acre) at the peak of the cycle, but in areas where sheep numbers were negligible the numbers rose to 1730 per ha. (700 per acre).

Voles have distinct food preferences. *Agrostis* spp. are most favoured, but they also eat *Deschampsia flexuosa*, *D. cespitosa*, *Holcus* spp., *Festuca rubra* and *F. ovina*. They tend to avoid *Juncus effusus*, *J. articulatus*, *Carex* spp., *Eriophorum vaginatum*, *Nardus* and *Molinia*, although in winter at high population densities they may be forced to eat these species (Charles, 1962). The digestive system of voles is less efficient than that of ruminants and since they are small animals their heat loss is relatively large. Therefore, voles eat much more food per unit body weight than other grazing animals in the area. The destruction caused by voles, however, is not confined to the amount of herbage they consume. In one study area they were found to eat an average of 8 g. dry matter per day while the average amount grazed and discarded was 4 g. per day (Charles, 1962).

Two vole plagues are known to have occurred in the last 80 years in the Southern Uplands, in 1875-76 and in 1891-92, although it is a matter of interest that no records exist of other outbreaks in the preceding 100 years. The last outbreak affected 40,000 ha. (100,000 acres) throughout Roxburghshire, Dumfriesshire, Kircudbrightshire, Selkirk-shire, Peeblesshire and Lanarkshire. The communities on the lower slopes, especially those providing early grazing for sheep, were extensively devastated and the voles subsequently moved to *Calluna* communities which in many areas also suffered heavy damage. Unfortunately, detailed botanical information relating to these outbreaks is lacking, but at a period of high population density within an area enclosed for afforestation in the Campsie Fells, Charles (1956) records that *Deschampsia cespitosa* was completely undermined by vole runs and apparently killed. In some areas there was much bare ground which was quickly colonised by *Cirsium* spp., *Digitalis purpurea*, *Holcus lanatus*, *H. mollis* and mosses which became temporarily dominant in the badly damaged patches. Young trees also suffered damage by ring-barking and root destruction. Working in a similar area in the Border region, Summerhayes (1941) showed that voles in moderate numbers caused limited damage to vegetation, the dominant grasses in different communities (*Molinia caerulea*, *Deschampsia cespitosa* and *Holcus mollis*) showing a reduction in luxuriance leading to more open communities richer in species.

The causes of the two great vole plagues is obscure, but it is perhaps significant that the principal areas of infestation occurred within the rainfall area of 127 cm. (50 in.) and over. Suggested causes (Elton, 1942) include the destruction of predators and inadequate burning and draining, but the phenomena have never been fully explained.

COMMUNITY TYPES

Early accounts and the development of modern ideas

Amongst the earliest accounts of the anthropogenic grasslands in Scotland were those of the Edinburgh area, north Perthshire, Forfar and Fife by Robert Smith (1900a, b) and R. and W. G. Smith (1905, 1911). These workers recognised the close relationship between topography, parent material, soil drainage and floristic composition and, in relation to these factors, described a number of pasture types which can be summarised as follows:

PLATE 26. Cattle grazing on alluvial *Agrostis—Festuca* grassland at the head of Glen Lochay, Perthshire.

PLATE 27. Blackface sheep gathered for supplementary feeding in winter. *Festuca—Deschampsia—(Nardus)* type 3 grass-heath in foreground and on steep slopes beyond. Cheviot Hills, Roxburghshire.

PLATE 28. *Vigorous growth of Pteridium aquilinum* on previously enclosed pasture land in S.W. Scotland. The area now provides virtually no grazing owing to the high frond density and the consequent paucity of herbage below the canopy.

PLATE 29. Replacement of Callunetum vulgaris (McV. and R.) by *Festuca—Agrostis* grassland and invasion by *Pteridium aquilinum* as a result of rabbit activity. The restriction of the more vigorous *Pteridium* to the peripheral area is thought to be the result of rhizome damage in the vicinity of the burrows. Near Cairn o' Mount, Kincardineshire.

(1) Grass pasture or grass/*Calluna* mixtures on moist or dry soils of variable base status but not including the most acid. These were *Agrostis—Festuca* grasslands.

(2) Grass-heath or grass-moor on soils of varying drainage usually with a layer of peaty humus. This group included *Deschampsia flexuosa*, *Nardus stricta*, *Molinia caerulea* grasslands and some *Calluna*/grass communities.

(3) Grasslands occurring mainly above 2000 ft. (608 m.) including communities rich in *Achemilla alpina* and *Vaccinium*/grass-heaths.

Crampton (1911) working in Caithness described the occurrence of various *Festuca—Agrostis* and *Nardus* communities on alluvial terraces and on soils derived from glacial drift. Elsewhere he associated the development of these and of *Molinia*-rich communities with the effects of flushing (i.e. natural irrigation) by spring water and attached importance to the base content of the water and to the intensity of irrigation. Crampton also noted the effects of excessive burning and sheep grazing in giving rise, on ombrogenous peats, to grassland communities rich in *Nardus stricta*. Later, Smith (1918), as the result of work in the Moorfoot Hills, recognised six vegetation types including the following grasslands: *Nardus* or *Molinia* dominant communities growing on soils with a surface layer of peaty humus, grass-heath on steep dry slopes merging with the *Nardus* grassland, and flushed or alluvial *Festuca—Agrostis* grassland. Subsequent accounts followed this broad classification although often upland grass-heath was not separated from related *Festuca—Agrostis* or *Nardus* dominant types. Thus, Tansley (1949) describes the following vegetation types as occurring in the forest zone:

Agrostis—Festuca grassland on well drained soils of pH 4·0-5·0. This was considered to be the upland equivalent of the lowland grass-heaths of Breckland and elsewhere.

Festuca—Agrostis grassland on soils derived from the harder limestones and the more basic rocks.

Nardus grassland on soils with acid damp raw humus or peat of variable depth.

Molinia grassland on acid peaty soils, wet but not waterlogged.

Pteridium dominant communities derived from *Agrostis-Festuca* grassland and other types by invasion.

Ulex dominant communities.

The nature of variation in the vegetation

It is now generally accepted that much of the floristic variation in the forest zone grasslands can be related to variations in grazing, soil moisture regime and soil base status. In recent years it has become progressively more apparent that much of the variation is continuous, lending itself to description in terms of gradients or in terms of a multi-dimensional continuum (Bray and Curtis, 1957). Floristic gradients have been observed by a number of workers. In Derbyshire, Balme (1953) has described in a limestone valley a continuous series of grassland communities related to topography and soil type. Similarly, in north Wales, Hughes (1958) considered that vegetation changes, in relation to rainfall, formed a continuous gradient although with departures from this at certain points where soil properties changed sharply. Ratcliffe (1959), working in the same region, described the vegetation in terms of three gradients related to soil base status, soil wetness and anthropogenic influences respectively, while more recently, Agnew (1961) has described the interrelationships of *Juncus effusus* communities in terms of a continuum related to changes in soil pH and other factors. In Scotland, Poore (1956) concluded, as a result of his studies in Breadalbane, that variation in vegetation was continuous and multi-directional and proposed that characterisation should be in terms of abstract reference points (noda) in the continuum, and recently McVean and Ratcliffe (1962) have published an account of the vegetation of the Scottish Highlands expressed in these terms. The nature of the floristic variation in *Agrostis—Festuca* grassland is well illustrated by data (Harberd, 1962) obtained from a small area in the Pentland Hills. Seven groups of sites were distinguished and arranged in a floristic sequence related to the sequence from most leached soils to most flushed soils (Table 18). Since flushing was by base rich spring water, increasing wetness was in this case associated with increasing soil pH. It will be seen from Table 18 that the mean abundance in the groups of a considerable number of species tended to rise or fall from one end of the series to the other. *Festuca rubra, Poa trivialis, Cardamine pratensis, Trifolium repens, Ranunculus repens, Sagina procumbens*, were more abundant on the wetter and more basic soils. In contrast, *Festuca ovina* and *Galium saxatile* were more abundant on the drier, acid soils becoming progressively less so as wetness and pH increased. Many other species had their peak in the central groups becoming progressively less abundant towards either end of the sequence. All these plant communities could be classed as *Agrostis-Festuca* grassland and the sequence is a good example of the variation to be found within what could be described as one vegetation type.

TABLE 18

Floristic Composition in Terms of Specific Frequency of a Series of Seven Groups
of Sites arranged in order of the Soil Sequence from most Leached (Group 1)
to most Flushed (Group 7)

Site Group	1	2	3	4	5	6	7
Log. soil water percentage	1·35	1·43	1·67	1·61	1·53	1·77	1·69
pH of surface soil	5·04	5·50	6·03	6·05	5·73	6·10	6·23
Mean No. of spp./site	9·3	13·0	18·2	16·7	15·5	14·6	12·7
Vaccinium myrtillus	5·0	6·7	...	...	...	...	...
Agrostis canina ssp. *canina*	...	3·3	...	...	2·0	...	...
A. canina ssp. *montana*	9·0	6·7	...	...	...	...	...
A. stolonifera	...	...	...	...	...	5·5	37·1
A. tenuis	91·0	93·3	84·3	98·3	96·0	92·7	65·7
Anthoxanthum odoratum	65·0	86·7	57·1	48·3	70·0	34·5	8·6
Briza media	...	...	42·9	6·7	4·0	1·8	...
Cynosurus cristatus	...	3·3	18·6	35·0	44·0	29·1	28·6

Site Group	1	2	3	4	5	6	7
Log. soil water percentage	1·35	1·43	1·67	1·61	1·53	1·77	1·69
pH of surface soil	5·04	5·50	6·03	6·05	5·73	6·10	6·23
Mean No. of spp./site	9·3	13·0	1 ·2	16·6	15·5	14·5	12·7
Deschampsia cespitosa	4·0	...	10·0	8·3	16·0	10·9	8·6
D. flexuosa	5·0	...	...	...	...	...	...
Festuca ovina	95·0	86·7	87·1	56·7	44·0	5·5	...
F. rubra	54·0	76·7	94·3	96·7	100·0	100·0	100·0
Holcus lanatus	...	...	2·8	8·3	6·0	...	...
H. mollis (2n=21)	...	...	...	3·3	...	...	31·4
H. mollis (2n=35)	23·0	...	...	...	20·0	14·5	11·4
Poa annua	...	...	...	...	...	3·6	34·3
P. pratensis	22·0	6·7	14·3	23·3	48·0	29·1	25·7
P. trivialis	2·0	...	5·7	15·0	22·0	49·1	77·1
Carex caryophyllea	12·0	50·0	74·3	53·3	22·0	3·6	...
C. flacca	...	3·3	51·4	21·7	2·0	1·8	...
C. panicea	...	...	...	...	4·0	...	...
C. pilulifera	...	...	8·6	...	...	...	...
Luzula campestris	50·0	90·0	51·4	56·7	28·0	5·5	...
Achillea millefolium	6·0	33·3	32·9	61·7	46·0	49·1	28·6
Alchemilla glabra	...	...	4·3	3·3	...	1·8	...
Bellis perennis	...	...	...	3·3	...	1·8	...
Campanula rotundifolia	1·0	16·7	4·3	1·7	...	...	...
Cardamine pratensis	...	...	11·4	5·0	22·0	54·5	60·0
Cerastium holosteoides	2·0	10·0	31·4	38·3	38·0	58·2	14·3
Cirsium spp.	...	...	1·4	...	...	...	...
Euphrasia spp.	...	6·7	31·4	33·3	44·0	23·6	...
Galium saxatile	65·0	30·0	2·8	6·7	...	...	...
G. palustre ssp. *palustre*	...	...	...	...	2·0	5·5	8·6
G. pumilum	...	...	2·8	20·0	6·0	9·1	2·9
G. verum	...	13·3	20·0	5·0	...	5·5	...
Leontodon autumnalis	...	...	2·8	1·7	...	...	...
Linum catharticum	...	...	4·3	...	...	...	...
Lotus corniculatus	1·0	3·3	24·3	6·7	...	...	...
Montia spp.	...	...	...	...	...	1·8	2·9
Oxalis acetosella	3·0	...	...	...	...	...	...
Plantago lanceolata	...	...	15·7	1·7	...	...	...
Potentilla erecta	19·0	10·0	18·6	3·3	...	1·8	...
P. sterilis	...	...	5·7	...	...	...	...
Prunella vulgaris	...	10·0	31·4	36·7	12·0	23·6	...
Ranunculus repens	1·0	...	1·4	10·0	22·0	30·9	54·3
Rumex acetosa	4·0	6·7	4·3	1·7	6·0	21·8	11·4
Sagina procumbens	...	...	...	11·7	14·0	34·5	65·7
Thymus drucei	1·0	...	45·7	5·0	...	...	...
Trifolium repens	17·0	60·0	74·3	81·7	70·0	90·9	97·1
Veronica chamaedrys	...	...	10·0	10·0	8·0	7·3	...
V. officinalis	1·0	...	...	...	...	...	...
Viola riviniana	1·0	16·7	44·3	18·3	2·0	1·8	...

Data taken from Harberd (1962)

Covering a wider range of environmental and floristic variation are the vegetation continua described by King (1962a) from the Cheviot Hills. The soil profile types here were arranged in a branching series, extending from leached, acid soils to flushed gleyed profiles relatively well supplied with bases:

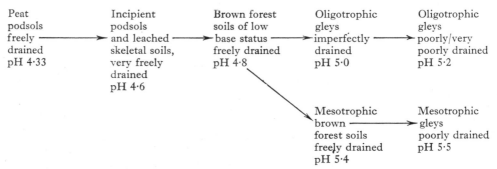

Peat podsols freely drained pH 4·33 → Incipient podsols and leached skeletal soils, very freely drained pH 4·6 → Brown forest soils of low base status freely drained pH 4·8 → Oligotrophic gleys imperfectly drained pH 5·0 → Oligotrophic gleys poorly/very poorly drained pH 5·2

Mesotrophic brown forest soils freely drained pH 5·4 → Mesotrophic gleys poorly drained pH 5·5

The vegetation changes associated with this sequence were found to be continuous for the most part, although relative discontinuities were noted in the form of co-incidental and complementary changes in cover-abundance of individual species or ranges of tolerance of small groups of species. The general nature of this vegetation can be seen from Fig. 34. The peat podsol and podsolic soils to the left of the diagram are associated with *Festuca ovina—Deschampsia flexuosa* grass-heath which gives way in turn to *F. ovina—Agrostis tenuis* grassland on brown forest soils of low base status. With increasing base status *Festuca rubra* and *Trifolium repens* occur and become progressively more prominent until on the wettest and most basic gley soils the vegetation is characterised by an abundance of *F. rubra* and *A. tenuis* associated with *F. ovina* and *Trifolium repens*.

So far reference has been made only to changes in floristic composition, but it is becoming increasingly apparent that intra-specific variations also occur in relation to environmental factors. These are produced as a result of the selective effect of the environment on genotypic variations within species giving rise to ecotypes or ecoclines (Turesson, 1922; Bøcher, 1949). In *Trifolium repens* for example physiological adaptation has been observed in relation to varying levels of calcium and phosphate (Snaydon, 1961) and in *Festuca ovina* to varying levels of soil calcium (Snaydon and Bradshaw, 1961). In the latter species the differences between extreme populations from high and low calcium habitats were as great as those reported between individual species of widely differing edaphic tolerances. Genecological differentiation in both morphology and maturity type has been demonstrated in *Calluna vulgaris* which exhibits ecoclinal variation in relation to changes in elevation and length of growing season (Grant and Hunter, 1962). Differentiation in respect of either maturity type, or morphology, or both has been reported in *Poa trivialis, Cerastium holosteoides, Carex caryophyllea* (Harberd, 1961) and *Trifolium repens* (King, 1963), in relation to factors associated with the environmental gradient from leached to mesotrophic flushed soils (cf. Table 18 and Fig. 34). It seems likely that further investigation will show that such differentiation is not uncommon amongst hill pasture species and that the existence of ecogenetic gradients within each of several species accounts for the continuous occurrence of a given community-type over a greater range of environmental variation than would otherwise be the case (McMillan, 1960).

Vegetation types

Since Tansley's *The British Isles and their Vegetation* was first published in 1939, a small number of studies have been published which deal with the composition of Forest zone grasslands in Scotland. These include Muir and Fraser (1939, 1940), Poore and Robertson (1948), Poore (1955), Asprey (1947), Nicholson and Robertson (1958), McVean (1961), Harberd (1962), Harper (1962), McVean and Ratcliffe (1962), King

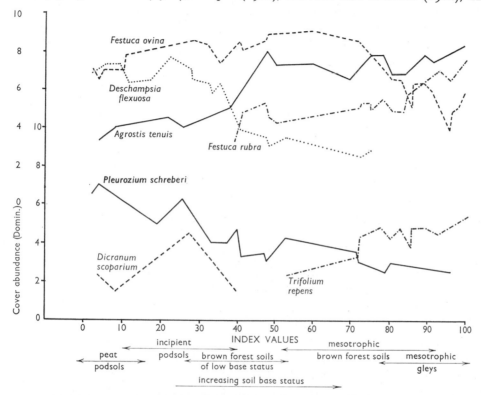

FIG. 34   Changes in cover-abundance of a number of species in relation to a sequence of soil profile types from peat podsols to brown forest soils of low base status and mesotrophic gleys. (Adapted from King, 1962a.)

(1962a). Additional information is available from certain *Memoirs on the Soil Survey of Great Britain*, Mitchell and Jarvis (1956) and Ragg (1960). With the exception of the account by McVean and Ratcliffe (1962), dealing with the Highland region, all the published data refer to comparatively small areas and there are great differences in the amount of information presented and in the methods of recording and describing the vegetation. The present account is based primarily on the data for the Highland area of McVean and Ratcliffe (1962) and on unpublished data from the Southern Uplands, Ochil Hills and the southern Highlands of King (1962b) and, for *Molinia* dominant communities, the data of Cross (1962). These consist of lists with estimates of cover-abundance (Domin's scale) from 127 stands. The lists have been arranged subjectively into groups on the basis of dominance and constancy placing emphasis, except in the case of zoo-plethismic communities, on those variations in floristic composition which were correlated with differences in soil profile type and, within the profile type, with differences in percentage base saturation of the soil. The resultant units are not edaphic community-types, however, since many other factors, including biotic factors, are correlated with variations in soil base status and profile type. Furthermore, some of the units comprise several variants differentiated principally in response to biotic factors and, although there is no reason why such variants should not be considered as separate units, they have not been separated here in order to reduce, so far as possible, the number of types. The presence of such variants in a community type is indicated by the inclusion of alternative or additional species in parentheses to the list of dominants in the tables. The floristic composition of these vegetation types is given in Tables 19 and 20 with the relevant soil data in Table 21. The composition of the associations and noda of McVean and Ratcliffe (1962) are summarised in Table 22 (p. 224).

In comparing the constancy data from these tables it should be remembered that the size of the sample plots are not the same in each of the three sets of data and in this respect, therefore, the results are not strictly comparable.

The community types have been arranged in groups, as follows, principally on the basis of their edaphic affinities:

Community types of peat podsols or oligotrophic peaty gley soils

Nardus—Festuca—Deschampsia type 2
Nardetum sub-alpinum (species-poor) (McVean and Ratcliffe)
Juncetum squarrossi sub-alpinum (species-poor) (McVean and Ratcliffe)
Molinia—Festuca—Deschampsia type 1

Nardus—Festuca—Deschampsia type 2 (Plate 33) is characterised by the dominance of *Nardus stricta* and *Festuca ovina* agg. *Deschampsia flexuosa* occurs in variable amounts, but is usually abundant. The type corresponds to the *Festuca—Deschampsia*-rich section on peat podsols in the continuum illustrated in Fig. 34 and merges with the adjacent *Festuca—Deschampsia*-rich section on incipient podsols. In addition to the dominants, the type is characterised by the constancy of *Vaccinium myrtillus*, *Agrostis canina*, *A. tenuis*, *Anthoxanthum odoratum*, *Carex binervis*, *Juncus squarrosus*, *Galium saxatile*, *Potentilla erecta*, *Hylocomium splendens*, *Hypnum cupressiforme*, *Pleurozium schreberi* and *Rhytidiadelphus squarrosus*. The soils are peat podsols or peaty gleyed podsols with from 10 to 30 cm. of mor humus or peat (pH 3·7-4·9) and the type commonly occupies much of the upper slopes of the hills in the Southern Uplands below the level of blanket peat. In this situation W. G. Smith (1918) associated it with redistributed peat, but it is equally characteristic of acid raw humus formed *in situ*. At least some stands appear to be derived biotically from Callunetum vulgaris as a result of grazing and burning (King, 1960) and mixtures of *Calluna* and *Nardus* may represent intermediate stages of the succession.

Species-poor Nardetum sub-alpinum described by McVean and Ratcliffe (1962) is a very similar type found on a similar range of soils. It is widespread in the central Highlands although less frequent in the north and west. The altitudinal range is from 305-702 m. (1000-2300 ft.), above this level merging with the chionophilous Nardeta (cf. Chapter 12).

Juncetum squarrossi sub-alpinum (species-poor facies) is frequently associated with Nardetum sub-alpinum and floristically rather similar. *Juncus squarrosus* is constant and the sole dominant. Additional constants are: *Agrostis canina*, *Anthoxanthum odoratum*, *Deschampsia flexuosa*, *Festuca ovina* agg., *Nardus stricta*, *Galium saxatile*, *Pleurozium schreberi*, and *Rhytidiadelphus squarrosus*. The type is most abundant in the central Highlands, but does not extend so far east as Nardetum sub-alpinum. The altitudinal range is 457-793 m. (1500-2600 ft.), extending into the low-alpine zone and the usual situation is on gentle slopes of up to 15°. The soils are gley podsols or shallow blanket peats of pH 3·3-4·1. At the highest elevations at which Juncetum squarrosi sub-alpinum occurs it may be a chionophilous type of vegetation. Species-poor Juncetum squarrosi is the same as the *J. squarrosus* communities found in Snowdonia, the English Lake District and the Cross Fell area (cf. Pearsall, 1950a; and Ratcliffe, 1959).

Molinia—Festuca—Deschampsia type 1 is characteristic of considerable areas in the Southern Uplands although it may have a wider distribution. It commonly occupies the upper slopes and rounded tops of the hills up to 457 m. (1500 ft.) and presents a characteristically under-grazed appearance, the herbage being from 30 to 40 cm. tall and often heavily tussocked. Floristically it is very similar to the *Nardus* type with which it is frequently in juxtaposition. The soils are generally peat podsols with gleyed A_2 horizons or base deficient, peaty gleys, both with up to 30 cm. of peat. The type may also occur on imperfectly drained peat podsols with about 15 cm. raw humus but showing evidence of lateral water movement at the base of the peat. This *Molinia* type is similar to the oligotrophic *Molinia* grasslands of the western Highlands but differs in its abundance of associated grasses such as *Festuca ovina*, *Agrostis tenuis* and *Deschampsia flexuosa*, and occurs on much shallower peat. McVean and Ratcliffe (1962) consider that the floristic composition of the *Molinia* dominant grasslands of the west Highlands, and of similar grasslands in Galloway, are adequately represented by the data for Molinieto—Callunetum and the *Molinia—Myrica* (mire see p. 435) from which they appear to have been derived by loss of the co-dominant species by human influence. These *Molinia* grasslands may occur on the lower hill slopes and on valley bottoms on peat typically about 50 cm. deep. The pH varies from 3·6 to 4·5 or from 3·8 to 6·1 for stands derived from Molinieto—Callunetum and the *Molinia—Myrica* nodum respectively. The soils are wet but characterised by water movement rather than stagnation.

Community types of leached podsolic soils

Festuca—Deschampsia—(Nardus) type 3

Although this type has floristic similarities to type 2 it seems to occupy a position intermediate between the *Nardus—Festuca—Deschampsia* type 2 and the *Festuca—*

Agrostis type 5. It is characterised by the dominance of *Festuca ovina* agg. with *Deschampsia flexuosa* rather less abundant. The intermediate character of the type is indicated by the cover-abundance and constancy values of the following species: *Sieglingia decumbens, Carex binervis, C. caryophyllea, C. panicea, Luzula campestris, L. multiflora, L. pilosa* and *Campanula rotundifolia*. *Nardus stricta* is always present and, in some stands, is so abundant as to be co-dominant. It is possible that this grassland type could be subdivided into a *Nardus*-rich and *Nardus*-poor facies (cf. King, 1962a). The associated soil types include acid skeletals, iron podsols, and brown forest soils of low base status which range from imperfectly to very freely drained with 3-5 cm. of surface mor or moder humus. The pH range is 4·1-5·1. These communities are found at any altitude in the forest zone but above about 305 m. (1000 ft.) the surface mor becomes thicker, the soil more podsolised and the vegetation merges with *Nardus—Festuca—Deschampsia* type 2. The type occurs in the Southern Uplands and in the central Highlands although in the latter it seems to be less common. Moss (1913) recognised a related type in the Pennines in open woods of *Quercus petraea* and *Betula* spp. and, in the same area, Adamson (1918) described a *Deschampsia flexuosa* rich grassland on steep slopes below the "peat edge". King (1962a) describes both a *Nardus*-rich and a *Nardus* poor variant of a similar grassland type in the Cheviot Hills. The type is most probably derived directly from *Vaccinium myrtillus*-dominated communities by sheep grazing pressure (see p. 196), and all variations can be found between this grassland and *Vaccinium*-heath, (cf. Ratcliffe, 1959; McVean and Ratcliffe, 1962). *Pteridium aquilinum* may invade this *Festuca—Deschampsia* grassland and, if the frond density becomes great enough, will eventually eliminate it completely (Plate 34).

Community types of freely drained acid soils

Festuca—Agrostis type 5
Species-poor Agrosto—Festucetum (McVean and Ratcliffe)

Species-poor Agrosto—Festucetum and *Festuca—Agrostis* type 5 clearly represent the same vegetation type. *Festuca ovina* agg. and *Agrostis tenuis* are the most abundant species and are associated with *A. canina, Anthoxanthum odoratum, Galium saxatile, Potentilla erecta, Rhytidiadelphus squarrosus* and *Hylocomium splendens*. Other species such as *Nardus stricta, Sieglingia decumbens, Carex pilulifera, Luzula campestris, Campanula rotundifolia*, and *Viola riviniana* are of frequent occurrence. The sward is dense and moderately well grazed. This is a widespread type of grassland occurring principally on brown forest soils of low base status or on leached skeletals. The humus is of the moder type and the pH ranges from 4·75 to 5·2. Drainage is either free or imperfect. The soils may be derived from glacial drift or from a wide variety of rocks except the very poorest such as quartzite (McVean and Ratcliffe, 1962). With increasing frequency of *Deschampsia flexuosa, Vaccinium myrtillus*, and hypnaceous mosses the type merges with

PLATE 30. Intermediate stage in the succession after burning Callunetum vulgaris (McV. and R.). *Erica* spp., *Festuca ovina* and *Nardus stricta* are prominent, while *Calluna* is regenerating in patches. *Alchemilla alpina* is also frequent. Near Dalwhinnie, Inverness-shire.

PLATE 31. *Festuca ovina—Deschampsia flexuosa—Agrostis* grass-heath at 1800 ft. (730 m.) on soil derived from mica schist. Sgurr a Mhaim, Glen Nevis, Inverness-shire.

PLATE 32. *Molinia—Festuca ovina—Calluna* community (cf. type 10), moderately species-rich and closely grazed on a poorly drained mesotrophic gley soil. *Festuca—Agrostis* grassland with scattered *Alnus* beyond. Bohuntine Hill, Glen Roy, Inverness-shire.

PLATE 33. Mosaic pattern of *Calluna* communities and grass-heath attributable to the effect of past fires. The grass-heath is mainly *Nardus—Festuca—Deschampsia* type 2. Gleann Beag, near the Devil's Elbow, Perthshire.

PLATE 34. Bracken (*Pteridium aquilinum*) and *Festuca—Deschampsia flexuosa* grass-heath (cf. type 3). Bracken cutting in the left background.

PLATE 35. Forest zone grasslands in the Cheviot Hills, S.E. Scotland. In the foreground is *Agrostis—Festuca* zoo-plethismic grassland on a hill top. The middle distance slopes show a mosaic of *Agrostis—Festuca* and *Festuca—Deschampsia* grassland communities, many of which are *Nardus* or *Pteridium*-rich. The lower summit plateau (506–649 m.) carries *Molinia*—or *Nardus—Festuca—Deschampsia* grass-heath (type 1 and 2) on peat podsol soils. In the background at 932 m. is the summit plateau of Cheviot covered with deep ombrogenous peat. This illustration shows the site of the sheep grazing behaviour studies of Hunter (1963).

PLATE 36

Festuca—Agrostis grassland on alluvial flats and the lower slopes of Glen Almond Perthshire. On higher ground to the right of the picture the grassland gives way to *Festuca—Deschampsia flexuosa* grass-heath (cf. type 3) and in turn to *Vaccinium—D. flexuosa* shrub-heath.

Deschampsia—Festuca grassland, while increasing abundance of *Festuca rubra* and basiphilous herbs indicates a transition to more mesotrophic *Festuca—Agrostis* types (e.g. type 9). These species-poor *Festuca-Agrostis* grasslands are of widespread occurrence in the Southern Uplands and the Highlands between 31 m. and 318 m. (100 ft. and 1250 ft.) but may be found up to 824 m. (2700 ft.) in the Highlands, especially in the drier south and east. In the west and north-west they are of much less frequent occurrence. Stands are frequently invaded by *Pteridium aquilinum* and, if the density of the fern is not excessive, *Holcus mollis* may become dominant or co-dominant with *Agrostis* and *Festuca* spp. With high fern density the grass sward is completely eliminated.

Community types of relatively basic soils freely or imperfectly drained

Festuca—Agrostis type 9
Alchemilleto—Agrosto—Festucetum (McVean and Ratcliffe)
Species-rich Agrosto—Festucetum (McVean and Ratcliffe)
Saxifrageto—Agrosto—Festucetum (McVean and Ratcliffe)

Apart from the dominance of *Festuca ovina* and *Agrostis tenuis* the most distinctive feature of the *Festuca—Agrostis* type 9 is the abundance of the more calcicolous species and, in comparison with *Agrostis—Festuca* type 10, the comparative absence of hydrophilic species. The list of constants is broadly similar to that of the *Festuca—Agrostis* type 5 on brown forest soils of low base status but is distinguished by the high frequency of such species as *Festuca rubra*, *Plantago lanceolata*, *Thymus drucei* and *Trifolium repens*. There are, in addition, many species which although frequent are not constants but, when taken together, they are very characteristic. Species in this category are *Briza media*, *Koeleria cristata*, *Sieglingia decumbens*, *Carex caryophyllea*, *Galium verum*, *Linum catharticum*, *Lotus corniculatus* and *Veronica officinalis*. The type is associated with freely or imperfectly drained mesotrophic brown forest soils (pH 5·1-6·0) with mull humus and a good crumb structure. The soils may be periodically flushed by base rich water or derived from relatively base rich parent materials. The sites recorded extend from 137 to 427 m. (450 ft. to 1400 ft.) and stands may be found throughout the Southern Uplands and in the Highlands although they do not cover large areas (Plate 36). The species-rich Agrosto—Festucetum is a very similar type, described by McVean and Ratcliffe (1962) from the Highlands. Stands of this association have been recorded from 152 to 792 m. (500 ft. to 2300 ft.) and are characterised by high cover values for *Agrostis* spp. and *Festuca ovina* agg. associated with a profusion of basiphilous herbs and bryophytes. The sward is closely grazed, less than 10 cm. high, and some of the herbs are dwarfed forms of species which are tall and robust when ungrazed e.g. *Alchemilla glabra*, *A. vestita*, *Rumex acetosa* and *Trollius europaeus*. The distribution of this Agrosto—Festucetum in the Highlands is co-extensive with that of calcareous rock and the soils are similar to those described for *Festuca—Agrostis* type 9. The pH range is from 5·3 to 7·2. Re-

lated to the species rich Agrosto—Festucetum is the Saxifrageto—Agrosto—Festucetum·
This is a closely grazed herb-rich grassland. *Agrostis* spp. and *Festuca ovina* agg. have a
consistently high cover and there is an abundance of basiphilous herbs and bryophytes,
amongst which *Selaginella selaginoides*, *Carex panicea* and *Saxifraga aizoides* are constants,
differentiating the type from species-rich Agrosto—Festucetum. Stands are small rarely
exceeding 10 sq. m. Although it occurs over the same range of altitude as the species-rich
type, Saxifrageto—Agrosto—Festucetum is more restricted in its distribution and has been
noted mainly on the calcareous schists between Breadalbane and Glen Clova. The soils
are dark brown silty clay loams with mull humus and a good crumb structure. They are
invariably flushed, receiving more continuous irrigation than those of species-rich
Agrosto—Festucetum. The pH range is from 6·5 to 7·0. As irrigation becomes more
continuous, the association grades into the *Carex panicea—Campylium stellatum* mire
(p. 437). Comparable types of grassland occur as fragments on calcareous soils in the
English Lake District and may exist in the Pennines; otherwise this association is confined
to the Highlands of Scotland. The Alchemilleto—Agrosto—Festucetum is also associated
with base rich soils but tends to occur at rather higher elevations than the other members
of this group. This association is characterised by many of the plants of species-poor
Agrosto—Festucetum but differs both in being floristically much richer and in the
abundance of *Alchemilla alpina*, which gives the vegetation its distinctive appearance.
Thymus drucei has a moderate cover and species indicative of more basic soils such as
Selaginella selaginoides, *Campanula rotundifolia*, *Ranunculus acris* and *Thalictrum alpinum*
are typically present. The grasses form a short sward in which a few shoots of *Vaccinium
myrtillus* sometimes occur. The altitudinal range is from 336 to 1007 m. (1100 ft. to
3300 ft.) and, at the lower levels, Alchemilleto—Agrosto—Festucetum may occur as patches
within the dwarf shrub-heaths or acidic grasslands. Above 763 m. (2500 ft.) and extending to 1007 m. (3300 ft.) the association is represented chiefly by the *Rhacomitrium*-rich
facies (not described in Table 22) which is floristically poorer and has affinities with the
Rhacomitrosum facies of Festuco—Vaccinietum (Chapter 11). At lower elevations the soils
are shallow, dark brown silty loams, loose textured and stony, developed on alluvium,
colluvium or scree material. Humus tends towards the mull type and the pH range is
5·3-6·0. Incipient podsolisation has been detected in one or two profiles. On the calcareous
mica-schist mountains between Breadalbane and Clova the association is well developed
on fairly base rich, unirrigated soils, as on the upper slopes of Ben Lawers. In other parts
of the Highlands it is found mainly on well-drained sites intermittently irrigated by base
rich water. The *Rhacomitrium*-rich facies is widespread in the western Highlands on
similar soils, but occurs in rather small patches except on the steep upper slopes of
Torridon sandstone mountains. Stands at the lower levels are clearly anthropogenic in
origin and Poore believes that even the stands which occur at the highest altitudes on
Ben Lawers may have been derived from other dwarf-shrub or herb-rich communities
by grazing. The association corresponds largely to the arctic-alpine grassland of W. G.
Smith (in Tansley, 1911). Patches of an identical *Alchemilla* grassland occur locally on
similar soils in the English Lake District but nowhere else in Britain.

Community types of moderately acid soils with impeded drainage

Festuca—Agrostis—(Nardus) type 6
Deschampsia—Festuca—Agrostis type 8
Molinia—Festuca—Agrostis type 7

Festuca—Agrostis type 6 is of common occurrence in the Southern Uplands below 381 m. (1250 ft.) on gentle drift covered slopes irrigated by drainage water from higher levels. It may also occur in the central Highlands. *Festuca ovina* agg. and *Agrostis tenuis* are generally co-dominant, although *Holcus lanatus* may sometimes be equally prominent. The type is distinguished from *Festuca—Agrostis* type 5 by the greater frequency of *Deschampsia cespitosa, Festuca rubra, Carex panicea, Carex* spp., *Luzula multiflora* and *Ranunculus acris* and by the lower frequency of *Calluna vulgaris, Sieglingia decumbens, Carex pilulifera* and *C. caryophyllea*. These floristic differences are associated with a change in soil conditions from freely drained oligotrophic brown earths to poorly, or very poorly, drained surface water gleys with up to 4 cm. of surface moder humus, and flushed by moderately acid water. The pH range is 4·9-5·5. With decreasing soil pH the type merges with the *Deschampsia cespitosa* type 8 and the *Molinia* type 9, while on more basic soils it passes into *Agrostis—Festuca* type 10. *Nardus stricta* is constant in type 6 but with variable cover values ranging from a trace to co-dominance with *Festuca* and *Agrostis* spp. It is probable that a *Nardus*-rich and a *Nardus*-poor facies could be distinguished, similar to those described by King (1962a) in the Cheviot Hills. The type overlaps with the species-rich Nardetum sub-alpinum which includes stands from higher elevations and from more basic soils. The closely related *Deschampsia—Festuca—Agrostis* type 8 is distinguished principally by the dominance of *Deschampsia cespitosa*, which may be overwhelming in well-developed, lightly grazed stands, although all stages can be found between these and *Festuca—Agrostis* type 6. Other floristic differences between these types are the increased frequency of *Agrostis stolonifera, Poa pratensis, Carex ovalis, Juncus effusus, Eurhynchium praelongum* and the decreased frequency of *Agrostis canina, Carex panicea, Potentilla erecta, Hylocomium splendens, Hypnum cupressiforme, Pleurozium schreberi, Polytrichum commune* and *Thuidium tamariscinum. Deschampsia cespitosa*, being unpalatable to sheep is generally under-grazed and this may contribute to the dominance of the species. The herbage in such communities is commonly 30-40 cm. tall. Cattle graze *Deschampsia cespitosa* more readily and, where they are numerous, stands may be grazed to 5 cm. and the associated *Festuca* and *Agrostis* species are then more prominent. The soils are gleyed, poorly or very poorly drained although not always very wet in summer. There is frequently a thin layer of moder humus and the pH varies from 4·6 to 5·2. The type is commonly found in hollows and drainage channels irrigated by moderately acid water or on alluvial flats subject to periodic inundation (Plate 36). This *Deschampsia cespitosa* grassland is truly anthropogenic, the recorded stands lying between 167 m. (550 ft.) and 457 m. (1500 ft.). It is quite distinct from Deschampsietum cespitosae alpinum of McVean and Ratcliffe (1962) which is found at elevations above 488 m. (1600 ft.). *Molinia—Festuca—Agrostis* type 7 is closely related to both the *Festuca*

—*Agrostis* type 6 and the *Deschampsia cespitosa* grasslands and is characterised by the overwhelming dominance of *Molinia caerulea* in association with *Festuca* and *Agrostis* and others pecies of moist *Festuca—Agrostis* grasslands. The soil is an acid gley, often humus-rich in the top 10 cm. and poorly or very poorly drained. The pH ranges from 4·75 to 5·10. The stands recorded are all from the Southern Uplands where the type sometimes occurs on the lower hill slopes on impervious drift derived from Silurian or Ordovician shales. The type may also occur in the Highlands.

Community types of mesotrophic soils with impeded drainage

Nardetum sub-alpinum (species-rich) (McVean and Ratcliffe)
Juncetum squarrosi sub-alpinum (species-rich) (McVean and Ratcliffe)
Agrostis—Festuca **type 10**
Molinia—Festuca—Agrostis **type 11**

The species-rich facies of Nardetum sub-alpinum of the Highlands has affinities with the *Festuca—Agrostis—(Nardus)* type 6 already described from the Southern Uplands, but includes stands both from higher elevations and from soils of higher base status. In this respect it is perhaps most closely related to *Agrostis—Festuca* type 10. *Nardus stricta* is dominant and the list of constants includes all those of species-poor Nardetum sub-alpinum together with the following additional species: *Agrostis canina, Carex echinata, C. panicea, C. pulicaris, Juncus squarrosus, Luzula multiflora* and *Ranunculus acris.* Associated with these are a large number of mildly calcicolous herbs which make the type easily distinguishable from the species-poor Nardetum sub-alpinum. Species-rich Nardetum is of local occurrence in the central Highlands and is confined to calcareous mountains where it occupies wet slopes where the drainage water comes from extensive areas of calcareous rocks, as on the flanks of the Ben Lawers range where the type is well developed. The soils are wet silty grey-brown loams with no surface raw humus. Gleying varies in intensity and may be pronounced. Closely related to this Nardetum is the species-rich Juncetum squarrosi sub-alpinum. *Juncus squarrosus* is dominant, *Nardus stricta* and *Festuca ovina* being next in abundance. Although only three stands have been recorded it is evident that the constants are common to both these species-rich facies. There is again an abundance of the same hydrophilous species, herbs and mosses. The Juncetum squarrosi sub-alpinum may be found together with the Nardetum in the central Highlands but does not extend so far east. The three recorded stands are from Breadalbane where the facies is widespread on soils receiving drainage from calcareous mica-schists. The soils are peaty gleys (pH 5·5-6·0) with a mull type of humus. *Agrostis—Festuca* type 10, like the last two community types, is a species-rich grassland. The dominant species are rather variable and although *Agrostis tenuis* is nearly always abundant, *Festuca rubra* and *F. ovina* agg. may sometimes be replaced as co-dominants by *Holcus lanatus* or *Nardus stricta.* The type contains many mildly calcicolous and hydrophilic species few of which have high constancy values but which, collectively, give the type a characteristic appearance. The constancy of *Briza media, Cynosurus cristatus,*

Holcus lanatus, *Carex panicea*, *Ranunculus acris*, *Trifolium repens* and *Acrocladium cuspidatum* together with the relative infrequency or absence of *Galium saxatile*, *Thymus drucei*, *Veronica chamaedrys*, *Hypnum cupressiforme* and *Pleurozium schreberi* distinguishes the type from the other closely related *Festuca—Agrostis* type 6 or type 9, with which it merges. The associated soil profile type is a poorly or very poorly drained gley with mull humus and a pH range from 5·3 to 6·1. The soils are flushed by moderately base-rich water (cf. Heddle and Ogg, 1936) but are not necessarily very wet in summer. Grazing intensity is variable and the herbage may be either closely grazed or reach 30 cm. or more in length. Stands are generally small, rarely exceeding 300 sq. m., but are found throughout the Southern Uplands, while in the central Highlands the distribution of the type is co-extensive with that of basic rocks (Plate 32). The closely related *Molinia— Agrostis—Festuca* type 11 is floristically similar to type 10 and is similarly characterised by an abundance of basiphilous and hydrophilous herbs. The soil type is a very poorly drained gley often with a humus rich **A** horizon. The pH range is 5·5-6·4. All the stands recorded are from the Southern Uplands, principally from the Ettrick-Eskdalemuir area, but the type may have a wider distribution.

Other community types

Agrostis—Festuca—Poa type 4
Luzula sylvatica grassland nodum (McVean and Ratcliffe)

Agrostis—Festuca—Poa type 4 (Plate 35) is a zoo-plethismic grassland dependent on the heavy deposition of dung and urine by sheep. The characteristic species are *Agrostis tenuis*, *Festuca ovina* agg. with *F. rubra* and *Poa pratensis*. These four species, sometimes with the addition of *Holcus lanatus*, make up the greater part of the sward. Other species are few in number and present only in very small amounts. Apart from those already mentioned, the species with the greatest constancy are: *Anthoxanthum odoratum*, *Campanula rotundifolia*, *Rumex acetosella*, *Rhytidiadelphus squarrosus*. The sward is moderately well grazed and usually very dense and vigorous. Stands of this type are found where sheep tend to lie at night, just below the edge of summit plateaux or on the lower summits and knolls in the Southern Uplands and the soils are those associated with these situations in this region; leached skeletals, iron podsols or brown forest soils of low base status with a surface layer of mor humus. The pH range is 4·2-4·6. Similar zoo-plethismic communities have been described from the St. Kilda group of islands by McVean (1961) and the type may also occur in the Highlands. The *Luzula sylvatica* grassland nodum is characterised by five constants in addition to the dominant namely, *Agrostis tenuis*, *Deschampsia flexuosa*, *Rumex acetosa*, *Rhytidiadelphus loreus* and *R. squarrosus*. The nodum is found on hill tops at about 457 m. (1500 ft.) elevation along the Atlantic seaboard. It is not known if the small patches of *Luzula sylvatica* commonly found in *Festuca—Agrostis* and *Nardus—Festuca* grassland throughout Scotland also belong to it. Stands vary in size from a few square metres to several hectares. Spence (1960) has

N

described similar stands of *Luzula sylvatica* on islands in Shetland lochs and on rock ledges in South Uist. Most of the soils examined consisted of a deep layer (up to 60 cm.) of moist or wet reddish-brown to black raw humus with a fibrous or friable structure.

INTERRELATIONSHIPS OF COMMUNITY TYPES

Edaphic relationships

The relationships among communities can be considered on the basis of their floristic and edaphic affinities without implying the existence of seral relationships, although these may often occur. In Fig. 35, the relationships of the community types to each other and to certain bog and mire communities described in other chapters, are summarised in terms of soil base status and drainage, or more precisely, in terms of the complex of factors correlated with these two edaphic gradients. The ordination of these types in relation to two environmental axes cannot account for the total floristic variation. In consequence, it should not be assumed that adjacent or overlapping types in Fig. 35 are necessarily as closely related as their proximity in one plane might suggest. For this reason, and also because the boundaries of community types may arbitrarily exclude intermediate stands, Fig. 35, by itself, does not provide any evidence for either continuous floristic gradients, or for discontinuities. Evidence from the literature indicates, however, that most if not all these grassland types are connected by gradients and that similar gradients also exist between them and certain mire or bog communities. For example, species-poor Juncetum squarrosi sub-alpinum has through one of its facies some affinity with ombrogenous bog. Other stands occur on ground where there are signs of lateral water movement and these grade into the soligenous mire, Sphagneto—Caricetum sub-alpinum which itself has a facies dominated by *Juncus squarrosus* instead of sedges (McVean and Ratcliffe, 1962 and Chapter 10). In terms of pH, species-poor Juncetum squarrosi is far removed from the species-rich facies and is more closely related to species-poor Nardetum sub-alpinum and *Nardus—Festuca—Deschampsia* type 2 with which it is frequently found (Fig. 35). Like these two *Nardus* types the Juncetum squarrosi may in some cases at least be derived from other heath community types by biotic factors (cf. Pearsall, 1950a) but in other places it seems to be differentiated from dwarf-shrub heath by soil conditions (McVean and Ratcliffe, 1962). *Nardus—Festuca—Deschampsia* type 2 is closely related to *Molinia* type 1 from which it seems to be differentiated principally by rather drier soil conditions and perhaps differences in the amount of lateral water movement in the surface peat (cf. Jefferies, 1915). No quantitative data exists on the moisture regimes of these soils and these conclusions are inferred from the topographical distribution of *Molinia* and *Nardus* stands relative to each other and to ombrogenous bog. As already stated, stands similar to those of *Nardus* type 2 were particularly associated by Smith (1918) with the zone of eroded and redistributed peat surrounding blanket peat on summit plateaux in the Moorfoot Hills, but the type is equally characteristic of shallow peats formed *in situ*.

With increasing irrigation and soil wetness, *Nardus* type 2 and Nardetum sub-alpinum (Fig. 35) may grade into Sphagneto—Juncetum effusi (McVean and Ratcliffe, 1962), although data on this point are lacking. A similar gradient may exist also between the Southern Upland *Molinia* type 1 and the Molinieto—Callunetum or the *Molinia*—*Myrica* mire of which McVean and Ratcliffe (1962) consider the Highland *Molinia* grasslands to be anthropogenic derivatives. Such a gradient might be associated with increasing depth of peat but other factors such as rainfall, past history, grazing pressure and the incidence of burning may all be of significance. From species-poor Juncetum squarrosi sub-alpinum to species-poor Agrosto—Festucetum there extends a floristic gradient associated with improved drainage, increased pH and a progressive reduction in the depth of surface organic matter from 20 or 30 cm. to 2 cm. or less. The *Agrostis*—*Festuca*—*Poa* type 4, associated with areas of sheep night-camps, and the *Nardus*-rich variant of *Festuca*—*Deschampsia* type 3 form biotic deviations from this gradient which corresponds with the first half of the local continuum illustrated in Fig. 34 (p. 185). Portions of it commonly occur as a topographical sequence from summit plateaux with peat podsol soils down a convex slope to lower levels.

On freely and imperfectly drained soils (Fig. 35), with increasing base status, the species-poor *Agrostis*—*Festuca* grasslands merge with the species-rich types including Alchemilleto—Agrosto—Festucetum. The latter differs from other freely drained, meso-trophic grasslands in its higher altitudinal range while McVean and Ratcliffe (1962) consider that it is also associated with soils of slightly lower fertility. Furthermore, in Scotland the type seems to be confined to the Highlands while the other *Festuca*—*Agrostis* types are widespread in their occurrence.

The species-poor and species-rich *Agrostis*—*Fesctuca* grasslands on free draining soils grade into the corresponding types on poorly drained soils, i.e. *Festuca*—*Agrostis* types 6 and 10. The *Nardus*-rich variants of these together with species-rich Nardetum sub-alpinum presumably represent a further modification due in part to the influence of biotic factors (cf. p. 192). Species-rich Juncetum squarrosi sub-alpinum in Breadal-bane is differentiated from species-rich Nardetum sub-alpinum by a greater degree of soil waterlogging (McVean and Ratcliffe, 1962) but, as with the species-poor facies, it is possible that biotic factors may also be involved here (cf. Pearsall, 1950a). The gradient associated with increasingly impeded drainage from species-rich Agrosto—Festucetum to *Agrostis*—*Festuca* type 10 may be continued into the *Juncus acutiflorus*—*Acrocladium cuspidatum* mire (Fig. 35) although the available data is not explicit on this point. A parallel gradient from the species-poor *Agrostis*—*Festuca* grasslands also may extend into the Sphagneto—Juncetum effusi or into the transitional types that occur between this association and the *Juncus acutiflorus*—*Acrocladium* mire (cf. McVean and Ratcliffe, 1962). *Molinia* types 7 and 11 appear to be differentiated from each other principally by soil base status (Table 20), but it is not clear what their relationship is to other types in Fig. 35 which have overlapping environmental ranges. The herb-rich *Molinia* type 11 seems to have some affinity with the *Juncus acutiflorus* mires (cf. McVean and Ratcliffe, 1962) and *Molinia* type 7 has an apparently close relationship with *Deschampsia cespitosa* type 8, but the differentiating environmental factors are not known. It appears, therefore, that these poorly, and very poorly, drained mesotrophic soils support a complex of overlapping community types which, although they have some floristic features in common, differ in many other characteristics, including the dominant species. Soil base status, drainage and biotic factors account for some of the total variation but much, especially that connected with *Molinia caerulea*, *Juncus squarrosus*, *Deschampsia cespitosa* and the *Juncus effusus* or *J. acutiflorus* mires, remains to be investigated more fully (cf. also discussion in Chapter 10).

Successional relationships

Where successions have taken place in the forest zone grasslands they have generally occurred in response to changes in soil or biotic influence or to a combination of both. In general, the plant successions in progress that are now most evident are those caused either directly, or indirectly, by biotic change although edaphic changes may also be associated with them. The widespread conversion of deciduous forest to dwarf-shrub heath or grassland in comparatively recent times and the associated fundamental changes in soil conditions is an outstanding example of this process (cf. Dimbleby, 1952a; McVean and Ratcliffe, 1962; Chapter 7). Starting with either pine or with oak-birch forest, this succession has taken place either through an intermediate stage of dwarf-shrub heath or, alternatively, the woodland may have given way directly to grassland, depending on the grazing intensity and on the circumstances of forest clearance. McVean and Ratcliffe (1962) have speculated that in the main period of deforestation, with lighter grazing pressure, the succession would be first to dwarf-shrub heath which, on acid soils in the Southern Uplands and in the Highlands, is still being converted to oligotrophic grassland by a combination of burning and grazing pressure (Plates 30 and 33). On the other hand, in recent years the forest has probably more often given place directly to grassland. On mesotrophic and eutrophic soils some species-rich grassland may have originated directly from woodland herb/grass communities, but the existence of herb-rich Callunetum (McVean and Ratcliffe, 1962) on these soils suggests that, as with the acid grasslands, some of the more basic grasslands also have been derived from shrub-heath. On the basis of ecological and historical evidence it can be assumed that *Calluna*-heath was at one time very much more widespread in the Southern Uplands than it is at the present day and its relative scarcity in this region in comparison with the central and south-eastern Highlands is to a considerable extent attributable to the differences in biotic history of the two regions, and to the lower sheep grazing intensities which prevail in the Highlands (cf. Fig. 30 and p. 271).

The conversion of dwarf-shrub heath to grassland is, in general terms, a function of the overall grazing intensity, modified by burning, and by selective grazing preferences both between communities and between species within a community.

The overall grazing intensity is determined by the ratio of the area occupied by community types supporting high grazing intensities to that occupied by those with only

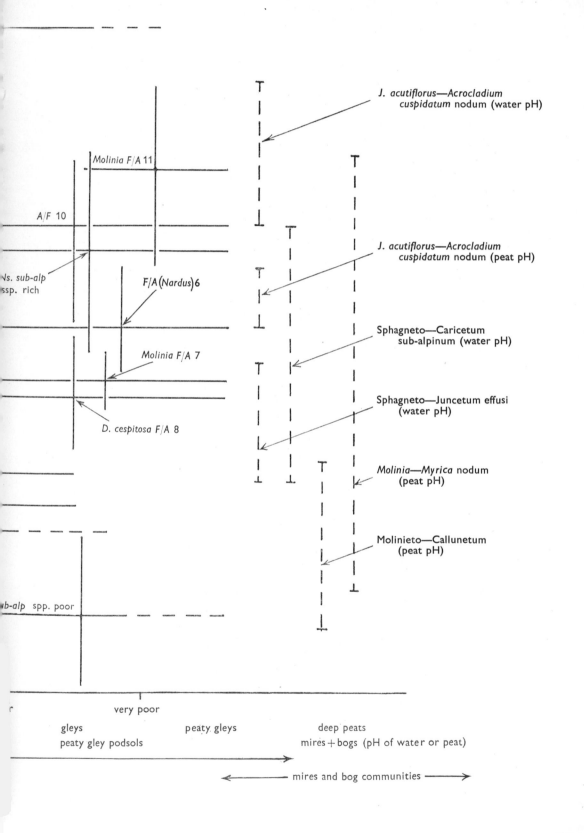

J. acutiflorus—Acrocladium
cuspidatum nodum (water pH)

Molinia F/A 11

A/F 10

J. acutiflorus—Acrocladium
cuspidatum nodum (peat pH)

Ns. sub-alp
ssp. rich

F/A (Nardus) 6

Sphagneto—Caricetum
sub-alpinum (water pH)

Molinia F/A 7

Sphagneto—Juncetum effusi
(water pH)

D. cespitosa F/A 8

Molinia—Myrica nodum
(peat pH)

Molinieto—Callunetum
(peat pH)

ub-alp spp. poor

very poor

gleys   peaty gleys   deep peats
peaty gley podsols   mires + bogs (pH of water or peat)

⟵ mires and bog communities ⟶

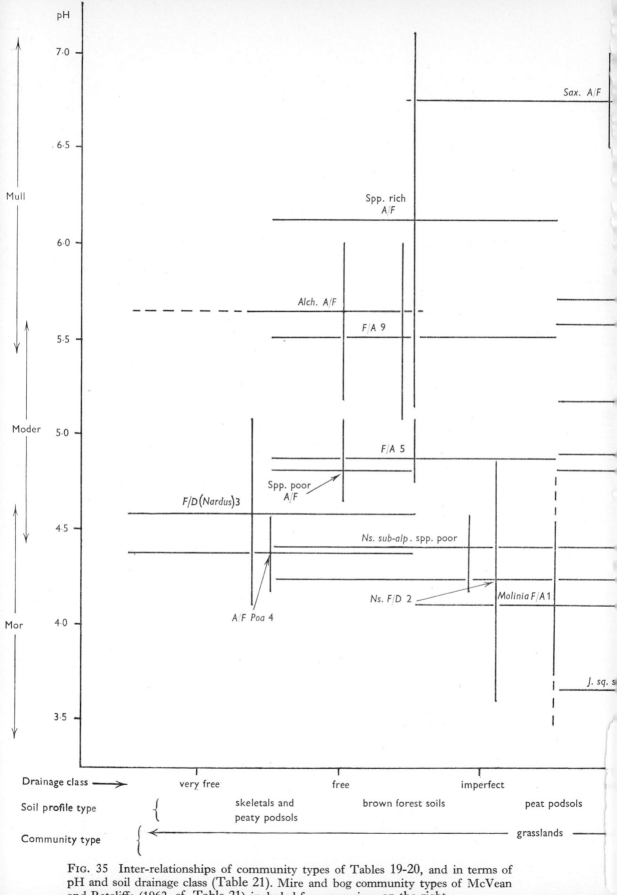

FIG. 35 Inter-relationships of community types of Tables 19-20, and in terms of pH and soil drainage class (Table 21). Mire and bog community types of McVean and Ratcliffe (1962, cf. Table 21) included for comparison on the right.

low intensities (Hunter, 1962a). The former group comprises *Festuca—Agrostis* grasslands, including *Pteridium*-rich variants, and may also include *Festuca—Deschampsia flexuosa* grass-heath; the latter group includes *Molinia* and *Nardus* grasslands and dwarf-shrub heath communities on podsol or peat podsol soils, together with ombrogenous bogs. Generally speaking, as the proportion of the area occupied by the first group increases, the overall grazing intensity may be expected to rise and with it the pressure on the communities of the second group. Under these conditions *Calluna*, and to a lesser extent *Vaccinium*-heath, tend to be replaced by some form of grassland (cf. Ratcliffe, 1959; McVean and Ratcliffe, 1962) although the ease with which this occurs for a particular stand will depend upon local variations of grazing intensity. These arise from the inter-action of a number of factors such as soil profile type, burning regime, stand location in relation to accessibility, exposure and the distribution of sheep home ranges within the grazing unit (Hunter, 1962b). These variations may account for the often patchy replace-ment of *Calluna* heath by grassland (cf. McVean and Ratcliffe, 1962) and also for the comparative rarity of species-rich *Calluna* heath on mesotrophic soils. Communities of the latter type might be expected to attract a higher than average grazing intensity, especially after burning, and would be converted to grassland at an overall stocking rate too low to affect *Calluna* heath on podsolic soils (McVean and Ratcliffe, 1962).

It will be apparent from what has been said that, depending on soil conditions and other factors, many types of grassland may be derived from dwarf-shrub heath. Referring to Fig. 35, it may be said that all the *Festuca—Agrostis* and *Festuca—Deschampsia flexuosa* grasslands, and probably Alchemilleto—Agrosto—Festucetum also, may be derived biotically from *Calluna* or *Vaccinium* heath. In addition, McVean and Ratcliffe (1962) consider that much *Molinia* dominant grassland in the west Highlands has originated from Molinieto—Callunetum or the *Molinia—Myrica* mire by loss of the dwarf-shrub component. *Molinia—Festuca—Agrostis* type 1 (Fig. 35) may have originated in a similar manner, but no evidence is available on this point. Under a regime of uncontrolled grazing by sheep the survival of *Molinia* in hill grasslands is largely due to the selective grazing habits of this animal. In many communities the species is seldom eaten by sheep and, therefore, in contrast to *Calluna*, is unaffected by changes in overall grazing intensity. Being deciduous it escapes grazing during the winter when, on oligotrophic *Molinia* communities, grazing intensity is highest, while in summer it is neglected except some-times in spring, when the young leaves are eaten (Hunter, 1962a). On the other hand, if it is systematically defoliated, as under a system of controlled grazing, *Molinia* becomes much less abundant in the sward and, under suitable conditions, may be eliminated altogether (Milton, 1940, 1947). Observation suggests that *Molinia* is more readily grazed by cattle than by sheep and, where cattle grazing intensity is high, it is probable that the species is under greater biotic pressure than when only sheep are present.

In addition to the grassland types already mentioned, many *Nardus*-rich grasslands are also derived from *Calluna* heath, but in many cases the change to *Nardus* dominance has probably taken place secondarily after *Festuca—Agrostis* or *Festuca—Deschampsia* grassland has first replaced *Calluna*. *Nardus—Festuca—Deschampsia* type 2, however, can be formed directly from *Calluna* heath (cf. Smith, 1916, 1918; Fenton, 1933) and, from observations on one succession in south-east Scotland, it has been suggested that the development of *Nardus* dominance is an intermittent process related to the natural life-cycle of unburned *Calluna* or to the burning cycle. Many cycles might be required before *Calluna* was completely displaced and the succession might take several decades to complete (King, 1960). Mixed *Calluna/Nardus* communities can probably be regarded as intermediate stages in this succession.

Nardus stricta also invades some *Agrostis—Festuca* grasslands and grass-heaths and, although soil base status and moisture regime have an important influence, this succession is generally regarded as being biotically determined. There is some evidence that on acid grasslands, for example, uncontrolled sheep grazing is favourable, while protection from grazing is unfavourable to this succession (Heddle and Ogg, 1936; Harris, 1939) and, in view of the relatively unpalatable nature of *Nardus* (cf. Milton, 1953; Hunter, 1962a), it is probable that it may be favoured through selective avoidance by grazing animals in many community types, particularly those of acid and damp soils. It has been suggested that the spread of *Nardus* in pastures has taken place following the historical replacement of cattle, ponies and wether sheep by breeding ewes on hill grazings (cf. p. 192), the former group of animals being less selective in their grazing habits (Roberts, 1959; Fenton, 1937). Fenton (1937) has associated the prevalence of *Nardus* in hill pastures of the Southern Uplands with the high density of sheep in this region (cf. Fig. 30, p. 171).

There is no clear evidence, however, that the difference in selectivity between these animals is critical, and it is possible that uncontrolled grazing is generally favourable to *Nardus*, the spread of this species in suitable habitats dating from the clearance of the forest and the widespread introduction of domestic grazing animals. However, while these considerations may apply to acid grasslands and possibly also to mesotrophic grasslands on wet soils, there is evidence that the success of *Nardus* as an invader may be influenced by soil conditions or by the composition of the community invaded. For example in south-east Scotland in *Festuca—Agrostis* communities on acid soils about pH 4·9, *Nardus* was recorded as a dominant where moister conditions prevailed as a result of flushing but not on drier, unflushed brown forest soils (King, 1962a). However, in the same region on very dry, freely drained but slightly more acid soils, where *Festuca ovina* and *Deschampsia flexuosa* were dominant, *Nardus* was also able to invade successfully and become dominant. On poorly drained gley soils the species was most successful where pH was lowest, in agreement with the findings of Heddle and Ogg (1936) that irrigation with spring water reduced the *Nardus* content of pastures, the effect being attributed to the base content of the water. It is possible, therefore, that some community types exist, of which species-rich Agrosto—Festucetum may be one, in which the species may, for edaphic reasons, be unable to succeed even when grazing conditions are favourable. An alternative explanation, which is not excluded by the data of Heddle and Ogg (1936), is that the degree of selectivity in grazing, as with intensity and seasonal distribution, may vary between community types and, contrary to the situation on acid grasslands, on such stands may be unfavourable to the development of *Nardus*. Low comparative grazing intensities with a relatively high ratio of winter to summer grazing are characteristic of *Nardus*-rich communities, but existing data do not make it possible to distinguish between the effect of increasing amounts of *Nardus* on grazing intensity as compared with that of decreasing amounts of *Agrostis tenuis*, *Festuca rubra*, *Poa pratensis* and *Trifolium repens* (Hunter, 1962a).

Another species whose abundance has been particularly associated with the biotic factor is bracken (*Pteridium aquilinum*). This is a woodland relic and, after the disappearance of the forest canopy, might be expected to have increased at the expense of other communities although, as with *Nardus stricta*, the spread of *Pteridium* is also said to have been hastened by the replacement of cattle by sheep grazing. On deep freely drained soils, especially in the west, where perhaps freedom from frost may be a factor (cf. Watt, 1954), bracken is able to invade *Agrostis—Festuca* grassland and to suppress it completely. Frequently however, dominance by the fern is less complete and grassland survives beneath the canopy sometimes modified by an increase in the proportion of *Holcus mollis*. Whether all such *Pteridium*/grass communities are successional is open to doubt and it is possible that, owing to the operation of unfavourable factors, many are in a state of relative stability, the fern being unable to increase further in density. In such communities the distribution of sheep grazing differs from that in *Agrostis—Festuca* grassland, but the grazing intensity and the pastoral value of the community type is high (Hunter, 1962a). *Pteridium* also invades newly burned *Calluna* heath especially when regeneration is slow and may possibly invade unburned stands also if the competitive power of *Calluna* is reduced by some other factor such as grazing (cf. Watt, 1955).

Although the presence of *Pteridium aquilinum* is largely associated with anthropogenic factors, edaphic influences are also clearly apparent. The association of *Pteridium* with free draining soils and its absence from wet soils has long been recognised (Tansley, 1949) and, more recently, comparative measurements of oxygen diffusion rates in soils (Poel, 1961) give support to the view that soil aeration is an important ecological factor for this species. It can probably be accepted that the general absence of *Pteridium* from soils waterlogged throughout the year is related to the low oxygen diffusion rates in such soils. The minimum level of aeration and the effects of seasonal and annual variation are not known, however, and until more information is available it will not be possible to determine to what extent this factor limits the spread of *Pteridium* into other communities.

The successional relationships between some of the community types on free draining soils in Fig. 35 and between these and improved grasslands is indicated by the experimental results of Milton (1940, 1947) and of Heddle and Ogg (1936). Milton (1940, 1947) applied lime (Ca) and phosphate (P), both alone and in combination with potassium (K) and nitrogen (N) at three sites in Wales. Two of these were *Festuca—Agrostis* communities, one of the species-poor type and the other rather more rich in species. The third was a *Molinia-Festuca* community. At each site the treatments were applied to small fenced plots grazed periodically by sheep (controlled grazing) and to unfenced plots open to continuous uncontrolled grazing. Over a period of 16 years under conditions of controlled grazing, the effect of applying Ca alone or Ca, P, K, N in combination was to cause the following generalised succession to occur:

	Phase 1 ⟶	Phase 2 ⟶	Phase 3
Predominant spp.	Agrostis spp. Festuca spp. or Molinia caerulea Festuca spp.	Agrostis spp. mainly A. tenuis Festuca spp. mainly F. rubra	Poa pratensis P. trivialis Agrostis spp. mainly A. tenuis Festuca spp. mainly F. rubra Holcus lanatus Trifolium repens
Less abundant associates	Anthoxanthum odoratum Nardus stricta Sieglingia decumbens Luzula campestris Carex spp. Galium saxatile Potentilla erecta	Holcus lanatus Poa pratensis Poa trivialis Trifolium repens	Traces of: Lolium perenne Dactylis glomerata Phleum pratense, etc.

The principal feature in the early stages was the elimination of *Molinia* and an increase of *F. rubra* and *A. tenuis*, while in the later stages *Poa* spp. became predominant with varying amounts of *Agrostis*, *Festuca*, *Holcus* and *Trifolium* spp. The succession reached phase 3 most quickly on the site which was in the first place richest in species. Application of P or P, K, N, caused the succession only to reach an intermediate stage, while the control plots remained *Festuca—Agrostis* dominant as in phase 1. The size of the response to manurial applications was greatly influenced by the nature of the grazing regime, the response being greatly reduced where grazing was uncontrolled. Under these conditions the succession did not advance beyond phase 2 and reached this stage only on the Ca and Ca, P, K, N plots at one site. Elsewhere the swards remained at an early stage, essentially *Festuca—Agrostis* or *Molinia—Festuca—Agrostis* in type, although with considerable variations in the balance of species.

Heddle and Ogg (1936) observed floristic changes similar to the early stages of this succession following the flushing of acid grasslands by base-rich water, and similar trends were also observed by Robertson and Nicholson (1961) after the application of lime and phosphate to *Nardus—Festuca* and *Agrostis—Festuca* swards. These changes were recorded on pastures open to continuous uncontrolled grazing and, although this may have limited the size of the response, evidence of Heddle and Ogg (1936) suggested that, when grazing was excluded altogether, the response to flushing was even less than where it was permitted. This succession from grass-heath to *Poa*-rich grassland is clearly related to increasing values for a complex of edaphic factors including soil base status, potassium and phosphate level (cf. Sonneveld *et al.*, 1959), and to nitrogen supply as well as to the nature of the grazing regime. It is not possible to identify the effects of individual edaphic factors although the data of Bradshaw *et al.* (1958, 1960a, 1960b) indicate some of the factors which may be involved. The nature of the grazing regime is, however, of very great importance, edaphic effects being severely limited if the regime is unfavourable, while the response to grazing may be similarly limited by edaphic conditions. The effect of certain grazing regimes is to complement the effects of increasing soil base status, causing the succession to advance further than it otherwise would do under a different regime. Hunter (1962a) has suggested that this interaction of biotic and edaphic factors is partly responsible for the plant succession associated with the change from base rich soils with mull humus to base deficient mor conditions, as a result of leaching. Thus soil leaching tends to be accompanied by a decline in the comparative grazing intensity and the nitrogen cycle, already slowed by the pedological changes, is further reduced by this decline, the combined effect of both factors being reflected in the associated changes in the vegetation. This succession from mesotrophic vegetation supporting a high grazing intensity to oligotrophic vegetation with a low grazing intensity is, in its essentials, the reverse of the early part of the succession already discussed from species-poor *Festuca—Agrostis* to *Poa*-rich grassland. The situation may be summarised, therefore, in terms of a single reversible succession (Fig. 36) of which the principal components, soil type, vegetation and grazing interact to form "an ecological unity, a given soil type, being accompanied by a characteristic vegetation, grazed in a characteristic manner" (Hunter, 1962a).

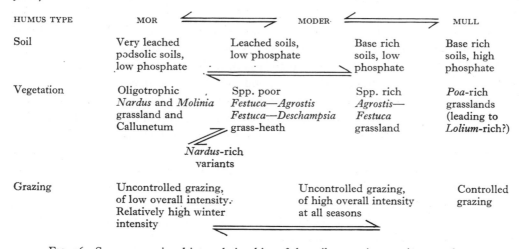

FIG. 36   Some successional interrelationships of the soil-vegetation-grazing complex.

SOME IMPLICATIONS OF VEGETATIONAL SUCCESSION

Soil development is influenced by climate, by the vegetation and its litter, and by the geological and lithological factors which determine the upper limit of nutrient availability. The major soil groups are linked with climate, but its effects on soil processes are modified by both parent material and by vegetation. Although vegetation shows relationships with climate, the species composition varies also with differences in soil within climatic zones, while different species in turn have their own influence on soil processes. There are in fact many instances of soil change following a change in vegetation (Handley, 1954).

The vegetational history of the Scottish uplands and the change from woodland to a variety of grassland and other communities reflects a fundamental change in the nature of the biological systems of these areas, the full implications of which are not yet clearly understood. This applies alike to changes induced by natural factors, such as climatic influences, and those resulting from alterations in the pattern of land usage. A shift in the balance within a complex of interacting factors which succession reflects, may bring about changes in both the rate and the nature of the associated processes. These can be studied and described, although it may not be possible to attach causal significance to a process, or to an organism, or sometimes even to indicate their precise roles in the organisation of the ecosystem.

Hydrological considerations

There is no evidence that rainfall on a regional scale is significantly influenced by vegetation (Hughes, 1949, and cf. Chapter 2), although the presence of forests may increase local precipitation through fog drip (Twomey, 1957; Geiger, 1959). In other respects the nature of plant cover often has a profound effect on the hydrological conditions of a site. These relationships have not been as widely studied in this country, as for example, in the United States. Coleman (1953), with special reference to conditions in that country, has ably reviewed the general relationships between vegetation and hydrology and reminds us of the characters inherent in all vegetation types which have a bearing on the water cycle: "Every vegetation cover is made up of three parts: the canopy of living and dead stems and leaves that stands clear of the soil, the accumulation of dead and decaying plant remains that lies on or near the soil surface and the living and dead roots and subsurface stems that permeate the soil." The kind of canopy determines the nature of rainfall interception, while the rooting characteristics may react on transpiration, thus having a bearing on water loss by evaporation. Indeed, the three phenomena of interception, transpiration and evaporation are all closely linked processes concerned with the loss of water to the atmosphere.

The first requirement for evaporation is the availability of water and the second a source of energy. Solar radiation is the source of energy and about 40 per cent. of the total income is used for evaporation.

Based on the physical consideration that total evaporation from all sources should be closely related to the intensity of incoming radiation, formulae have been worked out which enable estimates of evaporation to be derived from meteorological measurements (cf. Chapter 2, p. 31). Thus, Thornthwaite's (1948) derivation is based on temperature while Penman (1948) used data on air temperature, vapour pressure, windspeed and duration of bright sunshine. There is no evidence that, within certain prescribed limits, the *potential* evaporation from vegetation should vary with the nature of the plant cover but, when water input is limited, the *actual* evaporation is governed by plant and soil characteristics such as rooting depth, soil depth, permeability and water storage. In very dry conditions, for example, the deeper the root system, the longer the plant can continue to extract water from the soil and so satisfy, at least to some extent, the capacity for potential evaporation. In his analysis of evaporation processes in the forest, Rutter (1958) has suggested that deep-rooted trees may thus remove several more inches of water from the soil than either shallow-rooted ones, or heather and many grasses, although the whole subject of the relation between transpiration rate and the amount of water in the soil is controversial. Evaporation and related processes in grassland communities have received little detailed study, but in their work on interception Burgey and Pomeroy (1958) indicated the importance which may attach to the ratio of the non-transpiring to the transpiring surfaces in determining the magnitude of the net interception loss; a fact which may have important implications in comparisons between different grassland communities and other types of vegetation. The importance of plant species and the different soil characteristics which their growth induces is illustrated by Dimbleby's observations (1952b). This author showed that under pine and birch on mor and mull profiles respectively, although having a common origin, the pine soil dried out much more readily in a rainless period than the birch mull. The pine roots were restricted to the surface while in the mull soil the birch rooted more deeply and the profile showed a more uniform distribution of roots. The distribution of moisture was also more uniform and the moisture holding capacity was considerably enhanced.

Catchment studies have shown that stream flow increases following deforestation and in temperate regions this increase appears to be of the order of 5-15 per cent. (Bates and Henry, 1928; Lieberman and Hoover, 1951; Rutter, 1956). The presence of woodland also influences the distribution of run-off, the effect being a tendency to reduce peak rates of discharge. Although forests are generally held to be superior to grassland in this respect, much depends on the intensity of stocking, compaction of the surface, soil porosity, the rate of infiltration and the presence or absence of a partly decomposed surface mat of plant remains. It is worth noting that a similar effect on run-off pattern to that resulting from deforestation has been shown to occur on high-level blanket bog, bearing abundant *Sphagnum* and heather (Conway, 1960), in response to draining and burning. On the two catchments exposed to these treatments, peak rates of discharge were greater than on the undisturbed catchments and flow rates were considerably more sensitive to fluctuations in rainfall.

Vegetation may, therefore, have a direct bearing on both the pattern and the rate of water disposal from a site and the distribution of water within the vegetation—soil complex and these factors must be considered in relation to the chemical and biological processes within it.

Soil biology

Pearsall (1950b) remarks that, ". . . generally in the uplands the process of leaching can only be retarded and not completely stayed". This leads to a gradual loss of nutrients in the surface soil where leaching tends to proceed more rapidly than weathering (cf.

Chapter 2). It is generally accepted that, in a variety of ways, changes in plant cover and in associated land use have influenced the rate of leaching and have, therefore, brought about changes in the distribution of the principal groups of upland soils, areas of former brown forest soils now showing podsolic features in varying degrees (Crompton, 1958). A most important feature in soil degradation is the change-over from mull to mor conditions. In some cases there may be a delicate balance between these two humus types and although many soil changes are not easily reversed, mull and mor represent components of a dynamic system which is to a large extent reversible (Handley, 1954).

Dimbleby (1952a) cited an example in north-east Yorkshire of the previous existence of deciduous forest on what is now *Calluna* moorland and demonstrated (Dimbleby, 1952b) that birch establishment resulted in the development of a richer soil fauna and mull characteristics in the podsolised profile. Rennie (1955, 1957) claimed, however, that the requirement of forest trees for calcium is heavy and that 60-70 years growth of birch fails to bring about more than a trivial amount of soil improvement. On the basis of soil nutrient content he claimed that after more than 2000 years of podsolisation the site may be capable only of providing sufficient minerals for early growth.

The mor soil has a characteristically high degree of acidity and nitrates are usually absent, nitrogen breakdown generally terminating in the production of ammonia compounds. This reflects the contrasting nature of the nitrogen transformations in mor as compared with mull, such processes presumably being influenced by a reduction in the number of suitable bacteria (Pearsall, 1950b). The decomposition of the organic matter in the mor of the podsolic soil is generally considered to be carried out predominantly by fungi while in the brown forest soil the bacteria are held to be primarily concerned (Fenton, 1947; Witkamp and van der Drift, 1961). In discussing the micro-organisms of mull and mor, however, Handley (1954) points out that no sharp differentiation can be made, such as bacteria being restricted to mull and fungi to mor. Acidity develops not only as a result of removal of bases through leaching but is apparently intensified through the metabolic processes of at least some fungi. Under laboratory conditions, acid formation has been shown to be considerably more active on base deficient media (Aristevskoya, 1956).

The nature and relationships of soil fauna in the mull⇄mor dynamic system have been described by many authors and discussed in reviews by Fenton (1947), Handley (1954), Murphy (1955) and Satchell (1958). Faunistic successions have been cited by Murphy (1955), while Cragg (1961) quotes data from several studies on high-level Pennine soils to show that the contrasting densities and distribution of various animal groups among four plant communities and bare peat, represent a declining series in terms of biological activity as follows:

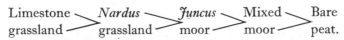

Limestone ⇄ *Nardus* ⇄ *Juncus* ⇄ Mixed ⇄ Bare
grassland   grassland   moor   moor   peat.

Although total biomass declined, the main animal groups responded in various ways to the different conditions. Thus, the Enchytraeidae showed their lowest biomass in limestone grassland and in bare peat and their highest values in the mixed mineral and peat soils of *Juncus squarrosus* moor and *Nardus* grassland. The Lumbricidae were found to have a considerable biomass as well as density in limestone grassland, but very low or negligible densities in other habitats. The same author, quoting Svendsen (1957), draws attention to the relative proportions of four species of Lumbricids found aggregated in sheep dung on alluvial grassland, a *Juncus effusus* community and on mixed moor. Earthworms react not only to major soil and vegetation differences but, as shown by work on grazed and ungrazed maritime grassland (Boyd, 1957), they may react fairly quickly to changes of a much lower order. In addition to the sequence described by Cragg, it is known that in degrading mull soils the population of earthworms declines (Crompton, 1953). Although marked differences in species distribution occur between brown forest soils and podsolic types (Bornebusch, 1930), Handley (1954) suggests that the litter of mor-forming plant species is either nutritionally unsuitable, or inadequate for earthworms or, if preliminary bacterial acitivity is necessary before the ingestion of plant material, that this may not occur in mor. The suggestion of a nutritional limitation for earthworms in mor is, in fact, supported by recent work (Satchell, 1962) on the nitrogen turnover in woodland mull by the large worm *Lumbricus terrestris*. Satchell estimates an annual turnover of about 100 kg./ha. and points out that this heavy demand in relation to the nitrogen returned in the litter is indicative of the probable intense competition for food amongst the soil fauna. The effect of pH, however, is probably of greater significance in determining both the occurrence of earthworms and the association of different species with various soil conditions, for Laverack (1960) has shown, in laboratory experiments, that markedly different threshold responses are exhibited by three species. Thus, *Allolobophora longa* rejected a pH of 4·4, *L. terrestris*, 4·2 and *L. rubellus* a pH of 3·8. These findings throw further light on the reasons for the different species distributions encountered in the field and the response of a given species to pedological changes which various authors have reported.

There is increasing evidence of the ecological importance of earthworms in soil processes (Edwards and Heath, 1962) not only through their direct influence on decomposition but also through their interactions on other organisms (Satchell, 1958; Ghilarov, 1962). Moreover, on the basis of work by Bloomfield (1955), Satchell (1958) suggests that earthworms may counteract the process of podsolisation through the production of colloidal material from soil and organic matter and the resorption by this of sesquioxides mobilised by leaf leachates. Recent work by Bocock and Gilbert (1957) and Witkamp and van der Drift (1961) on the disappearance of leaf litter on contrasting soils under woodland, and also studies of sheep dung decomposition on grazed communities on mull and mor (White, 1960), show clearly the kind of differences in the rate and nature of organic residue disposal associated with faunal activity and other agencies in the soil surface layers under different intensities of podsolic influences. Indeed, one of the important functions of the larger soil animals in mull is considered to be the physical mixing of soil constituents which their activity brings about.

Soil fauna are obviously intimately concerned with soil processes and some

indication of their significance may be judged by Cragg's (1961) finding on Pennine soils
that, in terms of biomass, the sheep represent only a small proportion of the total annual
production in moorland areas. Nevertheless, it is asserted (Handley, 1954) that soil
animals cannot be regarded as primary determinants, as the nature of the vegetable
debris controls the fauna. Handley considers that the process of soil development can
only be understood in terms of a multi-variable system, but Murphy (1955) suggests that
in cases of mor turning to mull there is good evidence of a step by step process, a change
of vegetation followed by a change in fauna, but the latter is not necessarily incidental to
the process and "there would seem to be an amalgam of these two factors, a mutualism
with the proviso that the vegetative change must come first".

Nutrient balance

In every biological system there is a circulation of nitrogen and other mineral
nutrients through the soil and plant components and their faunal associates. The uptake
of nutrients by plants and intake of food by animals is a more or less continuous
process and similarly, materials of plant and animal origin are being continuously
returned to the soil through the litter and in animal excreta. In the natural ecosystem the
death and eventual decay of whole plants and animal bodies releases nutrients temporarily
immobilised in them and so completes the cycle. Some of the agents associated with this
cycle, or series of cycles, have already been discussed, but the various pathways and
interactions are numerous and complex and in the present state of knowledge the
integrated processes of any given ecosystem cannot be comprehensively portrayed. In
relation to woodland, however, the kind of problems which are raised have been clearly
defined in a recent report of the Nature Conservancy (1960) from which the following
diagram is taken (Fig. 37).

In any given ecosystem, whether woodland, grazing or aquatic, the basic problems
are essentially the same and, under management by man to provide a harvest of plant or
animal products, the natural balance is upset; the system being exposed to considerably
greater demands on the total fund of nutrients. Thus, the requirements for scientific
management can only be defined with any certainty when the main parameters are known.

No attempt will be made to construct a balance sheet for a particular site under
natural conditions or to indicate the deviations which take place as soil and plant succession proceeds. A brief account of the magnitude of selected parameters, however, will
serve to illustrate the problem.

Nutrients move into the active biological system in precipitation, through the
fixation of atmospheric nitrogen and through the weathering of soil minerals, and are
lost from it principally through run-off and leaching. Chemical processes in the soil may
also influence the balance between effective gain or loss by rendering certain elements
available or unavailable to the plant. It is difficult, at present, to ascribe realistic values to
these processes although limited data on rainfall input (Egnér and Eriksson, 1955-60) is
of interest. This shows a wide variation over the British Isles, the actual input being

determined by the amount of rainfall and proximity to the sea and possibly by other factors as well. An indication of the range of variation in Scotland in terms of calcium input is given by the mean figures for the two-year period 1959-1960 in samples collected

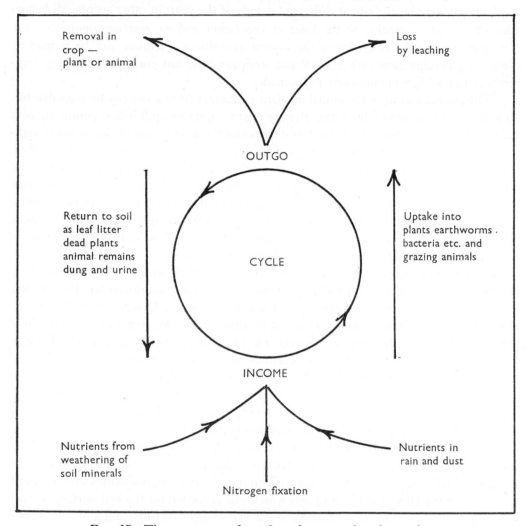

FIG. 37   The movement of nutrient elements other than carbon, hydrogen and oxygen through the ecosystem. (Adapted from *Report of the Nature Conservancy*, 1960, p. 60.)

at Eskdalemuir and Stornoway (Robertson, Crisp and Nicholson, 1962; Egnér and Eriksson, 1955-60).

		Rainfall		Calcium	
		(mm.)	(in.)	(kg./ha.)	(lb./acre)
Eskdalemuir	. .	1638	64·5	6·5	5·8
Stornoway	. .	1150	45·3	25·3	22·6

The fate of nutrients brought in by rain is likely to be determined by many factors such as the extent of vegetation cover, the chemical and biological nature of the surface, soil horizons, soil porosity, the characteristics of run-off and the physiological activity of plants growing on the site at different periods of the year; in other words, all factors which may vary according to the kind of vegetation and its reaction upon the soil. Net accession, or the efficiency of the system in nutrient retention, can be judged by comparing precipitation with run-off and drainage loss, but current data is too fragmentary to enable generalisations to be made.

The annual loss through animal or plant extraction from a site can be considerable. In a review of European literature Rennie (1955, 1957) has published comprehensive data on the chemical composition of forest trees and the distribution of elements throughout the various plant parts. On the basis of his estimates, a site growing pines for timber, assuming clear felling, would lose on the average, 4·3 kg. of calcium and 0·37 kg. of phosphorus per hectare per annum (3·8 lb. Ca and 0·33 lb. P per acre) over a 100-year period. By comparing such figures with the quantities of nutrients present in poor upland soils of the type commonly afforested, Rennie concludes that timber production on these soils, without a compensating addition of nutrients, is bound to lead to degeneration of the soil and its ultimate exhaustion for cropping purposes.

A calculation of nutrient loss in terms of Ca and P through the removal of sheep products under similar conditions provides an interesting comparison. The average annual removal at a grazing intensity of 1 sheep per 1·6 ha. (4 acres) would be of the order of 0·22 kg. of calcium and 0·11 kg. of phosphorus per ha. (0·2 lb. Ca and 0·1 lb. P per acre). Although the contrast between the two systems is striking, it is difficult to evaluate the different ecological implications of the systems without more detailed knowledge of the overall net gains and losses incurred under the two forms of use. It should also be emphasised that only calcium and phosphorus have been compared and no attempt has been made to evaluate the nitrogen balance which is likely to be critical and of particular significance where animal products are removed.

Under pasture management in large grazing units other factors are also involved. For example, heather burning is practised to enable a level of animal output to be maintained which would be impossible without it at the stocking intensities which prevail. Considering the large quantities of ash which are deposited on the soil surface at each burn, it is only necessary to postulate a small percentage loss following a burn to arrive at an annual average loss to the system which exceeds that due to animal production. On a soil on which the three communities, *Agrostis—Festuca*, *Calluna*, and dense *Pteridium* are interchangeable it is clear that the removal of nutrients via the animal declines from the first to the last, while in terms of total nutrient loss under management for sheep pasture, the loss from *Calluna* grazings may well exceed that from the more heavily grazed *Agrostis—Festuca* grasslands. Thus, the management technique may give rise to greater nutrient loss than animal output in itself, and it is at least arguable that the net loss may be drastically reduced, despite the increased rate of animal removal, through converting heath to grassland on suitable soils, by raising the grazing intensity, and thus eliminating burning. Similarly, although the incursion of bracken is generally deplored, it may represent in ecological terms a desirable change arresting the process of soil degradation.

There is increasing evidence that in the planning of land use programmes and, in particular, for land of inherent low fertility, further work is necessary on the conception of soil-plant-animal systems not only from the standpoint of their impact on internal processes but also from the point of view of their relative efficiencies in controlling the nutrient input:output ratio in relation to all sources of gain and loss. Furthermore, it is often too readily assumed that the use of the forest zone for animal production is unsound land usage, but many of the factors on which such a conclusion is based may be the result of current management practice rather than the effects of sheep grazing *per se*. The lack of grazing control inherent in present practice and the need for frequent burning results in vegetational trends of an undesirable kind with reactions throughout the entire system.

Considerations of various kinds, embracing chemical and biological activity in the soil, grazing behaviour and management effects, throw some light on the kind of relationships which may exist in the forest zone not only historically between woodland and grassland but between interchangeable communities having a common origin and existing today in juxtaposition. It is clear that any form of vegetation management has a distinct bearing on vegetation and soil processes, indeed on a whole range of ecological relationships within the system, and the nature of these should be understood in any system where natural vegetation is utilised or controlled. The changes induced by forest destruction were undoubtedly profound but the effect of subsequent practices in deforested areas may have had an ecological significance of a comparable magnitude.

REFERENCES

ADAMSON, R. S.   1918   On the relationships of some associations of the Southern Pennines, *J. Ecol.*, **6**, 97-109.

AGNEW, A. D. Q.   1916   The ecology of *Juncus effusus* L. in North Wales. *J. Ecol.*, **49**, 83-102.

ANON.   1956   *Inventory of the Ancient and Historical Monuments of Roxburghshire.* H.M.S.O., Edinburgh.

ANON.   1837   *Liber Sancte Marie de Melros*, ed. C. Innes. Edinburgh.

ARISTEVSKOYA, T. V.   1956   The role of micro-organisms in the podsol forming process. *6th Int. Congr. Soil Sci.*, Moscow, 40-45.

ASPREY, G. F.   1947   The vegetation of the islands of Canna and Sanday, Inverness-shire. *J. Ecol.*, **34**, 182-193.

BALME, O. E.   1953   Edaphic and vegetational zoning on the Carboniferous limestone of the Derbyshire dales. *J. Ecol.*, **41**, 331-344.

BARRETT-HAMILTON, GERALD, E. H.   1910-21   *A history of British mammals.* Pt. 10, 184-185. London.

O

BATES, C. G. and HENRY, A. J. 1928 Forest and stream-flow experiment at Wagon Wheel Gap, Colorado. *Mon. Weath. Rev., Suppl. Wash.*, **30**, 1-79.

BLOOMFIELD, C. 1955 A study of podsolisation VI. The immobilisation of iron and aluminium. *J. Soil Sci.*, **6**, 284-292.

BÖCHER, T. W. 1949 Racial divergences in *Prunella vulgaris* in relation to habitat and climate. *New Phytol.*, **48**, 285-314.

BOCOCK, K. L. and GILBERT, O. J. W. 1957 The disappearance of leaf litter under different woodland conditions. *Plant & Soil*, **9**, 179-185.

BORNEBUSCH, C. H. 1930 The fauna of the forest soil. Skovbundens dyseverden. *Forstl. Forsøgsvr. Dan.*, **11**, 1-224. (In Fenton 1947. Original paper not consulted).

BOULET, L. J. 1939 *The ecology of a Welsh mountain sheep walk.* Ph.D. Thesis. University College of Wales, Aberystwyth.

BOYD, J. MORTON 1957 Comparative aspects of the ecology of Lumbricidae on grazed and ungrazed natural maritime grassland. *Oikos*, **8**, 107-121.

BRADSHAW, A. D., LODGE, R. W., JOWETT, D. and CHADWICK, M. J. 1958 Experimental investigations into the mineral nutrition of several grass species. Part I. Calcium level. *J. Ecol.*, **46**, 749-757.
1960a Part II. pH and Calcium level. *J. Ecol.*, **48**, 143-150.

BRADSHAW, A. D., CHADWICK, M. J, JOWETT, D., LODGE, R. W. and SNAYDON, R. W. 1960b Experimental investigations into the mineral nutrition of several grass species. Part III. Phosphate level. *J. Ecol.*, **48**, 631-637.

BRAY, J. R. and CURTIS, J. T. 1957 An ordination of the upland forest communities of southern Wisconsin. *Ecol. Monog.*, **27**, 325-350.

BURGEY, R. H. and POMEROY, C. R. 1958 Interception losses in grassy vegetation. *Trans. Amer. geophys. Un.*, **39**, 1095-1100.

CHADWICK, M. J. 1960 *Nardus stricta* L. in *Biol. Flora Br. Isles, J. Ecol.*, **48**, 255-268.

CHARLES, W. N. 1956 The effects of a vole plague in the Carron valley, Stirlingshire. *Scot. For.*, **10**, 201-204.
1962 Private communication.

COLEMAN, E. A. 1953 *Vegetation and Watershed Management.* New York.

CONWAY, V. M. and MILLAR, A. 1960 The hydrology of some small peat-covered catchments in the Northern Pennines. *J. Inst. Wat. Engrs.*, **14**, 415-425.

CRAGG, J. B. 1961 Some aspects of the ecology of moorland animals. *J. Ecol.*, **49**, 477-506.

CRAMPTON, C. B. 1911 *The Vegetation of Caithness in relation to the Geology.* Cambridge.

CROMPTON, E. 1953 Grow the soil to grow the grass: Some pedological aspects of marginal land improvement. *Agriculture, Lond.*, **60**, 301-308.
1958 Hill soils and their production potential. *J. Brit. Grassl. Soc.*, **13**, 229-237.

CROSS, C. 1962 Unpublished data.

DARLING, F. FRASER 1937 *A herd of Red deer.* Oxford.
1955 *West Highland Survey.* Oxford.

DIMBLEBY, G. W.   1952a The historical status of moorland in north-east Yorkshire. *New Phytol.*, **51**, 350-354.

1952b Soil regeneration on the north-east Yorkshire moors. *J. Ecol.*, **40**, 331-341.

DOUGLAS, R.   1798 *General view of the Agriculture of Roxburgh and Selkirk.* Edinburgh.

EDWARDS, C. A. and   1962 The role of soil animals in breakdown of leaf material. *Proc.*
HEATH, G. W.   *Colloquium on soil fauna, soil microflora and their relationships,* 305-312. Oosterbeek.

EGNÉR, HANS and   1955-60 Notes on data on the chemical composition of air and precipi-
ERIKSSON, ERIK   tation. *Tellus,* **7-12**.

ELTON, C.   1942 *Voles, Mice & Lemmings.* Oxford.

FARROW, E. PICKWORTH 1916 On the ecology of the vegetation of Breckland. II. Factors relating to the relative distributions of *Calluna* heath & grass heath in Breckland. *J. Ecol.*, **4**, 57-64.

FENTON, E. W.   1933 The vegetation of an upland area (Boghall Glen, Midlothian). *Scot. geogr. Mag.*, **49**, 331-354.

1937 Influence of sheep on the vegetation of hill grazings in Scotland *J. Ecol.*, **25**, 424-430.

FENTON, G. R.   1947 The soil fauna: with special reference to the ecosystem of forest soil. *J. Anim. Ecol.*, **16**, 76-93.

FLUX, JOHN F. C.   1962 *The ecology of the Scottish mountain hare,* Lepus timidus scoticus, *Hilzheimer.* Ph.D. Thesis. University of Aberdeen.

FRANKLIN, T. B.   1952 *A History of Scottish Farming.* Edinburgh.

GAFFNEY, V.   1959 Summer sheilings. *Scot. Hist. Rev.*, **38**, 20-35.

GEIGER, RUDOLF   1959 *The climate near the ground.* Cambridge, Mass. U.S.A.

GHILAROV, M. S.   1962 On the interrelations between soil-dwelling invertebrates & soil micro-organisms. *Proc. Colloquium on soil fauna, soil microflora & their relationships,* 177-181. Oosterbeek.

GRANT, S. A. and   1962 Ecotypic differentiation of *Calluna vulgaris* in relation to
HUNTER, R. F.   altitude. *New Phytol.*, **61**, 44-55.

GRAY, M.   1957 *The Highland Economy* 1750-1850. Edinburgh.

HANDLEY, W. R. C.   1954 Mull and mor formation in relation to forest soils. *Bull.* For. *Comm. (Lond.),* **23**.

HARBERD, D. J.   1961 The case for extensive rather than intensive sampling in genecology. *New Phytol.*, **60**, 325-338.

1962 Application of a multivariate technique to ecological survey. *J. Ecol.*, **50**, 1-17.

HARPER, P. C.   1962 The soils & vegetation of Lammermuir. *J. Ecol.*, **50**, 35-51.

HARRIS, T. M.   1939 Notes on a fencing experiment. *J. Ecol.*, **27**, 383.

HEDDLE, R. G. and   1936 Irrigation experiments on a Scottish hill pasture. *J. Ecol.*, **24**,
OGG, W. G.   220-231.

HEWSON, R.   1955 The mountain hare in the Scottish islands. *Scot. Nat.*, **67**, 52-60.

1962 Food & feeding habits of the mountain hare, *Lepus timidus scoticus,* Hilzheimer. *Proc. zool. Soc., Lond.*, **139**, 415-426.

HUGHES, J. F.   1949   The influence of forests on climate and water supply. *For. Abstr.*, **11**, 145-153; 283-292.

HUGHES, R. E.   1958   Sheep population and environment in Snowdonia. (N. Wales). *J. Ecol.*, **46**, 169-190.

HUME, C. W.   1939   The rabbit menace. *Emp. J. Exp. Agric.*, **7**, 132-138.

HUNTER, R. F.   1954   The grazing of hill pasture sward types. *J. Brit. Grassl. Soc.*, **9**, 195-208.

    1961   Sheep stocking rates on Scottish hill pastures; Unpublished.

    1962a   Hill sheep and their pasture, a study of sheep-grazing in South-east Scotland. *J. Ecol.*, **50**, 651-680.

    1962b   Home range behaviour in hill sheep. In *Grazing* (ed. D. J. Crisp); Proc. 3rd symposium on grazing. Brit. Ecol. Soc., Bangor.

JEFFERIES, T. A.   1915   Ecology of the purple heath grass (*Molinia caerulea*) *J. Ecol.*, **3**, 93-109.

KING, J.   1960   Observations on the seedling establishment and growth of *Nardus stricta* in burned Callunetum. *J. Ecol.*, **48**, 667-677.

    1962a   The *Festuca—Agrostis* grassland complex in S.E. Scotland. *J. Ecol.*, **50**, 321-355.

    1962b   Unpublished data.

    1963   Ecotypic differentiation in *Trifolium repens. Plant & Soil*, **18**, 221-224.

LAVERACK, M. S.   1961   Tactile and chemical perception in earthworms—II Responses to acid pH solutions. *Comp. biochem. physiol.*, **2**, 22-34.

LIEBERMAN, J. A. and HOOVER, M. D.   1951   Stream-flow frequency changes on Coweeta experimental watersheds. *Trans. Amer. geophys. Un.*, **32**, 72-76.

LINTON, ANDREW   1918   *The grazing of hill pastures.* Lewis & Co. Selkirk.

McMILLAN, C.   1960   Ecotypes and community function. *Amer. Nat.*, **94**, 245-255.

McVEAN, D. N.   1961   Flora and vegetation of the islands of St. Kilda & North Rona in 1958. *J. Ecol.*, **49**, 39-54.

McVEAN, D. N. and RATCLIFFE, D. A.   1962   *Plant Communities of the Scottish Highlands.* H.M.S.O., London.

MILTON, W. E. J.   1940   The effect of manuring, grazing and cutting on the yield, botanical and chemical composition of natural hill pastures. I Yield & Botanical Section. *J. Ecol.*, **28**, 326-356.

    1953   The palatability of herbage on undeveloped grasslands in West-central Wales. *Emp. J. Exp. Agric.*, **21**, 116-122.

MILTON, W. E. J. and DAVIES, R. O.   1947   The Yield, Botanical & Chemical composition of natural hill herbage under manuring, controlled grazing and hay conditions. I Yield & Botanical Section. *J. Ecol.*, **35**, 65-95.

MITCHELL, B. D. and JARVIS, R. A.   1956   *The Soils of the Country round Kilmarnock.* Edinburgh.

MOSS, C. E.   1913   *Vegetation of the Peak District.* Cambridge.

MUIR, A. and FRASER, G. K.   1939/40   Soils & vegetation of the Bin and Clashindarroch Forests. *Trans. Roy. Soc. Edinb.*, **60**, 233-341.

MURPHY, P. W.   1955   Ecology of the fauna of forest soils. In *Soil Zoology*. (Ed. D. K. McE. Kevan.) London.

NICHOLSON, I. A. and ROBERTSON, R. A.   1958   Observations on the ecology of an upland grazing in N.E. Scotland with special reference to Callunetum. *J. Ecol.*, **46**, 239-270.

PEARSALL, W. H.   1950a   Report of Meeting of British Ecological Society. *J. Ecol.*, **38**, 176.

1950b   *Mountains and Moorlands*. London.

PEARSALL, W. H. and PENNINGTON, W.   1947   Ecological History of the English Lake District. *J. Ecol.*, **34**, 137-148.

PENMAN, H. L.   1948   Natural evaporation from open water, bare soil and grass. *Proc. Roy. Soc.*, **A193**, 120-145.

POEL, L. W.   1961   Soil aeration as a limiting factor in the growth of *Pteridium aquilinum*. *J. Ecol.*, **49**, 107-111.

POORE, M. E. D.   1955   The use of phytosociological methods in ecological investigations. III. Practical applications. *J. Ecol.*, **43**, 606-651.

1956   The use of phytosociological methods in Ecological investigations. IV. General discussion of phytosociological problems. *J. Ecol.*, **44**, 28-50.

POORE, M. E. D. and ROBERTSON, V. C.   1948   The vegetation of St. Kilda in 1948 with an appendix by H. Godwin. *J. Ecol.*, **37**, 82-99.

RAGG, J. M.   1960   *The Soils of the Country round Kelso & Lauder*. Edinburgh.

RATCLIFFE, D. A.   1959   The vegetation of the Carneddau, North Wales. I Grasslands, heaths and bogs. *J. Ecol.*, **47**, 371-413.

RENNIE, PETER J.   1955   The uptake of nutrients by mature forest growth. *Plant & Soil*, **7**, 49-95.

1957   The uptake of nutrients by timber forest and its importance to to timber production in Britain. *Quart. J. For.*, **51**, 101-115.

Report of the Committee on Hill Sheep Farming in Scotland (1944) H.M.S.O. Edinburgh.

Report of the Nature Conservancy for the year ended 30th September, 1960. H.M.S.O. London.

Report of the Red Deer Commission, 1960. H.M.S.O. Edinburgh.

RITCHIE, JAMES   1920   *The influence of man on animal life in Scotland*. Cambridge.

1925   Increase of mountain hare in the Scottish lowlands. *Scot. Nat.*, 47-48.

1929   The spread of the mountain hare in the Scottish lowlands and border country. *Scot. Nat.*, 169-175.

ROBERTS, R. A.   1959   The ecology of human occupation and land use in Snowdonia. *J. Ecol.*, **47**, 317-323.

ROBERTSON, G.   1810   *A general review of the agriculture of the county of Kincardineshire; or, the Mearns*. London.

ROBERTSON, R. A., CRISP, D. J. and NICHOLSON, I. A.   1962   *Chemical composition of precipitation in Great Britain*. Unpublished compilation of data.

ROBERTSON, R. A. and NICHOLSON, I. A.   1961   The response of some hill pasture types to lime and phosphate. *J. Brit. Grassl. Soc.*, **16**, 117-125.

RUTTER, A. J.   1958   The effects of afforestation on rainfall and run-off. *J. Inst. Pub. Health Eng. July*, 119-138.

SATCHELL, J. E.   1958   Earthworm biology & soil fertility. *Soils & Fertilisers*, **21**, 209-219.

                            1962   Nitrogen turnover by a woodland population of *Lumbricus terrestris. Proc. Colloquium on soil fauna, soil microflora and their relationships*, 238-243. Oosterbeek.

SMITH, R.   1900a   Botanical Survey of Scotland. I Edinburgh district. *Scot. geogr. Mag.*, **16**, 385-415.

                           1900b   Botanical Survey of Scotland. II North Perthshire district. *Scot. geogr. Mag.*, **16**, 441-467.

SMITH, R. and W. G.   1905   Botanical Survey of Scotland. II & IV Forfar and Fife. *Scot. geogr. Mag.*, **21**, 4-23 & 57-83.

SMITH W. G.   1911   In *Types of British Vegetation*. Grass moor association, 282-286; Arctic-alpine vegetation, 288-329. I (ed. A. G. Tansley). Cambridge.

                            1916   *Heather & Heather burning with special reference to sheep grazings.* Report of Enquiry 1912-15 Unpublished. Edinburgh & East of Scotland College of Agriculture.

                            1918   Distribution of *Nardus stricta* in relation to peat. *J. Ecol.*, **6**, 1-13.

SNAYDON, R. W.   1961   *Population differentiation in* Trifolium repens. Ph.D. Thesis. University of Wales.

SNAYDON, R. W. and   1961   Differential response to calcium within the species *Festuca*
  BRADSHAW, A. D.   *ovina* L. *New Phytol.*, **60**, 219-234.

SONNEVELD, F.,   1959   Influence of phosphate on the botanical composition and on the
  KRUIJNE, A. A. &   grade of quality of herbage. *Neth. Journ. Agric. Sci.*, **7**, 40-50.
  DE VRIES, D. M.

SPENCE, D. H. N.   1960   Studies on the vegetation of Shetland. III Scrub in Shetland and in South Uist, Outer Hebrides. *J. Ecol.*, **48**, 73-95.

STEVEN, H. M. and   1959   *The Native Pinewoods of Scotland*. Edinburgh.
  CARLISLE, A.

SUMMERHAYES, V. S.   1941   The effect of voles (*Microtus agrestis*) on vegetation. *J. Ecol.*, **29**, 14-48.

SVENDSEN, J. A.   1957   The distribution of Lumbricidae in an area of Pennine moorland. *J. Anim. Ecol.*, **26**, 411-421.

SYMON, J. A.   1951   The hill grazing output of Scotland. Part I. *Scot. Agric.*, **31**, 109-112.

                            1959   *Scottish Farming Past & Present*. Edinburgh.

TANSLEY, A. G.   1949   *The British Islands and their Vegetation*. Cambridge.

THOMPSON, V. H. and   1956   *The Rabbit*. London.
  WORDEN, A. N.

THORNTHWAITE, C. W.   1948   An approach towards a rational classification of climate. *Geogr. Rev.*, **38**, 55-94.

TROW-SMITH, R.   1957   *A History of British Livestock Husbandry* 1700-1900. London.

TURESSON, G.   1922   The genotypical response of the plant species to the habitat. *Hereditas*, **3**, 211-250.

TWOMEY, S.   1957   Precipitation by direct interception of cloud water. *Weather*, **12**, 120-122.

WALKER, J.   1812   *An Economical History of the Hebrides & Highlands of Scotland.* Vol: I. Edinburgh.

WATSON, P. J. and   1956   Reflections on hill land improvement. *Herb. Abstr.*, **26**, 137-145.
GREGOR, J. W.

WATT, A. S.   1954   Contributions to the ecology of bracken (*Pteridium aquilinum*). VI Frost & the advance & retreat of bracken. *New Phytol.*, **43**, 117-130.

WATT, A. S.   1955   Bracken versus heather, a study in plant sociology. *J. Ecol.*, **43** 490-506.

WHITE, E.   1960   The distribution and subsequent disappearance of sheep dung on Pennine moorland. *J. Anim. Ecol.*, **29**, 243-250.

WITKAMP, M. and   1961   Breakdown of forest litter in relation to environmental factors. *Plant & Soil*, **15**, 295-311.
DRIFT, J. VAN DER

TABLE 19

Floristic Composition of Community Types 1-5 in Terms of Mean
Cover-Abundance (Domin) and Constancy or Presence Classes 1-10

Designation: Type		1		2		3		4		5	
Dominants		Molinia Festuca Deschampsia		Nardus Festuca Deschampsia		Festuca Deschampsia (Nardus)		Agrostis Festuca Poa		Festuca Agrostis	
No. of stands		10		14		18		8		10	
Sample area		16–64 sq. m.		32 sq. m.		32 sq. m.		32 sq. m.		32 sq. m.	
Altitude		15–437 m. 50–1500 ft.		305–610 m. 1000–2000 ft.		152–437 m. 500–1500 ft.		305–487 m. 1000–1600 ft.		107–381 m. 350–1250 ft.	
Soil profile type*		PP PGP PG		PP PGP		P OSk OB		OSk OB		OB OSk	
Drainage class†		i–p		f–p		vf–i		vf–f		f–i	
		Pres.	Mean c–a	Const.	Mean c–a	Const.	Mean c–a	Const.	Mean c–a	Const.	Mean c–a
Calluna vulgaris		4	0·8	5	0·9	6	1·2	...	...	7	2·2
Empetrum nigrum		...	...	2	0·3	2	0·3	...	...	...	...
Erica cinerea		...	...	...	...	...	...	...	...	3	1·0
E. tetralix		2	0·6	1	0·2	...	...	...	...	1	0·5
Helianthemum chamaecistus		...	...	...	...	...	...	...	...	3	0·7
Salix repens		...	...	...	...	...	...	...	...	1	0·2
Sorbus aucuparia		...	...	...	...	1	0·1	...	...	...	...
Vaccinium myrtillus		9	2·9	9	2·9	9	3·5	...	...	5	1·4
V. vitis-idaea		...	...	3	0·3	...	...	...	...	2	0·2
Blechnum spicant		...	...	2	0·4	3	0·7	...	...	1	0·3
Lycopodium clavatum		...	...	...	...	...	...	...	...	3	0·3
Pteridium aquilinum		1	0·1	...	...	1	0·2	...	...	4	1·5
Selaginella selaginoides		...	...	...	...	1	0·1	...	...	...	...
Thelypteris limbosperma		...	...	...	...	1	0·3	...	...	...	...
Agrostis canina		9	3·1	10	5·1	10	5·3	8	1·8	10	4·8
A. tenuis		3	0·3	8	2·7	10	4·4	10	8·7	10	5·9
Anthoxanthum odoratum		6	1·6	7	3·3	10	3·9	10	2·8	10	3·2
Deschampsia cespitosa		...	...	...	...	2	0·3	6	2·3	1	0·2
D. flexuosa		10	6·0	10	6·0	10	5·8	6	1·8	6	2·0
Festuca ovina		10	6·8	10	7·7	10	7·2	10	6·6	10	8·3
F. rubra		...	...	3	0·5	1	0·1	9	4·6	7	2·1
Helictotrichon pratense		...	...	...	...	1	0·1	...	...	2	0·4
H. pubescens		...	...	...	...	...	...	...	...	2	0·4
Holcus lanatus		1	0·2	...	...	...	...	4	2·6	2	0·4
H. mollis		...	...	...	...	1	0·3	3	1·3	1	0·1
Molinia caerulea		10	9·0	3	0·9	5	1·3	...	...	1	0·2
Nardus stricta		7	3·1	10	8·8	8	4·6	4	1·0	8	3·8
Poa annua		...	...	...	...	...	...	1	1·0	...	...
P. pratensis		...	...	1	0·3	1	0·4	9	5·3	1	0·1
Sieglingia decumbens		...	...	1	0·3	4	1·0	...	...	9	2·2
Trisetum flavescens		...	...	...	...	...	...	1	0·3	...	...
Carex bigelowii		...	...	1	0·3	...	...	...	...	...	...
C. binervis		...	...	7	2·2	4	1·1	2	0·8	2	0·4
C. caryophyllea		...	...	...	...	2	0·7	1	0·1	7	2·2
C. echinata		1	0·2	...	...	...	...	...	...	...	...
C. flacca		...	...	1	0·1	...	...	...	...	...	...
C. nigra		4	0·7	...	...	...	...	1	0·1	...	...
C. panicea		1	0·2	6	1·3	5	0·8	...	...	4	0·9
C. pilulifera		2	0·4	7	1·8	9	2·6	1	0·2	10	2·8

	1 Pres.	Mean c–a	2 Const.	Mean c–a	3 Const.	Mean c–a	4 Const.	Mean c–a	5 Const.	Mean c–a
C. pulicaris	...	...	...	...	...	...	...	...	2	0·6
Carex spp.	1	0·1	...	...	...	...	...	...	...	...
Juncus effusus	...	...	...	...	1	0·1	...	...	...	...
J. squarrosus	7	1·9	10	3·2	2	0·6	1	0·2	3	0·9
Luzula campestris	...	...	1	0·2	6	2·1	6	1·2	6	2·3
L. multiflora	7	1·6	9	3·5	5	2·0	...	...	3	0·8
L. pilosa	6	1·7	7	2·0	5	1·2	...	...	2	0·4
L. sylvatica	3	0·7	4	0·9	3	0·4	1	0·4	...	...
Dactylorchis maculata	...	...	...	...	1	0·1	...	...	...	...
Eriophorum angustifolium	1	0·3	...	...	...	...	...	...	...	...
E. vaginatum	3	0·9	...	...	...	...	...	...	...	...
Narthecium ossifragum	...	...	...	...	1	0·2	...	...	...	...
Trichophorum cespitosum	3	0·9	1	0·1	2	0·3	...	...	1	0·1
Achillea millefolium	...	...	...	...	1	0·1	6	1·1	4	1·1
Alchemilla alpina	...	...	...	...	1	0·2	...	...	2	0·9
A. vestita	...	...	...	...	...	...	...	...	1	0·2
Anemone nemorosa	...	...	...	...	2	0·4	...	...	1	0·3
Campanula rotundifolia	...	...	...	...	4	0·9	8	1·8	9	2·3
Cerastium holosteoides	...	...	...	...	1	0·1	2	0·3	3	0·6
Cirsium palustre	...	...	1	0·1	...	...	...	...	...	...
Conopodium majus	...	...	...	...	1	0·1	...	...	2	0·5
Crepis paludosa	...	...	...	...	...	...	...	...	1	0·1
Euphrasia spp.	...	...	...	...	...	...	...	...	3	0·7
Galium saxatile	10	3·3	10	4·7	10	4·1	8	2·2	8	2·9
G. verum	...	...	...	...	...	...	...	...	1	0·2
Gentianella campestris	...	...	...	...	...	...	...	...	1	0·1
Hieracium pilosella	...	...	...	...	1	0·1	...	...	1	0·2
Hyperichum pulchrum	...	...	...	...	...	...	...	...	1	0·1
Lathyrus montanus	...	...	...	...	2	0·3	...	...	2	0·3
Leontodon spp.	...	...	...	...	...	...	...	...	1	0·1
Lotus corniculatus	...	...	...	...	...	...	...	...	3	0·7
Melampyrum pratense	1	0·1	...	...	...	...	...	...	...	...
Oxalis acetosella	...	...	2	0·2	2	0·3	...	...	...	...
Pedicularis sylvatica	...	...	...	...	1	0·2	...	...	...	...
Pinguicula vulgaris	...	...	...	...	1	0·1	...	...	...	...
Plantago lanceolata	...	...	...	...	...	...	...	...	3	0·4
Polygala serpyllifolia	...	...	...	...	2	0·5	...	...	4	0·7
Polygonum viviparum	...	...	...	...	1	0·1	...	...	...	...
Potentilla erecta	10	2·6	10	3·2	10	3·8	2	0·4	9	3·5
Prunella vulgaris	...	...	...	...	...	...	...	...	2	0·3
Ranunculus acris	...	...	...	...	1	0·1	...	...	2	0·4
R. repens	...	...	...	...	...	...	...	...	1	0·1
Rumex acetosella agg.	...	...	1	0·1	3	0·6	10	2·2	3	0·7
Succisa pratensis	...	...	...	...	2	0·3	...	...	3	0·6
Thymus drucei	...	...	...	...	3	0·6	...	...	...	...
Trientalis europaea	...	...	...	...	...	...	...	...	1	0·1
Trifolium repens	...	...	...	...	...	...	4	0·4	1	0·2
Veronica officinalis	...	...	...	...	1	0·2	...	...	6	1·2
V. serpyllifolia	...	...	...	...	...	...	...	...	1	0·1
Viola riviniana	...	...	...	...	3	0·6	...	...	2	0·3
Viola spp.	...	...	...	...	...	...	...	...	3	0·7
Atrichum undulatum	...	...	...	...	...	...	...	...	1	0·1
Aulacomnium palustre	1	0·2	...	...	...	...	...	...	...	...
Breutelia chrysocoma	...	...	...	...	...	...	...	...	1	0·1
Bryum spp.	1	0·1	...	...	...	...	...	...	...	...

[continued]

	1 Pres. Mean c–a		2 Const. Mean c–a		3 Const. Mean c–a		4 Const. Mean c–a		5 Const. Mean c–a	
Campylopus flexuosus	3	0·6	...	...	1	0·2	...	...	1	0·3
C. pyriformis	...	...	3	0·6	1	0·2	...	...	...	...
Dichodontium pellucidum	...	...	1	0·1	...	...	...	...	...	...
Dicranum scoparium	8	2·0	7	1·9	7	2·1	...	...	4	0·9
Ditrichum heteromallum	...	...	1	0·2	1	0·1	...	...	...	...
Eurhynchium praelongum	...	...	...	...	1	0·2	2	0·6	...	...
Hylocomium splendens	8	2·8	8	3·1	10	4·8	2	0·3	8	3·3
Hypnum cupressiforme	10	4·3	10	3·7	8	3·3	5	1·0	7	2·6
Isopterygium elegans	...	...	...	...	1	0·1	...	...	...	...
Leptodontium flexifolium	3	0·4	1	0·1	...	...	...	...	...	...
Leucobryum glaucum	1	0·1	...	...	...	...	...	...	1	0·1
Mnium hornum	4	1·0	2	0·4	2	0·3	...	...	1	0·3
M. undulatum	...	...	...	...	1	0·4	...	...	...	...
Plagiothecium undulatum	9	2·3	7	2·2	3	0·8	...	...	...	...
Pleuridium acuminatum	...	...	1	0·1	...	...	...	...	...	...
Pleurozium schreberi	10	5·0	10	5·3	10	5·1	3	0·6	8	3·3
Pohlia nutans	6	1·5	1	0·3	1	0·2	...	...	...	...
Polytrichum alpestre	3	0·5	...	...	...	...	...	...	...	...
P. commune	6	2·3	7	2·4	7	2·7	...	...	5	1·5
P. formosum	...	...	1	0·1	2	0·4	...	...	1	0·2
P. juniperinum	1	0·2	...	...	2	0·5	...	...	2	0·5
P. piliferum	...	...	1	0·2	1	0·1	...	...	...	...
P. urnigerum	...	...	...	...	2	0·4	...	...	...	...
Pseudoscleropodium purum	2	0·3	4	1·3	5	1·8	5	1·4	9	3·3
Rhacomitrium canescens	...	...	...	...	2	0·3	...	...	...	...
R. lanuginosum	...	...	...	...	1	0·2	...	...	...	...
Rhytidiadelphus loreus	1	0·4	1	0·3	2	0·7	...	...	1	0·3
R. squarrosus	9	3·4	8	3·6	10	3·8	10	3·5	9	3·7
R. triquetrus	...	...	...	...	2	0·5	...	...	1	0·3
S. capillaceum	...	...	2	0·1	1	0·1	...	...	1	0·4
Sphagnum girgensohnii	...	...	...	...	1	0·1	...	...	...	...
Thuidium tamariscinum	...	...	...	...	2	0·7	...	...	4	1·0
Barbilophozia floerkii	...	...	1	0·2	4	0·8	...	...	...	...
Calypogeia trichomanis	3	0·7	1	0·2	3	0·4	...	...	...	...
Cephalozia bicuspidata	...	...	...	...	1	0·1	...	...	1	0·1
Cephaloziella hampeana	2	0·3	1	0·2	...	...	...	...	...	...
Diplophyllum albicans	...	...	...	...	1	0·2	...	...	...	...
Lophocolea bidentata	6	1·9	7	1·8	6	1·4	...	...	5	1·2
L. bicuspidata	...	...	...	...	1	0·1	...	...	...	...
Lophozia ventricosa	2	0·5	...	...	1	0·2	...	...	...	...
Marsupella emarginata	...	...	...	...	1	0·2	...	...	1	0·1
Mylia taylori	...	...	...	...	1	0·1	...	...	...	...
Plagiochila asplenioides	...	...	...	...	1	0·1	...	...	...	...
Ptilidium ciliare	1	0·2	6	1·5	6	1·7	...	...	2	0·4
Cladonia sylvatica	...	...	...	...	4	0·7	...	...	3	0·3
C. pyxidata	...	...	...	...	1	0·2	...	...	...	...
C. uncialis	...	...	...	...	1	0·1	...	...	...	...
Cladonia spp.	...	...	1	0·3	...	...	...	...	...	...
Peltigera canina	...	...	...	...	1	0·1	...	...	...	...

*　PP = peat podsol
PGP = peaty gleyed podsol
PG = peaty gley
P = podsol
OSk = oligotrophic skeletal

OB = oligotrophic brown forest soil
MB = mesotrophic brown forest soil
OG = oligotrophic gley
MG = mesotrophic gley

†　f = free　　p = poor　　vf = very free　　i = imperfect

Data of King (1962) and Cross (1962)

TABLE 20

Floristic Composition of Community Types 6-11 in Terms of Mean
Cover-Abundance (Domin) and Constancy or Presence Classes 1-10

Designation: Type	6		7		8		9		10		11	
Dominants	Festuca Agrostis (Nardus)		Molinia Festuca Agrostis		Deschampsia Festuca Agrostis		Festuca Agrostis		Agrostis Festuca		Molinia Festuca Agrostis	
No. of stands	18		10		7		12		10		10	
Sample area	32. sq. m.		16–64 sq. m.		32 sq. m.		32 sq. m.		32 sq. m.		16–64 sq. m.	
Altitude	262–381 m. 850–1250 ft.		244–366 m. 800–1200 ft.		167–457 m. 550–1500 ft.		137–427 m. 450–1400 ft.		15–311 m. 50–1020 ft.		244–366 m. 800–1200 ft.	
Soil profile type*	OG		OG		OG		MB		MG		MG	
Drainage class†	p–vp		p–vp		p–vp		f–i		p–vp		vp	
	Const.	Mean c–a	Pres.	Mean c–a	Const.	Mean c–a	Const.	Mean c–a	Const.	Mean c–a	Pres.	Mean c–a
Calluna vulgaris	2	0·4	1	0·2	...	...	5	1·4	...	...	1	0·4
Empetrum nigrum	1	0·2	...	...	...	...	...	...	...	...	...	...
Erica tetralix	1	0·1	1	0·3	...	...	...	...	...	...	...	...
Helianthemum chamaecistus	...	...	...	...	...	...	1	0·1	...	...	...	...
Salix repens	...	...	...	...	...	...	...	...	...	...	1	0·3
Vaccinium myrtillus	3	0·6	...	...	...	...	5	1·3	...	...	...	...
V. vitis-idaea	1	0·1	...	...	...	...	1	0·2	...	...	...	...
Blechnum spicant	1	0·1	...	...	...	...	...	...	...	...	...	...
Equisetum palustre	...	...	...	...	...	...	...	...	...	...	1	0·1
Pteridium aquilinum	...	...	1	0·1	...	...	1	0·3	...	...	...	...
Selaginella selaginoides	3	0·3	...	...	...	...	1	0·1	...	...	1	0·2
Thelypteris limbosperma	...	...	...	...	...	...	...	...	...	...	1	0·2
Agrostis canina	**10**	**4·7**	**10**	**5·7**	4	1·4	9	3·8	9	3·1	9	4·0
A. stolonifera	...	...	...	...	6	2·4	...	...	2	2·0	3	1·1
A. tenuis	**10**	**5·5**	7	3·8	**10**	**5·0**	**10**	**6·8**	**10**	**6·7**	9	4·9
Anthoxanthum odoratum	**10**	**3·7**	**10**	**4·2**	**10**	**3·7**	**10**	**4·2**	**10**	**4·5**	**10**	**4·1**
Briza media	1	0·1	...	...	...	...	7	1·5	8	1·4	7	1·8
Cynosurus cristatus	...	...	...	...	...	...	1	0·2	8	2·4	3	0·7
Dactylis glomerata	...	...	...	...	1	0·3	1	0·1	...	...	...	...
Deschampsia cespitosa	9	2·3	6	2·3	**10**	**8·0**	5	1·0	**10**	**3·6**	8	2·4
D. flexuosa	1	0·1	1	0·4	...	...	2	0·4	...	...	...	...
Festuca arundinacea	...	...	...	...	3	0·7	...	...	3	0·6	3	1·0
F. ovina	**10**	**5·8**	**10**	**5·5**	9	3·3	**10**	**8·0**	**10**	**4·4**	**10**	**5·9**
F. rubra	9	3·5	4	1·5	7	4·0	**10**	**4·3**	**10**	**5·2**	**10**	**4·2**
Helictotrichon pratense	...	...	...	...	...	...	2	0·6	2	1·0	2	0·6
H. pubescens	2	0·5	2	0·4	3	0·7	3	0·9	3	0·8	5	1·6
Holcus lanatus	6	1·9	**10**	**2·8**	9	3·4	6	1·9	**10**	**4·5**	**10**	**4·1**
H. mollis	2	0·5	1	0·2	3	0·9	...	...	1	0·2	1	0·2
Koeleria cristata	...	...	...	...	...	...	5	1·2	...	...	...	...
Molinia caerulea	3	0·5	**10**	**8·6**	1	0·4	1	0·1	5	1·1	**10**	**7·9**
Nardus stricta	9	4·9	7	2·7	**10**	**2·9**	6	2·7	8	3·7	9	3·6
Poa pratensis	4	1·0	...	...	9	2·4	1	0·2	6	1·9	5	1·2
P. trivialis	1	0·1	...	...	1	0·1	...	...	3	0·5	1	0·3
Sieglingia decumbens	2	0·2	2	0·6	1	0·3	7	2·1	2	0·5	2	0·5
Trisetum flavescens	...	...	...	...	...	...	...	...	1	0·2	2	0·6
Carex bigelowii	1	0·2	...	...	...	...	...	...	...	...	...	...
C. binervis	2	0·6	...	...	...	...	1	0·2	...	...	...	...
C. caryophyllea	1	0·1	...	...	3	0·9	6	1·7	3	0·7	4	1·2

[continued]

	6 Const.	Mean c–a	7 Pres.	Mean c–a	8 Const.	Mean c–a	9 Const.	Mean c–a	10 Const.	Mean c–a	11 Pres.	Mean c–a
C. demissa	1	0·2	...	...	...	...	...	...	...	...	...	...
C. disticha	...	...	...	...	3	0·9	...	...	1	0·1	...	...
C. echinata	3	0·9	1	0·4	3	0·6	...	...	2	0·6	2	0·3
C. flacca	1	0·1	5	1·9	1	0·7	2	0·3	4	1·0	3	1·2
C. hostiana	...	...	...	...	...	...	...	...	...	...	1	0·2
C. nigra	5	1·6	3	0·7	4	1·1	...	...	6	1·9	8	2·7
C. ovalis	3	0·7	...	...	10	2·4	...	...	3	1·3	1	0·4
C. pallescens	...	...	...	...	...	...	...	...	3	0·8	2	0·5
C. panicea	9	3·0	5	1·3	6	1·9	3	0·5	10	3·9	7	3·1
C. pilulifera	6	1·3	...	...	4	0·7	9	3·0	4	0·8	2	0·5
C. pulicaris	5	1·1	...	...	...	...	3	0·4	5	1·7	6	1·8
C. rostrata	...	...	2	0·9	...	...	...	...	...	...	1	0·3
Carex spp.	...	...	...	...	...	...	...	...	...	...	1	0·4
Juncus acutiflorus	3	0·9	9	3·3	7	2·3	...	...	6	2·3	7	2·8
J. bulbosus	...	...	1	0·3	...	...	...	...	...	...	...	...
J. conglomeratus	4	1·1	2	0·5	4	1·1	...	...	5	1·6	4	1·3
J. effusus	6	2·0	3	0·7	10	2·9	...	...	6	1·8	3	0·7
J. squarrosus	6	1·3	3	0·8	3	0·6	3	0·7	3	0·8	2	0·4
Luzula campestris	2	0·4	...	...	1	0·1	6	1·8	2	0·3	...	...
L. multiflora	6	3·0	5	1·4	7	2·0	4	1·4	7	3·0	8	2·2
L. pilosa	1	0·2	...	...	...	...	1	0·1	...	...	1	0·2
L. sylvatica	1	0·1	...	...	...	...	...	...	...	...	...	...
Dactylorchis maculata	1	0·1	...	...	...	...	...	...	...	...	1	0·1
Eriophorum angustifolium	2	0·4	2	0·4	...	...	...	...	...	...	1	0·4
Narthecium ossifragum	...	...	4	1·4	...	...	...	...	...	...	1	0·1
Trichophorum cespitosum	1	0·1	1	0·3	...	...	...	...	...	...	1	0·1
Achillea millefolium	...	...	...	...	...	...	4	1·4	...	...	...	...
A. ptarmica	1	0·2	5	1·2	...	...	1	0·1	4	0·5	8	1·2
Ajuga reptans	...	...	...	...	1	0·4	...	...	...	...	4	1·0
Alchemilla alpina	...	...	...	...	...	...	2	0·3	...	...	...	...
A. glabra	...	...	...	...	...	...	1	0·1	...	...	...	...
A. vestita	1	0·1	...	...	...	...	2	0·3	1	0·2	...	...
Anemone nemorosa	5	0·8	3	0·8	...	...	2	0·5	1	0·1	3	1·0
Angelica sylvestris	1	0·1	1	0·3	...	...	...	...	...	...	1	0·3
Campanula rotundifolia	1	0·2	...	...	...	...	6	1·9	...	...	...	...
Cardamine pratensis	3	0·4	6	0·5	2	0·7	...	...	7	1·3	...	...
Cerastium holosteoides	4	0·5	...	...	1	0·1	7	1·1	7	1·2	6	0·8
Cirsium arvense	1	0·1	...	...	...	...	...	...	1	0·2	...	...
C. palustre	4	0·5	4	1·0	6	0·9	1	0·1	7	1·2	8	1·5
C. vulgare	...	...	...	...	...	...	2	0·2	...	...	...	...
Conopodium majus	2	0·5	...	...	3	0·7	3	0·4	1	0·2	2	0·2
Digitalis purpurea	...	...	1	0·1	...	...	...	...	...	...	...	...
Epilobium palustre	2	0·2	2	0·3	...	...	...	...	2	0·3	2	0·4
Euphrasia agg.	1	0·1	1	0·2	...	...	2	0·3	1	0·1	...	...
Filipendula ulmaria	1	0·3	1	0·3	...	...	...	...	5	1·6	...	...
Galium saxatile	8	2·0	7	2·3	7	1·9	9	2·9	4	0·6	7	1·5
G. uliginosum	3	0·4	...	...	2	0·9	...	...	3	0·7	6	1·5
G. verum	...	...	...	...	1	0·3	5	1·0	1	0·2	...	...
Galium spp.	...	...	1	0·3	...	...	...	...	...	...	...	...
Geum rivale	...	...	...	...	...	...	...	...	1	0·3	...	...
Hieracium pilosella	...	...	...	...	...	...	3	0·4	...	...	1	0·1
Hieracium spp.	1	0·1	...	...	...	...	...	...	...	...	1	0·3
Hypericum pulchrum	...	...	...	...	...	...	1	0·1	...	...	...	...
Lathyrus montanus	...	...	...	...	1	0·4	2	0·4	1	0·1	...	...
L. pratensis	3	0·4	2	0·4	3	0·7	...	...	5	1·4	5	1·4
Leontodon autumnalis	1	0·1	...	...	...	...	...	...	1	0·1	...	...

	6 Const.	Mean c–a	7 Pres.	Mean c–a	8 Const.	Mean c–a	9 Const.	Mean c–a	10 Const.	Mean c–a	11 Pres.	Mean c–a
Leontodon spp.	...	...	1	0·2	...	...	...	...	...	...	4	0·8
Linum catharticum	...	...	...	...	...	...	2	0·2	1	0·2	...	...
Lotus corniculatus	...	...	...	...	...	...	6	1·8	1	0·4	1	0·3
L. pedunculatus	1	0·2	...	...	4	1·1	...	...	...	...	2	0·7
Lysimachia nemorum	2	0·2	2	0·6	...	...	1	0·2	3	0·6	5	0·9
Parnassia palustris	...	...	2	0·5	...	...	...	...	...	...	...	...
Pedicularis palustris	...	...	1	0·1	...	...	1	0·1	...	...	...	...
Plantago lanceolata	1	0·2	3	0·6	1	0·1	8	2·0	6	1·6	...	...
Polygala serpyllifolia	1	0·1	...	...	...	...	2	0·3	...	...	...	...
P. vulgaris	...	...	...	...	...	...	...	...	1	0·2	...	...
Polygonum viviparum	2	0·4	...	...	...	...	1	0·2	...	...	...	...
Potentilla erecta	**9**	3·2	**9**	3·0	7	2·1	**10**	3·7	**10**	3·3	**10**	3·5
Primula vulgaris	1	0·1	...	...	...	...	3	0·5	1	0·2	3	0·7
Prunella vulgaris	3	0·6	1	0·3	1	0·4	...	...	5	1·6	3	0·9
Pulicaria dysenterica	...	...	...	...	...	...	...	...	...	...	1	0·1
Ranunculus acris	7	1·9	4	0·9	7	2·0	7	1·6	**10**	3·5	9	2·6
R. auricomus	...	...	...	...	...	...	...	...	1	0·1	...	...
R. bulbosus	...	...	...	...	...	...	2	0·3	...	...	...	...
R. ficaria	...	...	...	...	1	0·3	...	...	2	0·3	2	0·5
R. flammula	...	...	...	...	...	...	...	...	...	...	1	0·3
R. repens	2	0·4	...	...	6	0·7	2	0·5	4	1·2	4	1·0
Rumex acetosella agg.	**8**	1·8	5	1·3	**9**	3·1	3	0·8	**8**	2·1	6	1·5
Stellaria graminea	3	0·4	4	0·7	6	1·1	...	...	5	0·6	5	1·0
Succisa pratensis	1	0·2	3	0·9	...	...	2	0·3	...	...	2	0·4
Taraxacum agg.	2	0·3	1	0·1	...	...	...	...	3	0·3	3	0·6
Thalictrum alpinum	1	0·1	...	...	...	...	...	...	...	...	...	...
Thymus drucei	...	...	...	...	...	...	9	2·8	...	...	...	...
Trientalis europaea	1	0·1	...	...	...	...	...	...	...	...	...	...
Trifolium pratense	...	...	...	...	...	...	1	0·2	1	0·1	...	...
T. repens	5	1·2	5	1·2	3	0·9	**8**	2·4	**10**	3·4	**8**	2·4
Urtica dioica	...	...	...	...	1	0·1	...	...	...	...	...	...
Veronica chamaedrys	...	...	...	...	1	0·1	2	0·4	2	0·4	3	0·8
V. officinalis	1	0·1	...	...	...	...	7	1·4	...	...	...	...
Vicia sepium	...	...	...	...	1	0·1	...	...	1	0·2	1	0·2
Viola palustris	2	0·3	...	...	1	0·3	2	0·4	2	1·0	2	0·3
V. riviniana	2	0·4	...	...	...	...	7	1·6	...	...	4	1·0
V. tricolor	1	0·1	...	...	...	...	3	0·8	...	...	...	...
Viola spp.	...	...	5	1·4	4	1·0	...	...	...	...	...	...
Acrocladium cuspidatum	4	0·9	3	0·9	3	0·6	1	0·3	**10**	3·5	5	1·7
Atrichum undulatum	3	0·7	1	0·2	1	0·3	2	0·6	5	1·1	1	0·2
Aulacomnium palustre	...	...	2	0·5	...	...	...	...	...	...	1	0·2
Brachythecium rutabulum	1	0·3	...	...	1	0·3	...	...	2	0·3	...	...
Breutelia chrysocoma	...	...	...	...	...	...	1	0·2	...	...	...	...
Bryum alpinum	...	...	1	0·2	...	...	...	...	...	...	...	...
B. pseudotriquetrum	...	...	...	...	...	...	1	0·1	...	...	...	...
Bryum spp.	1	0·2	...	...	3	0·7	...	...	3	0·4	1	0·1
Campylopus flexuosus	...	...	1	0·2	...	...	...	...	...	...	...	...
Climacium dendroides	2	0·2	...	...	...	...	...	...	2	0·4	2	0·6
Ctenidium molluscum	...	...	...	...	...	...	1	0·3	2	0·3	...	...
Dichodontium pellucidum	1	0·1	...	...	...	...	1	0·2	...	...	...	...
Dicranella heteromalla	1	0·1	...	...	...	...	...	...	1	0·1	...	...
D. palustris	1	0·1	...	...	...	...	...	...	...	...	...	...
Dicranum scoparium	2	0·3	3	0·8	...	...	5	0·9	...	...	1	0·1
Eurhynchium praelongum	6	1·8	7	1·9	**10**	4·0	1	0·4	7	2·1	3	1·1
Fissidens adianthoides	...	...	1	0·2	...	...	...	...	...	...	...	...
Hylocomium splendens	**9**	3·2	7	2·9	6	1·6	**10**	4·3	**8**	2·9	**8**	3·4

[continued]

	6 Const.	Mean c–a	7 Pres.	Mean c–a	8 Const.	Mean c–a	9 Const.	Mean c–a	10 Const.	Mean c–a	11 Pres.	Mean c–a
Hypnum cupressiforme	7	1·4	6	1·9	...	...	8	2·4	2	0·7	6	1·8
Mnium hornum	4	0·7	...	...	...	...	2	0·3	...	...	2	0·3
M. punctatum	2	0·2	...	...	...	...	1	0·1	...	...	...	...
M. undulatum	6	1·2	5	1·2	6	1·1	5	0·9	7	1·8	6	1·7
Mnium spp.	...	...	1	0·2	...	...	...	...	...	...	1	0·1
Philonotis fontana	1	0·2	...	...	...	...	...	...	...	...	...	...
Plagiothecium undulatum	2	0·3	3	0·6	...	...	...	...	...	...	...	...
Pleuridium acuminatum	1	0·1	...	...	...	...	2	0·2	3	0·4	...	...
Pleurozium schreberi	8	2·0	5	1·9	...	...	6	2·1	1	0·3	4	1·4
Pohlia nutans	1	0·1	...	...	...	...	...	...	...	...	1	0·1
Polytrichum commune	9	2·5	4	1·2	4	0·7	2	0·5	2	0·5	3	0·9
P. juniperinum	...	...	...	...	...	...	1	0·2	...	...	...	...
P. nanum	...	...	...	...	...	...	...	...	1	0·1	...	...
P. urnigerum	1	0·3	...	...	...	...	...	...	...	...	...	...
Pseudephemerum nitidum	...	...	...	...	1	0·3	...	...	...	...	...	...
Pseudoscleropodium purum	9	3·4	9	2·7	9	3·6	10	4·1	10	4·0	8	3·6
Rhacomitrium canescens	...	...	...	...	...	...	1	0·1	...	...	...	...
Rhytidiadelphus loreus	1	0·2	...	...	...	...	1	0·2	...	...	...	...
R. squarrosus	10	3·9	9	3·8	10	4·4	10	4·6	10	5·0	8	3·7
R. triquetrus	...	...	...	...	...	...	3	1·0	...	...	1	0·2
Sphagnum palustre	1	0·1	1	0·2	...	...	...	...	...	...	...	...
S. plumulosum	1	0·4	3	1·2	...	...	...	...	...	...	...	...
Sphagnum spp.	1	0·3	...	...	...	...	...	...	...	...	1	0·1
Thuidium tamariscinum	9	2·8	6	2·2	6	1·7	5	1·8	8	3·0	4	1·0
Calypogeia trichomanis	1	0·2	3	0·7	...	...	...	...	...	...	3	0·6
Cephalozia bicuspidata	1	0·1	...	...	...	...	...	...	...	...	...	...
Cephaloziella hampeana	1	0·1	...	...	...	...	...	...	...	...	...	...
Fossombronia pusilla	...	...	...	...	...	...	...	...	1	0·2	...	...
Lophocolea bidentata	8	1·8	10	2·8	6	1·4	7	1·7	7	1·5	7	1·8
L. cuspidata	1	0·1	...	...	...	...	...	...	...	...	...	...
Lophozia ventricosa	...	...	1	0·2	...	...	...	...	...	...	...	...
Pellia epiphylla	2	0·1	1	0·2	...	...	1	0·1	...	...	...	...
P. neesiana	...	...	...	...	...	...	...	...	1	0·1	...	...
Pellia spp.	...	...	...	...	...	...	...	...	1	0·1	...	...
Ptilidium ciliare	...	...	...	...	...	...	2	0·3	...	...	...	...
Riccardia multifida	1	0·1	1	0·2	...	...	...	...	...	...	...	...
Scapania undulata	...	...	1	0·2	...	...	...	...	...	...	...	...
Solenostoma triste	1	0·1	...	...	...	...	...	...	...	...	...	...

* PP = peat podsol   OB = oligotrophic brown forest soil
PGP = peaty gleyed podsol   MB = mesotrophic brown forest soil
PG = peaty gley   OG = oligotrophic gley
P = podsol   MB = mesotrophic gley
OSk = oligotrophic skeletal

† f = free   p = poor
i = imperfect   vp = very poor

Date of King (1962) and Cross (1962)

TABLE 21

Summary of Soil Chemical Data for Community Types 1-11. Mean values for each community type for samples taken from **A** horizon except where otherwise stated.

(Exchangeable cations as m.equiv./100 gm. oven-dry soil, P_2O_5 as mg./100 gm. oven dry soil)

Designation: Type	1	2	3	4	5
Dominants	Molinia Festuca Deschampsia	Nardus Festuca Deschampsia	Festuca Deschampsia (Nardus)	Agrostis Festuca Poa	Festuca Agrostis
No. of stands	10	14	18	8	10
Soil profile type	PP PGP PG	PP PGP	P OSk OB	OSk OB	OB OSk
Drainage class	i–p	f–p	vf–i	vf–f	f–i
Loss on ignition	...	43·2*	20·5	21·18	14·4
Exch. Ca (m.equiv.)	...	1·7*	0·66	1·04	1·00
Exch. K (m.equiv.)	...	0·82*	0·47	0·72	0·30
Total exch. capacity (m.equiv.)	...	69·25*	29·46	30·00	20·50
% base saturation	...	5·78	6·35	9·94	8·40
pH	4·16	4·21	4·73	4·48	4·99
Total P_2O_5 (mg.)	...	298·0*	247·0	349·0	167·0
Sol. P_2O_5 (mg.)	...	11·70*	2·26	6·15	0·93

Designation: Type	6	7	8	9	10	11
Dominants	Festuca Agrostis (Nardus)	Molinia Festuca Agrostis	Deschampsia Festuca Agrostis	Festuca Agrostis	Agrostis Festuca	Molinia Festuca Agrostis
No. of stands	18	10	7	12	10	10
Soil profile type	OG	OG	OG	MB	MG	MG
Drainage class	p–vp	p–vp	p–vp	f–i	p–vp	vp
Loss on ignition	18·7	...	16·2	13·5	14·8	...
Exch. Ca (m.equiv.)	4·24	...	3·70	6·20	8·49	...
Exch. K (m.equiv.)	0·39	...	0·38	0·39	0·37	...
Total exch. capacity (m.equiv.)	26·64	...	23·02	23·63	22·67	...
% base saturation	23·65	...	22·66	34·40	50·18	...
pH	5·15	4·96	4·97	5·54	5·64	5·66
Total P_2O_5 (mg.)	269·5	...	237·0	180·0	242·0	...
Sol. P_2O_5 (mg.)	2·44	...	2·39	1·10	3·90	...

* Data for peat or humus layer. Values for exchangeable constituents and P_2O_5 are high due to volume/weight distortion on drying peat.

Data of King (1962) and Cross (1962)

TABLE 22

Floristic Composition of Community Types of McVean and Ratcliffe (1962) in Terms of Mean Cover-Abundance (Domin) and Constancy Classes 1-10

Description	Nardetum sub-alpinum species-poor	Nardetum sub-alpinum species-rich	Juncetum squarrosi sub-alpinum species-poor	Juncetum squarrosi sub-alpinum species-rich*	Agrosto-Festucetum species-poor	Alchemilleto-Agrosto-Festucetum	Agrosto-Festucetum species-rich	Saxifrageto-Agrosto-Festucetum	Luzula sylvatica grassland nodum
Number of stands	14	8	10	3	20	14	16	12	7
Sample area	2–8 sq. m.	4 sq. m.	2–10 sq. m.	4 sq. m.	4 sq. m.	1–4 sq. m.	4–16 sq. m.	4 sq. m.	4 sq. m.
Altitude	305–823 m.	381–701 m.	503–823 m.	548–823 m.	31–823 m.	335–853 m.	152–701 m.	335–701 m.	427–671 m.
	1000–2700 ft.	1250–2300 ft.	1650–2700 ft.	1800–2700 ft.	100–2700 ft.	1100–2800 ft.	500–2300 ft.	1100–2300 ft.	1400–2200 ft.
Slope	3°–32°	5°–40°	2°–33°	7°–25°	0°–40°	0°–45°	0°–40°	5°–38°	3°–40°
Cover (average)	100%	100%	100%	100%	100%	90–100%	95–100%	95–100%	95–100%

Species	N.s-p Const	c-a	N.s-r Const	c-a	J.s-p Const	c-a	J.s-r Const	c-a	A-F s-p Const	c-a	Alchem. Const	c-a	A-F s-r Const	c-a	Saxifr. Const	c-a	Luzula Const	c-a
Betula spp. (seedlings)																		
Calluna vulgaris	3.6	0.5	1.0	0.1														
Dryas octopetala											2.9	0.4	1.3	0.2	2.5	0.3		
Empetrum hermaphroditum			1.0	0.4					0.5				5.0	1.3	3.3	0.6		
Erica tetralix								0.7			5.0	0.9	0.6	0.2	0.8	0.2		
Helianthemum chamaecistus													1.9	0.5	2.5	0.6		
Rubus idaeus															0.8	+		
R. saxatilis			1.0	0.3									1.9	0.8	0.8	0.3		
Salix aurita													1.3	0.2				
S. herbacea			1.0								0.7	0.1			0.8	0.1		
S. phylicifolia															0.8	0.1		
Sorbus aucuparia			1.0	0.3	6.0	1.3			5.5	1.4	0.7	0.1	3.1	0.7	0.8	0.1	5.7	2.7
Vaccinium myrtillus	6.4	1.7			1.0	0.1					6.4	1.8	1.9	0.3			1.4	0.4
V. vitis-idaea	0.7	0.1									2.9	0.8	0.6	0.1				
Blechnum spicant	1.4	0.2							2.0	0.4	2.1	0.4	0.6	0.1	0.8	+	2.9	0.4
Botrychium lunaria	0.7	0.1							0.5	0.1	1.4	0.4						
Dryopteris filix-mas			4.0	0.7									0.6	0.1				
Equisetum palustre								0.3			0.7	0.2						
E. sylvaticum											0.7	0.1						
Lycopodium alpinum									0.5	0.1			1.3	0.1	0.8			
L. selago																		
Pteridium aquilinum	0.7	0.1	3.0	0.5				1.7			7.1	1.5	3.8	0.9				
Selaginella selaginoides											1.4	0.1			8.3	1.8		
Thelypteris dryopteris											1.4	0.1						
T. limbosperma																		

	1	2	3	4	5	6	7	8	9	10	11	12	13	14	15	16	17	18
Agrostis canina	6·4	3·1	9·0	3·0	9·0	2·7	:	3·0	8·0	3·3	3·6	1·1	5·6	1·6	8·3	2·4	1·4	0·6
A. stolonifera	0·7	0·1	3·0	0·8	3·0	1·2	:	1·0	10·0	6·3	10·0	3·7	10·0	4·6	6·7	2·9	8·6	2·2
A. tenuis	10·0	4·1	10·0	3·3	9·0	2·8	:	3·0	9·5	3·8	9·3	2·7	8·1	2·5	4·2	1·0	7·1	1·7
Anthoxanthum odoratum	9·3	2·9	9·0	3·4	9·0	:	:	:	:	:	:	:	:	:	:	:	:	:
Arrhenatherum elatius	:	:	1·0	0·5	:	:	:	:	:	:	:	:	0·6	0·2	4·2	0·9	:	:
Briza media	:	:	3·0	0·3	:	:	:	:	1·5	0·4	:	:	0·6	0·5	:	:	:	1·0
Cynosurus cristatus	5·0	1·0	4·0	1·0	:	2·5	:	4·5	1·9	1·2	3·6	0·8	1·9	1·3	5·8	1·2	2·9	1·0
Deschampsia cespitosa	4·3	1·2	10·0	3·5	9·0	2·5	:	4·0	3·8	0·9	2·9	0·6	3·8	0·5	:	:	:	2·2
D. flexuosa	9·3	4·6	10·0	1·2	10·0	4·2	:	4·0	9·5	4·7	10·0	5·2	10·0	5·3	10·0	4·8	5·7	1·7
F. ovina agg.	1·4	0·3	4·0	1·0	:	:	:	1·0	1·0	0·2	2·9	0·7	8·1	3·0	5·8	1·8	2·9	0·8
F. rubra	:	:	6·0	1·9	:	:	:	1·5	0·5	0·4	:	:	0·6	0·2	2·5	0·5	:	:
Helictotrichon pratense	0·7	0·2	3·0	0·8	:	:	:	0·5	1·9	:	:	:	1·9	0·1	:	:	:	:
Holcus lanatus	0·7	0·2	3·0	0·8	:	:	:	0·5	0·6	0·2	:	:	0·6	0·6	:	:	:	:
Molinia caerulea	10·0	7·3	10·0	7·2	9·0	4·0	:	6·0	6·3	1·8	5·7	1·3	6·3	2·3	5·0	1·4	7·1	1·3
Nardus stricta	:	:	:	:	:	:	:	:	:	:	:	:	0·3	1·3	:	:	:	:
Poa pratensis	2·1	0·6	1·0	0·3	:	:	:	2·0	5·0	0·8	0·7	0·1	5·0	1·8	3·3	0·7	:	:
Sieglingia decumbens	:	:	:	:	:	:	:	:	:	:	:	:	:	:	:	:	:	:
Carex bigelowii	0·7	0·2	:	:	5·0	1·7	:	2·0	1·3	0·5	2·1	0·5	1·3	0·3	:	:	1·4	0·3
C. binervis	5·7	1·1	3·0	0·5	1·0	+	:	3·0	1·3	0·7	0·7	0·2	1·3	0·4	:	:	1·4	0·2
C. capillaris	:	:	:	:	:	:	:	:	:	:	:	:	0·6	0·3	4·2	0·8	:	:
C. caryophyllea	:	:	:	:	:	:	:	:	:	:	:	:	5·0	0·8	2·5	0·5	:	:
C. demissa	:	:	3·0	0·7	:	0·7	:	0·5	0·1	:	0·7	0·2	1·9	0·2	4·2	0·9	:	:
C. dioica	:	:	:	:	:	+	:	:	:	:	:	:	0·6	0·2	:	:	:	:
C. echinata	:	:	10·0	2·9	10·0	2·7	:	2·0	0·5	0·5	:	:	5·0	1·9	2·5	0·8	1·4	0·2
C. flacca	:	:	3·0	0·7	:	0·7	:	:	:	:	:	:	:	:	2·5	0·2	:	:
C. hostiana	:	:	1·0	0·3	:	:	:	:	:	:	:	:	0·8	0·2	0·8	0·2	:	:
C. lepidocarpa	:	:	:	:	:	:	:	:	:	:	:	:	0·8	0·2	0·8	0·2	:	:
C. nigra	4·0	:	4·0	1·0	:	1·7	:	1·5	0·5	:	:	:	1·3	0·3	0·8	0·2	2·9	0·6
C. pallescens	4·3	1·1	9·0	3·2	1·0	3·7	:	2·5	0·7	0·7	0·7	0·1	3·8	1·0	8·3	3·7	:	:
C. panicea	9·3	2·1	:	:	:	:	:	6·5	1·5	6·4	1·2	:	4·4	0·8	:	:	1·4	:
C. pilulifera	7·1	1·3	9·0	2·5	1·0	2·0	:	0·5	0·1	2·9	0·6	:	4·4	1·1	9·2	2·7	1·4	:
C. pulicaris	0·7	0·2	:	:	:	:	:	:	:	:	:	:	2·5	0·4	:	:	:	:
Coeloglossum viride	:	:	:	:	:	:	:	:	:	:	:	:	:	:	:	:	:	:
Endymion non-scriptus	:	:	5·0	1·1	1·0	0·7	:	0·5	0·5	0·1	0·5	0·1	0·6	:	0·8	0·1	1·4	0·3
Eriophorum angustifolium	:	:	:	:	:	:	:	1·0	1·0	0·2	6·4	1·2	3·8	0·8	9·2	2·7	1·4	0·2
E. vaginatum	:	:	:	:	:	2·0	:	:	:	2·9	:	0·6	4·4	1·1	:	:	:	:
Juncus acutiflorus	5·0	:	1·0	0·3	3·0	1·0	:	:	:	:	:	:	2·5	0·4	:	:	:	:
J. articulatus	:	:	:	:	:	:	:	:	:	:	:	:	:	:	:	:	:	:
J. effusus	0·7	0·1	4·0	0·8	:	1·0	:	0·5	0·5	0·1	0·5	:	0·6	:	0·8	0·1	:	:
J. kochii	:	:	:	:	:	0·7	:	1·0	:	1·3	0·3	:	:	:	:	:	:	:
J. squarrosus	5·0	1·5	4·0	0·8	4·0	7·3	:	4·5	1·3	1·4	0·3	:	3·8	0·8	4·5	0·1	4·3	1·6
Luzula campestris	2·1	0·6	10·0	3·5	10·0	:	:	3·0	0·9	0·7	0·7	0·2	4·4	0·8	3·0	0·1	1·4	0·3
L. multiflora	7·1	1·3	:	2·0	:	:	:	5·0	1·3	5·7	1·1	:	3·1	0·4	5·0	0·3	1·4	0·2
L. pilosa	0·7	0·2	9·0	:	3·0	0·7	:	:	:	:	:	:	:	:	:	:	:	:
L. spicata	:	:	:	:	:	:	:	:	:	:	0·7	0·1	1·3	0·1	:	:	:	:

[continued]

P

	Const.	Mean c–a	Const.	Mean c–a	Const.	Mean c–a	Const.	Mean c–a	Const.	Mean c–a	Const.	Mean c–a	Const.	Mean c–a	Const.	Mean c–a	Const.	Mean c–a
L. sylvatica	1·4	0·1	1·0	0·3	...	...	...	...	3·0	0·6	0·7	0·1	2·5	0·4	0·8	0·2	**10·0**	6·0
Narthecium ossifragum	2·1	0·3	1·0	0·3	...	...	...	1·0	...	...	...	...	0·6	0·1	...	...	...	...
Orchis mascula	...	...	...	...	...	...	...	...	...	...	...	...	...	...	0·8	0·1	...	...
Trichophorum cespitosum	2·1	0·4	3·0	0·5	...	...	...	...	1·5	0·4	1·4	0·2	...	...	...	...	...	...
Achillea millefolium	2·1	0·4	...	...	...	...	...	...	1·0	0·3	2·1	0·4	3·8	1·2	2·5	0·5	...	...
A. ptarmica	...	...	3·0	0·5	...	...	...	...	0·5	0·1	...	...	...	...	...	...	...	...
Alchemilla alpina	...	...	3·0	0·6	...	...	...	...	1·5	0·4	**10·0**	6·2	5·0	1·7	4·2	1·1	2·9	0·6
A. filicaulis	...	...	1·0	0·4	...	...	...	...	...	...	...	...	1·3	0·3	0·8	0·3	...	...
A. glabra	...	...	3·0	0·7	...	...	...	...	...	...	2·1	0·4	2·5	0·8	7·5	2·7	...	...
A. vestita	...	...	3·0	0·7	...	...	...	...	0·5	0·1	1·4	0·5	5·0	1·2	4·2	1·4	...	...
A. wichurae	...	...	1·0	0·5	...	...	...	...	...	...	...	...	...	...	2·5	0·9	...	...
A. xanthochlora	...	...	1·0	0·3	...	...	...	...	...	...	0·7	0·2	...	...	0·8	0·3	...	...
Anemone nemorosa	3·0	0·4	...	...	...	...	...	...	...	...	...	...	...	...	0·8	0·1	...	...
Angelica sylvestris	...	...	3·0	0·4	...	...	...	...	...	...	0·7	0·1	...	...	...	...	...	...
Antennaria dioica	...	...	...	...	...	...	...	...	...	...	0·7	0·1	2·5	0·3	...	...	...	...
Arabis hirsuta	...	...	...	...	...	...	...	...	...	...	...	...	0·6	0·1	...	...	...	...
Armeria maritima	...	...	...	...	...	...	...	...	...	...	...	...	1·9	0·2	...	...	...	...
Bartsia alpina	...	...	...	...	...	...	...	...	...	...	...	...	...	...	0·8	0·1	...	...
Bellis perennis	...	...	...	...	...	...	...	...	...	...	...	...	3·8	1·4	2·5	0·6	...	...
Caltha palustris	...	...	1·0	0·1	...	...	...	...	...	...	...	...	...	...	...	...	...	...
Campanula rotundifolia	2·1	0·5	4·0	0·9	...	...	...	...	1·0	0·3	5·0	1·2	6·3	0·6	5·8	1·3	...	...
Cardamine flexuosa	...	...	1·0	0·1	...	...	...	...	...	...	0·7	0·1	...	...	...	...	...	...
C. pratensis	...	...	...	...	...	...	...	...	...	...	...	...	...	...	0·8	0·2	...	...
Cerastium alpinum	...	...	...	...	...	...	...	...	...	...	0·7	0·1	...	...	...	...	...	...
C. holosteoides	0·7	0·1	5·0	0·8	...	...	...	1·3	3·5	0·6	0·7	0·1	5·0	0·9	2·5	0·4	2·9	0·3
Cherleria sedoides	...	...	...	...	...	...	...	...	...	...	...	...	0·6	0·1	...	...	...	...
Cirsium heterophyllum	...	...	1·0	0·6	...	...	...	...	...	...	...	...	3·1	0·3	0·8	0·3	...	...
C. palustre	...	...	1·0	0·3	...	...	...	...	...	...	0·7	0·1	0·6	0·1	0·8	0·1	...	...
C. vulgare	...	...	...	...	...	...	...	...	...	...	...	...	0·6	0·1	0·8	0·1	...	...
Conopodium majus	...	...	...	...	...	...	...	...	...	...	...	...	0·6	0·2	...	...	...	...
Crepis paludosa	...	...	1·0	0·3	...	...	...	1·0	...	...	...	...	...	...	1·7	0·3	...	...
Epilobium palustre	...	...	1·0	0·3	...	...	...	1·0	...	...	...	...	...	...	...	...	...	...
Euphrasia spp.	1·4	0·2	**8·z**	1·8	...	...	...	1·7	3·5	0·7	5·7	1·4	1·8	6·9	6·7	1·6	...	...
Filipendula ulmaria	...	...	3·0	0·8	...	...	...	...	...	...	...	...	1·9	0·4	1·7	0·1	...	...
Fragaria vesca	...	...	...	...	...	...	...	...	...	...	...	...	0·6	0·1	2·5	0·3	...	...
Galium boreale	...	...	1·0	0·1	...	...	...	...	...	...	0·7	0·1	1·3	0·3	1·7	0·1	...	...
G. saxatile	!·?	3·3	!·z	1·5	;z·z	3·9	...	+	;z·z	3·8	**8·7**	2·2	5·6	1·4	2·5	0·3	4·3	1·2
G. verum	...	...	1·0	0·4	...	...	...	...	0·5	0·1	1·4	0·3	2·5	0·4	3·3	0·5	...	...
Gentianella campestris	...	...	...	...	...	...	...	...	...	...	0·7	0·2	1·3	0·1	1·7	0·3	...	...
Geranium sylvaticum	...	...	1·0	0·1	...	...	...	...	...	...	...	...	1·3	0·3	0·8	+	...	...
Geum rivale	...	...	3·0	0·6	...	...	...	1·0	...	...	2·1	0·4	3·8	0·8	3·3	0·9	...	...
Gnaphalium supinum	...	...	...	...	...	...	...	...	...	...	1·4	0·2	...	...	...	...	...	...
Heracleum sphondylium	...	...	...	...	...	...	...	...	...	...	...	...	0·6	0·1	...	...	...	...
Hieracium pilosella	...	...	...	...	...	...	...	...	...	...	...	...	2·5	0·6	0·8	0·2	...	...

Species	1	2	3	4	5	6	7	8	9	10	11	12	13	14	15	16	17
Hieracium spp.			0·6	5·0	0·3	1·3		0·1									
Hypericum pulchrum			0·1	0·8	0·2	1·3	0·7							0·1	1·0		0·7
Hypochoeris radicata			0·2	0·8	0·1	1·3		0·1	0·5					0·3	1·0	0·1	1·4
Lathyrus montanus					0·3	1·9	0·7							1·9	8·0	0·2	
Leontodon autumnalis			0·9	4·2	0·7	2·5	1·4	0·4	2·0	2·7				0·4	3·0		
Linum catharticum			1·6	9·2	0·7	3·1	1·4	0·1	0·5	1·3							
Lotus corniculatus			0·8	4·2	1·2	3·8		0·1	0·5								
Lysimachia nemorum			0·3	0·8	0·4	1·3				0·7				0·4	1·0		
Melampyrum pratense	0·2	1·4	0·3	0·8	0·3	1·9		0·3	2·0								
Mercurialis perennis	0·7	2·9			0·3	1·9											
Oxalis acetosella			0·1	0·8	0·2	0·6	2·1							0·1	1·0	0·4	
Oxytropis campestris			0·1	0·8													
Parnassia palustris			0·2	0·8						1·0							0·7
Pedicularis sylvatica										1·3				0·3			
Pinguicula vulgaris			0·4	2·5	0·1	0·6	0·7	0·1	0·5					1·1	1·0	0·2	1·4
Plantago lanceolata			1·8	5·0	2·3	5·6	2·1	0·6	2·5						4·0		
P. maritima			0·3	0·8	0·1	1·3											
Polygala serpyllifolia			0·3	1·7	0·4	2·5	2·1	0·4	1·5					0·3	1·0	0·5	3·0
Polygonum viviparum			2·8	8·3	1·2	3·8	1·4	0·2	0·5	2·7				1·3	5·0	0·3	1·4
Potentilla crantzii			0·4	4·2													
P. erecta	2·1	7·1	0·1	0·8	0·2	0·6	5·0	3·5	9·0			1·1	4·0			3·1	10·0
P. sterilis			0·1	0·8	0·3	1·3											
Primula vulgaris			2·0	8·3	2·3	8·1	2·9	0·1	0·5	1·3				0·6			
Prunella vulgaris	0·3	1·4	1·8	6·7	2·4	8·1	5·7	1·0	4·5	1·3				2·1			
Ranunculus acris					0·1	0·6		0·1	0·5								
R. ficaria														0·5	3·0		
R. flammula					0·1	0·6		0·1	0·5					0·3	1·0		
Rhinanthus minor agg.			0·3	0·8						0·3							
Rubus chamaemorus	2·1	8·6										0·2	1·0				
Rumex acetosa					0·9	3·8	2·9	0·6	3·0			0·3	1·0			0·3	1·4
Sagina procumbens					0·2	1·3	1·4										
Saussurea alpina			3·8	10·0	0·2	0·6	1·4										
Saxifraga aizoides			+	0·8	0·3	0·6	1·4										
S. hypnoides			1·1	4·2													
S. oppositifolia																	
Sedum anglicum								0·2	0·5								
S. rosea																	
Senecio jacobaea			0·3	1·7	0·1	0·6	0·7							0·3	1·0		
Sibbaldia procumbens			0·5	1·7	0·3	1·9	1·4										
Silene acaulis					0·6	1·9	0·7							0·1	1·0		
Solidago virgaurea					0·1	0·6	2·1							+	1·0		
Stellaria graminea					1·1	4·4	1·4	0·3	2·0					1·4	5·0		
Succisa pratensis					1·0	3·8			1·5					1·3	6·0	0·2	0·7
Taraxacum officinale agg.			0·7	3·3	0·1	0·6		0·3		0·3							
Teucrium scorodonia			0·8	3·3													

[continued]

Each column group below gives paired values: **Const.** and **Mean (c-a)**.

	1 Const.	1 c-a	2 Const.	2 c-a	3 Const.	3 c-a	4 Const.	4 c-a	5 Const.	5 c-a	6 Const.	6 c-a	7 Const.	7 c-a	8 Const.	8 c-a	9 Const.	9 c-a
Thalictrum alpinum	..	..	4·0	0·6	..	..	3·0	..	..	..	4·3	1·0	3·1	1·0	3·3	0·9	..	..
Thymus drucei	2·1	0·4	1·0	0·4	1·5	0·5	..	..	1·5	0·5	8·6	4·3	8·1	2·8	10·0	3·7	..	..
Trifolium repens	2·1	0·3	5·0	0·9	2·5	0·8	1·0	..	2·5	0·8	2·1	0·6	4·4	1·6	2·5	0·3	..	..
Trollius europaeus	..	..	..	..	..	..	..	..	..	..	0·7	0·1	1·9	0·4	2·5	0·3	..	..
Valeriana officinalis	2·1	0·2	..	..	..	..	..	..	..	..	..	..	1·3	0·1	..	..	..	..
Veronica chamaedrys	..	..	1·0	0·3	..	..	..	..	1·0	0·2	2·9	0·4	1·3	0·3	2·5	0·3	..	..
V. officinalis	..	..	1·0	0·3	..	..	..	..	1·5	0·6	0·7	0·1	3·1	0·5	..	..	..	..
V. serpyllifolia	..	..	..	..	..	..	..	..	..	..	..	..	1·3	0·1	..	..	..	..
Vicia sepium	..	..	1·0	0·3	..	..	..	..	..	..	..	..	0·6	0·1	..	..	..	..
V. lutea	..	..	..	..	..	..	..	..	..	..	..	..	..	..	..	..	..	..
Viola palustris	3·6	0·9	4·0	1·0	..	..	..	..	..	..	..	..	..	..	..	..	..	..
V. riviniana	5·7	1·4	5·0	1·4	8·0	1·9	..	..	8·0	1·9	7·9	2·0	6·3	2·0	8·3	2·2	..	..
Acrocladium cuspidatum	..	..	5·0	1·3	..	..	2·3	..	..	..	0·7	0·1	3·1	0·6	3·3	0·5	..	..
A. stramineum	..	..	1·0	0·3	..	..	..	..	..	..	..	..	..	..	..	..	..	..
Anomobryum filiforme	..	..	..	..	..	..	..	..	..	..	..	..	..	..	0·8	0·1	..	..
Antitrichia curtipendula	..	..	..	..	..	..	..	..	0·5	0·1	..	..	..	..	0·8	+	..	..
Atrichum undulatum	0·7	0·1	3·0	0·3	..	..	1·7	..	..	..	0·7	0·1	1·3	0·2	..	..	..	..
Aulacomnium palustre	..	..	3·0	0·3	..	..	..	..	..	..	..	..	..	..	..	..	..	..
A. turgidum	..	..	..	..	..	..	..	..	..	..	..	..	0·6	0·1	..	..	..	..
Barbula fallax	..	..	..	..	..	..	..	..	..	..	..	..	0·6	0·1	0·8	0·1	..	..
Brachythecium glareosum	..	..	..	..	..	..	..	..	..	..	..	..	1·3	0·3	..	..	..	..
B. rivulare	..	..	1·0	0·3	..	..	1·0	..	..	..	..	..	..	..	..	..	..	..
Breutelia chrysocoma	0·7	0·1	..	..	..	..	..	..	..	..	2·1	0·6	2·5	0·8	1·7	0·3	..	..
Bryum pallens	..	..	..	..	..	..	1·7	..	..	..	..	..	1·3	0·4	0·8	0·1	..	..
B. pseudotriquetrum	..	..	1·0	0·1	..	..	1·7	..	..	..	..	..	1·3	0·3	2·5	0·5	..	..
Campylium protensum	..	..	..	..	..	..	..	..	..	..	..	..	0·6	0·2	3·3	0·6	..	..
C. stellatum	..	..	..	..	..	..	1·3	..	..	..	..	..	1·3	0·3	0·8	0·2	..	..
Campylopus fragilis	..	..	..	..	..	..	..	..	..	..	1·4	0·1	1·3	0·3	..	..	..	..
Climacium dendroides	..	..	4·0	0·6	..	..	..	..	..	..	..	..	..	..	1·7	0·4	..	..
Cratoneuron commutatum	..	..	..	..	..	..	..	..	..	..	..	..	1·7	0·4	2·5	0·6	..	..
Ctenidium molluscum	..	..	1·0	0·1	..	..	..	..	..	..	2·1	0·7	5·6	1·8	10·0	2·8	..	..
Dicranella heteromalla	..	..	..	..	..	..	..	..	..	..	..	..	..	..	..	..	..	..
Dicranum bonjeani	..	..	1·0	0·1	..	..	..	..	..	..	..	..	5·6	0·6	..	..	..	..
D. fuscescens	..	..	..	..	..	..	..	..	..	..	..	..	..	..	..	..	..	..
D. majus	..	..	2·0	0·3	..	..	..	..	..	..	..	..	..	..	..	..	..	..
D. scoparium	2·1	0·4	..	..	..	..	..	..	..	..	3·6	0·6	5·0	0·8	2·5	0·3	5·7	0·7
Distichium capillaceum	..	..	..	..	..	..	..	..	..	..	..	..	..	..	0·8	0·2	..	..
Ditrichum flexicaule	..	..	..	..	..	..	..	..	..	..	..	..	..	..	5·8	1·8	..	..
Drepanocladus revolvens	..	..	..	..	..	..	0·7	..	..	..	..	..	1·9	0·4	..	..	..	..
D. uncinatus	..	..	..	..	..	..	..	..	..	..	1·4	0·2	0·6	0·1	4·2	0·8	..	..
Entodon orthocarpus	..	..	..	..	..	..	..	..	..	..	..	..	..	..	4·2	0·8	..	..
Eurhynchium praelongum	..	..	..	..	..	..	..	..	..	..	..	..	..	..	1·4	..	1·4	0·2
Fissidens adianthoides	..	..	..	..	..	..	..	..	..	..	0·6	0·2	0·6	0·2	2·5	0·4	..	..

Species	1	2	3	4	5	6	7	8	9	10	11	12	13	14	15	16	17	18
F. cristatus					0·2	1·3												
F. osmundoides			0·5	1·7	0·3	1·9	3·3	9·3	4·2	10·0	3·7		1·7	6·0	2·8	10·0	2·9	8·6
Hylocomium splendens	2·4	7·1	2·1	5·8	2·9	8·8	0·1	0·7									0·8	3·0
Hypnum callichroum					0·1	0·6	0·6	2·9	0·9	4·0								
H. cupressiforme	0·8	4·3	0·9	4·2	1·0	3·8												
H. hamulosum					0·2	0·6	0·1	0·7	0·4	2·0								
Leucobryum glaucum																		
Mnium cuspidatum		1·4			0·2	1·3	0·1											
M. hornum	0·3		0·1	0·8				1·4	0·1	0·5	2·3						0·3	1·4
M. orthorrhynchum		1·7	0·2	0·8	0·2	1·3	0·1				1·3				0·8	4·0		
M. pseudopunctatum			0·3	1·7			0·1	0·7	0·1	0·5	1·0				0·6	3·0	0·1	0·3
M. punctatum																		
M. seligeri					0·4	1·9	0·1										0·1	
M. stellare			0·6	3·3	0·1	0·6					2·7				0·8	4·0	0·1	
M. undulatum					0·1	0·6												
Neckera complanata																		
Oligotrichum hercynicum			0·2	0·8			1·9	7·9	0·4	1·5	3·3							
Philonotis fontana							0·1	0·7	1·6	6·0					0·3	1·0		
Plagiothecium silvaticum									1·1	3·5			1·1	4·0				
P. undulatum	0·2	1·4			0·8	1·3	1·3	5·0	1·0	4·0	1·7		2·2	9·0	0·3	1·0	0·3	1·4
Pleurozium schreberi	1·2	4·3			0·2	5·0					1·3						2·6	7·1
Pohlia nutans	1·7	7·1	0·8	3·3			0·1	0·7	0·1	0·5			0·5	2·0			0·6	3·0
Polytrichum alpinum	0·4	1·4	0·2	0·8			0·2	2·1	+	0·5			0·9	4·0	0·3	1·0	0·6	3·6
P. commune	1·2	4·3	1·1	4·2	1·2	5·0	0·6	2·1	1·3	4·5								
P. juniperinum																		
P. piliferum																		
P. urnigerum					0·4	1·9									1·6	6·0	0·6	3·6
Pseudoscleropodium purum	1·0	4·3	0·3	1·7			0·8	3·6			0·7		0·6	2·0	0·1	1·0		10·0
Ptilium crista-castrensis	0·3	1·4	0·1	0·8			0·1	0·7	0·2	0·5			3·5	10·0			0·3	1·4
Rhacomitrium canescens					0·4	1·9	1·5	5·7							0·1	1·0		0·7
R. fasciculare							0·7	0·7	0·3	1·0					0·3	9·0		0·7
R. lanuginosum																		
Rhodobryum roseum	0·6	2·9	0·1	0·8	1·0	4·4	1·9	6·4	0·3	4·5	1·0				2·4	3·0	0·6	3·6
Rhytidiadelphus loreus			1·3	5·8	1·6	8·1	1·9	6·4	1·5	8·0					0·4	1·0	0·6	3·6
R. squarrosus	2·8	8·6	1·8	6·7	1·4	5·0	0·9	3·6	1·9	2·5			0·3	1·0	0·4	3·0		
R. triquetrus	2·6	8·6							0·7	0·5								
Sphagnum auriculatum	0·3	1·4																
S. capillaceum																		
S. contortum																		
S. girgensohnii					0·1	0·6	0·1	0·7	0·1						0·6	1·0		
S. palustre															0·4	1·0		
S. plumulosum															0·5	1·0		
S. recurvum															0·1	1·0		
S. robustum															0·1	1·0		
S. squarrosum															0·1	1·0	0·2	0·7

[continued]

Species	Const.	Mean (c–a)	Const.	Mean (c–a)	Const.	Mean (c–a)	Const.	Mean (c–a)	Const.	Mean (c–a)	Const.	Mean (c–a)	Const.	Mean (c–a)	Const.	Mean (c–a)	Const.	Mean (c–a)	Const.	Mean (c–a)	Const.	Mean (c–a)
S. warnstorfianum			2·1																			
Thuidium delicatulum		0·7			1·0	0·3					2·1	0·6			3·3	0·5	5·0	0·9			1·4	0·6
T. tamariscinum	2·1		8·0	1·8				0·7	2·1	0·6	2·9	0·6	1·7	0·5	3·8	1·0	6·0	2·3			
Tortella tortuosa									2·9				5·8	1·7	3·1	0·6					
Trichostomum brachydontium													0·8	0·3							
Anastrepta orcadensis	0·7	0·1			1·0	0·1				0·5	0·1				1·3	0·1	0·5	0·1			2·9	0·4
Bazzania tricrenata															1·3	0·1					
Barbilophozia barbata	1·4	0·2			1·0	0·1				0·5	0·2						0·5	0·2			
B. floerkii					4·0	0·6				1·0	0·2				1·9	0·2	1·0	0·2			
B. hatcheri			1·0	0·3				0·7	0·1				0·8	0·2							
B. lycopodioides								0·7	0·1												
Calypogeia fissa			1·0	0·3											1·3	0·2					
C. trichomanis	0·7	0·1								0·5	0·1				0·6	0·1	0·5	0·1			
Chiloscyphus pallescens											0·7										0·7	
C. polyanthus			1·0	0·3						0·5	0·1				2·5	0·3					0·7	
Diplophyllum albicans	1·4	0·3								0·5		0·7	0·1	3·3	0·8	2·5	0·3			1·4	0·2
Frullania tamarisci								0·7	0·1						2·5	0·3			1·4	0·2	
Herberta adunca			8·0	1·5			1·7							1·3	0·2					
Lophocolea bidentata	3·6	0·6			4·0	0·8		0·7		2·1	0·2	0·8	0·2	2·5	0·4	2·0	0·4	1·4	0·2	
Lophozia incisa										0·7	0·1									
L. ventricosa							2·0	0·7	0·1						0·5	0·1	1·4	0·2	
Nardia scalaris			5·0	0·6										0·6	0·1					
Pellia fabbroniana			5·0	0·6										0·6	0·1					
Pellia spp.					5·0	1·2		0·7	0·1									
Plagiochila asplenioides											2·5	0·3	2·5	0·4					
Porella platyphylla										0·8	0·1	0·8	0·1					
Preissia quadrata										1·7	0·2	1·7	0·2					
Ptilidium ciliare	3·0	0·5	1·0	0·1			1·0	5·0	0·3		0·8	0·2			1·5	0·3		
Riccardia pinguis	3·0	0·5	1·0	0·1	5·0	1·2	1·0	5·0	0·7							
R. cf. sinuata			4·0	0·5												
Scapania aspera										2·5	0·3	0·6	0·2				
S. crassiretis	0·7	0·1						0·6	0·2	0·6	0·2					
S. gracilis	0·7		1·0	0·4			1·0						0·6	0·2			
S. irrigua							0·3									
S. nemorosa			1·0	0·1			0·7	0·1		0·8	0·1	1·3	0·1			0·8	0·1
S. undulata			1·0	0·1			1·4	0·4								
Tritomaria quinquedentata			1·0	0·3			0·7	0·1	1·3	0·3	3·3	0·6	1·3	0·3		
Cetraria aculeata							0·7	0·1	0·5	0·1	0·7	0·1	1·7	0·3	0·6	0·1	0·6	0·1
C. islandica							0·7	0·1				0·6	0·1	0·6	0·1
Cladonia bellidiflora							0·7	0·1				
C. coccifera							1·4	0·4			0·8	0·1		
C. gracilis							0·7	0·1				1·4	0·3
C. impexa							0·7	0·1				

	1	2	3	4	5	6	7	8	9	10	11	12	13	14	15	16	17	18
C. pyxidata	0·7	0·1	:	:	1·0	0·1	:	:	:	:	1·4	0·2	1·3	0·2	4·2	0·6	1·4	0·3
C. rangiferina agg.	0·7	0·1	:	:	1·0	0·1	:	:	0·5	0·1	0·7	0·2	:	:	:	:	:	:
C. sylvatica	0·7	0·1	:	:	1·0	0·1	:	:	0·5	0·1	3·6	0·7	:	:	:	:	:	:
C. tenuis	:	:	:	:	:	:	:	:	0·5	0·1	:	:	:	:	:	:	:	:
C. uncialis	:	:	:	:	:	:	:	:	:	:	1·4	0·3	:	:	:	:	:	:
Peltidea aphthosa var. leucophlebia	:	:	:	:	:	:	:	:	2·0	0·2	3·6	:	1·3	0·2	2·5	0·4	:	:
Peltigera canina	:	:	:	:	:	:	:	:	:	:	:	:	4·4	0·6	1·7	0·2	1·4	0·2
Solorina saceata	:	:	:	:	:	:	:	:	:	:	:	:	:	:	0·8	0·1	:	:

* Only three stands available, constancy values omited.

CHAPTER 7

DWARF-SHRUB HEATHS

G. H. GIMINGHAM

In literature, legend and in the affections of the people, heath vegetation has a central place among the characteristic features of Scottish landscape, and heather (*Calluna vulgaris*), the most widespread dominant, has acquired the status of a national flower. The communities of which the heathlands are composed occupy extensive areas, being in some cases particularly fine examples of their kind (Plates 37 and 38), and form part of a series which extends throughout much of Britain and the neighbouring oceanic and sub-oceanic parts of W. Europe, from S.W. Norway to Spain. While in many parts of this area heathlands are now rapidly being replaced by plantations and farm land, in Scotland heath is still retained and regarded by many as a vegetation-type which is not only attractive but valuable. Its value lies in the provision of grazing throughout the year in climates and on soils and terrain where to substitute a richer herbage would at present be uneconomic. Considerable stocks of sheep, and in some districts cattle also, are supported, while extensive areas are managed as grouse-moor or "deer forest" for sporting purposes: in numerous instances the requirements of sheep and grouse are combined. In the past the extent of heathland has been even greater, occupying much of the Lowlands now claimed by agriculture, industry and urban development. Today, the heaths with which this chapter is concerned, those of the forest zone or land below the tree limit, reach their greatest extent in the foothills, glens and lower slopes of the upland regions of the country. They are represented also in coastal districts, but only in a fragmentary way in the intervening territory. Similar communities occur on drained, or drying, peat-bogs.

The W. European heath formation extends from low-arctic and montane climatic regimes to conditions approaching those of the Mediterranean. An oceanic type of climate, however, is essential for its development, which requires not only the absence of temperature extremes but also an abundant and well-distributed rainfall with maintenance of a generally high atmospheric humidity. Under these conditions, heaths will develop on acidic soils, generally of low fertility, wherever forest is excluded. The whole of Britain falls within their climatic range and in Scotland there are few districts lacking examples of some type of heath community, although in the lowlands they may be confined now to small areas unfit for agriculture. However, they are clearly more vigorous

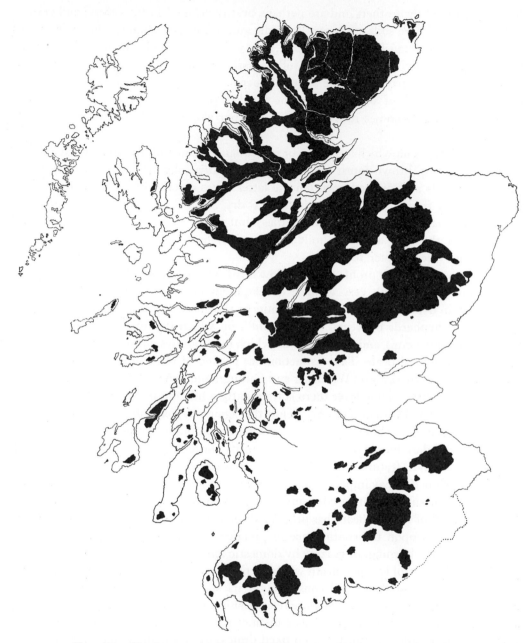

Fig. 38   Heath areas in Scotland. (Map compiled by C. L. Whittles (1950), *The Scottish Beekeeper*, **26**.) There is no map available showing the full extent of dwarf-shrub heaths in Scotland. However, the map reproduced here, restricted to areas in which *Calluna vulgaris* is extensively dominant, gives a useful impression of the general distribution of heathland.

in some districts than others and are perhaps best developed in the central and eastern upland regions where soils are generally acidic and of low base status, while rainfall lies between about 435 and 870 mm. (25-50 in.) per year (Fig. 38). On the more fertile soils, for example on many of the Perthshire hills, grassland often has a competitive advantage over heath, particularly under the added influence of grazing. Heath also largely gives place to other types of vegetation on the blanket peat of the hyper-oceanic western districts, where it becomes restricted to the steeper slopes or other very freely drained habitats.

The soil types on which heaths occur in Scotland include blown sand on fixed dunes (silicate syrosem), brown forest soils of low base status (oligotrophic braunerd), semi-podsols, podsols and drained peat. On the latter types a series of related communities may be traced from sites with free drainage ("dry" heath communities) to those with impeded drainage ("wet" heath communities), but where the substratum is waterlogged for much of the year and peat-building is active, heath is replaced by related bog communities (see Chapter 10).

The most usual soil profile to find below heath vegetation in Scotland is that of the iron humus podsol, with very variable development of the A_0 (raw humus) horizon. Differences in depth of this horizon contribute to the general distinction made by game-keepers and shepherds between "hard ground", on which the organic horizon is quite thin (up to about 5 cm.), and "soft ground" which incorporates podsolic soils with deeper organic horizons and peats. This distinction has proved of value in ecological investigations (Whittaker, 1960, 1961; Whittaker and Gimingham, 1962; see also Metcalfe, 1950). Beneath the purely organic layer there is frequently a horizon in which leached mineral grains are associated with humus (A_1). Below this again a typical ash-grey A_2 horizon may be visible, but in soils on which *Calluna* has long been dominant this may be masked by the presence of dark humic matter in some quantity throughout. A thin iron pan beneath the A_2 is a common feature under *Calluna*-dominated vegetation, and where this pan is strongly developed it may impede drainage, leading to gleying of the A_2 horizon and peat formation at the surface, with accompanying vegetational changes (cf. Plate 2 and p. 45).

Over most of its area heath has originated only after forest clearance, and its maintenance depends upon the continuance of practices which preclude a return of trees, normally periodic burning, or grazing by domestic animals, or a combination of both. In the absence of control by man, heath would in many cases give place to other vegetation, usually scrub or woodland, and consequently its status must be described as "semi-natural". It bears, however, a very close relationship to the climatic regime of W. Europe and, to this extent, can be regarded as a distinct regional formation occurring naturally where exposure, soil immaturity (as on fixed dunes) or occasionally soil infertility, limit the entry of trees. Indeed, on certain heathlands, once part of the native forest, trees will not nowadays readily recolonise, even where protected from burning and grazing, while commercial afforestation, although possible, is attended by certain difficulties. Such cases lead to unresolved debate on the status of heath vegetation, which on the one hand can be regarded as semi-natural if its origin was initially dependent on forest clearance, or, on the other, as a natural development in harmony with the environment, the role of man being merely that of "triggering-off" or accelerating a more or less natural replacement of forest by heath.

Apart, however, from the poorest soils and most exposed situations, a cessation of control by burning or grazing normally soon results in an invasion by birch (*Betula* sp.), often with rowan (*Sorbus aucuparia*)—as occurred on parts of several moors (for example Dinnet, Aberdeenshire) during and shortly after the 1939-45 war when staff for managing large acreages was lacking (cf. p. 270). Birch, sometimes accompanied or followed by Scots pine (*Pinus sylvestris*), may before long establish a closed canopy. However, "muir-burn" (the regular firing of heathland) is employed not only to prevent tree regeneration but also to promote new, young growth of *Calluna* which provides an important proportion of the diet of sheep and cattle when grazed on the heath, and of the red grouse (*Lagopus scoticus*). The rotational burning of sections of the "moors", which in Scotland is carried out as far as possible in the early spring but also to a considerable extent in autumn, is thus a fundamental aspect of moorland management and an ecological factor having profound effects (cf. p. 272).

The first ecological descriptions of Scottish heaths were those by R. Smith (1900), W. G. Smith (1902, 1905, 1911) and Hardy (1904). It is surprising, particularly in view of the importance of heathlands in the economy of the more sparsely populated parts of the country, and of the tensions between the interests of sheep-farming, sport and forestry in their use and development, that until recently they received little further attention from ecologists. Tansley (1949) in *The British Islands and their Vegetation* could do no more than base a brief account of Scottish heaths on the section contributed by W. G. Smith to the "Types of British Vegetation" (1911). Since then, however, a number of papers bearing on aspects of the ecology of heaths in Scotland have begun to dispel ignorance of the history of these communities, the influences at work in them, and the potentialities for their development. Several organisations such as the Nature Conservancy, the Hill Farming Research Organisation and the Macaulay Institute for Soil Research as well as University Botanical Departments and the Colleges of Agriculture are actively promoting research in this sphere, and the following account owes much to recent work in several of these centres.

GENERAL ASPECTS OF COMMUNITY STRUCTURE AND PHYSIOGNOMY

Dominant species and life-forms

Scottish heathland vegetation is in the main dominated by heather (*Calluna vulgaris*), which sometimes forms virtually pure stands over extensive areas. Since this species is a community dominant throughout such a wide range of habitat conditions there is considerable floristic diversity in the communities established under its influence (pp. 253-267). The use of the term "Callunetum" so common in the literature, therefore conveys little ecological information in the absence of further qualification.

Other species of Ericaceae such as *Erica cinerea*, *E. tetralix*, *Vaccinium myrtillus*, *V. vitis-idaea*, *Empetrum nigrum* and *Arctostaphylos uva-ursi* are often associated with *Calluna*, and under appropriate conditions one or more of these may equal it in importance or replace it as dominant. The leading species are all much branched, woody dwarf-shrubs. *Calluna* is often 0·75 m. in height and may exceed 1 m. (Plates 39 and 40), *Vaccinium myrtillus* may sometimes equal it, while *Erica cinerea*, *Vaccinium vitis-idaea* and *Erica tetralix* are generally shorter. All these, however, under favourable conditions are nanophanerophytes (renewal buds between 25 cm. and 2 m. above soil surface), but may behave as chamaephytes (renewal buds up to 25 cm. above surface) in more severe habitats. In *Empetrum nigrum* and *Arctostaphylos uva-ursi* the chamaephyte life-form is the more usual.

Apart from the occurrence of isolated trees or tree seedlings, the only other life-form of importance among the flowering plants of heath communities is the hemicryptophyte, into which fall most of the important grasses and sedges, e.g. *Deschampsia flexuosa*, *Molinia caerulea*, *Nardus stricta*, *Trichophorum cespitosum*, *Eriophorum* spp., *Carex binervis*, *C. pilulifera*, etc.

Table 23 gives a series of biological spectra from a variety of heath communities in Scotland, showing that in terms of species the hemicryptophytes may often be in excess of the combined figures for nanophanerophytes and chamaephytes, but the latter always contribute the greater cover and mass of the vegetation. The same is true of the examples of Scandinavian heaths included for comparison.

Stratification

Where scattered trees or tree seedlings occur these may be regarded as pioneers or relics of forest communities rather than as integral components of heath vegetation. Occasionally, however, shrubs such as *Juniperus communis* and *Ulex europaeus* occur with some regularity or form patches in heath communities, but they are scarcely now as typical a feature of Scottish heaths as they are of some related Scandinavian or W. European ones. Since the stratum they represent is so discontinuous or localised it has little effect on conditions below it and is ignored in the following discussion.

A closed canopy is normally formed by *Calluna*, at least in stands exceeding 5-8 years of age, sometimes in association with other species. Its height depends upon the habitat and the age of the stand: it may either be very uniform in an even-aged stand, such as frequently results from regeneration after burning, or undulating in an uneven-aged stand. Whereas in the former the canopy is often uninterrupted over large areas, in the latter there may be frequent gaps where the centre of an old bush has died out. On hill slopes the vegetational profile may resemble a series of descending waves owing to the main frame-branches of all plants becoming decumbent and parallel in the downward direction, so that the canopy of each bush comes to overlap the basal parts of the next below it.

Calluna-dominated communities are generally more or less distinctly stratified and

TABLE 23

Representation of Life-forms in Selected Examples of Heath Communities

Locality	Community-type	Proportion of species in each Raunkiaer Life-form Group as % total number of Phanerophyte species				No. of Phanerophyte species	No. of Bryophyte species	No. of Lichen species
		N*	Ch	H	G			
Yesnaby, Orkney	Oceanic *Calluna—Erica cinerea*	14·3	28·6	57·1	...	14	8	2
Daviot, Inverness-shire	*Calluna—Vaccinium*	11·1	22·2	55·6	11·1	18	7	2
Strathfinella Hill, Kincardineshire	*Calluna—Vaccinium*	11·5	15·4	65·4	7·7	26	16	4
Dinnet, Aberdeenshire	*Calluna—Arctostaphylos*	9·1	22·7	68·2	...	22	10	5
Forvie, Aberdeenshire	*Calluna—Empetrum nigrum*	...	16·7	83·3	...	12	7	11
Karmøy, S.W. Norway	Oceanic *Calluna—Erica cinerea*	14·3	10·7	67·9	7·1	28	11	4
Hallandsåsen, S.W. Sweden	*Calluna—Vaccinium*	17·6	11·8	58·8	11·8	17	11	3
Nörrevosborg, W. Jutland, Denmark	*Calluna—Empetrum nigrum*	16·7	33·3	33·3	16·7	6	6	12

N* = Nanophanerophytes   H = Hemicryptophytes

Ch = Chamaephytes   G = Geophytes

Based on flora lists from areas of 40 sq. m.

this stratification is associated with the development of characteristic micro-climatic regimes which are of importance in the regeneration of *Calluna* itself and other species of the community, and in the establishment of tree seedlings. In well-developed heath communities, common in the moist upland regions, four strata may be differentiated. (Simpler versions which appear in other habitats are described later, p. 239.)

Heaths with dense canopy and four strata. The most complex type of stratification frequently takes a form such as the following:

(i) *Calluna* canopy at its densest between 25 cm. and 40 cm. above ground, scattered branches extending to between 60 and 80 cm. or more.

(ii) Second stratum, discontinuous, at about 10-20 cm., consisting of subordinate dwarf-shrubs (e.g. *Vaccinium* spp., *Empetrum nigrum*) and grasses or sedges (e.g. *Deschampsia flexuosa*, *Carex binervis*, *Eriophorum* spp. or *Trichophorum cespitosum*).

(iii) Third stratum, at about 5-10 cm., of robust mosses, e.g. *Pleurozium schreberi*, *Hylocomium splendens* and low-growing herbs, e.g. *Potentilla erecta*, *Galium saxatile*.

(iv) Fourth stratum, the "ground stratum", of mat-forming or short erect mosses, e.g. *Hypnum cupressiforme*, *Pohlia nutans* and lichens.

Micro-climatic conditions. These strata exert marked effects upon micro-climatic conditions. Light intensity is reduced by the *Calluna* canopy to less than 20 per cent. of that in the open, while at ground level under the additional strata it may fall to below 0·5 per cent. This factor alone plays a large part in controlling the establishment of plants beneath the canopy and restricts the regeneration of *Calluna* itself to gaps in the canopy, since individuals will not normally survive long under less than 40 per cent. daylight.

The close-packed arrangement of shoots at the periphery of the bush is effective in retarding air-movement. For example, when a wind speed of 2·6 m./sec. (8½ ft./sec.) was recorded at 1 m. above ground on a heath near Aberdeen, the speed at canopy-level was only about 0·8 m./sec. (2⅓ ft./sec.). At ground level below dense moss strata air-flow is normally eliminated except perhaps when gales are blowing above, since as Geiger (1959) points out, "the retarding effect of a low plant cover is relatively less, the higher the wind velocity". The above measurements closely parallel those given by Stocker (1923) for a heath near Bremerhaven.

Temperature and humidity conditions also relate very closely to stratification, but although several investigators (e.g. Delany, 1953; Stoutjesdijk, 1959) have measured temperature profiles on passing from the air above heath vegetation down through the canopy to the ground, comprehensive data on this are lacking. Table 24 (p. 240) gives some representative measurements from Scottish heaths. In cloudy weather there is little difference between the temperature of the air surrounding the *Calluna* shoots at canopy level and that at a height of 1 m. above ground. In still, sunny weather, however, the temperature at canopy level may be several degrees higher. This may produce a local drop in relative humidity and consequently promote evaporation from the plants. In windy weather, by contrast, there is rather more mixing of the air; temperature and humidity differences are then lessened, although the marked reduction of air movement at canopy level already noticed will tend to maintain them to some extent.

Rather little solar radiation penetrates the canopy in this type of community, so that temperature usually remains lower and more constant within, while humidity is higher. The moss strata generally remain moist except in drought periods, and at ground level an even more constant environment is maintained, slow to warm up and yet well protected from intense cold. In summer the ground temperature is usually between 2° and 5° lower than that of the canopy, while relative humidity is normally about 80 per cent., frequently remaining for long periods about 95 per cent. As Leyton (1955) and others have pointed out, *Calluna* vegetation of this kind is effective in conserving surface moisture. This is an important factor affecting community composition and may also have some influence on the establishment of planted tree seedlings.

In winter, reduction in temperature by radiation away from the plants on clear, cold nights will reverse the pattern described above, being greatest in the upper part of the canopy. This may lead in frosty weather to thick deposits of rime on the shoots. Where, as so often, the surface of the canopy is undulating, the slight hollows may be shaded from the low winter sun throughout much of the day and the rime will then remain clothing the shoots. In warmer weather, these shaded patches may remain saturated with moisture as the rest drys out during the day.

Simpler types of community structure. In habitats less favourable for the development of the complex type of community structure one or more of the main strata may be lacking, while those represented may be less dense, or interrupted by gaps. A very common type is that in which the canopy produced by a luxuriant even-aged stand of *Calluna*, resulting from well-controlled burning management, becomes so dense as to exclude all other strata with the exception of a sparse ground stratum of mosses or lichens developed in patches beneath the thinner parts of the canopy. Elsewhere the ground is covered in a thick deposit of *Calluna* litter.

The drier substrata often lead to a lower and more patchy *Calluna* canopy, usually at about 20-30 cm., with an irregular second stratum of subordinate dwarf-shrubs such as *Erica cinerea* at about 15 cm., and a more or less well-developed ground stratum of mosses and lichens. In very exposed situations this type of structure may be reduced still further to two strata only, with a low, even, but not dense, *Calluna* canopy at about 10-15 cm. and a discontinuous ground stratum consisting predominantly of lichens. In both cases much bare ground is visible from above and a micro-climatic regime considerably different from that described in the previous section is operative. Light intensity at ground level is often as high as 60 per cent. of that above the vegetation, and where the *Calluna* canopy is low and rather open it seldom falls below 20 per cent. Correspondingly, more radiation reaches the lower levels, and maximum temperatures in sunny weather may be recorded at ground level rather than in the canopy (Delany, 1953).

TABLE 24

Examples of Temperature and Humidity Profiles in *Calluna* Communities

Height above ground at which determinations were made (cm.)	Series 1 Sun after frost T (°C.)	R.H. (%)	Series 2 Sun after frost T (°C.)	R.H. (%)	Series 1 Heavy cloud T (°C.)	R.H. (%)	Series 2 After 1 hr. full sun, following heavy cloud T (°C.)	R.H. (%)	Series 1 Hazy sun, no wind T (°C.)	R.H. (%)	Series 2 Full sun, light wind T (°C.)	R.H. (%)	Series 1 Windy, with drizzle T (°C.)	R.H. (%)	Series 2 Clearing after rain T (°C.)	R.H. (%)	Series 3 Sun after rain T (°C.)	R.H. (%)	Series 4 Full sun, moderate wind T (°C.)	R.H. (%)
100	5·7	70·0	6·8	66·0																
90																				
80																				
70																				
60																				
50	5·8	69·5	7·5	67·5																
40			8·6	62·5	3·3	93	4·4	94·5	14·8	62·0	14·4	56·5					14·2	72		
30			7·6*	70·0*	3·2	88	4·4	90·5	14·4	65·5	14·2	63·5	11·2	90	13·2	71	15·2	73	16·5	61
20	6·8	67·5											11·1	93	13·3	78			16·1	62
10	5·0*	96·5*	5·4*	94·0*																
Ground level	5·0*	94·5*	5·2*	96·5*	3·2*	88*	3·7*	95·5*	13·4*	75·5*	13·0*	79·5*	11·2*	93*	10·3*	99*	13·7*	95*	14·3*	85*

January: Forvie, Aberdeenshire

January: Cairn-Monearn, Kincardineshire

A warm February day: Netherley, Kincardineshire

July: hill slopes near Lochinver, Sutherland

* Readings taken amongst mosses.   - - - - Level of *Calluna* canopy.   T(°C.)—Temperature.   R.H.(%)—Relative humidity.

Conversely, in winter conditions there may be more loss of heat from the lower parts of the plants and from the ground than in the more complex types of structure, leading to greater fluctuations in the micro-climate at ground level. Similarly, desiccating conditions may prevail more frequently at ground level.

In certain dune heaths, the low *Calluna* bushes become dome-shaped with an exceedingly dense development of the shoots at the periphery, often stimulated by grazing. This canopy is generally formed at only 10-20 cm. above the ground surface, thus enabling the more robust mosses such as *Pleurozium schreberi*, *Hylocomium splendens* and *Rhytidiadelphus triquetrus* to grow out to the periphery, intermingling their branches with the shoots of *Calluna*. This fusion of the *Calluna* canopy with the taller of the two moss strata results in so great a reduction of light intensity below (readings as low as 0·02 per cent. have been recorded) that any further colonisation at surface level is excluded. Apart from gaps or thin portions in the canopy, below which *Hypnum cupressiforme*, *Cladonia* spp. and a few others may be present, the ground is covered only by *Calluna* litter and the dead parts of the larger mosses.

In the majority of wet heaths *Calluna*, if present, is variable in height and produces only a weakly developed and open canopy below which *Erica tetralix* and other species may form a stratum at about 20-25 cm., sometimes fairly uniform but never dense. The lack of a dense canopy, together with the more or less permanent supply of ground-water, permits development of a continuous ground stratum usually dominated by *Sphagnum* spp. Relative humidity of the air is thus maintained at high levels close to the ground in spite of the lack of a dense protecting canopy. According to the weather conditions, there is a more or less rapid decrease in humidity on passing upwards. Greater freedom of air-movement obtains in this type of structure than in some of the others, resulting in less appreciable stratification of temperature.

Stratification of root systems

Some information on the spatial arrangement of root systems in certain types of Scottish heathland soils is given by Boggie (1956). Under conditions of free drainage abundant *Calluna* roots are found to a considerable depth as, for example, to the base of a 0·75 m. deep podsol profile in Kincardineshire, with a few penetrating even more deeply between the boulders which form a continuous **C** horizon below. Among mosses or in deep moist litter *Calluna* stems, often procumbent at the base, become buried and give rise to adventitious roots which densely occupy the upper 3 cm. of the soil profile. Between this and a depth of about 10 cm. the larger roots are closely intertwined, while below this level the finer descending roots are rather less concentrated (Plate 41). Roots of *Deschampsia flexuosa* may also extend throughout the full depth of the profile.

A similar pattern is observed in shallower podsolic soils, except that where downwardly growing *Calluna* roots meet an indurated horizon, frequent in Scotland between depths of 60 cm. and 70 cm., they spread out laterally and form a close mat which can be peeled off intact when the loose soil above is removed. This is sometimes also seen just above a thin iron pan (Plate 41).

Q

On dune heaths *Calluna* roots may extend throughout depths of 80 cm., or more, of blown sand, often ceasing only at a junction between the sand and an underlying denser material such as clay or a buried, compacted "fossil" soil. Rhizomes and roots of *Carex arenaria* are frequently closely intertwined with those of *Calluna* down to similar depths, although at the lower levels these are probably dead. A dense stratum of adventitious roots is again evident just below the soil surface, where accumulating blown sand and litter deposited by *Calluna* and mosses surrounds the contorted stem bases.

A strikingly different pattern characterises heaths developing on peat. Here, while species such as *Eriophorum vaginatum* send active roots down to 50 cm. or more, those of *Calluna* are restricted in depth, for example to the upper 20 cm., the majority occupying only the top 5-10 cm. Below this they spread horizontally as if they had come against a barrier, sometimes extending outwards to distances of over 60 cm. It is probable that this limited rooting zone corresponds to the part of the soil lying above a water-table, at least in summer, providing a medium which is aerated and oxidising.

Boggie, Hunter and Knight (1958) have further shown, by the use of radioactive tracers, that in Scottish heaths even where the rooting depth of *Calluna* is considerable, active uptake of ions is very much greater in the upper 10 cm. of soil than below. On mineral soils this applies also to other species of the community, but on deep peat, species such as *Trichophorum cespitosum*, *Eriophorum vaginatum* and *E. angustifolium* show substantial uptake from lower levels.

FLORISTIC COMPOSITION OF HEATH COMMUNITIES

It is a feature of lowland heath communities that, although there is very considerable floristic diversity resulting in a number of associations, *Calluna vulgaris* is almost always present. It is not necessarily always the dominant, although as already mentioned, this is frequently the case. Very few other species have such a high percentage presence when all types of heath are considered; it may be approached in Scotland by some mosses such as *Pleurozium schreberi*, *Hypnum cupressiforme*,* *Dicranum scoparium* and perhaps *Hylocomium splendens*, but even these may be lacking on the lichen-rich dune heaths.

The abundance of *Calluna* in most heaths has a great influence on the representation of other species, owing to its marked reaction upon the habitat. Besides the influences mentioned in connection with stratification of the communities, *Calluna* deposits litter which, under the Scottish climate, gives rise to a raw humus constituting is in general an acid (pH 3·4-3·9), moisture-retaining, poorly aerated material with a high C/N ratio, in which nitrification is slow. Species which flourish in such a habitat are limited in number: the average of the total number of species, including bryophytes and lichens, in 4 sq. m. samples of seventeen heathland stands was 17. Certain stands occurring on soils of relatively high base status are excluded from this figure; the mean total number of species in five of these was 41. (Figures from McVean and Ratcliffe, 1962.)

* The var. *ericetorum* is widespread, but other forms occur as well. Forms and varieties of this complex species have not been distinguished in the following discussion and Tables.

Details of the several, more or less distinctive, assemblages of species on heaths are given below, but there are certain general features applying to Scotland as a whole. The first of these is the widespread occurrence of *Erica cinerea*, which is a regular component of the communities on all but the wetter soils. This fact alone relates the heaths of Scotland (and Britain in general) to those of the Faeroes, W. Norway, and N. and W. France, rather than to those of Sweden, Denmark, N. Germany, Holland, etc. In other words, Scottish examples belong to the more oceanic groups of heath communities. The frequent occurrence of certain other species, e.g. *Carex binervis*, *Blechnum spicant*, *Listera cordata*, *Dactylorchis maculata* ssp. *ericetorum*, *Plagiothecium undulatum* reinforces this conclusion.

A further feature of the floristic composition of Scottish heaths, resulting from their geographical situation, is that a number of species having northerly types of distribution are frequent while others of southern affinities common on English heaths are generally lacking. So for example, *Trientalis europaea*, *Empetrum nigrum*, *Vaccinium vitis-idaea* and *Hylocomium splendens* are familiar in Scottish heaths; whereas *Ulex minor* and *Cuscuta epithymum* are generally absent. From this angle many Scottish heaths may be related to those of Scandinavia rather than to those of N. Germany, the Low Countries, France, etc., and this is emphasised by the importance of *Vaccinium myrtillus* and *V. vitis-idaea* (also in places *Arctostaphylos uva-ursi*) which indicate affinities with the heaths of S.W. Sweden. An interesting exception to this trend is *Genista anglica* which is prominent in certain heaths of N.E. and N. Central Scotland, as well as in England, while on the Continent it becomes a regular component of heath communities only from N. Germany southwards (Fig. 39, pp. 244, 245). In this respect the Scottish heathland flora shows an interesting parallel to that of the province of Halland in S.W. Sweden, where there is a limited penetration of "southern" species into an otherwise Scandinavian and "northern" assemblage.

Directions of variation in floristic composition

Considerations such as those just mentioned suggest that several distinct trends of variation in floristic composition may be recognisable, each associated with variations in one of the more important environmental factor-complexes ("directions of variation", cf. Sjörs, 1950). Although in the section devoted to Communities (p. 251) an attempt will be made to recognise and describe a number of more or less distinctive "types", heath vegetation presents a complex series of varying combinations of species better regarded as a continuum of variation, the "types" simply representing the more commonly occurring variants. Such variations in floristic composition depend, for example, upon:

   (i) differences in the macroclimate between different parts of the country,
   (ii) differences in altitude, introducing climatic variations similar to (i),
   (iii) local habitat variation with accompanying differences in microclimate and soil factors,
   (iv) differences in past history, including past duration of heath vegetation, varying types of management (burning, grazing, etc.).

Treating these in turn, some account may be given of floristic diversity in Scottish heaths.

(i) Certain species rise or fall in abundance, or reach the limits of their geographical range, in relation to climatic gradients between one part of the country and another.

Variation from south to north is seen in the increasing prominence of *Empetrum nigrum*, and perhaps also of *Vaccinium myrtillus*, *V. vitis-idaea*, *Trientalis europaea*, *Cladonia rangiferina*, etc., in the heaths on passing northwards through Scotland. This may be attributed to increasing climatic severity, which is emphasised by the occurrence of species such as *Festuca vivipara*, *Arctostaphylos uva-ursi*, *Empetrum hermaphroditum*,

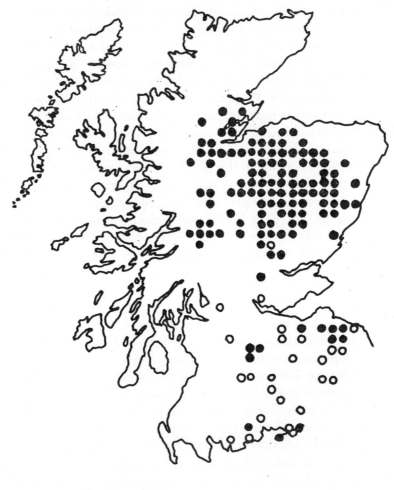

○   Before 1930

●   1930 onwards

FIG. 39A. Scottish distribution of *Genista anglica*. (From: *Atlas of the British Flora*, 1962, p. 100.)

Juniperus communis ssp. *nana*, *Lycopodium selago*, *Cetraria islandica* in heaths at low altitudes towards the north.

Variation which may be related to increasing "oceanicity" of the climate towards the west and the northern coastal regions (with Orkney and Shetland) includes the increased prominence of *Erica cinerea* wherever soils remain freely drained, while *Vaccinium vitis-idaea* and to a lesser extent *V. myrtillus* decline or drop out. *Trientalis europaea* is also more prominent in eastern than western heath communities. Other species illustrating this direction of variation are

FIG. 39B Outline of the general distribution of *Genista anglica*.

Carex binervis, *Hypericum pulchrum*, *Empetrum nigrum*, *Blechnum spicant*, *Dactylorchis maculata* ssp. *ericetorum*, *Selaginella selaginoides*, *Rhacomitrium lanuginosum*, *Rhytidiadelphus loreus* and *Pleurozia purpurea*, all of which become more frequent in heath communities of the more highly oceanic regions. Sample areas in such communities also normally give longer lists of mosses and especially of leafy liverworts. In particular, a number of species largely confined in the east to moist habitats such as woods, damp rocks, etc., appear with some regularity in western heaths: for example, *Dicranum majus*, *Isothecium myosuroides*, *Mnium hornum*, *M. undulatum*, *Thuidium tamariscinum*, *Diplophyllum albicans* and *Frullania tamarisci*. Similarly, species which on the east figure largely in the wetter types of heath community sometimes have a wider ecological range in the west: among these are *Erica tetralix*, *Salix repens*, *Breutelia chrysocoma*, and *Rhytidiadelphus squarrosus*.

(ii) Increasing altitude normally gives rise to a direction of variation similar to that related to increasing climatic severity ((i) above). The cover contribution of the *Vaccinium* spp., for example, frequently increases with altitude, while certain upland species such as *Antennaria dioica*, *Lycopodium selago* and *Juniperus communis* ssp. *nana* may begin to contribute significantly to communities even below the potential forest limit.

(iii) Among "directions of variations" arising from local habitat differences are the following:

(*a*) Changes in community composition on approaching the sea coast. *Festuca rubra*, for instance, becomes a regular component of maritime heaths, while examples very close to the sea may contain *Armeria maritima*, *Plantago maritima* and *Sedum anglicum*, or, where the substratum consists mainly of wind-blown sand as on dune heaths, *Ammophila arenaria* and *Carex arenaria*. A further frequent component of maritime heaths is a group of species indicative of mineral enrichment of the soil (see section (*c*)) such as *Thymus drucei*, *Succisa pratensis* and sometimes *Antennaria dioica*. This enrichment may in some cases come from the deposition of blown sand, but it probably derives also from solutes contained in fine spray and rain from clouds coming in across the sea, especially in the west.

(*b*) Differences in the composition of communities on slopes of differing exposure. Such differences occur where all habitat factors apart from local climate are more or less uniform and are well shown, for example, on the low conical hills of Lewisian gneiss on the north-west coast of Scotland. Examination of a number of stands of *Calluna—Erica cinerea* heath communities on the more freely drained sites below 305 m. (1000 ft.) demonstrated the striking restriction of certain species of the "northern" element of the flora, such as *Vaccinium myrtillus* and *Empetrum nigrum*, to north-facing slopes (Fig. 40). Other species, although less prominent components of the communities, are either similarly restricted or else more numerous on northern than southern slopes, as for example, *Lycopodium alpinum*, *Hylocomium splendens*, *Cetraria islandica* and seedlings of *Sorbus aucuparia*. Bryophytes in general are more prominent on the north sides of hills both as regards number of species and cover contributed. Certain members of the "oceanic" element in the flora also appear to be more widespread and numerous on northern faces than in corresponding communities with southerly exposure; they include *Blechnum spicant*, *Hypericum pulchrum* and *Rhacomitrium lanuginosum*. Southern slopes are characterised by earlier flowering of species such as *Erica cinerea*.

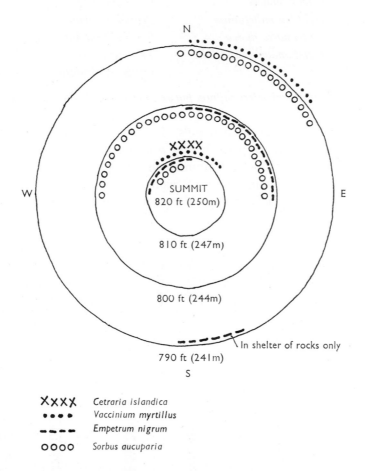

FIG. 40 Diagram illustrating limitation of certain species to the north facing slopes on contours at three altitudes around a symmetrical hill near Lochinver, Sutherland.

(c) Variation in soils from types poor in available mineral nutrients to ones which are rather richer. This is accompanied by increasing floristic richness in the community, such that at one end of the range are communities with as few as six species of flowering plants, mainly Ericaceae (but with bryophytes and particularly lichens in addition), while at the other, numerous species of grasses and herbs may be included of which the following list gives some examples:

Anthoxanthum odoratum	*Euphrasia* spp.
Sieglingia decumbens	*Hypochoeris radicata*
Carex nigra	*Linum catharticum*
Carex panicea	*Polygala vulgaris*
Achillea millefolium	*Prunella vulgaris*
Antennaria dioica	*Succisa pratensis*
Campanula rotundifolia	*Thymus drucei*
	Lotus corniculatus

A few mosses, such as *Pseudoscleropodium purum*, are perhaps also rather characteristic of "herb-rich" heaths.

(*d*) Variation from freely drained soils, through types with impeded drainage, to those which are seasonally or permanently waterlogged. This hydrologic sequence, which may be found on soils derived from almost any parent material, is so frequently repeated in the undulating topography of Scotland that it may be treated as a "soil-vegetation catena" (Fig. 41). The floristic variation usually starts with heaths rich in

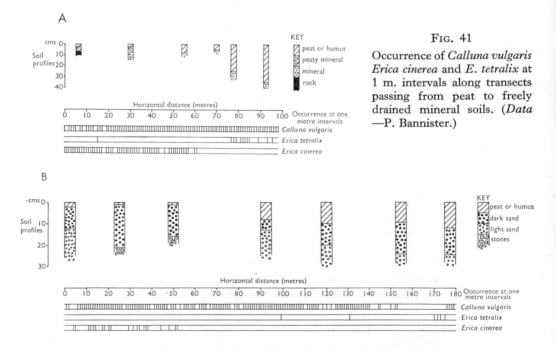

FIG. 41

Occurrence of *Calluna vulgaris* *Erica cinerea* and *E. tetralix* at 1 m. intervals along transects passing from peat to freely drained mineral soils. (*Data* —P. Bannister.)

Erica cinerea on the most freely drained profiles, often admixed with *Calluna, Deschampsia flexuosa* and sometimes *Vaccinium myrtillus*. When drainage is impeded, leading perhaps to gleying, *E. cinera* is lacking, *Calluna* is dominant and *Erica tetralix* may enter together with *Juncus squarrosus*. With further deterioration of drainage and increase in the quantity of water retained in the rooting region, *E. tetralix* increases in abundance, and may be associated with *Molinia caerulea, Nardus stricta, Pedicularis sylvatica, Narthecium ossifragum*, etc. *Calluna* decreases, and is excluded under conditions of prolonged water-logging when a "wet-heath" community results, dominated by *E. tetralix* with *Trichophorum cespitosum, Eriophorum vaginatum, Myrica gale, Carex echinata, Polytrichum commune, Sphagnum*, etc. This grades into the bog communities characteristic of wet peat. Such sequences, with continuous transition from one end to the other, which may be only a few yards apart or a mile or more, may occur on any heath-covered slope. The same pattern of variation occurs despite differences related to local climate, soil parent material, etc.

(*e*) Certain features of floristic composition are also associated with the variation from soils which are largely mineral in content with a shallow A_0 horizon of raw humus ("hard ground") to those having a considerable depth of organic "top" ("soft ground"— raw humus or peat). It is difficult to separate the effects of these factors from those related to the hydrologic characteristics of the habitat, but *Erica cinerea* for example belongs mainly to soils with little organic accumulation at the surface, and this tendency is shown even more strongly by *Arctostaphylos uva-ursi*. It is brought out again by variation in the bryophytic stratum from communities in which short turf-forming species are prominent to those with dense mat or weft forms, or sometimes *Sphagnum*.

(iv) Variations due to differences in the past history of heathland areas may be separated into those dependent largely on the time-interval since the origin of the community and those related to management practices.

(*a*) Certain aspects of floristic composition may vary with the time-interval since the initial derivation of heath from forest. "Younger" heaths may be rich in shade-tolerant species such as *Deschampsia flexuosa* and other indicators of woodland conditions (a possible example being the beautiful moss *Ptilium crista-castrensis*, a local component of Scottish heaths), while in longer-established communities there has been ample time for the entry of species excluded from forest, e.g. *Erica cinerea*, and suppression of the grasses. It has often been held that the occurrence of species such as *Anemone nemorosa, Oxalis acetosella* and *Polypodium vulgare* in heaths is a sign of recent derivation from woodland, but they also occur in long-established heaths both in Scotland and on the Continent, as well as at altitudes above the normal limit of forest.

(*b*) Grazing. Detailed observation and experiment on the influence of grazing animals has been largely confined to sheep. With increasing grazing intensity the dominance of *Calluna* is at first enhanced (under relatively mild grazing) so that its increasing cover tends to exclude other species including *Erica cinerea* (Gimingham, 1949). Many herbaceous species are also progressively eliminated, and this factor may account partially for the scarcity of species such as *Polypodium vulgare*. Thus, Spence (1960) has pointed out that in South Uist and Shetland, *Polypodium* is a regular component of the vegetation of ledges and islands in lochs, which are not subjected to grazing and burning. Further increase in grazing intensity damages *Calluna*, which may be eliminated in favour of grasses. This change (cf. Tansley, 1949) takes place more readily on base-rich soils where a productive pasture composed, for example, of *Festuca ovina* with *Agrostis* spp., etc., may result, but where *Pteridium aquilinum* is present in the area it may be given the opportunity to spread to serious proportions. Alternatively, on acid, base-poor soils *Deschampsia flexuosa* may increase and some surface erosion may take place in dry habitats, while in wet conditions *Nardus stricta*, *Molinia caerulea* or *Trichophorum cespitosum* may become dominant in almost pure stands.

Cattle and deer also contribute to the effects of the grazing factor on the composition of moorland communities. They may be responsible for the failure of tree-seedling establishment and, along with burning, for the very localised occurrence of shrubs such as *Juniperus communis*, so prominent a feature of N.W. European heaths (cf. also Chapter 6).

(*c*) Burning. Directions of variation resulting from the occurrence of fire depend upon its intensity (the temperatures reached) and frequency. A single very hot fire, in which the whole vegetation is destroyed and the surface humus or peat ashed down to depths of 10 cm. or more, may entirely alter the composition of the vegetation for many years. The temperatures produced in such fires, starting accidentally or from failure to control a routine burn in dry windy weather, have never been measured, but they certainly exceed 800°C. The organic horizon of the soil may be destroyed over considerable areas, erosion gulleys may form, and colonisation of the sterilised, leached mineral surface may be very slow. One such area in Inverness-shire examined five years after the fire, had the following community:

> *Polytrichum juniperinum* and *Ceratodon purpureus* (co-dominant).
> *P. piliferum* and *P. commune* (frequent).
> Occasional plants of *Calluna vulgaris*, *Agrostis tenuis*, *Deschampsia flexuosa*, *Festuca ovina*, *Juncus squarrosus*, *Nardus stricta*, *Carex nigra*, *Anthoxanthum odoratum*, *Rumex acetosella*, *Aira praecox*.

In time, however, it may be presumed that there would be renewed formation of a raw humus horizon and a heath community would return.

In the well-controlled fires employed in the management of many heathlands, temperatures just above ground surface seldom exceed 800°C. and normally fall between 300°C. and 500°C. (Whittaker, 1961). The practice of burning at more or less regular intervals, however, may cause more permanent differences in the flora than the occasional severe fire. With extremely frequent fires (e.g. at intervals of from one to six years), the heathland community characteristic of any particular region of Scotland may be modified by the elimination of all herbaceous species lacking buried perennating organs. Even such species as *Vaccinium vitis-idaea* may be lost, and the dominance of *Calluna* reduced, since although it regenerates readily after fire it is not amongst the species which re-establish cover most rapidly. Consequently *Pteridium aquilinum* (cf. p. 273), *Vaccinium myrtillus*, *Nardus stricta*, *Molinia caerulea*, and *Juncus squarrosus* may be among the invaders, according to the moisture regime of the habitat. Certain other resistant species may multiply, including *Carex pilulifera* and other *Carex* species, *Blechnum spicant*, etc.

This type of community grades into those produced by a less frequent burning routine, with intervals often of eight to fifteen years between fires. This is normal burning practice, designed to maintain the dominance of *Calluna* at its maximum. It leads to the progressive elimination not only of species most sensitive to fire but also of those sensitive to competition with *Calluna*. Almost pure stands of *Calluna*, with few associates other than bryophytes and lichens, may be produced over large areas. Still longer intervals between fires permit a richer floristic composition to be maintained approaching that of unburnt areas in the same district.

The actual floristic composition of Scottish heathland communities is, therefore, a product on the one hand of climatic and edaphic factor-complexes varying in different directions across the country and, on the other, of varying intensities of influences exerted directly or indirectly by man both at present and in the past. The composition of any particular community can be interpreted fully only with reference to all these influences. In this type of vegetation perhaps more than in most others the chances of similar groupings of controlling factors occurring in many distinct localities are low. The variation in community composition is correspondingly great, and may be in the nature of a more or less continuous network of trends. Any particular example of a heathland community may be regarded as occupying a point on this network, with related types occurring along the numerous different directions of variation produced by gradients in the various controlling factors.

The Communities

Despite what has just been said it remains possible to compare the composition of many examples of Scottish heathland communities and to group those which are most alike. Amongst the first to attempt this was W. G. Smith (1905, 1911) who suggested the following simple scheme:

HEATHER ASSOCIATIONS:
(a) Heath or dry heather moor (Heide) where *Calluna vulgaris* occurs with *Erica cinerea* and associates which prefer dry soils.
(b) Heather moor (Heide moor) thoroughly dominated by *Calluna vulgaris* and associates preferring a slight depth of peat:
   (i) exclusively *Calluna*, often on sloping ground;
   (ii) *Calluna* and *Erica tetralix*, peat deeper and moister.
(A "mixture of Grass Heath and Heather Associations" is also recognised.)

In establishing these groups, reference was made both to the chief dominants and to an aspect of the habitat—the nature of the substratum. Tansley (1949), however, took the view that there was "no good vegetational distinction" between "*Calluna* heath" and "*Calluna* moor" (as described by Smith) but, as can now be shown, Smith had merely picked on one "direction of variation", that which occurs on passing between "hard" and "soft" ground. Tansley, contrasting "upland heaths" with "lowland heaths", emphasised the altitudinal "direction of variation". Both treatments are, however, inadequate for the purpose of establishing a convenient grouping of those communities which are most alike and occur in similar habitats.

In 1940 Muir and Fraser, by detailed description of the heath communities in a restricted area of Aberdeenshire, produced a useful grouping of heath communities based on the leading dominants. While recognising that it was impossible to tell how far this scheme would apply to other parts of the country, Zehetmayr regarded it as the most complete description of Scottish heath vegetation available to him in 1960 for his bulletin on "Afforestation of Upland Heaths", and he summarises it as follows:

DRY HEATH TYPES:

Calluna—Erica cinerea

Calluna with abundant *Erica cinerea* forming the ground cover, subsidiaries not very frequent and usually suppressed.

Calluna—Vaccinium myrtillus

Calluna dominant, with abundant *V. myrtillus* co-dominant; *V. vitis-idaea* generally frequent.

Calluna—Arctostaphylos

Calluna dominant but open. Undergrowth of *Arctostaphylos*. Many subsidiaries.

Calluna—Deschampsia—Vaccinium myrtillus

Calluna dominant but open; subdominant or locally co-dominant *Deschampsia flexuosa* and *Vaccinium myrtillus*.

MOIST HEATH TYPES:

Calluna—Deschampsia flexuosa

Calluna dominant, with occasionally flowering, partly suppressed *D. flexuosa* abundant. Turf usually quite covered.

Calluna—Vaccinium

Calluna dominant, with suppressed or poor growth of *V. myrtillus* and *V. vitis-idaea* abundant. Turf exposed and showing growth of encrusting lichens.

Calluna—Nardus

Calluna normally dominant, with *Nardus* sub-dominant or co-dominant. *Pleurozium schreberi* the chief moss, along with patches of *Sphagnum*.

Submoorland types

Variable subtypes characterised by the presence of peat, subsidiary and co-dominant plants such as *Erica tetralix, Eriophorum vaginatum, Trichophorum cespitosum, Carex* and *Juncus* spp. abundant or locally abundant. *Sphagnum* spp. and *Pleurozium schreberi* usually the most frequent mosses.

EXPOSURE TYPES:

(Details of "Dry Eroded *Calluna*" and "Wet *Calluna—Cladonia*".)

It is now possible to suggest a more comprehensive scheme of groups, resulting from the scrutiny of tables recording the floristic composition of some 300 sample areas of heathland stands in Scotland. Since, as indicated above, these communities exhibit more or less continuous variation, grouping is at best an arbitrary division. Different arrangements could be adopted with equal success while transitional examples between groups will always occur. However, the following groups each incorporate those stands in which the chief species (i.e. those with quantitatively the largest contribution) are substantially the same, and the lists of associated species, although variable, show greater affinities than differences.

Since communities having sufficient floristic similarity to be placed in the same group can only occur where broadly similar habitat conditions prevail, a grouping of this kind should be of some service when vegetation is to be used as an indication of habitat potentialities. It will also express the climatic and geographical affinities of the community type, since each group will contain different proportions of species having essentially northern, southern, oceanic, continental and other distribution patterns. Bøcher (1943) surveyed the whole North Atlantic Heath Formation on this basis and it is convenient to list Scottish groups (some of which coincide with his) under his main headings—the "Euoceanic Series" and the "Scano-Danish (Scotch) Series".

Euoceanic Series

This title was given by Bøcher to heath communities occurring along the highly oceanic seaboard of western Europe, all of which contain a relatively high proportion of species showing "oceanic" patterns of distribution. At least two rather distinctive types appear in Scotland.

Calluna—Empetrum hermaphroditum communities. A convenient starting-point for a survey of some of the main groups into which Scottish heaths can be divided on floristic grounds is provided by one representing some of the extremes of variation to be found at low altitudes. On the islands in certain Lochs in Shetland, Spence (1960) has found and described examples of communities dominated by *Calluna*, with *Empetrum hermaphroditum* playing a prominent role (Table 25, p. 280). *E. hermaphroditum* enters into low-lying heath communities elsewhere in Shetland and in the Hebrides (e.g. South Uist: Spence, 1960), but on the level plateaux of peat characteristic of the centres of these islands in Shetland lochs it is a regular member of a type of community including other species of markedly northern, submontane affinities, as well as a strong oceanic component. Among the former are *Juniperus communis* ssp. *nana*, elsewhere in Britain belonging largely to mountain heaths ("Juniperetum nanae", McVean and Ratcliffe, 1962), *Euphrasia scottica*, *Vaccinium vitis-idaea* and *V. uliginosum*. The high constancy of *Potentilla erecta* (100 per cent.) and to a lesser extent of *Deschampsia flexuosa* (83 per cent.) are also features of northern heath-types (see Gimingham, 1961). Among the oceanic components are *Blechnum spicant* (32 per cent.), *Carex binervis* (50 per cent.), and *Rhacomitrium lanuginosum* (32 per cent., locally dominant). *Erica cinerea* however, is sparsely and irregularly represented, and this, together with the high constancy of *Rhinanthus minor* agg. and the montane element, appear to be among the features differentiating this from other Euoceanic heath community-types.

Altitudinal and edaphic range. The lochs with islands on which these communities are represented are situated at altitudes ranging from 8 to 150 m. above sea-level. The substratum is peat over 1 m. in depth, overlying boulders or bedrock of sandstone or granite-diorite.

Distribution. In the form described this community appears to be restricted in Scotland to Shetland. However, further surveys may reveal similar communities in the north-west coastal region and islands. Some of the characteristics mentioned above might then prove to be local features of the Shetland examples.

Relationship to other communities. These communities are clearly related to the *Vaccinium—Empetrum hermaphroditum* communities so common above the tree-line on Scottish mountains (cf. Chapter 11). Indeed, as Spence demonstrates, mean monthly temperatures at sea-level in Shetland are equivalent to those at 359 m. in the central Highlands, and those at 305 m. in Shetland equivalent to 762 m. in the central Highlands. The climate in which the communities under discussion develop may, therefore, properly be described as sub-alpine, and relationships with other sub-alpine communities are to be expected. Their situation, however, at low altitudes on an off-shore archipelago with a more oceanic climatic regime than that of the central Highlands introduces relationships with the other oceanic heath types (see below) and, together with the northerly geographical situation, produces a marked similarity to certain heaths in the Faroes (Bøcher, 1940). Here, a *Calluna—Empetrum* (*E. nigrum* and *E. hermaphroditum*) type of community very similar to the Shetland ones has been described. It is, however, often rich in *Vaccinium myrtillus* and so relates in turn to the *Empetrum—Vaccinium* heaths of the Faroes and, for example, South Greenland.

Ecological history. It is striking that in Shetland these communities are virtually confined to islands in lochs, which have largely escaped the influence of grazing and burning. In the neighbouring moorland, subject to the effects of these factors, *Empetrum hermaphroditum* plays a less important part while *Erica cinerea* becomes more prominent, and a community similar to the *Calluna—Erica* type described below results, but lacking *Juniperus*, *Polypodium vulgare*, *Rhinanthus minor*, etc. Alternatively, wetter conditions lead to the prominence of *Trichophorum cespitosum*, *Eriophorum* spp. and *Molinia caerulea*.

Calluna—Erica cinerea heaths, containing numerous species with oceanic affinities. The dominant is sometimes *Erica cinerea*, usually *Calluna* with abundant *E. cinerea*. These communities, widespread in the coastal and oceanic parts of Scotland, exhibit *Erica cinerea* at its most vigorous, usually in association with *Calluna*, but with *Empetrum* and *Vaccinium* spp. only occasionally represented and then in relatively small quantities (Table 25). As in the preceding type, *Potentilla erecta* is highly constant, and *Agrostis* spp. (especially *A. tenuis*) are regular components. *Hypnum cupressiforme* is of chief importance amongst the mosses, with *Dicranum scoparium* and *Hylocomium* *splendens* frequently well represented. *Pleurozium schreberi*, however, is abundant only in a few examples and may be sparse or lacking. Lichens are poorly represented. Among the oceanic species which either reach relatively high levels of constancy, or else are abundant when present, are *Blechnum spicant, Hypericum pulchrum, Carex binervis*, and *Dactylorchis maculata* ssp. *ericetorum*. Numerous others, especially bryophytes, figure in the list although their occurrence is less regular.

Variants include :

(α) *"Herb-rich" variants.* A number of examples of heath communities showing the characteristic features of this group include also better representation of a series of herbaceous species generally regarded as indicative of soils in the medium to higher ranges of base-status (e.g. *Antennaria dioica, Anthoxanthum odoratum, Euphrasia* sp., *Hypochoeris radicata, Sieglingia decumbens, Solidago virgaurea, Succisa pratensis, Thymus drucei, Pseudoscleropodium purum*). The stands contributing to column 3 in Table 25 include examples from semi-podsols developed over somewhat calcareous schist, and in maritime localities from soils enriched by wind-blown beach sand or perhaps by rain water brought in with westerly winds from over the Atlantic (cf. Gorham, 1956). The presence of *Armeria maritima* and *Plantago maritima* in certain stands probably reflects the influence of the latter factor.

(β) *"Dune heath" variants.* Certain west-coast sand-dune systems are highly calcareous (Chapter 4), but there are also numerous others in which the succession on the older, fixed dunes and on fixed flat expanses of blown sand leads to dune heath. Here, *Erica cinerea* may be the pioneer dwarf shrub (Plate 42), sometimes producing large dome-shaped bushes scattered amongst *Ammophila*, well before it is joined by *Calluna* and the separate shrubs coalesce to form *Calluna—Erica* communities essentially similar to those discussed above (Table 25, col. 4). This behaviour of *Erica cinerea* under highly oceanic climatic conditions provides a strong contrast to its reduced role in otherwise similar dune systems on the east coast, where *Calluna* or sometimes *Empetrum nigrum* may be the pioneer dwarf shrub (cf. pp. 257 and 264).

The dune-heath communities rich in *Erica cinerea* tend also to be more or less "herb-rich", reflecting perhaps both the relatively favourable base-status of the blown sand and the maritime situation. Species such as *Lotus corniculatus, Viola riviniana* and *Veronica officinalis* are regular. These communities, however, are to some extent distinguished from the rest by such plants as *Ammophila arenaria* (although usually in a more or less degenerating condition), *Carex arenaria, Festuca rubra* and *Rhytidiadelphus triquetrus,* these species being characteristic of dune heaths in general (see also p. 264).

Altitudinal and edaphic range. Most of the examples of this group which have been examined belong to low altitudes ranging from the dune heaths at a few metres above sea-level to about 90 m. Some of the "herb-rich" representatives are developed at higher altitudes, in relation to the occurrence of base-rich soil parent materials, e.g. up to 350 m. The substratum varies from blown sand with a slight admixture of humus, through shallow unstratified brown soils with deep-burrowing earthworms, to shallow podsolic soils in which, however, the surface layer of raw humus (A_0) is never thick, seldom exceeding 5 cm., and leaching is not pronounced. As shown above (p. 255), *Erica cinerea* is favoured by freely drained soils.

Distribution. Heaths of this group occur mainly close to the north and west coasts and in the outlying islands, but also scattered here and there in suitable localities elsewhere in the country.

Relationship to other communities. Relationship with *Calluna—Empetrum hermaphroditum* heaths has already been indicated. The Scottish Euoceanic *Calluna—Erica cinerea* heaths bear a very close relationship to similar communities in the hyperoceanic region of W. Norway (e.g. in the region of Haugesund and Jaeren peninsula: Nordhagen, 1921; Bøcher, 1940; Gimingham, 1961) and to closely comparable ones in the Faroes (Bøcher). In the opposite geographical direction they merge gradually into the *Calluna—Erica cinerea—Ulex gallii* heaths of Wales; while within Scotland various communities containing both *Erica cinerea* and *Vaccinium* spp. in appreciable quantities, or both *E. cinerea* and *Arctostaphylos uva-ursi*, link the Euoceanic to the Scano-Danish (Scotch) Series.

The "herb-rich facies of Callunetum vulgaris" described by McVean and Ratcliffe (1962) can be regarded as identical with the herb-rich variant of the Euoceanic *Calluna—Erica* heaths described here.

Ecological history. The origin and development of heaths rich in *Erica cinerea*, apart from those on sand dunes, have been little investigated. It is well known that, where present, the contribution of *E. cinerea* to heath vegetation is increased, at least temporarily, after burning. This may follow perhaps from the drying out and improvement of drainage and aeration of the surface soil layers following fires. It is possible, therefore, that burning may be a factor concerned in the wide-spread occurrence of this type, especially where examples lie outside the most oceanic parts of the country. Any factors which reduce the competitive vigour of *Calluna* and retard the development of raw humus at the soil surface favour *Erica cinerea*, and this relates presumably to the association of this group of communities with oceanic regimes, and with relatively base-rich soils. On the other hand, factors such as sheep grazing of moderate intensity, which enhance the competitive effects of *Calluna*, will reduce *E. cinerea* (Gimingham, 1949). On the more fertile soils heavier grazing tends to eliminate both species, and many *Calluna—Erica cinerea* communities can be replaced by grassland under appropriate management.

Scano-Danish (Scotch) Series

Certain of the heaths reaching their optimal development in south-west Scandinavia show close affinities to those of the rather less highly oceanic parts of Scotland. The series so constituted was given the above title by Bøcher, distinguishing it from the Dutch-German Series and the Baltic-Submontane Series.

Scottish representatives of this series appear to fall conveniently into four groups (Table 27, p 288).

Calluna—Erica cinerea heaths with the oceanic floristic element reduced, but in which *Vaccinium* spp. are absent or insignificant.

Communities of this kind, occurring fairly frequently in the eastern half of Scotland, may be regarded as occupying a more or less intermediate position between the oceanic *Calluna—Erica cinerea* heaths, and the widespread *Calluna—Vaccinium* heaths (below, p. 258). Indeed, they may in several instances merely represent versions of one of these community-types impoverished by frequent burning and regular grazing. This view is further supported by the fact that they show few distinctive floristic features, and, apart from an occasional "herb-rich" example, are poor in species of flowering plants. Besides *Calluna* and *Erica cinerea* the only species occurring with some regularity are *Carex pilulifera* and *Trichophorum cespitosum*; even *Potentilla erecta* is no longer so regular or important a component (Table 27, col. 1). Mosses may be well represented, and when this is so the balance is similar to that described above for the oceanic *Calluna—E. cinerea* heaths, with *Hypnum cupressiforme* of chief importance. In other examples, lichens, especially *Cladonia pyxidata*, are widespread.

Variants include:

(a) *Stands dominated by* Calluna vulgaris *alone* (Table 27, col. 2). Further reduction in the community structure is observed when *Calluna* is dominant in almost pure stands, having no associated dwarf shrubs. Such communities occur frequently, especially in east Scotland, but also for example on dunes in the west. Most commonly they belong to heaths in the agricultural lowlands, now surrounded by farmland and often restricted in area by reclamation. This suggests that they may have been much modified in the past; in many cases they have been frequently burnt. The absence of *Erica cinerea* may be due either to somewhat poorly drained or peaty soils reducing its competitive vigour in relation to *Calluna*, or to grazing or other factors enhancing the dominance of *Calluna* to the virtual exclusion of all else. Other features of the flora of these communities bear a similarity to those described in the preceding paragraph, as for example the leading role of *Hypnum cupressiforme* among the mosses, while both *Pleurozium schreberi* and *Hylocomium splendens* are sparse. It seems appropriate, therefore, to treat these types together, although it is not suggested that all communities in which *Calluna* is the sole representative of the dwarf shrubs have originated in the same way or bear the same relationships to other groups. Indeed, it is highly probable that similar communities may be derived from former *Calluna* with *Vaccinium* heaths by the operation of the factors mentioned. (The "Callunetum vulgaris" of McVean and Ratcliffe (1962) contains stands referable

R

here, although the majority relate to the *Calluna—Vaccinium* heaths, see below.) It is difficult to regard these communities as anything more than much modified or reduced versions of related types, or intermediates between the more clearly recognisable groups, occupying habitats which are neither strongly oceanic nor suitable for the other typical associates of *Calluna*, such as *Vaccinium* spp., *Arctostaphylos uva-ursi* or *Empetrum nigrum*.

(β) *Calluna* with *Erica cinerea* and *Arctostaphylos uva-ursi* (Table 27, col. 3). Examples are met with in parts of the eastern foothills of the Grampian and Cairngorm massifs, and perhaps elsewhere, combining the features of the heaths placed in this section with strong representation of *Arctostaphylos uva-ursi* (Plate 38). They lack, however, the very typical assemblage of species which characterise the *Calluna* with *Arctostaphylos* communities described as a distinct main type below. Indeed, *Calluna*, *Erica cinerea*, *E. tetralix*, *Arctostaphylos uva-ursi* and *Hypnum cupressiforme* are the only species which appear to reach high constancy values in the rather small set of samples examined, and this suggests again that these are probably to be regarded as transitional stands between the *Calluna—Erica cinerea* and *Calluna—Arctostaphylos* types or as reduced versions derived from one or the other. One stand in which *Vaccinium myrtillus* is frequent suggests a possible relationship with *Calluna—Vaccinium* heaths.

Edaphic range. These communities are found mainly on "hard ground". There is frequently a thin accumulation of litter and raw humus, up to about 5 cm. in depth, overlying a shallow mineral profile which may be clearly or obscurely podsolised (podsol ranker). Sometimes the organic top may rest directly on stony till or rock debris decaying *in situ* (ranker). A few examples on peat have been noted, where the surface has become thoroughly drained and is no longer moistened by a ground-water table.

Calluna—Vaccinium heaths, usually including Empetrum nigrum and often also Erica cinerea. This group of heath communities is probably the most important and characteristic of Scotland as a whole. It is extremely widespread, occurring in suitable habitats throughout the whole country, and frequently extends in one form or another over large areas (Plate 37). Many of the best grouse moors and hill grazings belong here. Typically, *Calluna* is dominant but both *Vaccinium myrtillus* and *V. vitis-idaea* are regularly present in varying quantities (Table 27, col. 5). *Erica cinerea* no longer plays the part it has in the preceding groups, although it is often present in a subordinate status, sometimes actually forming a discontinuous lower stratum below the canopy of *Calluna*. *Empetrum nigrum* becomes a component of high constancy, but its bulk and cover are seldom great. Other general features are the regularity with which *Deschampsia flexuosa* occurs, and the reduced role of *Potentilla erecta*, *Agrostis* spp., *Blechnum spicant* and other species prominent in one or more of the preceding groups. Chief among the mosses is now *Pleurozium schreberi*, with *Hypnum cupressiforme* very regularly accompanying it but quantitatively in second place. *Hylocomium splendens* is also a characteristic species of high constancy; *Dicranum scoparium* and *Polytrichum commune* are slightly less regular. Lichens, although not prominent, are generally represented, particularly by *Cladonia sylvatica* and *C. uncialis*. Additional bryophytes becoming constant in certain western examples of this heath type are *Plagiothecium undulatum*, *Anastrepta orcadensis*, *Bazzania tricrenata* and *Scapania gracilis*.

The proportions in which the two *Vaccinium* spp. occur vary but, at least in the lowland heaths, examples in which *V. vitis-idaea* is present but *V. myrtillus* is absent are rare. On the other hand, heaths containing *V. myrtillus* extend well beyond the range of conditions in which *V. vitis-idaea* plays a part, especially towards the oceanic west. For this reason, some authors such as Bøcher (1943) have preferred to constitute a community-type based on strong representation of *V. myrtillus* (the "Myrtillion boreale"), with *V. vitis-idaea* as an additional component in examples from certain parts of the geographical range. However, Scottish experience suggests that heaths with both *Vaccinium* species represent the fullest expression of this community-type, which should therefore be described in these terms. Those with only one of the two species may then be treated as variants occurring under conditions which eliminate the other.

Variants include:

(α) Calluna *with* Vaccinium myrtillus*; V. vitis-idaea *absent* (Table 27, col. 5). In these examples *Erica cinerea*, although not more than about 57 per cent. constant, is often abundant. *Potentilla erecta* is also perhaps rather better represented than is often the case in the heaths with both *Vaccinium* species. Otherwise the general description given above applies equally here.

(β) *Communities dominated by* Vaccinium myrtillus, *in which* Calluna *is reduced or lacking*. In lowland regions *V. myrtillus* is seldom dominant, but patches of limited extent occur in which other dwarf shrubs are suppressed or excluded. These sometimes mark the site of former woodland and are then of a temporary nature, but they occur in heathland by rock outcrops, and especially among large boulders or scree with deep crevices. Sometimes *V. myrtillus* also becomes dominant on very exposed ridges or ledges (cf. Pearsall, 1950: "*Vaccinium* edge"), or, perhaps temporarily, as a result of overburning when the vigour of *Calluna* is reduced (Elliott, 1953).

Variations in soil conditions may also produce variants in community composition, as in previous types. The following are among the most distinctive variants:

(γ) *Herb-rich variants*. On the richer soils, communities of the *Calluna* with *Vaccinium* spp. type may show a flora enriched with additional species, such as those mentioned in connection with similar variations in the *Erica cinerea* heaths. However, perhaps in view of the soil conditions normally associated with *Calluna—Vaccinium* heaths this does not here seem to be such a pronounced tendency.

(δ) *Moist variants*. A number of examples, however, contain an important component of species otherwise characteristic of wet heaths. These are clearly transitional between the *Calluna—Vaccinium* type of community and certain of the wet heaths developed in otherwise similar sorts of habitat (cf. p. 265 and Chapter 10). In some cases *Trichophorum cespitosum*, *Juncus squarrosus* or *Eriophorum vaginatum* are among the prominent species, and along with them *Erica tetralix* and *Sphagnum* spp.; while more occasionally *Nardus stricta*, *Molinia caerulea*, *Pedicularis sylvatica*, *Rubus chamaemorus* and *Aulacomnium palustre* are associated.

Altitudinal and edaphic range. Communities containing *Calluna* and both species of *Vaccinium* occur in mountainous regions up to altitudinal limits varying between 750 m. and 1850 m. (cf. Chapter 11 and Metcalfe, 1950). Many of these are essentially similar to the types described here, incorporating, however, some additional montane species (such as *Chamaepericlymenum suecicum*, and *Empetrum hermaphroditum* in place of *E. nigrum*). The features of floristic composition given in this section apply largely to examples lying below about 600 m., but there is no sharp distinction from those at higher levels. There is no lower altitudinal limit, examples of this community-type occurring down to sea-level. However, below about 100 m. on the east side of Scotland and 360 m. on the west, *Vaccinium vitis-idaea* is normally excluded and the variant containing *V. myrtillus* only occurs.

Although this community-type is represented over a considerable range of soil moisture conditions, in other respects the soil-type is rather clearly defined. It is one in which there is an appreciable depth of raw or peaty humus, and so ranges only from drained or drying peat to podsol rankers, semi-podsols and podsols. Most characteristic of these is thin peat over a podsol with thin iron pan, but other substrata include truncated podsols and stabilised scree with accumulated raw humus in the crevices, as well as podsolic gleys. These soils are invariably acid, the pH at the surface normally falling within the range 3·6-4·5.

Towards the wetter extremes of this edaphic range species typical of wet heaths increase in prominence, producing communities of the type described as moist variants (δ); where a parent-material of slightly higher base-status leads to a less markedly podsolised profile with a shallower A_0 horizon, herb-rich variants may arise (γ).

Distribution. Widespread in the hilly districts of Scotland, and in the lowlands where soils are relatively acid and of low base-status. The complete version, with both *Vaccinium* species, is most frequent in north, east and central Scotland, and elsewhere at the higher altitudes. The variant containing *V. myrtillus* only, however, extends into all the lowland and coastal regions and in the west is also prominent on the hills.

Relationship to other communities. Scottish *Calluna—Vaccinium* communities are closely similar in composition to an important heath-type in western Sweden, extending also into S. Norway, Denmark and more isolated stations, e.g. on north-facing slopes, in N. Germany and Holland. In these areas the leading species are the same as those in Scotland with a few important differences. Chief among these is the absence on the Continent of certain oceanic species, especially *Erica cinerea* and *Blechnum spicant*, and the presence of a small number of more Continental species, lacking in Scottish heaths, such as *Arnica montana, Scorzonera humilis* and *Dicranum rugosum*. Otherwise the floristic composition, including that of the bryophytic stratum, of examples from the two regions is closely similar. Damman (1957) examining the Swedish examples, named them "Hylocomieto—Callunetum", giving prominence to the role of *Hylocomium splendens* in the bryophyte stratum. This is broadly a northern-oceanic species and serves to differentiate these communities from more southern or Continental heaths. Among other species used to differentiate the Swedish "Hylocomieto—Callunetum" from more southern heath-types, the following also occur in the equivalent Scottish communities: *Luzula pilosa, Cladonia rangiferina, Lycopodium clavatum, L. selago, Trientalis europaea, Anemone nemorosa*. It is reasonable to regard the Scottish type as a somewhat more oceanic version of the Scandinavian.

Since the range of the *Calluna—Vaccinium* heaths overlaps that of the highly oceanic *Calluna* with *Erica cinerea* communities in Scotland, there is intergradation between them and many transitional examples are found which could readily be placed in either group, with *E. cinerea* normally contributing considerable cover. In other cases, *Calluna* is overwhelmingly dominant, with other dwarf-shrubs contributing little cover. Recognising that, at least in heaths situated below the natural tree limit, this may be a result of anthropogenic factors, McVean and Ratcliffe (1962) placed all such stands from the Highland region in a single "Callunetum vulgaris" based on the dominance of *Calluna* and the constancy of *Dicranum scoparium, Hylocomium splendens, Hypnum cupressiforme* and *Pleurozium schreberi*. Most of the stands listed in their table could clearly be associated with the *Calluna—Vaccinium* heaths described above since they contain varying quantities of *Vaccinium* spp., while a few seem to link with the variant (α) of *Calluna—Erica cinerea* heaths (p. 257).

At higher altitudes the communities described in this section grade into the "Vaccinieto—Callunetum" of McVean and Ratcliffe.

Calluna—Arctostaphylos heaths, with Erica cinerea and often Genista anglica, Pyrola media, Lathyrus montanus, etc. Certain heaths from the upland regions of central and eastern Scotland in which *Calluna, Arctostaphylos uva-ursi* and *Erica cinerea* figure prominently, contain also a number of interesting species not regularly found in other heath types. Indeed, the basic assemblage of species is so strikingly similar from stand to stand, even in widely separated areas, that this community-type is one of the most clearly defined and readily recognisable among the heaths, contrasting with the variable nature of those hitherto described. Among the most constant species are *Agrostis tenuis, Deschampsia flexuosa, Festuca ovina, Lathyrus montanus, Lotus corniculatus, Potentilla erecta, Pyrola media, Vaccinium vitis-idaea,* and of the mosses *Hypnum cupressiforme* is again the chief species, while both *Pleurozium schreberi* and *Hylocomium splendens* are often well represented, with *Dicranum scoparium* somewhat less regular. Some other species, while not reaching such a high degree of constancy, are also very typical of this heath-type. Most conspicuous of these is *Genista anglica*, only sparingly represented in other heath-types but abundant in some examples of *Calluna—Arcto-*

staphylos heaths, particularly in the glens of the eastern Grampians, such as Glen Esk, Deeside, Speyside, etc. Considering only this portion of the area within which *Calluna—Arctostaphylos* heaths occur, the constancy of *Genista anglica* is high, and this applies equally to the moss *Dicranum spurium* which, in examples such as Dinnet Moor, is very abundant and, at least in Scotland, of apparently high fidelity to this type of community. Certain additional species are also characteristic when associated in this community-type, although each ranges widely into other communities and none is invariably present. Examples, many of them indicative of a soil base-status approaching that of the herb-rich variants of other types, include *Antennaria dioica, Anthoxanthum odoratum, Carex pilulifera, Campanula rotundifolia, Hypericum pulchrum, Listera cordata, Solidago virgaurea, Succisa pratensis, Veronica officinalis* and *Viola riviniana* (Table 27, col. 6).

The physiognomy of the community is usually characterised by a patchy canopy of *Calluna*, many of the gaps being occupied by a mat of *Arctostaphylos*. As old bushes of *Calluna* open up in the centre or die out, *Arctostaphylos* creeps into the new gaps, often spreading some distance from its original anchorage. Twisted, prostrate woody stems of *Arctostaphylos* are everywhere found partially buried under new growth of *Calluna*. Patches of bare ground are also frequent, occupied by a rich lichen flora in which the species concerned vary considerably from stand to stand, the more regular perhaps being *Cladonia sylvatica, C. impexa* and *C. pyxidata* var. *chlorophaea* (= *C.* "*chlo rophala*").

Altitudinal and edaphic range. Calluna—Arctostaphylos heaths of this type are perhaps more limited altitudinally than the other types described, occurring mainly between the limits of 225 m. and 600 m. They are well represented in the east central Highlands of Scotland, figuring in the survey by McVean and Ratcliffe (1962) and also in Chapter 11 (p. 484). The substratum is often a shallow, well-drained and rather stony soil ("hard ground") of a podsolic type, but with little accumulation of raw humus (A_0) and sometimes with indistinct profile development. Parent materials are perhaps of rather higher base status than those leading, for example, to the deep podsols of the *Calluna—Vaccinium* heaths, but some examples, e.g. Glen Dye on sandy morainic material, are clearly differentiated iron-humus podsols with thick deposition layers of iron and humus in the **B** horizon showing downwardly directed "tongues". In Glen Tanar (Whittaker, 1960) similar communities occur on oligotrophic braunerde, and at Dinnet an excellent example is found on a semi-podsol which was probably under cultivation about 1870. Here there is only a very thin, 6 mm. ($\frac{1}{4}$ in.) accumulation of raw humus, having a pH of 5·0, and the upper 23 cm. (9 in.) of soil, corresponding approximately to plough depth, consist of a more or less uniform admixture of organic and mineral material, grey-brown in colour, about 80 per cent. base-saturated and with abundant burrowing earthworms (Boggie, 1956).

Distribution. The distribution of this heath type (Fig. 42) includes the counties of Angus (Glen Esk), Kincardine (Glen Dye), Aberdeen (Deeside—including GlenTanar Dinnet, Pannanich, etc.), Inverness (Glen Banchor, Allt Mor, Glen Mauckic, Dal-whinnie, Daviot) and Perthshire (Blair Atholl, Keltney Burn).

Relationship to other communities. An account of this heath-type is given by McVean and Ratcliffe (1962) under the title "Arctostaphyleto—Callunetum". On the whole, it is rather clearly distinct from others in Scotland, with the exception perhaps of the *Calluna—Erica cinerea* communities of the less oceanic character. As mentioned in connection with these (p. 258) some apparently transitional examples containing *Arctostaphylos* occur.

Rather strangely, this community-type seems also to bear only slight relationship to Scandinavian heaths containing *Arctostaphylos*. In western Norway, as in the very north of Scotland, *Arctostaphylos* occurs in the highly oceanic *Calluna—Erica cinerea* heaths, and it is these communities which show greatest floristic affinity with those discussed in this section. Communities from S.W. Sweden containing *Arctostaphylos* are much more akin to the *Calluna—Vaccinium* type and may contain more continental species such as *Genista pilosa* and *Arnica montana*; those in Denmark are generally rich

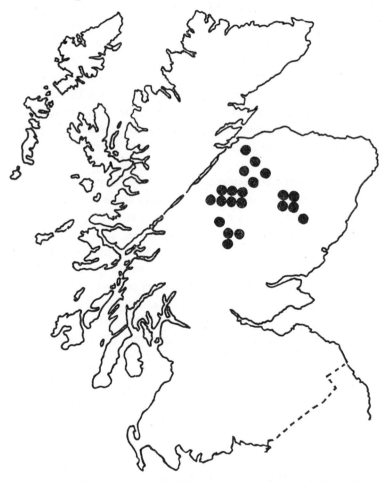

FIG. 42 Distribution of *Calluna-Arctostaphylos* heaths with *Erica cinerea, Genista anglica, Pyrola media, Lathyrus montanus,* etc. (After McVean and Ratcliffe, 1962.)

in *Empetrum nigrum* and although usually including *Genista anglica* show few of the other species here associated with *Arctostaphylos*, linking more closely with next group to be described.

    Calluna—Empetrum nigrum communities of dry habitats. Communities in which *Calluna* and *Empetrum nigrum* are the chief species on dry freely drained soils such as blown sand although widespread, for example, in Denmark, are extremely restricted in Scotland. They are confined to old fixed, maritime sand dunes where the sand is siliceous with a low lime-content, in a few places on the north-east and north-west coasts. *Empetrum nigrum* is vigorous and abundant, extending continuously among the *Calluna* or colonising open sites and spreading in big circular patches derived from a single individual. *Erica cinerea* is often present, but *Vaccinium* spp. are lacking. Other flowering plants of high constancy are those of dune heaths in general such as *Ammophila arenaria*, *Carex arenaria*, *Festuca rubra* (or *F. ovina*), *Galium verum* and the moss *Rhytidiadelphus triquetrus*. Otherwise, the only characteristic features of the community-type are its richness in lichen species, again variable from stand to stand but with *Cladonia impexa*, *C. sylvatica* and *Cetraria aculeata* perhaps among the most typical. Chief among the mosses is *Hylocomium splendens*, but *Pleurozium schreberi*, *Hypnum cupressiforme* and *Dicranum scoparium* are also constants. As with other maritime sands, species indicative of at least moderate base-status occur with some frequency, such as *Holcus lanatus*, *Campanula rotundifolia*, *Anthoxanthum odoratum*, *Thymus drucei*, *Lotus corniculatus*, *Viola riviniana* and *Luzula campestris* (Table 27, col. 7).

    A variant is:

        (*a*) Empetrum-*lichen communities lacking* Calluna. In parts of the habitats occupied by the dry *Calluna-Empetrum* communities there are stands in which *Calluna* is lacking altogether and a version dominated by *Empetrum nigrum* results (Plate 43). This is rich in lichen species, especially *Cladonia sylvatica*, *Cetraria aculeata* and *Cladonia furcata*, but contains few other components apart from *Teesdalia nudicaulis* and a small group of mosses, including *Ceratodon purpureus*, *Polytrichum piliferum* and, where sand deposition occurs, *Rhacomitrium canescens*. Landsberg (1955) suggests that this type of community is in fact seral, developing in areas which, although generally stable, are locally subject to sand erosion or deposition. This accords with the pioneer role of *Empetrum* on some dune heaths on the coasts of Sweden and Denmark, and the stabilising effect of prostrate colonies of *Empetrum* may lead to an increase in the proportion of *Calluna* and the formation of a closed dune heath community.

    Altitudinal and edaphic range. In the form described, this community type occurs only within about 30 m. (100 ft.) of sea-level and only on well-drained, stabilised sand at a pII of 4·8-6·0. It occurs where sand has blown over slopes near to the sea, on old fixed dune ridges, and on the irregular hummocky dunes representing the trailing "arms" of an eroded U-shaped dune. The soil profiles may show varying degrees of podsolisation.

PLATE 37. Heathland scenery in N.E. Scotland. On hills in distance *Calluna—Vaccinium* heath, in foreground *Calluna—Erica tetralix* heath on soils of impeded drainage.

Photo D. Jenkins

PLATE 38. Heathland scenery in N.E. Scotland, near Banchory, Aberdeen-shire. Foreground: *Calluna—Arctostaphylos uva-ursi* heath on shallow soil with thin organic "top". Many boulders at surface.

PLATE 39. Dome-shaped form of a mature bush of *Calluna vulgaris* growing without direct competition from neighbouring individuals (top of rule is 1 m. from ground surface).

PLATE 40. Degenerate bush of *Calluna vulgaris* showing central gap caused by death of oldest frame-branches and outward collapse of others. Peripheral branches are still producing green shoots and flowers.

Photos I. Moir

(A)   (B)

PLATE 41. (A) Soil profile, and (B) distribution of *Calluna* roots in heath
at Dinnet, Aberdeenshire. Note dense aggregation of roots just below
soil surface, some extending to lower horizons and spreading out just
above the iron-pan. Samples prepared by R. Boggie.

PLATE 42
Entry of a bush of *Erica cinerea* among *Ammophila arenaria*, etc. on a dune system at the Bay of Luce, Wigtownshire.

PLATE 43
Empetrum nigrum—lichen community on old stabilized dunes near Collieston, Aberdeenshire (Sands of Forvie).

PLATE 44
Calluna—Erica tetralix wet heath, with *Empetrum nigrum* and foliage of *Eriophorum angustifolium*. Near Aberdeen.

PLATE 45

Dune heath at Sands of Forvie, Aberdeenshire. *Calluna vulgaris* in building phase after burning a degenerating stand (old charred stems still visible). Windward eroded slopes of U-shaped dunes in background.

Photo E. M. Birse

PLATE 46

Pattern of regenerating *Calluna* stands of various ages after burning in strips. Foreground: a peat-hag, and hollow eroded down to parent material. Glen Dye, Aberdeenshire: Clach-na-Ben in distance.

PLATE 47

Mosaic of stands of differing age produced by rotational burning— Geallaig Hill, Crathie, Aberdeenshire. The pattern is emphasized by snow lying on the ground on the sites of recent fires.

Photo D. Jenkins

PLATE 48. Charred stems of old *Calluna* plants after burning. Such plants fail to regenerate vegetatively, and reconstitution of vegetational cover, mainly by seedling establishment, is slow.

Photo E. Cormack

PLATE 49. Cyclical change in a *Calluna—Vaccinium vitis-idaea* community. A gap phase has formed in an old *Calluna* bush, the dead stems being colonized by *Hypogymnia physodes*. The ground is occupied by mosses (*Hypnum cupressiforme*, *Pleurozium schreberi*, etc.) and *Vaccinium vitis-idaea* is spreading into the gap. The rule measures 1 m.

Distribution. Well developed on parts of the Aberdeenshire coast, especially at the sands of Forvie (Landsberg, 1955), and smaller patches in Kincardineshire. Also in places on the coast of Wester Ross and perhaps elsewhere.

Relationship to other communities. This type of heath community, occupying a rather distinctive habitat, shows few links with other Scottish types. Apart from the prominence of *Empetrum nigrum* there is little similarity with the type of wet heath in which *Empetrum* also plays an important part (below). Both floristically and ecologically these two *Empetrum*-rich community-types are widely separated, while under conditions somewhat intermediate between them, the role of *Empetrum* is reduced, e.g. in the *Calluna—Vaccinium* communities. This constitutes an ecological problem which is at present under investigation.

Communities showing the closest relationship to those grouped in this section occur in Denmark, especially Jutland (Bøcher, 1943). As in Scotland, they contain very few species of phanerogams apart from those associated with a substratum of blown sand, and are usually rich in lichens, especially *Cladonia sylvatica, C. impexa* and *C. "chlorophaea"*. Apart from the scarcity or absence of *Hylocomium splendens*, the bryophytic component is also closely similar. Related communities occur on dunes on the coasts of S.W. Sweden, and in inland localities in N. Germany, N.E. Holland, etc. (Gimingham, 1961).

Heaths on soils of impeded drainage or rather deep organic "top"

Calluna—Erica tetralix heaths rich in Empetrum nigrum (Table 26, p. 284, col. 1). Where peaty humus builds up above a gleyed podsolic profile or on deeper peat, *Calluna—Erica tetralix* communities are frequent, and those of the less extremely wet substrata may include *E. nigrum* as a constant component (Plate 44). Beneath the dwarf shrubs, the bryophytic stratum is dominated by *Sphagnum* spp. Most of the species with high constancy-values are characteristic of wet habitats: *Eriophorum vaginatum, Juncus squarrosus, Polytrichum commune, Aulacomnium palustre,* and with slightly lower constancy, *Narthecium ossifragum, Eriophorum angustifolium* and *Trichophorum cespitosum;* the last tending to be more abundant in stands with *E. vaginatum* scarce or absent. *Drosera rotundifolia* is frequently present.

The occasional occurrence of species typical of the drier heath-types suggests that the floristic differences are not as great as they might appear, and good evidence for relationship is provided by the high constancy of *Pleurozium schreberi* and *Hypnum cupressiforme*—the former usually contributing appreciable cover. On the west of Scotland and on higher ground, *Vaccinium myrtillus* and *Hylocomium splendens* may also be present.

A variant is:

(a) In the extreme north of Scotland, similar habitats may exhibit communities of *Erica tetralix* and *Empetrum nigrum*, lacking *Calluna* but similar in other respects to those described above.

Altitudinal and edaphic range. From little more than sea-level (e.g. behind or between dune ridges where erosion down to the water table has taken place) to about 500 m. in the hills. Mainly on *Sphagnum* peat or related peats and peaty humus.

Distribution. Widespread through the northern part of the country in suitable habitats.

Relationship to other communities. As mentioned above, links are discernible between this type of community and the *Calluna—Vaccinium* heaths, and no doubt the two groups represent different portions of a direction of variation following a gradient in soil moisture regime. Very similar stands occur in S.W. Sweden, Denmark and N.E. Holland, the chief difference being the apparently much reduced role of *Sphagnum* and the frequent occurrence of *Vaccinium uliginosum*. Many of these examples are very rich in species of hepatics.

Calluna—Erica tetralix wet heaths. This important complex of related communities occurs widely where drainage conditions maintain more or less permanently saturated conditions at the surface of an acid soil or peat, although not such as to lead to active peat-building. Such communities may occupy small hollows, or large shallow basins where drainage water collects, or breaks in the slope of a hill where seepage water comes to the surface. Alternatively they may form a zone, sometimes wide and sometimes narrow, towards the foot of a hill slope between the drier heath community above and true bog or "poor fen" below. This zonation may be seen in miniature in dune slacks on the more acid dune systems where the drier *Calluna* with *Ammophila* and *Carex arenaria* is separated by a very narrow zone of *Calluna* with *Erica tetralix* from the floor of the slack, which is frequently dominated by *Salix repens*. Apart from *Calluna* and *Erica tetralix*, the important species tend to be those ranging also into various types of bog community (Chapter 10) such as *Trichophorum cespitosum* and *Narthecium ossifragum*. In a number of the stands *Molinia caerulea* is a prominent component and in some examples, although not all, it is best represented where *Trichophorum* is weakest. *Eriophorum vaginatum*, *E. angustifolium*, *Juncus squarrosus* and *Carex panicea* also have high cover values in certain stands but are absent from others. Insufficient work has been done to establish the reasons for these variations, or the relationships between stands in which these species are differently grouped. *Pleurozium schreberi* and *Hypnum cupressiforme* remain the most constant mosses, *Sphagnum* is usually important and frequently associated are *Aulacomnium palustre*, *Leucobryum glaucum*, *Rhytidiadelphus squarrosus*, *Polytrichum commune* and *Dicranum scoparium*. Hepatics are usually represented, sometimes in considerable abundance and diversity.

Variants include:

On the basis of the occurrence of the associated species characteristic of wet oligotrophic habitats, the following subdivisions may be suggested, although it is sometimes difficult to distinguish between them:

(α) *Rich in* Trichophorum cespitosum (Table 26, col. 2).

(β) *Rich in* Molinia caerulea (Table 26, col. 3).

(γ) Calluna—Erica tetralix *communities with neither of the above species prominent* (Table 26, col. 4).

(δ) Erica tetralix *dominant with* Calluna *sparse or absent.*

(ε) *Herb-rich variants* on slightly flushed peats or other soils; these include many of the species also characterising herb-rich variations of other heath-types.

Altitudinal and Edaphic range. Mainly a lowland complex of communities, from sea-level to about 550 m., over gleyed podsolic profiles, shallow wet peat and skeletal soils kept moist by seepage or run-off.

Distribution. Throughout Scotland.

Relationship to other communities. Related wet heaths are common in the sector of N.W. Europe running from Holland through N. Germany to Denmark and the western half of S. Sweden. Similar types occur throughout much of England, but are replaced in S. England and N. France by communities characterised by a number of highly oceanic species. The variants (α) and (β) above are similar to groups of stands entitled "Trichophoreto—Callunetum" and "Molinieto—Callunetum" by McVean and Ratcliffe (1962).

Species which constitute the *Calluna—Erica tetralix* communities also play a part in the mosaic of the hummock-hollow complex of acid bogs, occupying the sides and tops of the hummocks (cf. pp. 450; 460).

Calluna—Eriophorum vaginatum wet-heath (Table 26, col. 5). A community type of rather distinctive physiognomy, consisting of tussocks of *E. vaginatum* interspersed among bushes of *Calluna*, is characteristic of hill peat in parts of Scotland. It ranges from about 150 m. to quite high altitudes (see Chapter 11), taking on a slightly different character above about 600 m. by the addition of montane species such as *Rubus chamaemorus* ("Calluneto-Eriphoretum", McVean and Ratcliffe, 1962). Few analyses from lowland examples are available, but apart from the species mentioned, *Polytrichum commune* is highly constant, often forming dense cushions, and *Sphagnum* spp. also constitute an important component. Areas of acid bog may pass into this community after modification by drainage, and in places it represents an ecotone between a loch-side zone of *E. vaginatum* and drier heaths above. Bog peat dominated by *E. vaginatum* (as at Cruden Moss, Aberdeenshire) may, if the surface begins to dry, be colonised by *Calluna*, the young plants appearing between the tussocks of *Eriophorum*, thus giving rise to *Calluna—Eriophorum* wet heath.

Where *Calluna—Eriophorum vaginatum* communities develop, the water table is frequently to be seen at the surface in the hollows between tussocks from November to February, although the upper horizons may dry out considerably in summer. The pH lies normally between 3·6 and 3·8, and base-saturation is generally less than 30 per cent.

DYNAMIC ASPECTS

The origins of heaths—maintenance and reversion

The authors of earlier accounts of British heathlands tended to expect them to constitute a vegetation-type, the chief units of which would conform in status and developmental history. Thus Tansley (1949), for example, regarded heaths of exposed coastal and high mountain habitats as climatic climaxes, while the remainder, occurring in regions having forest as their theoretical climax vegetation, had to be fitted into his framework as "sub-climaxes", arrested at a particular stage of seral development by edaphic, biotic or anthropogenic factors. While fully aware of the evidence that many examples of heathland had been derived in the past from forest, as clearly indicated in 1911 in *Types of British Vegetation*, he finally concluded (1949) that the heath formation could only be summarised as representing a seral stage in the development of climax woodland on acid soils. This view may be criticised on the ground that the interpretation has been forced to fit the theoretical framework, but recent work has shown that it is rather the attempt to summarise the status of heathlands in a simple manner which is misplaced. Research on the vegetational history of Scotland has shown that here, as elsewhere, heathlands have had numerous different types of origin, and that numerous different factors may be concerned in various combinations in their production. Some heaths, such as those of mountain and coast, may, as Tansley suggested, arise in the course of plant successions. Even here it is often difficult to obtain objective evidence of the unaided replacement of earlier seral stages by heath communities and the question as to whether the latter are themselves seral or climax is equally difficult to settle. For the rest, the ecological history of each area requires independent investigation. In many cases derivation from forest is indicated, but whether this has followed either more or less "natural" changes in climate or soil, or has resulted from the clearance of forest by man, remains a matter for debate. Still other heaths occupy areas formerly grassland or peat bog. These different types of origin will be briefly examined in turn.

Origin in the course of plant succession. It has always been assumed that dune heaths arise in the course of the prisere on blown sand, if conditions of pH, calcium content, etc., become suitable (Plate 45). Transects passing inland across a simple non-calcareous system frequently demonstrate the location of dune heath in dry hollows or flat areas between ridges which have passed through the stage of surface fixation, or on the older stabilised ridges themselves where pH at the surface has fallen to about 6·5 or less. The difficulty confronting this simple explanation is to find evidence of invasion by the heath plants. Detailed examination of the transition zones between fixed dune communities and dune heath on four Aberdeenshire dune systems failed to yield any seedlings or young plants. These zones contain scattered bushes of *Calluna* and *Erica cinerea*, but all were well established or old plants, often compact and dome-shaped and sometimes, in the case of *Calluna*, degenerating (Ritchie, 1951). Such cases suggest a regression rather than an advance of dune heath, and there is evidence that this may be a result of intensive grazing by rabbits which are responsible for the dense, hemi-spherical form of the bushes.

Nevertheless, even if colonisation by heath plants is spasmodic and confined to infrequent periods of relief from rabbit grazing, it is still a seral development and evidence should be forthcoming for this. Such evidence may be found, for example, in the presence of large numbers of dead *Carex arenaria* rhizomes in the sand beneath certain dune heaths in which the species is no longer present (Boggie, 1956), and in the frequent occurrence of degenerating clumps of *Ammophila arenaria* amongst the heather. Further, the entry of a single plant of *Calluna* into the dune pasture community at St. Cyrus, Kincardineshire, can be dated with certainty to the period 1952-53, a time when the rabbit population was reduced by myxomatosis. This at present is still the only individual in the area, but since the soil pH is not more than 6·2 and calcium carbonate content is below 1·5 per cent. (in spite of some base-enrichment from weathering lavas of nearby cliffs), it may be expected to spread unless prevented by renewed grazing or other factors. The lack of dune heath behind so many Scottish non-calcareous dune systems may perhaps be ascribed, to some extent, to the influence of grazing animals.

Little can be said with certainty about the further seral development of dune heaths, once established. Low shrubs such as *Ulex europaeus* sometimes enter but are seldom important. *Juniperus communis* occurs in examples of dune heaths from Tain on the Dornoch Firth northwards. Species of *Salix* occur in the wetter situations, and occasional seedlings of *Sorbus aucuparia* and *Betula* spp. may be found. It is reasonable to suppose that some type of woodland would eventually develop, at least in the more sheltered situations, if protected from burning and grazing.

Origin from forest. Pollen analyses of peat deposits in various parts of Scotland carried out by Durno (1956, 1957, 1958, 1959) often show an increase in ericoid pollen following upon the transition from Boreal to Atlantic times. This, accompanied by a reduction in total tree pollen, is evidence for some degree of replacement of forest by heath as a result of climatic change before the influence of man was felt (Fig. 43). Generally, however, such heath was transitory and followed by a return of forest. More striking expansions of heath are indicated in Neolithic and Iron Age times from about 2500 B.C., leading eventually to lasting replacement of forest by heath, particularly from the Iron Age (c. 500 B.C.) onwards. This increase first appears in coastal examples and only later in more inland sites where, in many cases, it is confined to a relatively "modern" period. Taking into consideration abundant additional evidence of the increasing activity of man during these times, it is difficult to avoid the conclusion that he played a large part in initiating and continuing the change. Men of late Neolithic cultures, followed by those of the Bronze Age, made their first settlements in coastal areas, where forest clearance would have started. Later this would have extended into more inland districts, to reach its climax in relatively recent times. At the same time, in the sub-atlantic period climatic conditions became rather more favourable for heath vegetation and less so for forest, and it remains impossible to judge the relative contributions of the two linked causes, climate and man, of the origin of many heaths from former forest.

That many heaths indeed occupy former forest sites is shown by the presence of fragments, or stumps, of trees preserved in peaty deposits beneath present-day heath vegetation, even to quite high altitudes (cf. Pearsall, 1950). Since the main dominants (e.g. *Calluna vulgaris*, *Vaccinium* spp.) and several of the other heath species are normally already present under the tree canopy, the extent of vegetational change is not great and examples may be followed on the sites of recently felled woodland. At first the cover of *Calluna* is often less than 50 per cent. and dominance may be shared with *Vaccinium myrtillus* and one or more grasses, often *Deschampsia flexuosa* which may contribute up to 80 per cent. cover at ground level. In the first few years after felling, the community is distinctly patchy reflecting the irregularities in the former tree canopy. Release from dominance by trees leads to the spread of such species as *Chamaenerion angustifolium*, *Agrostis* spp., *Carex pilulifera*, *Galium saxatile* and *Rumex acetosella*. Some others characteristic of the woodland community such as *Dryopteris dilatata* retain their place.

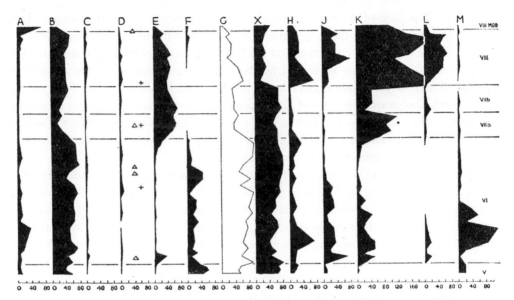

Fig. 43   Pollen diagram from St. Fergus Moss, Aberdeenshire. (S.E. Durno (1956), *Scot. geogr. Mag.*, **72**, 180.) Note temporary rise of Ericoid pollen in Zone VIIa, and marked lasting increase in VIII.

> Arboreal species: A. pine (*Pinus*): B. birch (*Betula*): C. oak (*Quercus*): D. elm (*Ulmus*): E. alder (*Alnus*): F. willow (*Salix*): G. hazel (*Corylus*).
> Non-arboreal species: H. grass (Gramineae): J. sedges (Cyperaceae): K. heaths (Ericaceae): L. bog moss (Sphagnales): M. ferns (Filicales).
> X. Total tree pollen expressed as a percentage of total pollen.
> △—ash (*Fraxinus*): +—lime (*Tilia*).
> Horizontal lines represent the limits of the pollen zones vi-viii.

Within about five years, however, the expanding bushes of *Calluna* begin to coalesce and the community composition approximates to the heath-type typical of the habitat concerned, with the slow entry of species such as *Erica cinerea* which may have been absent from the original woodland.

Reversion from heath to woodland. Heaths which have replaced destroyed forest are seldom stable communities, except in very exposed habitats or perhaps where long-established on poor soils. In the absence of measures such as burning and grazing, which lead to their perpetuation, they show signs of vegetational change after a time. This first becomes evident in the opening out of the *Calluna* canopy as the plants mature, with subsequent appearance of gaps where the centre of an individual bush has become degenerate. Space for colonisation by other species is then available, since *Calluna* does not rapidly replace itself on the same spot. Sometimes such spaces are filled by other species of the community (p. 274), but under suitable conditions they provide situations in which tree seedlings will establish and develop when undisturbed by fire and grazing animals. First to appear are usually *Betula* spp. and *Sorbus aucuparia*, but if seed-parents are not too distant *Pinus sylvestris* also colonises. On soils of moderate base status the beginnings of birch scrub may be evident within about ten years of the cessation of burning, and as the tree canopy closes *Calluna* cover diminishes while that of grasses expands. These changes may be slow as *Calluna* persists in shade for a number of years, although failing to regenerate, but in some examples as at Dinnet and Cambus O'May, Aberdeenshire, conversion to birch wood with predominantly grassy ground flora may occur within about twenty years.

Origin from bog. The stratigraphy of the upper horizons of peat beneath present-day heath communities on drained or drying bog sites often gives clear evidence of the relatively recent replacement of *Sphagnum*-dominated communities by *Calluna*. Undoubtedly in many cases this is the result of artificial drainage. Even where there has been no interference with the former bog surface itself, drainage and cultivation of the surrounding countryside may lead to a lowering of the water-table and produce a similar result. Sometimes repeated burning of bog vegetation leads to sufficient drying of the surface for the spread of *Calluna*. Once again, however, it may be that to some extent relatively recent climatic changes have contributed to the change.

Calluna and other wet-heath species constitute a component of the former bog communities, usually occupying the upper parts of hummocks which are often inter-spersed with pools and channels (cf. Chapter 10). Whenever any part of the bog surface lies above the direct influence of a water-table, for whatever reason, for a considerable period of the year, it becomes open to colonisation by *Calluna*. Wet-heath communities may rapidly develop over former bog, and frequently as drying-out proceeds and *Calluna* becomes increasingly dominant, species of the former communities persist for long periods, in particular *Eriophorum angustifolium* and *E. vaginatum*, both of which root deeply in the wetter peat levels.

Relationship with grassland communities. Fenton (1935, 1949) and others have commented upon the possibility of reversible transitions between heath and grassland communities produced by grazing animals (cf. Chapter 6). On relatively fertile soil, intensive grazing may lead to the replacement of heath by *Agrostis—Festuca* grassland by way of a transitional grass-heath stage. This has been observed in Speyside, Perthshire and elsewhere, and the many instances of abrupt boundaries between heath communities and grassland where a fence divides moorland, lightly grazed by sheep, from the lower-lying, more heavily grazed "in-bye" land of a farm, provide additional evidence (cf. Plates 28 and 29). In other habitats, and especially where rabbit-grazing has a marked effect upon the vegetation, *Deschampsia flexuosa* may become the dominant grass. Abandoned fields sometimes revert to heath, but overgrazing by sheep may permit a more or less permanent replacement of heather by *Pteridium aquilinum* (bracken). On peatlands, replacement of heath under heavy grazing (often reinforced by burning) by *Nardus stricta* or *Molinia caerulea* is also often virtually irreversible.

Secondary successions following burning

Although the standards of good moorland management are not always observed, they normally demand burning in small strips or patches rather than large areas. A spatial patchwork then results with each patch at a different stage in the recolonisation succession (Plates 46 and 47). Tansley drew attention in 1939 to the lack of any detailed studies of successions following burning on Scottish heaths. As regards the first few months of recolonisation this remains largely true, but it is now possible to summarise certain types of development more fully. Descriptions are given by Fenton (1949) and more detailed studies have been reported by Whittaker (1960). Two main types of sequence may be recognised.

(1) *In which* Calluna *is slow to recover and temporary dominance is attained by other species*

(*a*) On "hard ground".

Calluna—Erica cinerea communities. Where the plants do not exceed 12-15 years of age before burning and the fire is of moderate intensity (temperature around 300°C.), both species begin to regenerate from stem bases during the subsequent year. For about two years the community is mixed, including: *Deschampsia flexuosa, Festuca ovina, Agrostis* spp. and *Carex pilulifera*, one or more of which may become dominant in small patches; mosses (e.g. *Polytrichum juniperinum, P. piliferum, Bryum* spp., *Ceratodon purpureus, Campylopus* spp.); and, in some instances, a rich selection of *Cladonia* spp. From about the third year onwards the canopy of *Calluna* and *Erica* begins to close up, with *Calluna* re-establishing dominance from about the fifth or sixth year.

If the ericaceous species are killed out, either because of their greater age before burning, or as a result of a more intense fire (e.g. 500-800°C.), their regeneration is entirely from seed (Plate 48). On "hard ground" this is a slow process, particularly in the case of *Calluna*. Sometimes such areas remain largely bare for a number of years, but in more favourable habitats *Deschampsia flexuosa* may exert temporary dominance. Usually, however, within two to five years a dense crop of seedlings is established, in which those of *Erica cinerea* may outnumber *Calluna*. This is followed by a period of dominance by *Erica cinerea* which may last up to five years or more. Repeated observations on fenced plots have shown, however, that the proportion of *Calluna* in the vegetation gradually increases until eventually it exceeds that of *Erica cinerea*.

Calluna—Arctostaphylos uva-ursi communities. By three years after burning, *Arctostaphylos* may be quantitatively the leading species, owing to regeneration from its extensive creeping and partly buried stems. Both *Arctostaphylos* and *Erica cinerea* may exceed *Calluna* in quantity until more than seven years after burning. *Vaccinium* spp., *Antennaria dioica, Carex pilulifera* and, to a lesser extent, *Potentilla erecta* also reappear early, developing from undamaged underground vegetative organs, while *Thymus drucei* and *Veronica officinalis* spread in the open community, particularly after three to five years. Species such as *Genista anglica*, *Pyrola media* and *Listera cordata* may not re-appear until about seven to ten years or more have passed.

(*b*) On "soft ground".

Calluna—Vaccinium communities. Again a temporary phase of dominance by *Deschampsia flexuosa* is often observed, but in many cases it is either followed, or replaced, by a rapid spread of *Vaccinium myrtillus* which, regenerating from rhizomes in the absence of competition with *Calluna*, may become dominant in about three years. *Erica cinerea* is also prominent and *Carex pilulifera* spreads quickly, but most other species of the community, including the majority of bryophytes, do not re-enter until after about four years. From about five years after burning *Calluna* begins to equal and surpass *Vaccinium*.

Communities rich in *Empetrum nigrum*. In a closely similar way, a phase of dominance by *Empetrum nigrum* lasting three to five years or longer may precede the re-establishment of cover by *Calluna*.

Burnt strips of hillsides frequently appear green in contrast to the surrounding brownish colour of *Calluna*, owing to the dominance either of *Vaccinium myrtillus* or *Empetrum nigrum*. However, regeneration of *Calluna*, whether vegetatively or from seed, is quicker and more uniform under the moister conditions provided by "soft ground", and a community not unlike that of the original stand is often established after about four years.

(2) *In which the original community is relatively rapidly reconstituted without intervening stages*

This occurs chiefly under very moist conditions, on peat.

(i) On peaty podsols or drained hill peat, where before burning *Calluna* was dominant with few associates, recolonisation is very largely by *Calluna*. There may be some spread of species such as *Juncus squarrosus*, *Trichophorum cespitosum*, *Nardus stricta* and *Eriophorum vaginatum* which are little damaged by fire, but only under conditions unfavourable for *Calluna* regeneration do any of these become dominant.

(ii) *Calluna—Erica tetralix* communities.

Erica tetralix, regenerating from rhizomes, develops along with *Calluna*, and owing to the wetness of the substratum few of the other species are severely damaged by a well-controlled fire. Thus *Carex panicea*, *Narthecium ossifragum*, *Potentilla erecta*, *Molinia caerulea* and *Trichophorum cespitosum* all produce new growth within the first year, while the outer surfaces of cushions of *Sphagnum* spp. and *Leucobryum glaucum* receive only slight singeing and become green within a few weeks.

The spread of bracken. Under conditions favourable for the regeneration of *Calluna*, burning does not normally lead to the conspicuous spread of *Pteridium aquilinum*. It may,

S

however, permit the entry of bracken into the community, but the competitive vigour of *Calluna* normally restricts it to a subordinate role or confines it to small patches. From this position it is ready to spread if the *Calluna* is allowed to become degenerate, or if its recolonisation after fire is delayed by heavy grazing, or as a result of excessive frequency of burning.

Cyclical change in heath communities

If individual bushes of heather are allowed to grow undisturbed by grazing or fire, the pioneer and building phases of growth are succeeded at an age of between fifteen and twenty years by a mature phase in which the central branches spread apart, intercepting less light. At an age of about twenty-five years, or more, these branches begin to die and the plant enters a degenerate phase, in which a gap of gradually increasing dimensions

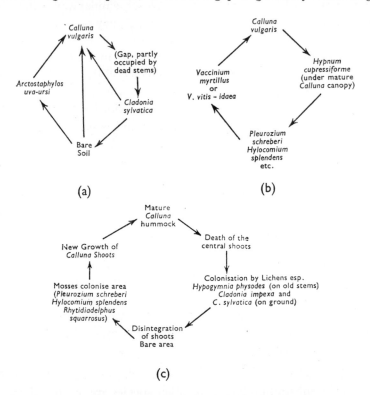

Fig. 44   Examples of cycles of change in heath communities: (a) In *Calluna-Arctostaphylos* communities (after Watt, 1947). (b) In *Calluna-Vaccinium* communities. (c) In dune heath.

develops in the centre of the bush (Plates 40 and 49). Watt (1955) was the first to draw attention to, and name, these phases in the morphological life-history of the plant. Since the bare spaces in the centre of degenerate individuals are more readily invaded by other species than by *Calluna* itself, a cyclical series of changes results in the plant community.

Such a cycle was described by Watt (1947) and Metcalfe (1950) in *Calluna—Arcto-staphylos* communities in the Cairngorm region, in which the gap phase is first occupied by *Cladonia sylvatica* anchored on the dead *Calluna* stems. When these disintegrate the *Cladonia* mat is disrupted, and the bare soil becomes covered by *Arctostaphylos uva-ursi* spreading vegetatively from nearby stems. Only later does *Calluna* spread back over the *Arctostaphylos* and replace it when the closed canopy creates dense shade (Fig. 44A).

In *Calluna—Vaccinium* communities similar cycles are observed in which the ground at the centre of the bush becomes occupied, often during the mature phase, by *Hypnum cupressiforme*. As the gap opens out, this is usually largely replaced by more robust mosses such as *Pleurozium schreberi*, *Hylocomium splendens* and *Plagiothecium undulatum*. The bryophyte mat is first penetrated by shoots of *Vaccinium myrtillus* or *V. vitis-idaea* derived from rhizomes, and one of these species may often be seen established in the centre of an old *Calluna* bush which has become ring-shaped in the degenerate phase (Fig. 44B and Plate 49).

Ritchie (1951) has drawn attention to a similar cycle of change in dune heath in which, however, *Calluna* itself recolonises after temporary occupation of the gaps by lichens and mosses (Fig. 44C).

The *Calluna* population in heathland areas which are not regularly burnt and only lightly grazed becomes in time uneven-aged, leading to a markedly patterned community in which other species occupy the gaps formed where plants have become degenerate or dead. Such areas may, for many years, exhibit a mosaic of patches in which different stages of the cycle are represented side by side. The occasional occurrence of a seedling of *Sorbus aucuparia*, *Betula* spp. or *Pinus sylvestris* in the centre of a gap suggests that in the absence of any arresting factor this structure is not stable, but would eventually permit colonisation and replacement by trees. It is, however, virtually impossible in Scotland to find areas in which to test these hypotheses in the presence of good evidence of freedom from grazing and burning for periods of about fifty years.

UTILISATION OF HEATH LANDS

At the present time heathlands are maintained over wide areas in Scotland for the purposes of sheep farming and the sport of grouse shooting. To a lesser extent, cattle are grazed on *Calluna* communities in certain parts. Here and there, in the more accessible regions, particularly during the last twenty years, small areas have been converted into pasture or arable land, but the only significant conversion of heathland is in the course of afforestation, which by 1957 had used well over 28,300 ha. (70,000 acres) of heathland (Zehetmeyer, 1960). The rival interests of extensive grazing and afforestation as uses of heathland periodically erupt in controversy over their relative importance and their long-term effects upon soil fertility, while the possibility of substituting some other, radically different form of land use is also raised.

The interests of sheep and grouse are served by basically the same type of moor management, which is designed to maintain much of the heather in its pioneer and building phases—when productivity of edible green shoots is at a maximum over a large part of a moor. This is achieved by regular burning of strips or patches on rotation such that, as far as possible, each patch is burned at intervals of between eight and about fifteen years, depending upon the habitat and community-type. If regeneration is effective a dense, even-aged stand develops in each patch, and stands of differing age form a large-scale mosaic over the moor. (Older heather is also held to be of value, since it is grazed particularly in winter and may provide keep in critical periods when younger and shorter vegetation is snow-covered. Grouse also require the additional cover it provides. However, it is probable that the majority of moors carry more than enough old heather.)

Treatment by periodic burning, while maintaining a good supply of *Calluna*, leads to impoverishment of the flora and of wild life in general. It has further been claimed that it causes general degradation of soil fertility, as a result of the loss of a certain proportion of the available mineral nutrients, deposited as ash on the soil surface, after each fire. However, insufficient long-term studies have been carried out to provide reliable support for or disproof of this theory. More important, perhaps, is the fact that perpetual mono-culture of *Calluna* leads to increasing soil podsolisation and hence reduced availability of nutrients, while the selective grazing habits of sheep, in Scotland virtually the only domestic animal on the moors, are such as to promote the spread of undesirable species including *Pteridium aquilinum* and *Nardus stricta*. Furthermore, the continual cropping of the animal produce from these communities, with negligible provision for the return of substances in the form of fertilisers, inevitably leads in time to habitat deterioration. It is difficult to contrast yields of sheep, cattle, grouse, etc., today with those in past decades or centuries owing to lack of comparability in the available statistics, while veterinary advances and improvements in methods of management might be expected to obscure any decline in yields. None the less, sheep densities of the order of one sheep to between 1·2 and 2·8 ha. (3 and 7 acres) can scarcely be regarded as an efficient form of land use while, merely in terms of productivity, the land devoted to grouse-rearing contributes little and this too appears to be on the decline.

In view of this it is easy to argue that afforestation is more productive, economically more rewarding, and a basically sounder form of land use, since it usually involves a supply of fertiliser to the land and normally, though not always, slowly promotes a return of fertility to the upper layers of the soil. Studies have now been made of the mineral requirements for afforestation of many heath soils, the most appropriate species to plant in the different communities and the most effective methods of planting (Zehetmayr, 1950). Recent research (Leyton, 1954) has thrown some light onto the "check" suffered by Spruce (*Picea abies*) resulting from the effects of competition when planted among *Calluna*. Thus, except in the most exposed localities, there are few areas of lowland heath which cannot be effectively afforested, and there is little doubt that an increase in acreage under forest would be beneficial.

Nevertheless, it is unsound to make direct comparisons between a system which has the resources of a large state enterprise and one which has grown up over the years in the form of relatively small farm units with little capital. Evidence is beginning to accumulate from various districts of the possibilities of improving heathland for agricultural purposes and, in particular, for carrying increased stocks of sheep and a higher proportion of cattle than at present, without an accompanying deterioration of fertility. There is no reason why investigations on large-scale application of fertilisers and control of grazing in difficult territory should not show the way to replace *Calluna* communities in the better habitats by more valuable pasture, while in poorer districts the quantity and quality of edible material produced by *Calluna* itself could similarly be improved. The hill-sheep industry remains an important part of the agricultural economy of the country, and in this way might be placed on an ecologically sounder foundation. Smaller, more productive areas devoted to sheep-farming would at the same time permit realisation of the equally legitimate claims of forestry for increased scope. In any event, a greater ecological diversity than is at present apparent in the Scottish heathlands would in the long run be of advantage to farmer, forester and ecologist, with little sacrifice of the appeal of the heather moors to the tourist and sportsman.

REFERENCES

BØCHER, T. W. — 1940 — Studies on the plant-geography of the North-Atlantic heath formation. I. The heaths of the Faroes. *K. Danske vidensk. Selsk., Biol. Medd.*, **15**, 1-64.

1943 — Studies on the plant-geography of the North-Atlantic heath formation. II. Danish dwarf shrub heaths in relation to those of north Europe. *K. Danske vidensk. Selsk., Biol. Skr.*, **2**, 1-129.

BOGGIE, R. — 1956 — *Plant Root Systems and Soils of Grassland and Heath.* Ph.D. Thesis, University of Aberdeen.

BOGGIE, R., KNIGHT, A. H. and HUNTER, R. F. — 1958 — Studies of the root development of plants in the field using radioactive tracers. *J. Ecol.*, **46**, 621-639.

DAMMAN, A. W. H. — 1957 — The south-Swedish *Calluna*-heath and its relation to the Calluneto—Genistetum. *Bot. Notiser*, **110**, 363-398.

DELANY, M. J. — 1953 — Studies on the microclimate of *Calluna* heathland. *J. Anim. Ecol.*, **22**, 227-239.

DURNO, S. E. — 1956 — Pollen analysis of peat deposits in Scotland. *Scot. geogr. Mag.*, **72**, 177-187.

1957 — Certain aspects of vegetational history in North-East Scotland. *Scot. geogr. Mag.*, **73**, 176-184.

1958 — Pollen analysis of peat deposits in Eastern Sutherland and Caithness. *Scot. geogr. Mag.*, **74**, 127-135.

1959 — Pollen analysis of peat deposits in the Eastern Grampians. *Scot. geogr. Mag.*, **75**, 102-111.

ELLIOTT, R. J. — 1953 — *The Effects of Burning on Heather Moors of the South Pennines.* Ph.D. Thesis, University of Sheffield.

FENTON, E. W. 1935 The transition from woodland and moorland to grassland in the Spey Valley and elsewhere. *J. Ecol.*, **23**, 56-68.

1949 Vegetation changes in hill grazings with particular reference to heather (*Calluna vulgaris*). *J. Brit. Grassl. Soc.*, **4**, 95-103.

GEIGER, R. 1959 *The Climate near the Ground*. Cambridge, Mass., U.S.A.

GIMINGHAM, C. H. 1949 The effects of grazing on the balance between *Erica cinerea* L. and *Calluna vulgaris* (L.) Hull. in upland heath, and their morphological responses. *J. Ecol.*, **37**, 100-119.

1961 North European heath communities: a 'network of variation'. *J. Ecol.*, **49**, 655-694.

GORHAM, E. 1956 On the chemical composition of some waters from the Moor House Nature Reserve. *J. Ecol.*, **44**, 375-382.

HARDY, M. 1904 *Equisse de la Géographie et de la Végétation des Highlands d'Écosse*. Paris.

LANDSBERG, S. Y. 1955 *The Morphology and Vegetation of the Sands of Forvie*. Ph.D. Thesis, University of Aberdeen.

LEYTON, L. 1954 The growth and mineral nutrition of spruce and pine in heathland plantations. *Imp. For. Inst. Paper*, **31**, 1-109.

1955 The influence of artificial shading of the ground vegetation on the nutrition and growth of Sitka spruce (*Picea sitchensis* Carr.) in a heathland plantation. *Forestry*, **28**, 1-6.

McVEAN, D. N. and RATCLIFFE, D. A. 1962 *Plant Communities of the Scottish Highlands*. H.M.S.O., London.

METCALFE, G. 1950 The ecology of the Cairngorms. Part II. The mountain Callunetum. *J. Ecol.*, **38**, 46-74.

MUIR, A. and FRASER, G. K. 1940 The soils and vegetation of the Bin and Clashindarroch forests. *Trans. Roy. Soc. Edinb.*, **60**, 233-341.

NORDHAGEN, R. 1921 Vegetationsstudien auf der Insel Utsire im westlichen Norwegen. *Bergens Mus. Aarb., Naturvid. raekke*, **1**, 1-149.

PEARSALL, W. H. 1950 *Mountains and Moorlands*. London.

RITCHIE, J. C. 1951 *An Ecological Survey of Heath Vegetation in the Region of Aberdeen*. Unpublished thesis, Department of Botany, University of Aberdeen.

SJÖRS, H. 1950 Regional studies in North Swedish mire vegetation. *Bot. Notiser*, **2**, 173-222.

SMITH, R. 1900 Botanical survey of Scotland. I. Edinburgh district. *Scot. geogr. Mag.*, **16**, 385-416.
II. North Perthshire district. *Scot. geogr. Mag.*, **16**, 441-467.

SMITH, W. G. 1902 The origin and development of heather moorland. *Scot. geogr. Mag.*, **18**, 587-597.

1905 Botanical survey of Scotland. III and IV. Forfar and Fife. *Scot. geogr. Mag.*, **21**, 4-23.

1911 "*Scottish Heaths*" in "*Types of British Vegetation*". (Ed. A. G. Tansley). Cambridge.

SPENCE, D. H. N.   1960   Studies on the vegetation of Shetland. III. Scrub in Shetland
                                  and in South Uist, Outer Hebrides. *J. Ecol.*, **48**, 73-95.

STOCKER, O.   1923   Die Transpiration und Wasserökologie nordwestdeutscher
                                  Heide- und Moorpflanzen am Standort. *Ztschr. für Bot.*, **15**,
                                  1-41.

STOUTJESDIJK, PH.   1959   Heaths and inland dunes of the Veluwe. *Wentia*, **2**, 1-96.

TANSLEY, A. G.   1949   *The British Islands and their Vegetation.* Cambridge.

WATT, A. S.   1955   Bracken versus heather, a study in plant sociology. *J. Ecol.*, **43**,
                                  490-506.

WATT, A. S.   1947   Pattern and process in the plant community. *J. Ecol.*, **35**, 1-22.

WHITTAKER, E.   1960   *Ecological Effects of Moor Burning.* Ph.D. Thesis, University of
                                  Aberdeen.
                          1961   Temperatures in heath fires. *J. Ecol.*, **49**, 709-715.

WHITTAKER, E. and   1962   The effects of fire on regeneration of *Calluna vulgaris* (L.) Hull
   GIMINGHAM, C. H.   from seed. *J. Ecol.*, **50**, 815-822.

ZEHETMAYR, J. W. L.   1960   Afforestation of upland heaths. *For. Comm. Bull.*, **32**. H.M.S.O.,
                                  Edinburgh.

Table 25

Synoptic Table showing Composition of Community-types in the Euoceanic Heath Series

Figures in these columns show % presence of each species in the stands sampled

	Calluna—Empetrum hermaphroditum communities	Calluna—Erica cinerea heaths		
		"Typical" examples	Herb-rich variants	Dune-heath variants
Localities	Islands in Shetland lochs	S. Uist, N. coast of Sutherland, Orkney	S. Uist, Sutherland, Ross-shire, Rhum, Shetland, Orkney, Aberdeenshire	Wigtownshire
No. of stands sampled	6	7	12	2
Sample area	Variable	4 sq. m.	4 sq. m.	4 sq. m.
Altitude range	Up to 150 m.	Up to 90 m.	15–350 m.	Up to 50 m.
Sorbus aucuparia	16	...	8	
Calluna vulgaris	100	100	100	++
Empetrum hermaphroditum	83	14	17	
E. nigrum	...	43	25	
Erica cinerea	16	100	100	++
E. tetralix	...	43	25	
Salix repens	...	29	25	
Vaccinium myrtillus	...	29	8	
V. vitis-idaea	16	...	8	
Blechnum spicant	32	57	50	+
Pteridium aquilinum	...	43	25	
Agrostis canina/A. tenuis	16	86	92	++
Anthoxanthum odoratum	16	43	75	
Deschampsia flexuosa	83	...	25	
Festuca ovina	...	...	58	
F. rubra	...	43	42	+
Molinia caerulea	10	43	42	
Nardus stricta	...	29	33	
Sieglingia decumbens	...	14	58	

[continued]

Carex binervis		25	57	50
Carex nigra			14	16
Carex panicea		58	29	
Dactylorchis maculata ssp. ericetorum		25	29	
Luzula campestris	++	17		16
L. multiflora		17		32
Trichophorum cespitosum		17	29	16
Campanula rotundifolia		8	29	
Euphrasia spp.		58		32 (E. scotica)
Galium saxatile	++	25	14	
G. verum			29	
Hypericum pulchrum		92	71	
Linum catharticum	++	33	14	
Lotus corniculatus		50	14	
Pedicularis spp.		17	29	
Plantago lanceolata		42	14	
Polygala serpyllifolia		58	29	
Potentilla erecta		92	86	100
Rhinanthus minor agg.		17		100
Rumex acetosa		8		32
Solidago virgaurea		17		50
Succisa pratensis		42	29	16
Thymus drucei	+	75	14	
Trifolium repens		25	14	
Veronica officinalis	++	8		
Viola riviniana	++	58	43	
Breutelia chrysocoma	+	17	14	
Dicranum scoparium		42	57	
Hylocomium splendens		67	71	
Hypnum cupressiforme	++	83	86	
Pleurozium schreberi	+	42	29	
Pseudoscleropodium purum		58	14	32
Rhacomitrium lanuginosum		17	14	
Rhytidiadelphus loreus		8	29	
R. squarrosus		42	29	
R. triquetrus		42	29	
Thuidium tamariscinum	+	25	14	
Diplophyllum albicans		17	29	

	Calluna—Empetrum hermaphroditum communities	Calluna—Erica cinerea heaths		
		"Typical" examples	Herb-rich variants	Dune-heath variants
Localities	Islands in Shetland lochs	S. Uist, N. coast of Sutherland, Orkney	S. Uist, Sutherland, Ross-shire, Rhum, Shetland, Orkney, Aberdeenshire	Wigtownshire
No. of stands sampled	6	7	12	2
Sample area	Variable	4 sq. m.	4 sq. m.	4 sq. m.
Altitude range	Up to 150 m.	Up to 90 m.	15–350 m.	Up to 50 m.
C. adonia rangiferina	...	29	8	++
C. sylvatica	...	14	17	

Additional species recorded in one only of the community-types included in this table:

Calluna—Empetrum	"Typical" examples	Herb-rich variants	Dune-heath variants
Juniperus communis ssp. nana 16	Arctostaphylos uva-ursi 29	Lonicera periclymenum 8	Aira caryophyllea +
Vaccinium uliginosum 16	Agrostis stolonifera 29	Rubus fruticosus agg. 8	A. praecox +
Polypodium vulgare 83	Campylopus flexuosus 14	Athyrium filix-femina 8	Ammophila arenaria ++
Eriophorum angustifolium 32	Dicranum majus 14	Lycopodium selago 17	Carex arenaria +
Luzula sylvatica 32	Leucobryum glaucum 14	Selaginella selaginoides 17	Sedum acre +
	Plagiothecium undulatum 57	Cynosurus cristatus 17	Veronica chamaedrys +
	Polytrichum commune 14	Festuca vivipara 17	Polytrichum juniperinum ++
	Cetraria islandica 14	Holcus lanatus 8	Lophocolea bidentata +
		Koeleria cristata 25	Ptilidium ciliare ++
		Carex flacca 8	Cetraria aculeata +
		C. pilulifera 50	
		C. pulicaris 42	
		Listera cordata 17	
		Alchemilla alpina 17	
		Anemone nemorosa 17	
		Angelica sylvestris 8	
		Antennaria dioica 58	
		Anthyllis vulneraria 8	
		Armeria maritima 8	
		Cirsium heterophyllum 17	
		Dryas octopetala 8	

Note: ++ = Occurring in both stands.
  + = Occurring in one stand.

Filipendula ulmaria	8
Galium boreale	17
Gentianella campestris	8
Geum rivale	17
Hieracium pilosella	17
Hypochoeris radicata	33
Lathyrus montanus	25
Leontodon autumnalis	17
L. hispidus	8
Lysimachia nemorum	8
Parnassia palustris	8
Plantago maritima	33
Primula vulgaris	25
Prunella vulgaris	25
Ranunculus acris	17
Taraxacum officinale agg.	8
Thalictrum alpinum	17
Trifolium pratense	17
Trollius europaeus	25
Vicia sepium	8
Acrocladium cuspidatum	17
Ctenidium molluscum	17
Drepanocladus uncinatus	8
Fissidens osmundoides	17
Isothecium myosuroides	17

Col. 1—Data from Spence (1960).   Col. 3—Includes data from McVean and Ratcliffe (1962).

Table 26

Synoptic Table showing Composition of Community-types in Heaths on Soils of Impeded Drainage, etc.

Figures in these columns show % presence of each species in the stands sample

	Calluna—Erica tetralix heaths rich in Empetrum nigrum	Calluna—Erica tetralix wet heaths			Calluna—Eriophorum vaginatum wet heath
		Rich in Trichophorum cespitosum	Rich in Molinia caerulea	Neither Trichophorum nor Molinia prominent	
Localities	Orkney, Inverness-shire, Aberdeenshire, Kincardineshire	Wigtownshire, Argyll, W. Ross, Sutherland, Inverness-shire, Moray, Nairn, Aberdeenshire, Kincardineshire, Angus	W. Ross, Inverness-shire, Aberdeenshire, Kincardineshire, Perthshire	Wigtownshire, Sutherland, Aberdeenshire, Kincardineshire, Perthshire	Aberdeenshire, Perthshire
No. of stands sampled	20	30	15	11	3
Sample area	4 sq. m.	4 sq. m.	4 sq. m.	4 sq. m.	Variable
Altitude range	10–500 m.	50–600 m.	50–300 m.	50–300 m.	50–400 m.
Calluna vulgaris	100	100	100	100	100
Empetrum nigrum	100	...	...	9	33
Erica cinerea	10	43	47	18	...
E. tetralix	85	100	93	100	100
Genista anglica	5	10	...	...	...
Myrica gale	...	...	33	9	...
Vaccinium myrtillus	10	13	20	18	...
V. vitis-idaea	5	3	7	...	...
Blechnum spicant	5	...	7	...	...
Agrostis canina/tenuis	15	7	20	27	...
A. stolonifera	15	...	7	9	...
Anthoxanthum odoratum	5	...	7	9	...
Deschampsia cespitosa	...	...	7	9	...
D. flexuosa	10	7	40	46	...
Festuca ovina	10	...	7	9	...
F. rubra	5	...	...	9	...
Molinia caerulea	10	40	100	9	...
Nardus stricta	25	3	33	36	...

	E	D	C	B	A
Carex arenaria	5	.	.	18	.
C. binervis	15	3	13	9	.
C. echinata	10	3	27	.	.
C. nigra	.	.	7	.	33
C. panicea	20	43	27	.	.
C. pilulifera	.	30	20	.	.
Eriophorum angustifolium	45	30	27	55	.
E. vaginatum	60	27	.	55	100
Juncus effusus	15	.	7	27	100
J. squarrosus	60	30	27	36	.
Listera cordata	5	.	7	.	.
Luzula multiflora	5	3	.	.	.
Narthecium ossifragum	50	67	33	46	33
Trichophorum cespitosum	40	100	67	18	33
Drosera rotundifolia	30	3	7	9	.
Galium saxatile	5	.	7	.	.
Hypericum pulchrum	.	.	7	9	.
Pinguicula vulgaris	5	10	7	9	.
Polygala serpyllifolia	.	3	27	9	.
Potentilla erecta	15	33	93	55	.
Rubus chamaemorus	5	.	.	9	.
Succisa pratensis	5	.	27	18	.
Veronica officinalis	.	.	7	27	.
Viola riviniana	.	.	7	9	.
Aulacomnium palustre	55	3	20	55	67
Breutelia chrysocoma	3	.	13	.	.
Campylopus flexuosus	.	13	13	.	33
Dicranum scoparium	30	33	40	73	100
Hylocomium splendens	20	20	67	36	.
Hypnum cupressiforme	80	70	73	82	100
Leucobryum glaucum	3	23	33	9	.
Mnium hornum	15	.	.	18	.
Plagiothecium undulatum	30	3	33	27	33
Pleurozium schreberi	95	27	67	82	67
Pohlia nutans	15	7	7	46	100
Polytrichum commune	60	13	.	73	33
P. juniperinum	10	3	7	9	100
Rhacomitrium lanuginosum	10	23	27	.	.

[continued]

	Calluna—Erica tetralix heaths rich in Empetrum nigrum	Calluna—Erica tetralix wet heaths			Calluna—Eriophorum vaginatum wet heath
		Rich in Trichophorum cespitosum	Rich in Molinia caerulea	Neither Trichophorum nor Molinia prominent	
Localities	Orkney, Inverness-shire, Aberdeenshire, Kincardineshire	Wigtownshire, Argyll, W. Ross, Sutherland, Inverness-shire, Moray, Nairn, Aberdeenshire, Kincardineshire, Angus	W. Ross, Inverness-shire, Aberdeenshire, Kincardineshire, Perthshire	Wigtownshire, Sutherland, Aberdeenshire, Kincardineshire, Perthshire	Aberdeenshire, Perthshire
No. of stands sampled	20	30	15	11	3
Sample area	4 sq. m.	4 sq. m.	4 sq. m.	4 sq. m.	Variable
Altitude range	10–500 m.	50–600 m.	50–300 m.	50–300 m.	50–400 m.
Rhytidiadelphus loreus	15	7	40	9	...
R. squarrosus	10	7	27	37	...
R. triquetrus	5	...	7	18	...
Sphagnum spp.	85	57*	73†	46†	67
Alicularia scalaris	...	...	7	9	...
Barbilophozia floerkii	5	3	...	...	...
Calypogeia trichomanis	10	3	7	36	...
Diplophyllum albicans	...	3	20	...	...
Gymnocolea inflata	15	...	...	9	33
Lophocolea bidentata	10	7	7	18	33
Lophozia ventricosa	5	7	7	...	33
Mylia anomala	...	...	...	9	...
Odontoschisma sphagni	...	7	27	...	...
Scapania gracilis	...	7	7	9	...
Cladonia "chlorophaea"	5	...	...	...	33
C. coccifera	...	7	20	9	33
C. gracilis	...	10	7	...	33
C. impexa	10	30	20	9	33
C. pyxidata	...	47	33	18	...
C. rangiferina	5	10	...	...	...
C. squamosa	10	3	7	...	33
C. sylvatica	25	17	13	9	33
C. uncialis	...	33	13	...	...

Additional species recorded in one only of the community-types included in the table:

Species	
Empetrum hermaphroditum	5
Holcus lanatus	5
Luzula campestris	5
Chamaenerion angustifolium	5
Viola palustris	5
Orthodontium lineare	5
Pseudoscleropodium purum	5
Cephaloziella sp.	5
Plagiochila asplenioides	5
Cladonia fimbriata	5
C. pityrea	5
Lecanora varia	5

Species	
Arctostaphylos uva-ursi	3
Betula nana	3
Juniperus communis ssp. nana	3
Lycopodium selago	7
Carex bigelowii	3
Dactylorchis maculata ssp. ericetorum	3
Juncus kochii	3
Antennaria dioica	3
Pedicularis sylvatica	3
Campylopus atrovirens	13
Dicranella heteromalla	3
Anastrepta orcadensis	3
Leptoscyphus anomalus	7
L. taylori	10
Pleurozia purpurea	7
Cetraria islandica	3
C. aculeata	7

Species	
Salix aurita	7
Equisetum sylvaticum	7
Festuca vivipara	7
Juncus conglomeratus	7
Trientalis europaea	7
Thuidium tamariscinum	13
Cladonia cornuta	7

Species	
Salix repens	27
Carex demissa	9
C. pulicaris	9
Juncus articulatus	9
Lotus corniculatus	9
Plantago lanceolata	9
Rumex acetosella	9
Taraxacum officinale agg.	9
Trifolium repens	9
Acrocladium cuspidatum	9
Ceratodon purpureus	9
Dicranella palustris	9
Calypogeia fissa	9
Lophozia excisa	9
L. incisa	9
Peltigera sp.	9

Species	
Cephalozia connivens	33
Cladonia furcata	33

Data from McVean and Ratcliffe (1962) have been incorporated in the above table.

* Species recorded include:
S. capillaceum
S. compactum
S. palustre
S. papillosum
S. plumulosum
S. robustum
S. rubellum
S. tenellum

† Species recorded include:
S. capillaceum
S. compactum
S. palustre
S. papillosum
S. plumulosum
S. robustum
S. rubellum
S. tenellum

‡ Species recorded include:
S. capillaceum
S. palustre
S. papillosum
S. rubellum

THE LOWLAND AQUATIC ZONE

T

CHAPTER 8

THE PHYTOPLANKTON OF THE SCOTTISH FRESHWATER LOCHS

A. J. BROOK

It has been estimated that there are well over one thousand freshwater lochs* in Scotland. These range in size from the very extensive Loch Lomond with an area of 71·2 sq. km. (27·5 sq. miles), the deep Lochs Morar and Ness (with depths of over 305 m. (1000 ft.), to the small, shallow Highland lochans which occur in considerable numbers, especially in the north-west of the country. In all they occupy an area of more than 880 sq. km. (340 sq. miles).

The first general review of the phytoplankton of these waters was published more than 50 years ago in a paper surveying this community in the freshwaters of the British Isles as a whole (West and West, 1909). The main features of the Scottish lake plankton were briefly described, but the summary was based only on the examination of the "net plankton" collected in the summer months from thirty-eight of the larger lochs. Another short account was given by Murray (1910) in a review of the biology of the Scottish lochs, but this again was based only on net collections taken, admittedly from a much larger number of lochs, during the course of the Bathymetric Survey. In both accounts, however, the main feature emphasised was the dominance of desmids, with diatoms occasionally abundant and Cyanophyta always poorly represented. On the basis of these accounts it would seem that a desmid-dominated plankton has been assumed to be typical of the whole country, with the result that, in what was probably the earliest biological classification of lakes, Teiling (1916) refers to the desmid-dominated, oligotrophic waters as *Caledonian* in contrast to the more productive, Cyanophytean-dominated *Baltic* type.

A detailed examination has recently been made of the "net phytoplankton" of over 200 Scottish lochs from all parts of the country and this more extensive survey has indicated that these earlier impressions of the plankton give neither a complete, nor an accurate picture. This is not surprising considering the comparatively small number of lochs examined in these earlier surveys and, especially in the case of the Wests, the

---

* The Scots words "loch" and "lochan" are used throughout this account and are synonymous with English "lake" and "tarn" or "mere", respectively.

290

limited and geologically similar areas in which the lochs are situated: i.e. Perthshire, Inverness, Ross-shire, Sutherland and the Outer Hebrides.

The present more extensive survey of the Scottish phytoplankton was initially undertaken to examine the validity of Nygaard's Phytoplankton Quotient Hypothesis (Nygaard, 1949), which is claimed to give a fairly reliable estimate of a lake's trophic status, that is, its inherent capacity to support life or its biotic potential. The Quotient Hypothesis is based on the supposition that certain algal groups, e.g. Cyanophyta, Chlorococcales, Centric Diatoms, etc., are specifically, most numerous in eutrophic lakes compared with others, e.g. Desmidiaceae, most species of which occur in oligotrophic waters. The Phytoplankton Quotient is the ratio between these two categories:

$$\text{The Compound Quotient} = \frac{\text{Cyanophyceae} + \text{Chlorophyceae} + \text{Centrales} + \text{Euglenineae}}{\text{Desmidiaceae}}$$

The quotients are determined simply by the enumeration of species obtained from net collections of phytoplankton. In trying to assess the validity of Nygaard's hypothesis it has been found that one of the great limitations is that it is not uncommon, in net collections, to find considerable numbers of adventitious forms from other lake habitats in addition to true plankters. In studying the Scottish plankton, especial attention has been paid to the desmids in this connection for it has been found that many adventitious forms of this group often occur in considerable numbers, especially in the smaller lochs. Thus, on the assumption that any desmid which occurs frequently and constantly in the plankton collected from the open water of large, deep lakes must be truly adapted to this habitat, it has been found that for the Scottish lochs, only 30 desmid taxa can be classified as limnoplanktonic, while only another 15 may be considered to be facultative plankters (Brook, 1959a). The Wests, however, list 223 desmids as occurring in the Scottish plankton and it is not surprising, therefore, that they stress the qualitative dominance of this algal group; a dominance which is by no means as well marked as their results would suggest.

The trophic status of Scottish lochs in terms of their phytoplankton

If care is taken to exclude all tychoplanktonic taxa in making assessments of the trophic status in terms of Nygaard's Phytoplankton Quotient, it has been found for eighteen Scottish lochs, for which other biological, chemical and physical data indicative of their productivity is available, that there is a remarkably good correlation between these data and the quotients so determined, as is shown in Table 28 (p. 292).

The quotients, and hence an indication of the trophic status, of some 200 lochs have been determined and 125 of these are plotted in Fig. 45 which thus shows the geographical distribution of plankton types. From this map the following general pattern of distribution of lake types in Scotland is apparent (p. 293).

Eutrophic lochs (quotients greater than 2·0) with Cyanophyta, Chlorococcales and Centric Diatoms most numerous, by species, and often showing water blooms in

TABLE 28

Loch	pH	Alkalinity (p.p.m. CaCO₃)	Compound Phytoplankton quotient	Bottom fauna	
				Nos./sq. ft.	g./sq. ft.
Loch Grosvenor	5·5–6·0	1·0–2·0	3/14 = 0·21	4·5	0·014
Loch Smuraich	,,	,,	3/11 = 0·27	14·8	0·029
Loch Rannoch	6·0–6·5	2·0–4·0	2/7 = 0·28	142·0	0·275
Loch Eigheach	,,	,,	7/25 = 0·28		
Loch Shiel	,,	,,	14/62 = 0·23		
Loch Rosque	,,	,,	7/16 = 0·44		
Loch a' Mhullaich	6·5–7·0	4·0–10·0	10/22 = 0·45		
Loch na Beiste Brice	,,	,,	7/11 = 0·65		
Lochindorbh	,,	,,	6/12 = 0·50		
Loch Cruinn	,,	,,	11/17 = 0·65	56·0	0·224
Loch Choin	,,	,,	circa 1·0	33·0	0·076
Loch Daimh Beg	7·0–7·5	10·0–30·0	9/10 = 0·9		
Loch Daimh Mhor	,,	,,	8/5 = 1·6		
Loch Freuchie	,,	,,	6/12 = 0·5		
Loch Kinardochy	,,	,,	<2·0 up to 3·0	38·0	0·141
Loch Moraig	7·5–8·5	30·0–80·0	16/6 = 2·7	264·0	0·572
Lochan an Daim	,,	,,	26/4 = 6·5	110·0	0·324
Loch Leven	,,	,,	17/2 = 8·5	190·0	1·014

summer and autumn. The majority are shallow lochs in fluvio-glacial deposits. They occur:

(a) In the area of Old Red Sandstone to the east of a line between Thurso and Helmsdale and south of this region between the Dornoch Firth and Inverness, including the Cromarty Firth and Black Isle.

(b) South of the Highland fault between Stonehaven and Helensburgh, down to a line between Girven and Dunbar, marking the southernmost extent of the central Lowlands.

(c) In the rich agricultural lowland areas of Galloway and Dumfries which border the Southern Uplands.

Oligotrophic lochs (quotients less than o·8) in which desmids are, by species, most numerous.

This group include most of the region known as the Scottish Highlands in the area to the north of the Highland fault. The most oligotrophic of these are the small lochans receiving acid drainage from peat and the numerous large, deep lakes of tectonic or glacial origin which are all mainly surrounded by moorland and receive their drainage off granitic rocks.

Mesotrophic lochs (quotients between o·8 and 2·0) which are intermediate in character between the two previous types. These occur:

(a) Towards the borders of the areas outlined in the two previous types. One of the best examples of this category is the increasingly eutrophic series of lochs extending from the edge of the Highland fault at Dunkeld into the rich agricultural land around Blairgowrie.

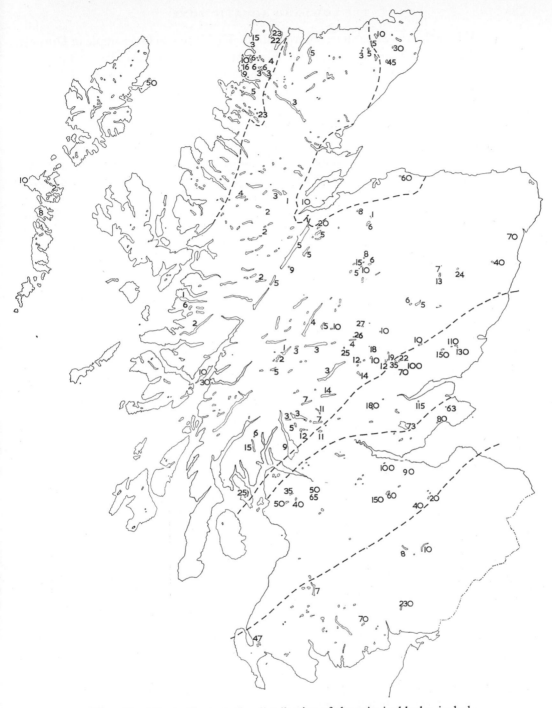

Fig. 45 Map to illustrate the distribution of the principal lochs, including those for which Nygaard's Compound Phytoplankton Quotient has been determined (values are given × 10), in relation to the major geological regions of Scotland. (cf. Fig. 10, p. 40).

(b) Where there are limestone outcrops in the Highlands, as for example in Durness, Assynt, Lismore, Islay, and the Blair Atholl and Tay limestone outcrops in central Perthshire. The character of these lochs varies considerably depending on the calcium content of the water. In some, e.g. Lismore and Durness in which alkalinities of over 100 p.p.m. $CaCO_3$ have been recorded, the plankton although typically eutrophic in its specific composition is quantitatively poor and, in consequence, the waters have considerable clarity throughout the year. Charophytes are often abundant and are inevitably lime-encrusted (cf. Chapter 9). In others, the influence of limestone is less well marked; charophytes although present are never abundant or lime encrusted, and the plankton, often quantitatively rich, is truly intermediate in character between the typically eu- and oligotrophic types. Good examples are Loch Bhac, Loch Kinardochy and Loch Earn in Perthshire.

This survey of the "net phytoplankton" of the Scottish lochs indicates clearly that a wide range of plankton and of lake types exist. Chemical analyses of the waters of 107 lochs, from which plankton has also been examined, have been carried out by Mr. A. V. Holden and his assistants at the Freshwater Fisheries Laboratory, Pitlochry and his results provide evidence of considerable chemical diversity. Both the chemical and biological analyses have been summarised in Table 29, from which it can be seen that

TABLE 29

Range of some Chemical Substances and Compound Quotients of Scottish Loch Waters

No. of Lochs	pH	Alkalinity p.p.m. $CaCO_3$	Hardness p.p.m. $CaCO_3$	Calcium p.p.m.	Magnesium p.p.m.	Sodium p.p.m.	Potassium p.p.m.	Chloride p.p.m.	Compound Quotient
2	4·0–5·0	...	4·0– 6·3	1·8– 2·2	1·8– 4·5	4·7 –11·0	0·20–0·35	?–19·4	0·08– 0·1
6	5·5–6·0	1·0– 2·0	6·2– 8·4	1·8– 5·8	2·0– 4·7	3·15– 3·45	0·20–0·25	6·6– 7·5	0·21– 0·7
14	6·0–6·5	2·0– 5·0	5·9– 12·4	2·8– 6·0	2·0– 6·3	2·7 –15·8	0·10–1·95	5·1–27·0	0·20– 1·5
33	6·5–7·0	4·0– 10·0	8·3– 23·0	4·9– 11·2	2·2–13·0	2·9 –25·0	0·20–1·05	5·8–32·3	0·33– 2·2
23	7·0–7·5	10·0– 30·0	14·0– 35·5	8·3– 29·2	3·1–17·4	2·7 –34·0	0·50–2·20	5·8–36·4	0·50– 3·5
13	7·5–8·0	30·0– 60·0	40·0– 86·0	25·0– 71·0	12·0–29·0	6·0 –20·8	0·65–2·23	8·7–34·5	1·0 –10·0
14	8·0–9·6	60·0–135	79·0–185·0	40·0–130·0	8·0–89·0	3·1 –36·9	0·50–4·70	32·8–59·2	1·4 –18·0

comparatively few of the lochs are markedly oligotrophic, with low pH and alkalinity values. Indeed, most are around neutral in their reaction with alkalinities between 15 and 30 and Plankton Quotients indicative of mesotrophy i.e. about 1·0. A remarkably high proportion are, however, distinctly alkaline with pH values often of 8·0 or more and having phytoplankton populations whose compositions are clearly indicative of eutrophy.

The limnoplanktonic species present in the summer plankton of 9 lochs of markedly different morphological types but which are fairly representative of the three trophic categories considered above, are listed in Table 32 (p. 294). Some of the physical and chemical characteristics of the lochs in this Table are as follows:

Loch Morar—Rock basin in granitic schists.
> Length 11·7 miles; area 10·3 sq. miles; mean depth 284 ft.; max. depth 1017 ft.; pH 6·5; alkalinity 2·4 p.p.m.$CaCO_3$.

Loch Achilty—A small rock basin remarkably deep for its small size.
> Length 0·87 miles; area 0·23 sq. miles; mean depth 51·8 ft.; max. depth 119 ft.; pH 6·5-7·0; alkalinity 4·0 p.p.m.$CaCO_3$.

Loch Aslaich—Small, narrow, drift-dammed loch in schists.
> Length 0·35 miles; area 0·3 sq. miles; mean depth 10·9 ft.; max. depth 26 ft.; pH 6·5; alkalinity 9·0 p.p.m.$CaCO_3$.

Loch Lomond—Typical valley rock basin which can be divided into two distinct sections:
> (*a*) upper deep narrow basin lying in metamorphic rocks;
> (*b*) a lower, wide shallow basin lying mainly in strata of Old Red Sandstone age.
> Length 22·6 miles; area 27·5 sq. miles; mean depth 121·3 ft.; max. depth 623 ft.; pH 6·6-7·0; alkalinity 4·4-9·0 p.p.m.$CaCO_3$.

Loch Ard—Rock basin lying along the outcrop of a belt of slates between two bands of grit.
> Length 2·3 miles; area 0·94 sq. miles; mean depth 43·9 ft.; max. depth 107 ft.; pH 6·5-6·8; alkalinity 10-15 p.p.m.$CaCO_3$.

Loch Kinardochy—A kettle hole with small limestone outcrop on western shore.
> Length 0·45 mile; area 41 acres; mean depth 8·9 ft.; max. depth 30 ft.; pH 6·8-7·4; alkalinity 18-26 p.p.m.$CaCO_3$.

Loch Leven—Large kettle hole in fluvio-glacial and lake deposits.
> Length 3·65 miles; area 5·3 sq. miles; mean depth 14·9 ft.; max. depth 83 ft.; pH 7·8-8·4; alkalinity 52-76 p.p.m.$CaCO_3$.

Castle Loch (Lochmaben)—Kettle hole on fluvio-glacial deposits.
> Length 0·83 mile; area 0·3 sq. miles; mean depth 8·6 ft.; max. depth 18 ft.; pH 7·6-8·4; alkalinity 60-74 p.p.m.$CaCO_3$.

Balgavies Loch—Lake ponded by drift on Lower Old Red Sandstone strata.
> Length 0·5 mile; area 0·08 sq. miles; mean depth 9·8 ft.; max. depth 31 ft.; pH 8·0-8·4; alkalinity 89-94 p.p.m.$CaCO_3$.

The distribution of species in the plankton

The Wests (1909) in a brief summary of the general distribution of species describe the Scottish plankton as Chlorophyceous and conspicuous for its abundant and varied desmid flora and mention by name *Xanthidium subhastiferum, Staurastrum anatinum, S. ophiura* and *S. jaculiferum* as noteworthy and widespread. This is a somewhat surprising list, for of these four species *S. anatinum*, in its various forms, is the only one which could be described as fairly general in its occurrence and then only in lochs of oligotrophic to moderately mesotrophic status and thus in the areas in which the Wests restricted their collecting. The varieties *hebridarum* and *depauperatum* of *Xanthidium antilopeum* are much more typical of the plankton in the areas in which the Wests collected than *X. subhastiferum* which is a comparatively rare species, as is also *S. ophiura*, while *S. jaculiferum* (now *Staurodesmus jaculiferus*) is by no means the most common species of this monospinous desmid genus. Furthermore, their comments concerning the general absence of other groups of green algae (Chlorococcales and Volvocales) applies only to the oligotrophic lochs, for these often occur in abundance in lowland waters as do species of Cyanophyta, which they also state to be poorly represented.

Murray (1910) in his account of the Scottish phytoplankton lists nine desmids and five diatom species as being generally distributed. The present investigation indicates that, especially in the case of the desmids, his conclusions are no longer valid. This is partly because several of the species listed have had to be abandoned, as the result of recent taxonomic studies, and partly because the present detailed study has shown that they are, in fact, restricted to lakes of fairly well defined trophic types. His list of supposedly generally distributed species is considered here with indications as to the actual distribution of these taxa in the light of recent investigations:

Desmidiaceae

    Closterium kutzingii—Only in oligo-mesotrophic lochs.

    Euastrum verrucosum—Only in oligo-mesotrophic lochs.

    Xanthidium antilopeum—Only the vars. *hebridarum* and *depauperatum* are common in the plankton and then only in oligo-mesotrophic lochs.

    Arthrodesmus incus—A "nomen dubium" (see Teiling, 1948).

    Staurastrum jaculiferum—Now *Staurodesmus jaculiferus* (see Teiling, 1948). Restricted to oligotrophic lochs.

    Staurastrum lunatum—Only in oligo-mesotrophic lochs.

    Staurastrum paradoxum—Now a "nomen dubium" (see Brook, 1959b).

    S. gracile—In *sensu* Brook (1959b), only in eutrophic lochs, but certainly not used in this restricted sense by Murray.

    Hyalotheca mucosa—A facultative plankter (see Brook, 1959a), oligotrophic-mesotrophic in distribution.

Diatomaceae

    Asterionella formosa—One of the few truly generally distributed plankters.

    A. gracillima—Now a "nomen dubium" included with the above species.

    Tabellaria fenestrata—See Knudson (1953).

    T. flocculosa—The var. *asterionelloides* is common at times in eutrophic lochs although it also occurs in those of mesotrophic status.

    Surirella robusta—Probably only a facultative plankter, mostly in meso- or slightly eutrophic lochs.

Even from this brief appraisal of the actual distribution of species previously considered as widespread, it is clear that a high proportion of them are in fact limited to lochs of fairly definite trophic type, although a number have no clear affinities and would seem to be tolerant of a wide range of nutrient levels. The distribution of species in relation to their apparent trophic preferences will now be considered group by group.

Distribution of Bacillariophyceae

The only diatom occurring exclusively in distinctly eutrophic lochs is *Melosira granulata* var. *angustissima* which has been found only in some of the lowland lochs in Forfar, Fife and Dumfriesshire. *Fragilaria crotensis*, *Fragilaria capucina*, *Synedra acus* var. *angustissima*, *Diatoma elongatum* and *Tabellaria flocculosa* var. *asterionelloides* are also common in most of the eutrophic lochs, although they also occur in the plankton of less rich waters of mesotrophic status.

Two diatom species which would seem to have their maximum development in mesotrophic lochs, although they also occur in oligotrophic and a few somewhat eutrophic lochs, are *Synedra acus* var. *radians* and the small centric diatom *Cyclotella glomerata* as well as *C. comta*.

Although *Tabellaria flocculosa* var. *flocculosa* and *Asterionella formosa* occur in all types of lochs, they are the only diatom taxa which are markedly abundant at times in oligotrophic waters.

The only diatom with a strictly limited distribution is *Rhizoselenia longiseta* which has so far only been recorded from Loch Lomond. *R. eriensis* is known to occur consistently in the spring plankton of a number of mesotrophic lochs in central Perthshire, but it may, in fact, have a much wider distribution.

Distribution of Chrysophyceae

Dinobryon divergens occurs in a high proportion of the lochs investigated, from oligo- to eutrophic status. Its variety *schauinslandii*, and *D. bavaricum*, *D. cylindricum*, and *D. sociale* are limited, however, to meso-oligotrophic lochs. *D. sociale* var. *americanum* must also be included in this category although it often occurs in abundance and is, at times, the dominant organism in the spring plankton of distinctly alkaline waters (see Brook and Woodward, 1956) in which production is normally poor. *Euroglena americana* may also predominate in the spring plankton of alkaline waters. Only *D. sertularia* seems to be restricted in its distribution to base rich lochs of eutrophic status.

Other members of the Chrysophyceae tend to occur either exclusively in the oligotrophic, or extend a little way into the mesotrophic, category; the commonest are the frequently large colonies of *Stichogloea doederleinii* and species of the genus *Mallomonas* of which *M. caudata* is most widespread. Mention must also be made in this connection of *Diceras chodati* which although not often seen in net plankton collections has nevertheless been present in significant numbers in quantitative collections in early summer from lochs in Perthshire and Sutherland (Brook, 1954).

Distribution of Dinophyceae

Ceratium hirundinella is the only generally distributed species of this group occurring in nearly every loch examined. It shows considerable variation in form from loch to loch and although this aspect of its biology has been investigated to some extent in the Scottish plankton (Murray, 1910), a more extensive study of the relation of form to trophic status might lead to some interesting results. *C. cornutum* is much less widely distributed and seems to be limited to oligotrophic waters.

Peridinium willei has been recorded from several meso- and very many oligotrophic waters and although other members of the genus and of the related *Glenodinium* and *Gymnodinium* have been found, none are common. However, a detailed investigation of the Dinophyceae of Scottish freshwaters has yet to be made.

Distribution of Cyanophyta

This group is, in general, most common both in abundance and number of species in the nutrient-rich waters of the more shallow lochs in the lowland areas of the country where they frequently give rise to considerable water blooms. The taxa most frequently giving rise to this phenomenon are *Aphanizomenon flos aquae*, *Microcystis aeruginosa*, *M. flos aquae*, *Anabaena circinalis* and the var., *macrospora*, and to a lesser extent by *Anabaena flos aquae*. Heavy blooms caused by *Oscillatoria aghardii* var. *isothrix*, *O. bornetii*, *O. limosa*, *Gloeotrichia echinulata* and *Anabaena planctonica* have also been observed.

Although the species *Coelosphaerium naegelianum*, *Gomphosphaeria lacustris* and *Oscillatoria tenuis* also occur in markedly eutrophic lochs, they are present at times in considerable abundance (although never producing blooms) in waters of mesotrophic status. *Anabaena flos aquae*, *Merismopedia tenuissima*, *Eucapsa alpina* and *Anacystis montana* occur in quite a number of oligotrophic lochs.

Distribution of Chlorophyta (excluding Desmidiaceae)

Of the motile Volvocales, only *Eudorina elegans* is widely distributed, being common at times in eu- and mesotrophic lochs, although it may also be conspicuous at times in the plankton of distinctly oligotrophic lochs. *Volvox aureus* would seem to be of very rare occurrence and is always confined to eutrophic waters. *Gonium sociale* has also been found in waters of similar status.

The most widely distributed, non-motile Isokont, although it has only recently been recorded in Scotland (Brook and Holden, 1957), is *Gemellicystis neglecta*. It has been found in a high proportion of all mesotrophic lochs examined as well as in a number of eutrophic lochs, thus confirming Lund's (1956) statement about its trophic requirements which were, that it is found in neither strongly eutrophic nor oligotrophic lakes. Algae which have been referred to the somewhat doubtful taxon *Sphaeocystis schroetii* seem to occur mostly in mesotrophic lochs but are never abundant.

With regard to members of the Chlorococcales, the majority of species tend to be associated with eutrophic conditions and the most common species are *Kirchneriella obesum*, *Scenedesmus opoliensis*, *S. armatus*, *S. bijugatus*, *Coelastrum microporum* and *Pediastrum duplex*. Other taxa, which, although often abundant in eutrophic lochs, also occur in waters of oligotrophic status are *Ankistrodesmus falcatus*, and its vars. *spiralis* and *acicularis*, *Scenedesmus quadricauda*, *Pediastrum boryanum* and *Dictyosphaerium pulchellum*. *Crucigenia rectangularis*, on the other hand, appears to attain its maximum development in mesotrophic lochs.

The genus *Botryococcus*, now accepted as a member of the Chlorophyta, is represented by three species. Of these *B. braunii* is the most common, occurring throughout the trophic range and occasionally abundant in waters of moderate eutrophy although it rarely produces significant blooms. The doubtful species *B. protuberans* (which it is believed may be only a growth form of *B. braunii*), occurs with the latter, especially in eutrophic waters. The quite distinctive *B. sudeticus* is oligotrophic in its distribution.

A number of other species of Chlorophyta which are of rare occurrence in the Scottish plankton have been recorded in various taxonomic papers (Brook, 1954, 1955, 1957a, 1958).

Distribution of Desmidiaceae

It is widely assumed that members of this group of the Chlorophyta are most commonly associated with waters of oligotrophic status. Thus it is interesting to find that a remarkable number of desmid species occur almost exclusively in eutrophic lochs and can be used as reliable indicators of high nutrient status (Brook, in press). The most noteworthy are *Staurastrum gracile* (*sensu* Brook, 1959a), *S. chaetoceras* and *S. planctonicum*, species which occur only in distinctly alkaline, shallow lowland lochs. *Staurastrum pingue* is another species which attains its greatest abundance in eutrophic waters, although, unlike the previous species, it seems to tolerate quite oligotrophic waters and thus it has a remarkably wide distribution in Scotland. It is interesting in this connection to note that although the British desmid flora is generally considered to have been quite exhaustively investigated, this species has been recorded for the British Isles only recently (Brook, 1958). In the past it has unquestionably been referred, along with several other taxa to the now abandoned "rubbish dump", *S. paradoxum*, a taxon which in consequence came to be recognised as ubiquitous and of cosmopolitan distribution (Brook, 1959a).

Other species tolerant of eutrophic conditions are *Cosmarium depressum* var. *achondrum* and *Closterium aciculare* var. *subpronum*. The latter is generally recognised as a calciphilous desmid and in some markedly calcareous lochs (i.e. on Lismore and in the Durness area) it may be the only desmid present in the plankton.

Also tolerant of fairly high nutrient status although occurring most frequently in less rich waters of mesotrophic status as well as in oligotrophic lochs are five species of *Staurastrum*. These are *S. furcigerum*, *S. cingulum* var. *obesum*, *S. lunatum* var. *planctonicum* and *S. pseudopelagicum*. Three species of *Staurodesmus* also fall into this category, *S. brevispinus*, *S. cuspidatus* and some forms of *S. curvatus*, as do *Cosmarium abbreviatum* var. *planctonicum* and *Euastrum verrucosum*.

Very few planktonic desmids are restricted to oligotrophic lochs although it seems that most species of *Staurodesmus*, other than those mentioned above, tend to be associated with waters of low trophic status. The most frequently occurring species of this genus in the Scottish lochs are *S. megacanthus* var. *scoticus*, *S. jaculiferus*, *S. sellatus*, *S. triangulatus* and *S. subtriangulatus*. Other desmids most frequently associated with oligotrophic lochs and never present in waters which could be classed as more than mesotrophic are the planktonic forms of *Staurastrum anatinum* (=f. *longibrachiatum*, *pelagicum*, *paradoxum*, etc. see Brook 1959a), *S. cingulum*, *S. longispinum* and *S. brasiliense*, the vars. *hebridarum* and *depauperatum* of *Xanthidium antilopeum*, the filamentous desmid *Spondylosum planum* and the colonial *Cosmocladium saxonicum*.

Some planktonic desmids seem to have a very localised distribution. This appears to be because these algae never reproduce sexually and populations of them are, therefore, clones which have propagated themselves for periods probably running into thousands of years. It is well known that the semicells of desmids are susceptible to considerable variation which may either be the result of mutation, or merely a reflection of a change of environmental conditions. Any mutation, in the absence of suitable resting stages (zygospores) by which dispersal can be effected will, of necessity, be confined and isolated within a given lake. In this way local races of various desmids with a very limited distribution may arise in a lake, or group of lakes, in a restricted area. Several taxa in the Scottish plankton would seem to fall into this category. They are as follows:

S. cingulum var. *affine* (West and West) Brook, which is considered to be a local race of *S. cingulum* var. *obesum* and is restricted in its distribution to Caithness, the Orkneys and Shetland Islands (Brook, 1959a).

S. pendulum var. *pinguiforme* Croasdale, forma (see Brook, 1959c), which is limited to a series of intercommunicating lochs of glacial origin in north Perthshire—Lochs Ericht, Eagheach, Rannoch and Tummel.

Xanthidium controversum var. *planctonicum* West and West, which would seem to be a local race of *X. antilopeum* with its distribution limited to north west Sutherland and a few lochs in the Outer Hebrides.

Xanthidium subhastiferum var. *murrayi* f. *triquetra* West and West, which is limited to Loch Lomond.

Euastrum verrucosum var. *planctonicum* West and West, which is considered to be an extreme form of the var. *reductum* and is limited to a few lochs in Sutherland (Brook, 1959b).

Quantitative studies and the periodicity of the Scottish freshwater plankton

With the exception of a somewhat superficial study of plankton periodicity by Bachmann (1908) it would seem that none of the earlier investigators of the Scottish plankton (West and West, 1909; Murray, 1910; Griffiths, 1939; Lind, 1951, 1952) were in a position to carry out quantitative examinations or add to the knowledge of their periodicity. However, as part of a series of investigations designed primarily to follow the effects of the addition of various mineral nutrients to lochs on the growth of brown trout (*Salmo trulta*), a number of detailed quantitative studies have been made over a period of several years on the phytoplankton of several lochs of differing types and nutrient status (Brook, 1957b; Brook and Woodward, 1956; Brook and Holden, 1957).

In some of the smaller lochs investigated in this connection, considerable and quite sudden fluctuations in plankton abundance have been observed (Brook and Woodward, 1956). Detailed studies of four lochs in the Tummel-Garry Catchment area of north Perthshire have shown that these fluctuations are primarily due to the effects of water inflow and outflow through these lochs. The magnitude of the influence of this factor depends on the volume of the loch, the extent of the catchment area and the amount of rain falling in this area. For purposes of comparison, a figure representing the replacement of water in each loch studied was determined by dividing the volume of water contained in a loch by the amount passing through for a given period, this replacement quotient being expressed in days. From this investigation it was found that estimates of the standing crop of plankton may give very misleading indications of the productivity of small lakes where there is a considerable flow of water through them.

Comparisons of communities other than the plankton and of some of the chemical characteristics of the four lochs investigated show how misleading such estimates can be. From a consideration of these other biotic and chemical characteristics, these lochs can be arranged in an ascending order of productivity (Table 30). It will be observed from

TABLE 30

The Productivity of Four Scottish Hill Lochs in terms of Submerged Macrophytes, Quantitative Evaluation of the Bottom Fauna, Chemical Characteristics and Average Zooplankton Density

	Loch Choin	Loch Kinardochy	Lochan an Daim	Loch Moraig
Replacement quotient . . .	16	91	5	26
Indicator macrophytes . . .	*Littorella, Lobelia*	*Littorella, Lobelia*	*Potamogeton natans*; some charophytes	*P. natans*; abundant charophytes
Bottom fauna per sq. ft.				
numbers	33	38	110	264
weight (g.)	0·076	0·141	0·324	0·572
pH	6·14–7·52	6·80–7·67	7·22–8·08	7·38–8·13
Alkalinity (p.p.m. $CaCO_3$) . .	1·6–7·8	11·0–29·0	23·0–52·8	35·8–85·6
Free ammonia (p.p.m.) . .	0·168–0·756	0·103–0·636	0·974–1·240	0·095–1·200
Silica (p.p.m. SiO_2) . . .	0·55–2·14	0·49–2·28	1·30–3·35	0·41–4·72
Zooplankton: average per visit (1950–52) per 100 l. . .	562	2790*	108	1211

* The 1952 figure for Loch Kinardochy. Figures for 1950 and 1951 are not included since they show the effects of treatment with rotenone in 1949-50 to eradicate pike.

this table that, in terms of bottom fauna, Lochan an Daim is about three times as rich as Loch Kinardochy in addition to being richer chemically. Comparisons of the average spring, and summer, standing crops of plankton in these lochs suggests, however, that

Loch Kinardochy with a Replacement Quotient (Re.Q) of 91 is much richer than Lochan an Daim with a very low quotient (Re.Q. 5) or even Loch Moraig (Re.Q. 26), thus showing that quite erroneous estimates of plankton production in small lakes may be obtained if these are studied without reference to the important physical factor of water replacement.

The results of various quantitative studies of the plankton of lochs where water replacement is not a significant factor, however, are summarised in Table 31. In this

TABLE 31

Trophic Status and Standing Crop of Phytoplankton of some Scottish Lochs

Loch	pH	Range of: Alkalinity (p.p.m. CaCO₃)	Compound Phytoplankton quotient	Standing crop of phytoplankton (organisms per ml.) min.	max.
Loch Tummel . . .	6·0–6·5	4–7	0·3	17	30
Loch Freuchie . . .	7·0–7·3	10–14	0·5	...	576
Straloch . . .	7·0–7·2	12–16	0·6	...	842
Loch Kinnaird . . .	7·0–7·6	14–20	1·0	...	672
Loch Kinardochy . . .	7·0–7·8	15–25	2·0	10	510
Loch Dunmore . . .	7·4–7·8	25–30	3·0	65	970
Loch Moraig . . .	7·8–8·2	70–84	2·7	60	1,800
Loch Leven . . .	8·0–8·5	45–60	13·0	1,020	17,000

table, the maximum and minimum standing crops of phytoplankton of lochs representative of a wide range of trophic status are listed. These quantitative results confirm the impression gained from the qualitative examination of the Scottish plankton, that a wide range of productivities occur and, as indicated by the Phytoplankton Quotient determinations, the largest populations occur in the shallow lochs in lowland areas. In a number of these lochs, waterblooms of blue green algae are of fairly frequent occurrence.

REFERENCES

BACHMANN, H.   1908 Vergleichende Studien uber das Phytoplankton von Seen Schotlands und der Schweiz. *Arch. Hydrob. Planktonk.* **3**, 80-83.

BROOK, A. J.   1954 Notes on some uncommon algae from lochs in the Tummel-Garry catchment area. *Trans. bot. Soc. Edinb.*, **36**, 209-214.

1955 Notes on some uncommon algae from lochs in Kinross, Perthshire and Caithness. *Trans. bot. Soc. Edinb.*, **36**, 309-316.

1957a Notes on freshwater algae, mainly from lochs in Perthshire and Sutherland. *Trans. bot. Soc. Edinb.*, **37**, 114-122.

1957b Changes in the phytoplankton of some Scottish hill lochs resulting from their artificial enrichment. *Verh. internat. Ver. Limnol.*, **13**, 298-305.

1958 Notes on algae from the plankton of some Scottish freshwater lochs. *Trans. bot. Soc. Edinb.*, **37**, 174-181.

1959a The status of desmids in the phytoplankton and the determination of phytoplankton quotients. *J. Ecol.*, **47**, 429-445.

1959b *Staurastrum paradoxum* and *S. gracile* in the British freshwater plankton, and a revision of the *S. anatinum*-group of radiate desmids. *Trans. Roy. Soc. Edinb.*, **63**, 26, 589-628.

	1959c	*Staurastrum pendulum* var. *pinguiforme*, *S. micron* f. *major* face *quadrata* and *S. micron* var. *perpendiculatum*, desmids new to the British freshwater plankton. *Nova Hedwigia*, **1**, 157-162.
BROOK, A. J. and HOLDEN, A. V.	1957	Fertilization experiments on Scottish freshwater lochs. I. Loch Kinardochy. *Sci. Invest. Freshwat. Fish. Scot.*, **17**.
BROOK, A. J. and WOODWARD, W. B.	1956	Some observations on the effects of water inflow and outflow on the plankton of small lakes. *J. Anim. Ecol.*, **25**, 22-35.
GRIFFITHS, B. M.	1939	The free-floating microscopic plant life of the lakes of the Isle of Raasay, Inner Hebrides. *Proc. Univ. Durham Phil. Soc.*, **10**, 71-87.
KNUDSEN, B. M.	1953	The diatom genus *Tabellaria*. II. Taxonomy and morphology of the plankton varieties. *Ann. Bot., N.S., Lond.*, **17**, 131-155.
LIND, E. M.	1951	The plankton of some lakes and pools in the neighbourhood of the Moor of Rannoch. *Trans. bot. Soc. Edinb.*, **35**, 362-369.
	1952	The phytoplankton of some lochs in South Uist and Rhum. *Trans. bot. Soc. Edinb.*, **36**, 37-47.
LUND, J. W. G.	1956	On certain planktonic palmelloid green algae. *J. Linn. Soc. (Bot.)*, **55**, 593-613.
MURRAY, J.	1910	The biology of the Scottish lochs. Part 1. The biology in relation to environment. *Bathymetrical Survey of the freshwater lochs of Scotland.* Vol. I, 275-312. Edinburgh.
NYGAARD, G.	1949	Hydrobiological studies of some Danish ponds and lakes. II. The Quotient Hypothesis, and some new or little-known phytoplankton organisms. *K. danske vidensk. Selsk.*, **8**.
TEILING, E.	1916	En Kaledonisk fytoplanktonformation. *Svensk Bot. Tidskr.*, **10**, 506-519.
	1948	*Staurodesmus*, genus novum. Containing monospinous Desmids. *Bot. Notiser*, **101**, 49-83.
WEST, W. & WEST, G. S.	1909	The British freshwater phytoplankton with special reference to the desmid plankton, and the distribution of British desmids. *Proc. Roy. Soc.*, **B81**, 165-206.

TABLE 32

Limnoplanktonic species present in summer plankton of nine lochs of markedly different morphological types and trophic status. (see p. 295 for details of lochs.)

	Morar	Achilty	Aslaich	Lomond	Ard	Kinardochy	Leven	Castle Maben	Balgavies
CHLOROPHYTA—									
CHLOROPHYCEAE:									
ZYGNEMATALES—(DESMIDIACEAE):									
Staurodesmus curvatus	+	+	...	...	...	+	...	...	...
var. *elongatus*	+	+	+	...	...	...	...	...	...
S. cuspidatus	+	+	...	+	...	...	...	...	...
S. megacanthus	...	...	+	+	...	...	...	...	...
S. sellatus	...	+	...	...	...	...	...	...	...
S. subtriangularis	...	+	+	...	+	...	...	...	...
S. triangularis	...	...	...	...	...	...	...	...	...
var. *indentatus*	...	+	...	...	...	...	...	...	...

[continued]

	Morar	Achilty	Aslaich	Lomond	Ard	Kinardochy	Leven	Castle Maben	Balgavies
Staurastrum anatinum	...	...	...	...	...	...	...	...	...
f. *paradoxum*	+	...	+	+	...	+	...	...	...
S. cingulum	+	+	...	+	...	...	...	...	...
var. *obesum*	...	...	...	...	...	+	...	...	...
S. chaetoceras	...	...	...	...	...	...	+	+	...
S. lunatum var. *planctonicum*	...	...	+	+	...	...	...	...	...
S. denticulatum	...	...	...	...	...	...	...	...	...
S. planctonicum	...	...	...	...	...	...	...	...	+
S. gracile	...	...	...	...	...	...	+	...	+
S. pingue	...	...	...	...	+	+	+	+	...
Cosmarium depressum var. *planctonicum*	...	...	...	...	...	+	+	...	...
C. contractum var. *ellipsoidium*	...	+	...	+	...	...	...	...	...
C. abbreviatum var. *planctonicum*	...	+	...	...	+	...	...	...	...
Closterium setaceum	...	...	...	+	...	...	...	...	...
C. aciculare var. *subpronum*	...	...	...	...	...	+	+	...	...
Cosmocladium saxonicum	...	...	...	+	...	...	...	...	...
Euastrum verrucosum	...	...	+	+	+	+	...	...	...
Spondylosum planum	...	+	...	+	+	...	...	...	...
Xanthidium antilopeum									
var. *depauperatum*	...	+	...	...	...	+	...	...	...
var. *hebridarum*	...	...	+	+	...	+	...	...	...
X. subhastiferum	...	+	...	...	...	...	...	...	...
var. *murrayi* f. *triquetra*	...	...	...	+	...	...	...	...	...
VOLVOCALES:									
Eudorina elegans	...	...	...	...	+	+	+	+	+
Volvox aureus	...	...	...	...	...	...	...	+	...
Gemellicystis neglecta	...	...	...	+	+	+	...	...	...
Tetraspora lacustris	...	...	...	...	+	+	...	...	...
Elakatothrix gelatinosa	...	...	...	...	...	...	+	...	...
CHLOROCOCCALES:									
Ankistrodesmus falcatus	...	...	...	+	...	+	+	...	...
var. *acicularis*	...	...	...	+	...	+	+	...	...
Botryococcus braunii	...	...	+	+	...	+	+	...	...
Coelastrum microporum	...	...	...	...	...	...	+	...	...
C. spharicum	...	...	...	...	...	...	...	...	+
Crucigenia rectangularis	...	...	...	...	+	+	...	...	...
Dictyosphaerium pulchellum	...	...	...	+	+	+	+	...	...
Kirchneriella obesum	...	...	...	+	...	...	+	+	+
Micractinium radiatum	...	...	...	...	...	...	+	...	...
Oocystis crassa	...	...	...	...	...	...	+	...	...
O. solitaria	...	...	...	...	...	+	+	...	...
Pediastrum boryanum	...	...	...	...	...	+	+	+	+
P. duplex	...	...	...	...	...	...	+	+	+
Quadrigula closteroides	...	...	...	...	+	+	...	...	...
Scenedesmus arcuatus	...	...	...	...	...	...	+	...	...
S. bijugatus	...	...	...	...	...	...	+	+	...
S. opoliensis	...	...	...	...	...	...	+	+	+

	Morar	Achilty	Aslaich	Lomond	Ard	Kinardochy	Leven	Castle Maben	Balgavies
S. obliquus	...	...	...	...	...	...	...	+	+
S. quadricauda	...	...	...	+	...	+	+	+	+
CHROMOPHYTA—									
CHRYSOPHYCEAE:									
Dinobryon bavaricum	...	...	...	...	...	+	...	...	...
D. cylindricum var. *palustre*	...	...	+	+	+	+	...	...	...
D. divergens	...	...	...	+	+	+	+	...	+
Mallomonas caudata	...	...	...	+	+	+	...	...	...
Stichogloea doederleinii	...	...	+	...	+	+	...	...	...
BACILLARIOPHYCEAE:									
CENTRALES:									
Cyclotella comta	...	...	...	+	...	+	+	+	...
C. glomerata	...	...	...	+	...	+	+	...	...
Melosira granulata	...	...	...	...	...	...	...	+	+
M. italica var. *subarctica*	...	...	...	+	...	+	+	...	...
Rhizosolenia longiseta	...	...	...	+	...	...	...	...	...
R. morsa	...	...	...	...	...	+	...	...	...
PENNALES:									
Asterionella formosa	+	+	+	+	+	+	+	+	+
Diatoma elongatum	...	...	...	...	...	...	+	...	+
Fragilaria capucina	...	...	...	+	...	...	+	...	+
F. crotonensis	...	...	...	...	...	...	+	+	+
Synedra acus var. *radians*	...	...	...	...	+	+	+	...	...
var. *angustissima*	...	...	...	...	...	...	...	+	+
Tabellaria flocculosa	...	...	+	...	...	...	...	...	...
var. *asterionelloides*	...	...	...	+	+	...	+	...	+
DINOPHYCEAE:									
Ceratium hirundinella	+	...	+	...	+	+	...	...	+
Peridinium willei	...	...	+	+	...	+	...	...	...
CYANOPHYTA—									
Anabaena circinalis	...	...	...	...	...	...	+	...	+
A. flos aquae	...	...	...	+	+	+	+	...	...
Aphanizomenon flos aquae	...	...	...	...	...	...	...	+	+
Anacystis montana	...	...	...	...	+	+	...	...	...
Chroococcus dispersus	...	...	...	...	...	+	+	...	...
C. limneticus	...	...	...	...	...	+	+	...	...
Coelosphaerium naegelianum	...	...	...	+	+	+	+	+	+
Eucapsa alpina	...	...	...	...	...	+	...	...	...
Gomphosphaeria lacustris	...	...	...	+	...	+	+	...	...
G. kutzingianum	...	...	...	...	...	...	+	+	...
Gloeotrichia echinulata	...	...	...	...	...	+	...	...	...
Microcystis aeruginosa	...	...	...	...	...	...	+	+	+
M. clathrata	...	...	...	...	...	...	...	...	+
M. flos aquae	...	...	...	...	...	+	+	+	+
Oscillatoria aghardii var. *isothrix*	...	...	...	+	...	...	+	+	...
O. geminata	...	...	...	...	...	...	+	...	+
O. tenuis	...	+	...	+	+	...	...	...	...

U

CHAPTER 9

THE MACROPHYTIC VEGETATION OF FRESHWATER LOCHS, SWAMPS AND ASSOCIATED FENS

D. H. N. SPENCE

INTRODUCTION, WATER AND SOILS

This chapter is based mainly on the results of a study of the principal macrophytic plant communities of Scottish freshwater aquatic habitats (listed in Tables 42 and 43, pp. 384 and 390) and the factors responsible for their distribution, carried out between 1958 and 1961. Previously three papers were published by George West (1905, 1910a, 1910b) of a botanical survey made for the Bathymetrical Survey of Scotland (Murray and Pullar, 1910). With its numerous excellent photographs West's work provided the principal account of the dominant phanerogamic and higher cryptogamic flora of aquatic habit of many lochs in the Ness area, Lismore, Galloway, Fife and Kinross. Apart from these papers the only published work on the subject and its sole reference in Tansley (1949) is Matthew's (1914) paper on the White Moss Loch.

Definitions. Readers of ecological descriptions of the vegetation of aquatic and waterlogged habitats are faced with a bewildering jargon. Terms used may be adaptations of Scandinavian, French, German or Russian words, sometimes translated and sometimes not, or special definitions of common English words—definitions which often differ in North American, British and continental usage. For a new account like this, invention of further terms is no solution and the least objectionable method still seems to be to give definitions of common English words which are developed from and conform reasonably with the usage of British ecologists.

Life forms and growth forms provide a basis for defining the terms submerged, floating-leaved, emergent or swamp, and fen vegetation.

Aquatic phanerogams or **hydrophytes** are all those plants which have their perennating buds exclusively or chiefly below the surface of standing water. They include:—

1. Species with emergent leafy shoots and emergent flowering shoots.

2. Species with floating leaves, with or without submerged leaves.

3. Species with submerged leaves only and with emergent or submerged flowering shoots (linear-leaved, broad-leaved and rosette species).

4. Non-rooting species.

The first three categories are rooted and the third category is subdivided on a basis of growth form. The first category may also be divided, into *total hydrophytes,* e.g. *Schoenoplectus lacustris,* which occurs as a dominant in a mean depth of summer water of almost 90 cm. and never less than 30 cm., and *partial hydrophytes* e.g. *Phragmites communis,* a species frequently dominant in 50 cm. and even 100 cm. of water but it may also predominate where the summer water table is more than 50 cm. beneath the soil surface. In order to define floating-leaved and submerged vegetation adequately, a number of important cryptogamic plants must also be considered, e.g. bryophytes and Characeae.

The definition of swamp used here is based on a combination of habitat factors and of the wider distribution of the predominant species.

Swamp vegetation exists on permanently, or seasonally, submerged substrata dominated typically by total, or partial hydrophytes with linear emergent leaves (emergent aquatics) and, less commonly, by helophytes. The summer water table in such a piece of ground may vary from more than 100 cm. above, to a few centimetres below, the soil surface. Swamp vegetation is restricted, as a term, to vegetation on areas adjoining open water, water which may be present in winter only. The terms hydrophyte and helophyte mean water and marsh plant respectively, but used in the broad sense of Clapham, Tutin and Warburg (1962) and not in the original, narrower sense of Raunkiaer (1937).

Because of their spatial and floristic connections with adjacent aquatic communities accounts of a number of topographically determined or topogenous mire communities are included; these are referred to hereafter as fen.

Fen vegetation comprises those stands dominated by partial hydrophytes and, perhaps typically, by helophytes, or by hemicryptophytes, in which the summer water table usually lies below the soil surface, and this soil is liable to be flooded in winter. Soils vary from organic to inorganic, soil reaction from alkaline to acid, and fens may be further classed by soil or comparative vegetational criteria as rich or poor.

The definitions of swamp and fen are arbitrary since the soil-vegetation types intergrade in nature. Curtis (1959, p. 365) from his work in Wisconsin, like Pallis (earlier) on the East Anglian fens, and others, claims that an evident dividing-line separates the truly aquatic from the terrestrial types, the latter occurring on soil flooded in spring but typically emersed during the growing season. Swamp (aquatic) cannot, however, be separated from fen (terrestrial) on the basis of water table alone because hydrophytes often transgress into seasonally emersed soils, helophytes into permanently submerged soils. Similar observations in the English Lakes likewise lead Pearsall (1918, p. 76) to conclude that no such line of demarcation is possible. He compromised by considering reedswamp from a dynamic viewpoint, both as "the climax aquatic community and pioneer fen community". Fen, as used here, includes fen, marsh and much valley bog as defined by Tansley (1949, p. 634) whereas swamp is more or less synonymous with his usage.

Floating-leaved and **submerged vegetation** comprise communities of which the prevalent species are submerged (except for floating-leaved types) all the year round. The plants are predominantly rooted in, or affixed to, the substratum, and comprise phanerogams (including *Lemna* and *Utricularia* spp.), vascular cryptogams, bryophytes and Characeae. The definition of total hydrophytes may be extended to include all species in the categories outlined above of which the perennating buds or other mechanisms lie exclusively below the water surface.

Hydrophytes possess a number of morphological and anatomical features which are generally regarded as having adaptive significance. Some of these features may determine whether a submerged rooted aquatic plant obtains most of its nutrients from the surrounding water via its shoots or via its roots. There is no *a priori* reason for deciding that one or other route is always more important and, in the absence of much experimental evidence, some writers have deduced that the shoot, others that the root, is the main means of entry for most nutrients. Clearly these conclusions have some bearing on the question of whether substrate, or, say, light controls the distribution of rooted plants in this environment. The subject is, therefore, deferred until after the vegetation and its habitat have been described (cf. p. 371 *et seq*).

Vegetation zones and plant succession. On the smooth banks of small lochs a long belt or zone of *Phragmites* reedswamp can often be seen lying parallel to the water's edge and bounded, in the loch itself, by a belt of *Nymphaea alba*. Closer examination may show that the reedswamp is preceded further up the bank by a zone where *Phragmites* is co-dominant with *Carex* spp. and that a further mixed zone marks the transition from reedswamp to floating-leaved vegetation. Under the water, at the outer edge of the *Nymphaea* zone, this edge may be seen to support dense submerged vegetation which in turn forms a zone (or zones) beyond the *Nymphaea*. There are, in other words, gradations in life form and in water table that might be expected to be correlated. It has been possible in the present study to test this assumption with data gathered at many sites. A second assumption (see, for example, Tansley, 1949, p. 582) that a spatial sequence of communities from, say, water lilies to reedswamp also represents plant succession can only be tested by knowing rates of change. This is a habitat where, because of frequent soil instability, rapid change in vegetation with time seems as implicit as it does on a sand dune. Evidence, however, brought in the section on "stability and change" (p. 378) throws doubt on the view that vegetational change in Scottish swamp and aquatic communities is normally rapid. In this account spatial sequences of plant communities are conveniently described in terms of zonation without implying any successional or temporal relationship.

Field method. For all localities visited, at least several plant communities were studied by means of one or more quadrats of from 1 to 16 sq. m. in extent. Note was taken of general features of vegetation such as zonation and broad extent of swamp and floating-leaved communities, in and around a given loch. The main dominants of the vegetation, or its visible portion, round the loch were rapidly noted. Quadrats were recorded in selected uniform areas of each of these dominants. Cover-abundance on Domin's 10-point scale has been estimated for all phanerogams, pteridophytes, bryophytes and Characeae, in almost 400 quadrats together with assessment of total plant cover as percentage of sample area. Plant height was determined as the mean of five flowering shoots (usually of the dominant) per quadrat and habitat features such as the level of water above or below the soil surface, were recorded. The same procedure was used for aquatic communities up to the limits of visible depth; for aquatic areas beyond this, list of specimens obtained with a grab were made. Details of soil and water sampling are given in the next section.

Each value for the quantitative attributes of a given stand, except height of vegetation, is the figure for one measurement taken on any day between July and early October in any of the three years 1958, 1959 and 1960.

Sample area and habitat range. The field data, including the quadrats, have been collected in over one hundred lochs and swamps from Shetland to Wigtownshire. The sample area covers more than five degrees of latitude or more than 650 km. (400 miles) from north to south. Table 42 provides a list of these localities, county by county, together with the communities examined in each.

Table 33 gives the percentage distribution of the 382 quadrats by growth-form classes of the predominant species:—

TABLE 33

Percentage distribution by growth form classes, of 382 quadrats
from the localities enumerated in Table 42.

HELOPHYTES	EMERGENT AQUATICS	OTHER AQUATICS 49			
		Rosette	Floating-leaved	Submerged broad-leaved	Submerged linear-leaved
4	47	25	25	15	35

The question arises of how far the vegetation so described is representative of the whole of Scotland. The total number of localities studied throughout Scotland barely exceed the number of freshwater lochs found in Galloway alone; the Outer Hebrides, well provided with freshwater and brackish lochs, were omitted and the larger Highland lochs are under-represented. In the latter lochs, however, the amount of soil available for colonisation relative to the surface area of water is very small while the vegetation of colonisable areas seems likely to be duplicated in smaller lochs with similar water chemistry and substrates. Most of the samples lie below 305 m. but broad latitudinal range compensates to some extent for this narrow altitudinal range. A few samples only are available from above 610 m. so that these altitudes, and hence the full climatic range available in Scotland, are under-represented.

Soil and Water Analysis

Samples were collected over a wide geographical and geological range from about one-fifth of the quadrats: beneath several swamp species in 1960 and, in 1961, mainly beneath submerged species. Soil samples under two or more species were taken from each station. Where these were lochs some floristic analysis had been carried out in a previous year and a water sample also was usually taken.

Estimates were made in the 1960 series of percentage oxidised carbon (% C), total nitrogen, exchange properties (total cation exchange capacity, exchangeable hydrogen, exchangeable metal ions) and pH. For soils gathered in 1961 percentage oxidised carbon, pH and conductivity were determined. In addition, weight loss following ignition (percentage loss on ignition) was estimated for most of the samples and a mechanical analysis was carried out by a short method in which silt and clay were not separated. pH, conductivity and alkalinity (total dissolved carbonate and bicarbonate, expressed as parts per million (p.p.m.) $CaCO_3$) of water samples were estimated within a week of collection then, after storage in a refrigerator at 5°C., two to three months later and six months later. Chloride content of a number of samples was also determined.

Methods are described below.

Every soil sample, comprising at least five sub-samples collected in the first 1–5 cm. beneath a given species, filled a $10 \times 10 \times 3$ cm. tin and upon return to the laboratory was stored in a refrigerator at 5°C. until needed for analysis. Polythene bottles containing water samples were stored likewise. pH and conductivity were measured on coned and quartered portions of fresh soil, the remainder being dried in a forced-draught oven at 80°C. for 4 hours. The samples were lightly ground, passed through a 2 mm. sieve and stored in stoppered bottles until required.

Oxidised carbon (% C) was estimated by Walkley and Black's method, loss on ignition by ignition in a muffle furnace for 2 hours, at 500°C., total nitrogen by Kjeldahl, exchange properties by Brown's titration method. Soil pH (electrometrically) and conductivity (by Mullard conductivity bridge) were estimated on 1:2 soil:water mixtures except for a few final samples (e.g. Kinord) for which these values were determined on the saturation extract (Jackson, 1958), after centrifuging for 5 minutes at 2500 r.p.m.

Mechanical analysis was carried out by the standard method although silt and clay fractions were not separated. One decantation only was made, at the estimated settling time through 10 cm. for the silt fraction. Since the oxidised carbon estimate by Walkley and Black's method is the result of a dichromate digestion, this figure forms the basis for the estimate of organic matter used in the mechanical analysis of each soil; the percentage silt plus clay, plus error, being 100 minus percentage organic matter minus percentage sand. This error is implicit in the given values of silt and clay and the drawback that the error cannot be estimated has been accepted in return for the saving of time spent on analysis.

Alkalinity (dissolved CO_3' and HCO_3') was measured in some soils and in all the water samples by titration against standard acid (Jackson, 1958). Results for water samples were originally expressed as m. equiv. CO_3', plus m. equiv. HCO_3', per litre. Dissolved carbonate was only noted in two very alkaline lochs where it occurred in minute quantities. Holden (unpublished) has carried out an extensive survey of the water chemistry of Scottish lochs and some of his pH and alkalinity results are used in the present account. Following Holden, alkalinity is expressed in p.p.m. $CaCO_3$ although there are theoretical objections (see, for example, Hutchinson, 1957, p. 667) to assuming that alkalinity is wholly due to calcium carbonate and bicarbonate. The chloride content of waters was measured by titration with saturated silver nitrate in potassium chromate (Jackson, 1958, p. 261).

Results are given in Tables 43 and 44 (pp. 390 and 392) of the soil properties measured under certain species, when predominant, and figures for pH, alkalinity and conductivity of water in the named lochs. Where results of analyses can usefully be applied to individual plant communities then the ranges and means of these properties are noted in the appropriate synoptic tables. It must be emphasised, however, that the number of soil samples taken from beneath one species never exceeded nineteen and that the range in values of percentage oxidised carbon, sand, etc., in these soils, taken from a number of different lochs, was very wide. The mean percentage oxidised carbon of the soil beneath any one species has not proved to be significantly different from the mean percentage oxidised carbon under any other species tested. This applies also to mean percentage sand, for example, or mean percentage silt plus clay.

The causal importance of a silt, for example, compared with a sand, lies presumably in the adsorptive properties of the silt. A submerged plant growing in sand may absorb nutrients from a root environment little different from that surrounding the shoot. The roots of plants on silt, however, may avail themselves through, for instance, contact exchange, of ions unavailable to the water or to shoots because of features such as an oxidised soil surface layer (see below); any aquatic soil with a high organic or inorganic colloidal fraction has similar properties. An overall balance may be achieved in a loch between the chemical properties of the water and of the various soils with which, directly or indirectly, certain communities seem connected so that one species may be typical of soil with 10 per cent. silt, another of soil with 80 per cent silt where metal ion saturation is, for example, 50 per cent. In a second (richer) loch an equivalent metal ion saturation may be achieved for the latter species with 40 per cent. silt.

The greatest divergence from the nutrient availability of the surrounding loch waters may be expected in these colloidal soils. Between lochs with waters of different chemical composition, therefore, fine texture or high cation exchange capacity in particular is not *a priori* likely to be meaningful. For ubiquitous species no correlation need be expected. There might, however, be a significant difference in the mean of such properties in soils underlying two species occupying lochs with more or less similar water chemistry. Some of the non-significance in the difference between means of measured soil properties results from the impossibility of pre-judging which species are "ubiquitous" or "restricted" in terms of water chemistry. A number of significant negative associations between some restricted species have, however, since been demonstrated. These might be explained, in part, by more detailed sampling, in terms of soil difference.

Water Chemistry. pH and alkalinity (p.p.m. $CaCO_3$) were measured on water from some thirty lochs, conductivity and chlorine content in about fifteen. Mr. Holden has supplied pH and alkalinity data for a further twenty lochs. The pH and alkalinity, of course, give oversimplified assessments of nutrient status; this was one of the reasons for measuring conductivity but such results are themselves difficult to interpret, partly because of regional variation in chloride content.

From the data in Table 34 conductivity can be seen to follow a downward trend from a peak in two calcareous maritime lochs of Sutherland (an Aigeil and Croispol) via the maritime low-alkaline lochs of Shetland to the non-calcareous inland lochs of the Ness area.

TABLE 34

Properties of the water of lochs in selected areas.

District	No. of samples	pH	Conductivity μmhos	Alkalinity p.p.m. $CaCO_3$	Chloride mgm./l.	Source of chloride reading
Sutherland: calcareous .	2	8·58	338	146	46·5	An Aigeil Croispol
Shetland . .	5	7·28	236	31	113·6	Spiggie*
Sutherland (rest) . .	4	7·15	93	21	11·9	An Loin Applecross
Ness . . .	4	6·71	82	16	11·1	Uanagan

* At one place L. Spiggie is less than 25 m. from the sea and may be liable to winter inundation by salt water.

High chloride content against relatively little bicarbonate contributes to the Shetland values of conductivity while the converse is the case with the calcareous maritime Sutherland lochs. Both sets, however, have far higher chloride and bicarbonate contents than the remaining Sutherland, and the Ness, lochs. Now Swindale and Curtis (1957) have been able to demonstrate a correlation between conductivity of the water, and the distribution of certain prominent aquatic species in Wisconsin. In Scotland maritime influences are bound to complicate matters through the varying effect of chloride supply on conductivity, since the increasing exposure found towards the north-west, and in the north and western isles, will cause gradients in the quantities of this and other ions, as the few figures already given indicate. Gorham (1958) studied the chemical composition of the daily precipitation in the English Lake District over a period of one year and showed a clear correlation between high chloride content of the rain water and winds blowing from the sea, that is, from the south-west. Holden (1961) has shown that in general chloride concentration in freshwater lakes varies with the distance of the lake from the coast. This parameter is estimated by Holden for Scottish lochs in a south-westerly direction; data from a wide range of localities in Scotland and from New Zealand and Holland fit a general equation which seems to be valid for distances of from 0·1 to 80 km. and probably more. Eventually, therefore, some correlation of the type found by Swindale and Curtis may be shown to exist in Scotland.

The alkalinity and pH of any body of water and indeed its general chemistry may fluctuate considerably during a single year. Data in Livingstone (1963, p. G.4) indicate that alkalinity may vary over this period by a factor of two (for example, 36–57 p.p.m.) in a humid climate such as that of Scotland and nearly three-fold (for example, 18–49

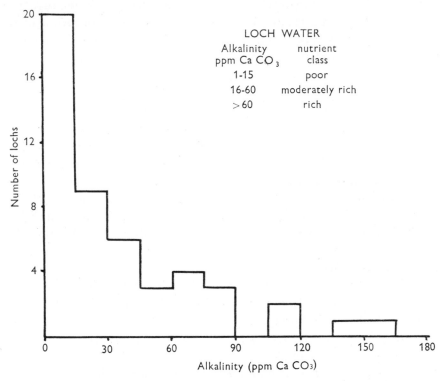

LOCH WATER	
Alkalinity ppm Ca CO$_3$	nutrient class
1-15	poor
16-60	moderately rich
>60	rich

FIG. 46. Distribution by alkalinity classes of the loch waters sampled during the survey. Each loch is represented by one sample.

p.p.m.) in a semi-arid climate. The pH of the water, sampled at the same season in two consecutive years, may also vary. Thus Holden (*in litt.*) gave values of pH 7·9 and 9·6 for two such samples from Forfar Loch, and there are further data in Livingstone. The ability of water plants to deal with such variation in the chemical environment will inevitably confound attempts to define the "preference" of all but some restricted species. Furthermore, consideration of the sources of these spatial and temporal variations in the chemistry of lake and river waters, such as are carefully reviewed by Livingstone (1963), shows that it is inadequate to represent the chemical analysis of the water of a lake by a single sample taken somewhere on its surface during summer. This inadequacy must, however, be accepted in the present study, in order to obtain an idea in terms of alkalinity and pH of a typical Scottish loch environment and to attempt some grouping into poor, moderately rich and rich types of water.

The distribution of the fifty lochs by alkalinity classes is given in Fig. 46. The class of 1–15 p.p.m. $CaCO_3$ comprises two-fifths of the samples, almost two-fifths more occur in the 16–60 p.p.m. class while the remaining fifth have alkalinity in excess of 60 p.p.m. For present purposes the nutrient status of lochs of 1–15 p.p.m. $CaCO_3$ is regarded as poor, those of the 16–60 p.p.m. $CaCO_3$ class as moderately rich and those in excess of 60 p.p.m. $CaCO_3$ as rich. (These three classes are included in the first two (<50, 50–150 p.p.m.) of the three classes used by Zimmerman (in Curtis, 1959, p. 390.)). For Scotland as a whole the sample distribution may be biased in favour of this last class but the distribution still reflects the fact that the largest volume of water and, more important for present considerations, the greatest area of shoreline, must lie in the 1–15 p.p.m. class.

Classification of sub-aqueous soils

Of the two kinds of dead organic matter present in water, the first is autochthonous organic matter consisting typically of decayed plankton but presumably including material derived from the decay of any aquatic plants growing in the water. **Gyttja** may be equated mainly with decayed planktonic material (cf. Hutchinson, 1957). The second fraction is allochthonous organic matter which originates outside the body of water and which consists of undecayed, inwashed plant debris and material derived from peat. This is **dy**. The peaty material imparts the strong brown colour to many waters, the problem of whether it is colloidal or dissolved being still undetermined (Hutchinson, 1957, p. 882).

Caspari in 1910 wrote an account of the deposits of Scottish freshwater lochs, basing his description upon a large number of soils collected at all depths from many lochs during the Bathymetric Survey. His three main classes of deposit were described as (1) sands and grits, (2) clays, which are largely inorganic, and (3) brown muds which contain variable quantities of organic matter. Beneath the layer of recognisable plant and animal remains which may overlie the predominant deposit of brown mud, was organic material which could be divided into two portions: the first, insoluble in dilute alkali, comprised the partially decomposed "first residues" of the remaining, often imported, plant and animal matter. The second portion, soluble in dilute alkali, gave a deep brown solution from which an iron-rich precipitate was formed in acid: this is the allochthonous organic matter.

From the analysis of the alkali extracts of a number of these muds Caspari (p. 265) found that the carbon content lay between 57·8 and 53·4 per cent. Estimates of percentage organic matter (% om) present were, therefore, made by multiplying the values for carbon by two. This is the factor used in the present account when deriving percentage organic matter from percentage oxidised carbon, the latter having been determined by Walkley and Black's method (cf. p. 310). These values for percentage organic matter may be compared directly with the estimates in sub-aqueous soils made, on a loss on ignition basis, by Pearsall (1918), Misra (1938) and Slack (1954).

The qualitative soil classification of Kubiëna (1953) has been applied to the sub-aqueous soils observed and analysed in the present survey. Kubiena's **A** division of sub-aqueous soils comprises three major groups or classes: **AA** sub-aqueous soils not forming peats, **AB** peat-forming sub-aqueous soils, and **BB** Anmoor-like soils. All these groups are present in Scotland although many of the four sub-groups of **AA**, raw soils, gyttja, dy and sapropels, frequently seem to merge (for reasons discussed on p. 316).

The raw soil or protopedon raw soil of **AA** includes "chalk-deficient sub-aqueous raw soil" which must, apart from boulders or rock, cover the greatest area of shoreline in Scottish lochs. It is a skeletal soil ranging in particle size from gravels to clays (cf. Caspari's "grits, sands" and "clays"), and is stable enough to allow some colonisation by higher plants or, sometimes, by an algal ("Afja") layer. It forms mainly sand and gravel bays and detrital fans which contribute the smallest-particled soils on most shores having any degree of turbulence. Whether these soils are likely, as the dynamic view would require, to develop further on most shores is doubtful; to call them raw soils may, therefore, be incorrect.

An extremely hard red-brown substrate in which pebbles and stones may be embedded has been seen in a number of lochs (Kinord, Clousta, Uanagan, Tarff). This is probably a limonite-rich sediment or ochreous mud (Caspari), lake ochre (Hutchinson) or dystrophic lake iron protopedon (Kubiëna). The origin of this sediment, consisting largely of concretions of $Fe(OH)_3$ and hydrated Fe_2O_3, is not fully known (see Caspari, 1910, p. 270; Hutchinson, 1957, p. 711; Ruttner, 1953, p. 75), but both aeration and humus-rich water, poor in electrolytes, seem necessary for its formation. Its relevance here lies in its sparsely colonised state, even where it occurs well within the photic zone.

The only certain example of lake marl, and lake chalk, raw soils were found in shallower parts of the limestone lochs of Croispol, Lanish and Calladail (in Durness) and L. Moraig (Perthshire).

Gyttja is described as a grey, grey-brown to blackish **AC** soil with good decomposition and mainly autochthonous organic matter. It occurs, probably as eutrophic gyttja, in a number of lochs like Lindores, Hempriggs, Leven and Spiggie where alkalinity is moderately high to high (more than 37 p.p.m. $CaCO_3$). It may tend towards iron sulphide muds, or sapropels, "very smelly **AG** soils, primarily autochthonous," (Kubiëna, 1953); these soils may lack higher plants and are often associated with pollution, e.g. much of Kilconquhar, Forfar or Carlingwark lochs. Gyttja-like mud occurs at the colonised bottom of L. Lowes and L. Garten, both "brown lochs" with alkalinity of 13·6 and 7·8 p.p.m. $CaCO_3$ respectively.

Dy is specified by Kubiëna as "essentially organic, muddy **AC** soil occurring at the bottom of acid, 'electrolytically poor' brown waters"; it is primarily allochthonous. Both flora and fauna of dy are described as poor to very poor. This simply does not apply to a large number of lochs of which the muds would, in qualitative terms, be described as dy (dygyttja). For example, the large delta fan of L. Uanagan of which the water is brownish but with alkalinity of 37 p.p.m. $CaCO_3$, is more or less completely covered by vegetation to a depth of more than 250 cm. The substrate beneath the **A** layer was variable even under one dominant while the physical composition of the **A** layer itself seemed to vary over short distances; there were considerable differences in the quantities of allochthonous plant remains. Yet over all these muds there was, in August 1960 and 1961, a distinct pale brown flocculation a few cm. deep, probably consisting mainly of $Fe(OH)_3$. The floor of L. naUala, in Sutherland, is covered with vegetation and its soil too bears an $Fe(OH)_3$-like precipitate in summer although, as in L. Uanagan, it is not biologically dy. In fact the alkalinity of L. Uanagan is higher than that of L. Lowes or L. Garten with their apparent gyttja deposits. There is probably continuous variation in the biological and chemical properties of these muds and of the mud-water systems, which prevents their being classed precisely as gyttja or dy. As Mortimer (1949, p. 66) points out, chemical analysis rarely seems to have been the basis for such classification while Slack (1954, pp. 234 and 235) also finds the terms difficult to apply, in his case to L. Lomond muds. Ruttner (1953. p. 170 *et seq.*) does not equate gyttja with rich waters; he emphasises rather the factors controlling the different biological processes in these muds. This will be done with the Scottish examples at the conclusion of this section.

The peat-forming, sub-aqueous soil group **AB** is represented in Scotland by fen, mainly *Phragmites* fen and *Carex* fen. Reference to accounts of communities in which these plants predominate, however, will show that many, particularly the sedges, occur on loch shores on predominantly inorganic soils.

A special sub-group, Peat gyttja, should be mentioned. This is now submerged terrestrial peat of which the surface has become somewhat altered by immersion. Many lochs from Shetland to Galloway have some deposits of peat gyttja. Frequently the material is water worn, with numerous "sink-holes". It may be colonised by *Nymphaea*, *Potamogeton natans*, *Schoenoplectus* or even *Littorella*. A mechnical analysis from L. an Ordain (Sutherland) is given in Table 44, p. 392.

The final group to be mentioned is Anmoor, in particular warp anmoor. This is waterlogged gley soil with gyttja-like humus forms, found in river valleys or on the shores of shallow lakes. The description fits precisely the typical soils found under stands of *Glyceria maxima—Iris pseudacorus*, *Equisetum fluviatile—Acrocladium*, *Typha latifolia—Lemna minor*, etc. Kubiëna points out that dried anmoor gradually changes to mull, spatial examples of which have been observed in the present study.

Oxidising and reducing muds. In most lakes in temperate climates, heating in spring from low temperatures causes separation of the water into an upper layer of circulating, relatively turbulent water, the epilimnion, and a deeper, colder, relatively undisturbed layer, the hypolimnion. The zone of sharpest temperature change per unit depth between these layers is the thermocline. The establishment of these horizontal layers marks the onset of thermal stratification which Mortimer (1941) has shown is accompanied by chemical stratification in the concentration of certain dissolved substances. The energy which distributes heat in a lake is derived mainly from wind. The stronger the wind the deeper and less steep the thermocline, the feebler the chemical stratification. A major effect of stagnation in the hypolimnion, that accompanies stratification, is an increase in the oxygen-free layer in the mud from just beneath, to above, the mud surface with consequent reduction (p. 370). Without seasonal stratification the mud surface stays permanently oxidised and "brown".

Oxygen concentration during summer stratification is, however, also linked with the trophic status of the lake water, generally forming, with increasing depth, either an orthograde or clinograde curve. With almost no depth change in oxygen concentration, even with stratification, the orthograde curve is typical of oligotrophic water. The fact, first noted by Caspari, that most muds in Scottish lochs are brown can be attributed then both to the size of these lochs and their nutrient-poor water. An overall fall with a sharp increase in the thermocline is typical of the clinograde curve of eutrophic lakes. The richer, mainly lowland lochs are more likely to develop muds with black reduced surfaces during stratification due to biological demands and, perhaps, oxygen depletion in the hypolimnion, with subsequent release from mud to water of variously-held nutrients. Further, in the last metre or so, close to the mud surface, the curve of oxygen concentration may steepen more sharply since even muds with oxidised surfaces become oxygen-free just below the surface (Mortimer, 1941; Ruttner, 1953). This and the fact that small bodies of water may, if sufficiently sheltered, be internally stratified even over a few decimetres' depth (Ruttner), mean that shallow, rich water lakes readily produce black reducing muds. Since most smaller Scottish lakes, or lochans, have poor water, low in electrolytes and alkalinity with consequently low oxygen consumption, oxidised muds are likely to predominate. As trophic status is closely connected with the form of the oxygen curve and measurement of the latter was outside the scope of the present work, the terms rich and poor water, based on alkalinity, are used in this account rather than eutrophic and oligotrophic. In general terms, the importance of these processes, however named, for rooted aquatics may lie in the extent to which a mud releases nutrients to the water or where it cannot do this, perhaps to the plants only.

CLASSIFICATION AND SYNOPSIS OF PLANT COMMUNITIES

The first step in classifying the vegetation has been the tabulation of quadrat data by dominant species, i.e. those contributing most areal cover. The next step is to inspect for the presence of possible differential and/or constant species. Constants are noted as useful. However, since the same species may be constant in different communities, which may have the same or different dominants, use is made, where possible, of the presence or absence of differential species to distinguish these communities. A stand occurs frequently in which the dominant is accompanied by a few other species which also contribute little cover. This is defined as a *pure stand* where there are not more than *six* accompanying species, of which the total cover-abundance is not more than *three*.

For reasons of space almost all the tables of individual quadrats for named dominant species are omitted from the present account. *Phragmites communis* for example forms at least three community-types totalling forty-three quadrats. The data for each community have been combined in a single column which gives the mean cover-abundance and percentage presence for each species together with the means of such attributes as plant height, percentage plant cover, etc. The columns are collected in synoptic tables which may comprise several communities of a single species (e.g. *Phragmites*, Table 50, p. 408), or a number of communities dominated by species of similar growth-from, e.g. *Nuphar lutea, Nymphaea alba, Potamogeton natans* (Table 48, p. 402). It is these columns, combined in synoptic tables, which form the basis in this chapter for the description of communities.

The scheme of classification is based on a combination, which was discussed at the outset, of growth-form and habitat. The habitat feature used is the summer and winter level of free water in relation to soil surface. The soil surface is the datum line for the water surface or *water level*. Where this lies above the soil surface, the depth of water is referred to as so many cm., or as a water level of so many cm.; where water level lies below the soil surface, its distance below is referred to as *minus* so many cm. Thus in soils with free water below the soil surface, the water level has a negative value with respect to zero at the soil surface.

The term *water table* is restricted to soils with the water level, or free water, below the soil surface. Where the depth at which free water occurs is being referred to specifically as the water table, the figure has a positive value.

Terminology. The basic vegetation unit or community-type where all layers are considered together, and which is defined by the dominant species, is the **sociation** (soc.). If a species dominates in more than one sociation, then these sociations are distinguished by the presence of differential and/or constant species. A community-type in which a species predominates seasonally or permanently as a pure stand is a *society*. The term **association** has been employed here to unite certain sociations, sharing one or more dominant and differential species which distinguish them from a group or groups of sociations related by floristics and growth-form, viz. *Potamogeton filiformis—Chara aspera* association and *Juncus fluitans—Lobelia dortmanna* association.

The term association has not, however, been applied evenly and the absence of named associations amongst, for example, the swamp community-types does not mean that none exist but that the tables of quadrats have not been studied closely enough to discern them, and that the necessary comparisons have not been made, either with related soligenous and ombrogenous mire communities, or with the extensive continental literature.

Synopsis

Aquatic communities on a permanently submerged substrate dominated by total hydrophytes:

Fully submerged species:
    (1) Linear- and broad-leaved species.
    (2) Rosetted species.

Floating-leaved species.

Communities are listed in alphabetical order of dominant species, followed by the number of the synoptic table in which they occur; sociations are binominal, the rest are societies.

Communities dominated by fully submerged species except, sometimes, *Littorella*.

	Table		Table
Chara aspera — Myriophyllum alterniflorum	45	*Lobelia—Littorella*	45
Elodea canadensis	46	*Juncus fluitans—Utricularia vulgaris*	45
Fontinalis spp.	46	*J. fluitans—Sphagnum subsecundum*	45
Isoetes lacustris	46	Linear-leaved *Potamogeton* spp. (*berchtoldii, obstusifolius, pectinatus, pusillus*)	46
Nitella opaca, N. opaca var. *brachyclema, N. translucens*	46	*Potamogeton filiformis—Chara*	45
Open *Littorella—Lobelia dortmanna*	45	*P. gramineus*	46
Littorella—Juncus fluitans	45	Broad-leaved *Potamogeton* spp. (*lucens, perfoliatus, praelongus, ×zizii, alpinus*	47
Littorella—Potamogeton filiformis	45	(original quadrats)	

(Tables 45, 46 and 47 are on pages 394, 398 and 400 respectively.)

Floating-leaved communities, dominated by *Nymphaea alba* (including ssp. "*occidentalis*"), *Nuphar lutea, Potamogeton natans—J. fluitans* (*Polygonum amphibium*) (*Sparganium minimum*, etc.), Table 48 (p. 402); (for *P. polygonifolius* see *Sphagnum subsecundum—J. bulbosus*, Table 54).

Swamp communities on permanently or seasonally submerged soil dominated chiefly by total or partial hydrophytes (emergent aquatics) and, to a lesser extent, by helophytes; fen communities on seasonally or periodically submerged soils, dominated by partial hydrophytes and perhaps chiefly by helophytes, or by hemicryptophytes.

	Table		Table
Carex lasiocarpa	51	*Filipendula ulmaria—Acrocladium*	53
C. lasiocarpa—Myrica gale	51	*Glyceria maxima—Iris pseudacorus*	53
C. nigra—C. panicea	52	*Juncus articulatus—Angelica*	53
C. nigra—Acrocladium	52	*Myrica gale—C. lasiocarpa*	51
C. paniculata—Angelica	51	*Phalaris arundinacea—Filipendula*	53
C. rostrata, C. rostrata — Equisetum fluviatile	50	*Phragmites communis—Sparganium minimum* and *P. communis—Littorella*	50
C. rostrata—Menyanthes	51	*P. communis*	50
C. rostrata—Acrocladium	51	*P. communis — Galium palustre* and *Ranunculus lingua*, and *Myrica*, variants	50
C. vesicaria—Veronica scutellata	51	*Potentilla palustris—Acrocladium*	53
Cladium mariscus—Myrica	49	*Schoenoplectus lacustris—J. fluitans*	49
Eleocharis palustris—Littorella	49	*Sphagnum subsecundum—Juncus bulbosus*	54
Equisetum fluviatile—Acrocladium	49	*Typha latifolia—Lemna minor*	49
Equisetum fluviatile—Littorella	49		

(Tables 49-54, pp. 404, 408, 412, 418, 420 and 424.)

THE PLANT COMMUNITIES

Fully submerged community types

Potamogeton filiformis—Chara aspera association; **Juncus fluitans— Lobelia dortmanna association** (Table 45); **Societies of Fontinalis, Elodea,**

Isoetes lacustris **and** *Nitella* **spp.**; *Potamogeton gramineus* **society**; **linear-leaved pondweed societies** (Table 46); **broad-leaved pondweed communities** (Table 47):

Potamogeton filiformis—Chara aspera **association** (Table 45). This association comprises three sociations, *Potamogeton filiformis—Chara aspera*, *Littorella uniflora—P. filiformis* and *Chara aspera—Myriophyllum alterniflorum*. For reasons of floristics and habitat they are considered together. *P. filiformis—Chara* has two constants, *Littorella* and *Chara aspera*, which are in turn dominant in each of the other two sociations. *Myriophyllum alterniflorum* is an additional constant. The *Chara aspera—Myriophyllum* sociation includes *Chara delicatula* var. *barbata* and *C. papillosum*, both of which become dominant in parts of the extensive *Chara* beds of L. Croispol (Plate 50) and L. Lanish. *Myriophyllum* occurs as a condensed shallow-water form in this community. Usually two, sometimes all three, communities are present in the same loch but they occupy different habitats. The first floristic hint of this is given in the mean total plant cover: one-eighth of the *P. filiformis* stands, one-fifth of the *Littorella* stands and almost half of the *Chara* stands reach 100 per cent. cover. The condensed var. *annulata* of *C. delicatula* and var. *lacustris* of *C. aspera* are only found in the first two communities but mainly in the first, *P. filiformis—Chara*, which rarely has anything but bare sand or gravel in the shallow zone above it. As plant cover increases so does depth of water, in both mean and range. These then are the first submerged communities encountered on entering the water, they occur in a definite order when present together and the evidence suggests that one, *P. filiformis—Chara*, must grow near the zone of maximum turbulence. *Chara—Myriophyllum* may occur first but in not less than 50 cm. water (L. Lanish). Open reedswamp on sand, mainly *Eleocharis*, is recorded in 5/11 cases in places above both *P. filiformis—Chara* and *Littorella—P. filiformis*.

The soil under *P. filiformis—Chara* is always sand (85 per cent. in L. an Aigeil). The sand is more or less interspersed with stones which at L. Watten cover 75 per cent. of the surface and thus restrict colonisation. At L. Spiggie, *P. filiformis—Chara* occurred on the limited sand at the south end and similarly, in shallow water only, at the north end of the loch on extensive sand which descends 1 m. below the water surface. Even as a subordinate species *P. filiformis* does not penetrate far into the *Chara* zone. Shallow water and sand may both be necessary for this species.

The soil beneath the *Littorella—P. filiformis* sociation is likewise sandy but since the community occurs in up to 70 cm. water it may overlap with the lake marls underlying *Chara—Myriophyllum* having 95 per cent. CaCO$_3$. Again, *Chara—Myriophyllum* may overlap for considerable distances with *Potamogeton pectinatus* (as in L. Croispol, Fig. 52c, p. 360). Extensive *Chara* beds occur in L. Leven and L. Lindores but these were not sampled in detail.

Waters. Both the available conductivity measurements were from lochs near the sea, L. Spiggie and L. an Aigeil, and were high (with respectively 114 and 45 mgm. Cl per l). All three communities are typical of water of moderate to high alkalinity, probably high conductivity, and calcareous and/or sandy substrates. The lochs either lie on limestone (L. Croispol), are associated with calcareous fluvioglacial deposits (Rescobie, Lindores) or calcareous sand and salt-spray (an Aigeil, Spiggie). West's (1905) list for limestone lochs on Lismore read similarly and clearly possessed all three communities. Af Rantzien (1951, p. 487) describes a similar *Chara aspera— Myriophyllum* community as the characteristic "elodeid" vegetation of shallow limestone lakes in Oland (Gotland) and in parts of the Swedish mainland.

Littorella can be seen from this evidence not to be confined "to non-calcareous lakes and ponds", as stated in Clapham, Tutin and Warburg (1962, p. 767). *Myriophyllum alterniflorum* is another ubiquitous species, its sometimes dense growth producing pure stands among sociations of this or the following association. On the other hand, material certainly identified as *M. spicatum* has been collected by the author only from deep water (*c.* 200 cm. or more) in rich-water lochs like Croispol, Lanish, Moraig and Watten; in some it forms dense, pure stands.

Juncus fluitans—Lobelia dortmanna **association** (Table 45). All these community-types except open *Littorella—Lobelia* share *J. fluitans* as a constant or dominant species; in addition, *Littorella* and *Lobelia* are dominant, constant, or, usually, prominent species. *Juncus bulbosus* is a familiar enough plant of damp acid ground; the *Atlas of the British Flora* (1962) illustrates both the abundance of the species and, most convincingly in southern England, its absence from chalk and limestone areas. Submerged in many lochs of the palaeogenic region, either as single plants or covering large areas, is a non-flowering aquatic form with tresses of hair-like leaves. This is *J. bulbosus* var. *fluitans*, or *J. fluitans* Lam., hereafter referred to as *J. fluitans*. Isolated plants may be a few centimetres high while plants in dense stands may be as much as 100 cm. long. The various intergrading forms—sterile, viviparous and normal—which connect the plants found in aquatic and terrestrial habitats are discussed by West (1905, p. 976) and by Glück (1936).

Lobelia dortmanna has a mainly highland distribution in the British Isles, being most plentiful in western regions. In Scotland it occurs, apart from Galloway, entirely north of the Highland line.

Open *Littorella—Lobelia* only has the constancy of *Eleocharis palustris* to distinguish it floristically from any of the following communities: it exists largely on negative attributes, consisting of those stands lacking a single dominant. It also has low plant cover, frequently less than 5 per cent. (mean 30 per cent.), the lowest species density of the six sociations and it occurs in the shallowest water. The soil is always sandy or gravelly, often hard and sometimes limonitic, and low in organic matter—a protopedon. The community occurs typically on the littoral shelf of terraces (p. 364). As with *P. filiformis—Chara*, the ground above and most of the ground on either side of this community is bare or only supports scant *Eleocharis palustris*.

With increasing depth in any locality having open *Littorella—Lobelia*, either the *Lobelia—Littorella* or the *Littorella—J. fluitans* sociations, are usually encountered. They are only distinguished by their dominants and either may predominate where both

X

Lobelia and *Littorella* occur. Wherever plant cover exceeds 50 per cent. a thin layer of organic sandy mud is often found under the *Littorella* sward and over coarser sediments In sheltered parts of some lochs or in lochans, *Littorella—J. fluitans* occurs on organic soils, frequently alternating with *J. fluitans—Utricularia* (see below); Grasswater contains examples of this. *Lobelia—Littorella* also occupies organic sediments, as at Neldricken. However, more than 75 per cent. of the stands of both communities overlie sandy soils. No consistent differences have been noted in the soils beneath the two communities or the depths of water at which they occur (cf. Fig. 47).

With open *Littorella—Lobelia* sociation on coarse soils in shallow water, *Littorella —J. fluitans* and *Lobelia—Littorella* are typical of less rich water than those which bear *Littorella—P. filiformis* in the shallows.

Apart from its occurrence as a constant in the three preceding communities, the stands in which *Juncus bulbosus* or its var. *fluitans* are dominant or co-dominant have been divided on floristic bases into three sociations of which two are described here. (For *Sphagnum subsecundum—J. fluitans*, see Table 54.) *Juncus fluitans—Utricularia* has as constants *Utricularia vulgaris*, *Myriophyllum alterniflorum* and *Potamogeton natans* while the second sociation has *Sphagnum subsecundum* var. *auriculatum*, *Ranunculus flammula* (including ssp. *scoticus*) and *P natans* (which may include some *P. polygonifolius*).

In the *J. fluitans—Utricularia* sociation, species density is, at 9·7, the highest in the association while plant cover in both sociations is high. Each sociation has a different mean, and range in depth of water above the soil. *J. fluitans—Utricularia* is typical of a water level around 70 cm. deep, *J. fluitans—Sphagnum* occurs in shallower (mean 11 cm.) water. Always with a high degree of cover, *J. fluitans* itself may vary from 10–15 cm. high, as on sand at L. Merkland, to, perhaps more typically, 50–100 cm. high at L. Meikle.

J fluitans—Utricularia illustrates a curious feature of aquatic vegetation In several lochs stretches of water have been noticed, some way out from the shore, apparently dominated by *Schoenoplectus lacustris*. Closer examination has shown that *Schoenoplectus* gives an areal cover of from 5–20 per cent and that it is, in fact, an emergent layer above a dense *J. fluitans—Utricularia* sociation (Fig. 48). The value of 20·2 for *Schoenoplectus* in the synoptic table is thus explained. Conversely where *Schoenoplectus* is dominant (Table 49) *J. fluitans* is a constant (Grasswater). The communities are closely related.

Soils. Of the fifteen samples under *J. fluitans—Utricularia* two were sandy and there is one sample (L. Kinord) of stiff, almost unaltered, clay from water depths of 110 cm. where the percentage oxidised carbon is only 5·25. The remaining samples were brown muds of from 1 cm. to more than 50 cm. in depth and soft or firm in texture, with up to 43 per cent. carbon. This maximum came from a small, shallow, fully colonised lochan (Flatpunds). The mud at L. an Loin had a buff-coloured layer over darker mud and contained freshwater snails. Thus the physical range of the soils was very wide, giving a mean percentage organic matter of 66 per cent.

J. fluitans—Utricularia has a range in pH of 6·73–7·99, conductivity 79–480 μmhos and alkalinity of 9·5–57 p.p.m. CaCO₃. This maximum alkalinity is reached, like that for *Littorella—J. fluitans*, in L. an Loin, a moderately rich loch lying mainly on Cambrian limestone. *J. fluitans—Utricularia* must cover large tracts of the shallower Highland lochs of generally low alkalinity; it occurs extensively at the head of L. Meiklie, L. Uanagan, in the north-west corner of L. Kinord, in L. Mallachie, L. Maberry, etc. In some lochans like L. na Uala (Sutherland) or L. Flatpunds (Shetland) the community covers almost the whole bottom. In the peaty lochans in the interior of Lewis, *J. fluitans* sometimes forms "great mats of vegetation" (Perring, 1961). *Juncus fluitans* is not apparently dominant over any considerable areas in the English Lake District; it forms

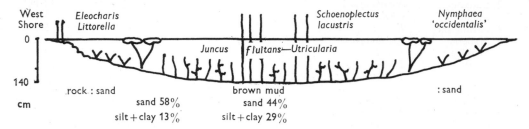

Fig. 48. West-east transect across Lochan na Uala, Sutherland, an oligo-trophic (poor water) lochan. Apart from the rocky margin to a depth of water of 70 cm., and open *Littorella—Lobelia* on sands beneath, to a depth of 100 cm., the floor of the loch comprises a sandy brown mud densely colonised by *Juncus fluitans—Utricularia* soc. Percentage sand and silt + clay is indicated at two points on the bottom.

a consocies with locally abundant *Callitriche* in not more than 3 m. depth of water on coarse silt or sand (Pearsall, 1920, p. 184). Pearsall notes *J. fluitans* is subdominant in shallow water with *Lobelia* and *P. natans*; this community must be analogous to the *Lobelia—Littorella* sociation or to the following, *J. fluitans—Sphagnum* sociation.

In shallower water, *J. fluitans—Utricularia* tends towards *J. fluitans—Sphagnum*, to *Littorella*, or to *Lobelia—Littorella* communities, or to reedswamp of *Phragmites* or *Eleocharis palustris*; it may form a mosaic with *Schoenoplectus lacustris*. In deeper water, the community gives way to floating-leaved vegetation or to a variety of broad-leaved, submerged pondweeds.

J. fluitans—Sphagnum subsecundum is a sociation of shallow water, of mean depth 11 cm., within what is normally the region (0–50 cm.) of greatest turbulence, i.e. Ruttner's (1953) "eulittoral", but this sociation contains much loosely fixed *Sphagnum* and it is presumably restricted to sheltered bays, lochans or small pools where turbulence is minimal or absent. Sometimes the sociation occurs on coarse sand, e.g. by the inlet of a small spring, with 1 per cent. oxidised carbon, but it may be more typical of soils rich in organic matter (from 20 to 41 per cent. oxidised carbon); the mean is 25 per cent. oxidised carbon. Pearsall's shallow water community, of the English Lakes, with prominent *J. fluitans* is typical of very organic peaty soil, the mean organic matter being

72 per cent.† The low pH (6·64–6·80) and alkalinity (<0·1 p.p.m. $CaCO_3$) of the few available water samples suggest this community is the opposite of *Chara—P. filiformis.*

TABLE 35

Depth of colonisation by macrophytic vegetation in a number of lochs

Lochs	Dominant species at greatest depth	Depth below which species is sole dom. and often sole species (m.)	Depth to which colonisation occurs (m.)	Max. depth of loch (m.)
1. Merkland	*Isoetes*	1·80	...	25·92
2. Uanagan	*Nitella opaca*	2·30	...	13·11
3. Lindores	*Chara*	1·60	2·50	3·05
4. Carlingwark	*Elodea*	1·40	2·90	5·18
5. Maberry	*Nitella opaca*	1·90	3·00	4·27
6. Magillie	*Isoetes*	1·80	2·80	4·27
7. Tarff	*Isoetes*	1·40	...	27·14
8. Merklie	*J. fluitans*	1·30	...	13·72
9. Clunie	*Elodea*	1·50	...	21·04
10. Spiggie	*Fontinalis*	2·20	3·50	12·50
11. Black	*Nitella opaca*	2·20	3·50	3·50
12. Croispol	*C. contraria*	4·00	8·00	79·00
13. Lowes	*Nitella opaca*	2·20	5·00	16·16
14. Rescobie	*Elodea*	0·70	1·20	7·01
15. Mochrum	*Nitella opaca*	0·80	2·50	3·96
16. White	*Pot. lucens*	0·90	3·40	11·59
17. Lomond	*Isoetes*	2·00	...	190·01
18. Lurgainn	*Isoetes*	2·40	...	47·58
19. Awe	*Isoetes*	2·50	...	93·63
20. Baile a Ghobhainn	*Fontinalis*	10·67	12·20	26·84 West
21. na h'Achlaise	*Littorella—J. fluitans*	0·80	2·00	8·54
		Depth below which named species prevail		
22. near Stack	*P. natans*	0·30	0·8	0·8*
23. Creagach	*Myrio./P. gram/Chara*	0·50	0·50	0·50*
24. Mhor	*P. obtusifolius/Nitella*	1·00	1·40	1·40*
25. Garten	*P. × sparganifolius/Nitella*	1·40	1·80	1·80*
26. na Uala	*J. fluitans—Utricularia*	1·00	1·30	1·30*
27. Hempriggs	*Fontinalis—P. perfoliatus*	1·90	3·00	3·00*
28. Kinord	*Nitella translucens—Isoetes*	1·50	1·70	3·66*

* In nos. 22 to 28, total plant cover of these communities is 100%, or nearly 100%.

After excluding certain ubiquitous species like *Equisetum fluviatile, Eleocharis palustris, Littorella* and *Myriophyllum alterniflorum,* comparison of the *J. fluitans— Lobelia* association and the *P. filiformis—Chara* association reveals one group of sociations

† Pearsall (1920, p. 200) lists the individual values and means for percentage organic matter of soil samples from beneath a number of aquatic species, e.g. nine "deep water" species. These means are used in his, and Tansley's (1949) subsequent, account. No species, however, is represented by more than 11 samples, the average like mine being 6. Ranges also tend to be wide, from 2–70 per cent. organic matter (mean 25 per cent.) for 8 samples under *Isoetes,* 24–95 per cent. (mean 44·7 per cent.) for 4 samples under *Sparganium.* Means are not reported as having been tested for significant differences.

typical of poor water (with mean alkalinity of 5, 14 and 17 p.p.m. $CaCO_3$) and another typical of rich water (mean alkalinity of 80, 73 and 83 p.p.m. $CaCO_3$). Among those species of more than spasmodic occurrence confined, in addition to *P. filiformis* and *P. pectinatus* (a known calcicole), to the calcicole association are *Zannichellia palustris*, *Chara papillosa*, *Chara deliculata* var. *barbata* and *C. rudis*. In the calcifuge association the differential species besides *J. fluitans* and *Lobelia* are *Isoetes*, *Subularia*, *Elatine hexandra* and possibly *Ranunculus flammula*.

The distribution of the two groups of communities is not quite mutually exclusive, for one or more sociation of each group occur in two of the lochs studied, L. Spiggie and L. an Loin. Only in L. Spiggie were the "key" species *P. filiformis* and *J. fluitans* seen growing together in the same small area, sociations dominated by either species covering far larger parts of the loch. L. Spiggie has the lowest alkalinity (37 p.p.m. $CaCO_3$) recorded for *P. filiformis*, while L. an Loin has the highest recorded alkalinity (57 p.p.m. $CaCO_3$) for *J. fluitans* and *Lobelia*, both of which are absent from L. Lindores, a loch of similar alkalinity that again contains *P. filiformis*. These figures may approach then the upper and lower alkalinity limits for *J. fluitans* and *P. filiformis* respectively.

Fontinalis, Elodea, Isoetes lacustris and Nitella spp. societies (Table 46) Whenever any of these species occurs as a dominant in a loch then it will usually be found to form stands at the deepest colonised zones. In any of the first twenty lochs listed in Table 35 it is found that, with increasing depth, a level is reached where only one species dominates; at this, or a slightly greater depth, that species also forms a pure stand. Rooted plants do not occur below the outer edge of these communities. In the tabulated examples 1 to 21 the depth to which colonisation penetrates is known approximately in thirteen cases: in the remainder, the maximum depth of water is certainly beyond the photic zone (cf. Fig. 47).

A large number of these deep water communities are dominated by *Fontinalis*, *Elodea*, *Isoetes* or *Nitella opaca*. Many similar examples were given by West (1905, 1910). Apart indeed from three charads of limestone lochs, only *Nitella opaca* and *Fontinalis* penetrated according to that author beyond 6·1 m. in the many Scottish lochs he examined, *Fontinalis* being recorded in as much as 12·2 m. of water. (*N. translucens* only reached 3·05 m. and the maximum depth for *Isoetes* was 6·1 m., a depth also reached by six pondweeds: West.) Only three stands of *Fontinalis* are listed but one of these at least is based on the exhaustive survey of about 130 hectares of the north end of L. Hempriggs where innumerable grabs failed to reveal anything but a very dense mat of *Fontinalis* and local societies of *P. perfoliatus*. This is an example from a shallow loch where colonisation at the maximum possible depth (3 m.) is 100 per cent. In other similar examples, like L. Kinord, there may be from two to several dominants or one dominant and several subordinate species—here neither photic nor substrate limits appear to have been reached.

The *Isoetes* data are based on stands more or less visible from the surface or from just underneath. This is reflected in the mean sample depth of 99 cm. while the species occurs from 3 cm. to more than 250 cm. (West's (1910a) figures are 60–500 cm.) so they are not necessarily typical stands of the whole range of *Isoetes*. Only *I. lacustris* stands are shown, since no stands dominated by *I. echinospora* were noted. One stand is recorded in which *Elatine hexandra* is dominant. *Spongilla lacustris*, the fresh water sponge, is often conspicuous and has a presence of 70 per cent. in this society. Amongst these societies it is, moreover, almost exclusive to *Isoetes*; elsewhere, only in the *Lobelia—Littorella* sociation (Table 45) does it make more than a slight contribution. It always occurred in poor waters.

From inspection of quadrats in which *Elodea* or *Fontinalis* predominate and, indeed, from the study of all quadrats of submerged community-types, these species appear to have mutually exclusive distributions. Under the five stands of *Elodea* summarised in the synoptic tables the soil was, as for *Fontinalis*, a silty black mud, a typical gyttja (a sample from L. an Choin had 16 per cent. sand, 58 per cent. organic matter, 26 per cent. silt and clay). In both Carlingwark and Rescobie the soil approaches a sulphuretted or iron sulphide mud.

Nitella species likewise occur on bottom muds but these may be black or brown. However, while *Nitella* species rarely occur with *Elodea* the species do seem to occur frequently with *Fontinalis*, although study of all quadrats in relevant communities indicates that this is unlikely to be a significant positive association. Pearsall records changes in vegetation at the mouth of the Black Beck, Esthwaite Water, between the years 1914–15 and 1929 (in Tansley, 1949). From his maps it is evident that where silting is considerable, *Fontinalis* is either succeeded by *Nitella* which in turn is followed by *Elodea*, or *Fontinalis* is replaced directly by *Elodea*. Here is some explanation of the negative association between *Fontinalis* and *Elodea*.

Fontinalis does sometimes predominate in water less than 30 cm. deep, on rocks, but neither *Nitella* spp. nor *Elodea* are dominant in water of much less than 100 cm. depth thus underlining their tendency to occur in less turbulent or more silty habitats. This is not so for *Isoetes*, which forms communities in from 3–300 cm. of water on skeletal, sandy or clay, soils so accounting perhaps for its weak association with *Fontinalis* and *Elodea*. *Isoetes* shows some ecological affinity with *Nitella opaca*, one such example (L. Kinord) having 46 per cent. sand and 3 per cent. oxidised carbon. In two other examples, lacking *Nitella*, from Merkland and Tarff, there was respectively 95·5 and 83·5 per cent. sand and 0·1 and 2·7 per cent. oxidised carbon. It is possible that association of *N. opaca* with mud is fortuitous, being rather the result of its tolerance of the low light intensity prevailing in deep, less turbulent, habitats. With *Fontinalis* too, the association with rocks, or with soft mud, may be indirect and there is some experimental evidence for this. Thus Ruttner (1953, p. 63) has shown that, unlike submerged phanerogams and many algae, many aquatic mosses cannot assimilate bicarbonate ions from the breakdown of $CaCO_3$: their carbon source must be CO_2. Ruttner observes that their physiological behaviour is reflected in their natural distribution. Aquatic mosses are found only where free CO_2 is present in the water, for example in springs, mountain streams, moorland pools and, in lakes, in the eulittoral (wave-beaten) zone, where there is exchange with the atmosphere, and at greater depths where CO_2 again increases.

The chemistry of the loch water in which these species occur is in most cases too little known for one to do more than indicate possible causal factors. Thus the *Nitella* communities have a pH range of from 6·9 (Garten) to 8 (Lindores) and alkalinity from less than 2 p.p.m. (Kinord) to 57 p.p.m. $CaCO_3$ (Lindores), which suggests poor to moderately rich waters. *Fontinalis* and *Elodea* range into rich waters. The tendency of *Isoetes lacustris* to be restricted to waters of palaeogenic regions, whether in Wales, the English Lake District, Galloway, or the Scottish Highlands, is reflected in the present alkalinity data (not more than 20 p.p.m. $CaCO_3$). The *Atlas of the British Flora* also shows that the species is normally lacking from chalk or limestone areas. The negative association between *Isoetes* and *Elodea* has been partly explained here on the basis of possible differences in underlying soils; in addition, *Elodea* is scarce and mainly lowland in Scotland.

Potamogeton gramineus society (Table 46). There are no constants, although *P. natans* reaches 60 per cent. and *Chara* spp. or *Nitella* spp. are present in 9/10 samples, in five cases having cover of over 5 per cent. In every sample *P. gramineus* occurs on, and surrounded by, bottom muds so that it typically forms mosaics with other species on a more or less level soil. *P. gramineus* is replaced in shallower water by *Chara*, *Nitella*, *Littorella* or *Juncus fluitans*; in deeper water it gives way in half the stands to *P. natans*, in another to *P. obtusifolius* and, in another, *P. praelongus*.

It occurs as a dominant in lochs of pH 7 to pH 8·2 and with a wide range in alkalinity of 9·2–89·6 p.p.m. $CaCO_3$. It is not, in Scotland at least, "absent from districts with calcareous soils" (Clapham, Tutin and Warburg, 1962, p. 949) since it forms communities in at least one limestone loch (Moraig) and is a member of several communities in other (Durness) lochs.

Linear-leaved pondweed societies (Table 46). *P. pectinatus*: the two available samples confirm its calcicolous nature; it is very abundant particularly at the south end of L. Croispol (pH 8·6, alkalinity 132 p.p.m. $CaCO_3$). The range of water depth is 60–250 cm. According to the *Atlas of the British Flora*, some 70 per cent. of the Scottish 10 km. squares having *P. pectinatus* are coastal (cf. *P. filiformis*); in England it is predominantly an inland plant.

The three remaining species all agree in occurring on bottom muds, in frequently reaching considerable heights (more than 1·5 m.) and in sharing *Nitella* spp. (rather than *Chara* spp.) as constants and, in three-quarters of the cases, *Callitriche hermaphroditica*. Samples are too few to generalise on their water "preference". Perhaps the absence of *Juncus fluitans*, *Lobelia* and *Subularia* from all these stands is important, although *J. fluitans* and *Lobelia* form communities in different parts of L. an Loin, Lowes, and *J. fluitans* in Spiggie—all lochs containing these pondweed communities. These societies are similar to Pearsall's (1918) "linear-leaved associes" of the English Lakes where, too, *Callitriche hermaphroditica* is prominent.

Broad-leaved pondweed communities (Table 47). There are an insufficient number of samples to consider the stands dominated by species other than *P. gramineus* as distinct communities although most of these species have in the course of this survey been seen to form extensive stands in many more than the few examples given here.

Floristically it seems possible that *P. perfoliatus* is closely associated with *Fontinalis* and that *Myriophyllum spicatum* may associate with *P. praelongus* and *P. lucens*. In some examples there are eight or ten accompanying species when ground cover is considerable and *P. perfoliatus*, although abundant, is not tall. In other cases, for example, *P. praelongus* at Lanish and Croispol, there are merely one or two accompanying species. In these two limestone lochs the pondweeds may exceed 4 m. in height while West (1905, p. 979) recorded plants of *P. perfoliatus* nearly 8 m. high in limestone Loch Baile a Ghobhainn on Lismore.

TABLE 36

The pH and alkalinity of seven lochs, and the minimum depth of water in which *Potamogeton praelongus* occurs as a dominant species.

Lochs	Lindores	Grass-water	Croispol	Lanish	Kinardochy	Uanagan	Spiggie	Mean
pH . . .	7·9	6·83	8·80	8·70	7·20	7·30	7·80	7·79
Alkalinity (p.p.m. $CaCO_3$)	52	20	135	78	20	37	37	54
Water depth (cm.)	200	150	300	200	180	300	...	220

In all cases the plants are growing on bottom muds. They may form a band along the top edge of such muds, being replaced in deeper water by species of different growth-form, like *Chara* or *Elodea*, or they may themselves form the deepest vegetation (as at White Loch, an Loin, Kinardochy, and see Fig. 47). As might be expected from their association with bottom muds all these species except *P. alpinus* predominate in deep water. *P. perfoliatus* is, exceptionally, dominant in as little as 100 cm. water, while the mean depth for ten *P. gramineus* stands was 100 cm., but the range is wide and this species may form societies in as little as 50 cm. water. For *P. praelongus* there are, in addition to the two stands listed, depth data from five other lochs (Lindores, Grasswater, Croispol, Uanagan and Kinardochy). The mean depth of the dominant in these seven samples is 220 cm., its shallowest being 150 cm. in Grasswater. West records *P. praelongus* with *P. perfoliatus* and *P. lucens* as deep water species, in from 180–600 cm. water.

Water Chemistry. *P. lucens* is a known calcicole (White Loch and Rescobie). *P. perfoliatus* is probably ubiquitous as, even in three stands, alkalinity ranges from 2–76 p.p.m. $CaCO_3$ while West records it as a dominant in limestone lochs on Lismore. The information on water recorded wherever *P. praelongus* (Table 36) was dominant, suggests that it occupies moderately rich to rich waters.

In the *Atlas of the British Flora*, *P. praelongus* is recorded in about sixty 10 km. squares in Scotland, either lowland or coastal, six being in Shetland. The distribution of neither *P. pectinatus*, a known calcicole, nor *P. praelongus* is correlated with squares containing more than 5 per cent. chalk and limestone but here a map of calcareous drift and sand (cf. *P. pectinatus* and *P. filiformis* in Orkney) would be needed. On the other hand, *Isoetes* and *Subularia* do fit well into non-calcareous areas based on surface geology just because these areas are highland and thus mainly free of drift. For *P. praelongus* as for *P. filiformis* (and *P. pectinatus*) there seems to be some connection with water rich in electrolytes, whether this results from bicarbonate and associated ions expressed in high alkalinity, or from the complex of ions in maritime regions indicated by high conductivity.

Floating-leaved community-types

Nymphaea alba sociation, **Nuphar lutea** including *pumila* (society, **Potamogeton natans—*J. fluitans*** sociation, **Polygonum amphibium** sociation (***Sparganium minimum,* etc.**) (Table 48). Stands of *N. alba* were divided into those · dominated by *N. alba* ssp. *occidentalis* and *N. alba* ssp. *alba* although intergrading forms undoubtedly exist (Heslop Harrison, 1955; Clapham, Tutin and Warburg, 1962) at, for example, L. an Choin and L. an Loin. Such a subdivision means that column 1 of Table 48 is based on only four stands but the difference is maintained since *Nymphaea* "*occidentalis*" is then seen to have *J. fluitans* as a constant, which indicates that this small water-lily is confined, in Sutherland for example, to poor waters. The highly calcareous L. an Aigeil, also in Sutherland, supports *N. alba* ssp. *alba*. In Scotland at least *N. alba* is far commoner than *Nuphar lutea* or *N. pumila*.

Most of the *N. lutea* stands possess *P. obtusifolius*, *Elodea*, *Hippuris* or *Lemna trisulca*, while a small group and, to judge by the range of *N. lutea* and the uncommonness of *N. pumila*, a less important group, contains *J. fluitans*.

There are a number of pure stands of *Nuphar lutea* where (as for *Phragmites*) there are not more than five accompanying species with cover abundance less than 3; the figure of 10 per cent. quoted in Table 37 for *N. lutea* is the maximum cover recorded in eleven stands. Comparison of *N.* "*occidentalis*", *N. alba* and *N. lutea* stands, in that order, shows a decrease in species density and in mean percentage plant cover, and maximum cover of accompanying species, at soil surface. Doubtless the submerged leaves of *Nuphar* reduce available light compared with *Nymphaea* while the shallower based *N.* "*occidentalis*" has the most developed community of the three. The twelve *N. alba* stands occur in slightly shallower mean depth of water than *N. lutea* while the ranges differ, *N. lutea* penetrating into deeper water; but these means, if in the right order, are probably too low because West (1910a) records *N. alba* in water up to 2·6 m. deep and *N. lutea* to 3·6 m. deep. Just as the smaller *N.* "*occidentalis*" occupies poorer water than *N. alba*, an environmental response is also suggested by the fact that it occurs, on average, in shallower water than *N. alba*.

J. fluitans is constant in *P. natans* stands, together with *Sparganium* spp. (*angustifolium, emersum* and *minimum,* mainly sterile specimens with sometimes uncertain identity). *Sparganium angustifolium* and *S. emersum* also form pure stands in poor waters (cf. L. Oich, L. an Ordain, Plate 51, L. Ken) but they have not been listed separately from those of *Juncus—Utricularia* or *P. natans—J. fluitans* with which sociations (particularly the latter) they frequently merge in poor water. A synoptic list for five aquatic *Polygonum amphibium* stands is included although there are insufficient data for comment (Table 48).

N. *alba* muds range from sand content of 7·6 to 85 per cent.; the other fractions are also variable. The mean percentage organic matter content is 47·7 per cent. and compares with figures of 25·7 per cent. given by Pearsall (1920) for average organic content of *N. alba* muds and 48·5 per cent. for *N. "occidentalis"* muds in the English Lakes. The pH of muds range from 5·30 (L. Stack) to 8·09 (L. an Aigeil). The pH of the

TABLE 37

Various quantitative attributes of stands of floating-leaved species.

	No. of stands	Mean no. of spp.	Mean plant cover on soil (%)	Max. cover of accompanying spp. (%)	Dominant in
Nymphaea alba ssp. occidentalis	4	10	64	75	mixed stands
Polygonum amphibium .	5	7	*c.* 50	*c.* 35	mixed stands usually
Potamogeton natans . .	15	6	55	35	pure stands usually
Nymphaea alba ssp. *alba* .	6	6	46	35	pure stands usually
Nuphar lutea . . .	11	5	44	10	pure stands

water lies between 6·4 and 8·6, conductivity between 71 and 375 μmhos, and alkalinity between 2·5 and 157 p.p.m. $CaCO_3$. *N. alba* therefore ranges on sandy, organic, or organic silty, soils from poor to rich waters.

For *N. lutea* there is less adequate information, the highest water pH being 7·9 and alkalinity 52 p.p.m. $CaCO_3$, which would make this a species of moderately rich water, yet Heslop Harrison (1955) maintains that *N. lutea* is typical of richer waters than *N. alba*. Certainly *N. lutea* predominates in southern England but not necessarily on chalk and limestone (cf. *Atlas of the British Flora*).

The soils under fifteen stands of *P. natans* were noted as eleven "soft muds", and four "firm (sandy) muds" and "sands". One soft mud (from Vidlin, Shetland) had 40 per cent. oxidised carbon (80 per cent. organic matter), 11 per cent. sand, 9 per cent. silt and clay. Pearsall gives 74·2 per cent. for average organic content of *P. natans* muds in the English Lakes. *P. natans* occurs in poor to rich water, of pH 6·8–9·4 with alkalinity from 5·2 to 117 p.p.m. $CaCO_3$, and is thus almost as wide-ranging as *N. alba*.

Zonation. With the possible exception of *Nuphar lutea* these species may be described as ubiquitous. It is, therefore, difficult to generalise about zonation. Both *Nuphar* and *Nymphaea* are commonly bounded on their shoreward side by reedswamp of *Phragmites*, *Typha*, *Carex rostrata*, *C. lasiocarpa*, *Schoenoplectus* (Plate 52), or *Equisetum fluviatile*. Where reedswamp occurs in large bodies of water on organic soils some lessening of wave action can be assumed; it is usually in a bay or perhaps the south-west corner of the loch. There may, or may not, be a zone of open reedswamp in which water-lilies co-dominate before the water-lily zone itself is entered. It may be deduced that reedswamp and water-lilies are able to ring certain small bodies of water just because of minimal wave action and the chance for some sediment to accumulate.

Where *Nuphar* or *Nymphaea* occur together, *Nuphar* usually occupies deeper water but either species may occur in mud above the summer water table. Water-lilies, in turn, are replaced in deeper water by broad or linear-leaved, submerged *Potamogeton* species, by *Nitella* species, *Elodea*, *Littorella*, etc., or by *P. natans*, which often forms a fringe in deeper water (Gamhna, Uanagan, cf. Figs. 47 and 49, p. 322 and 338).

P. natans can colonise sandier soils, where these may be supposed to result from turbulence, than the water-lilies. *P. natans* can also dominate in deeper water than these plants (West, 1910a, records 6 m.). With increasing depth of water, *P. natans* can replace reedswamp (*Carex rostrata*, or *Eleocharis palustris*), *N. alba*, *J. fluitans*, *Lobelia*, *Littorella* or *Nitella* and, in turn, it can give way to any of these floating-leaved or submerged species.

Swamp and fen community-types

Schoenoplectus lacustris—*J. fluitans* sociation, Eleocharis palustris— Littorella sociation, open Equisetum fluviatile society, (Sparganium erectum society), Typha latifolia—Lemna minor sociation and Cladium mariscus— Myrica gale sociation (Table 49).

Schoenoplectus lacustris—*J. fluitans* sociation. There are two constants— *J. fluitans* and *Sparganium minimum*. *Schoenoplectus* occurs as a subordinate species of the *J. fluitans—Utricularia* sociation, often in adjoining stretches of water, so that the sociations intergrade. When dominant, *Schoenoplectus* had a mean cover/abundance value of 6, or 30 per cent. and, when subordinate, of 4–5 or 15 per cent. The "open reedswamp" of Tansley (1949, p. 595) is in fact here *J. fluitans* with emergent *Schoenoplectus*. Cover at soil surface in pure reedswamp was 55 per cent. compared with 88 per cent. in open swamp.

The mean depth of water was 88 cm. above which the plant had a mean height of 125 cm., but it was never seen to predominate in less than 30 cm. water and that figure may be an extreme, being a value for L. Dernaglar in 1959 when the loch was 40 cm. below its usual September level. This means that, on gently sloping ground, *Schoenoplectus* swamp is normally separated from the shore by an intervening zone of submerged vegetation, *J. fluitans* or *Littorella* (Plate 68), or of floating-leaved vegetation (Plate 53).

The soil was always firm, due partly to the root mat, but texture was very variable. One-third of the stands overlay submerged peat-gyttja full of water-worn sink-holes; one such mud had 30 per cent. oxidised carbon, 7·6 per cent. sand and 33 per cent. silt plus clay. A grey silty mud from the detrital fan at L. Uanagan had 25 per cent. oxidised carbon, 26 per cent. sand and 24 per cent. silt plus clay but a mud from Sandy Water, Shetland, had 81 per cent. sand and only 6·8 per cent. silt plus clay. A silty substrate is not always present but the species may typically occupy a more silty soil than the closely related *J. fluitans—Utricularia* sociation. The mean percentages of silt plus clay were 15 per cent. (six samples) under *Juncus* and 30 per cent. (five samples) under *Schoeno-plectus*. More reliable perhaps is the observation that at L. Uanagan and L. an Loin where the communities adjoin each other, the *Juncus* stands overlie two or three times less silt plus clay than the *Schoenoplectus* stands, and about twice as much carbon. In the English Lakes, according to Pearsall (1920, p. 195), *Schoenoplectus lacustris* has an average organic content of 43 per cent. and prefers the more organic soils.

   Zonation. As a dominant, *Schoenoplectus* is replaced in shallow water by *Phragmites—Littorella, Littorella,* or *J. fluitans—Utricularia,* in deep water by *P.x zizii, Nitella, J. fluitans—Utricularia* or *Isoetes* (Fig. 47). *Schoenoplectus* forms the characteristic (open) reed-swamp in the English Lakes, though of local distribution, and in the Ant Broads, Norfolk.

   Schoenoplectus tabernaemontani was examined only in South Uist, and at Kilconquhar where it was accompanied by *Ranunculus lingua;* it is not listed here.

   Eleocharis palustris—Littorella sociation (Table 49). Only *Littorella* may be a constant in this widespread community but half the stands possess *J. fluitans* while three of the others have *P. filiformis* or *P. pectinatus*. The community occurs in shallow water of from 8–55 cm. depth (mean 28 cm.), (West, 1910a, quotes 0–45 cm.); the dominant itself has a mean height above water of 20 cm., mean cover-abundance value of 5, and the soil surface is typically less than half colonised (having a mean plant cover of 43 per cent.). Species density is 8·3, reaching a maximum of 14.

   Generally this can be taken as the typical reedswamp of shallow water on exposed shore, shores of sands and gravels, but not of deposited silts or organic matter. *Equisetum fluviatile* tends to dominate on similar soils in deeper water while *Eleocharis*, in turn, is the constant in open *Littorella—Lobelia* of exposed sandy shores. All but two of the samples were on firm sand, the sand content in four of these ranging from 64 to 92 per cent. The percentage of oxidised carbon in twelve samples of the fourteen analysed varied from 0·7 to 3·2. The shallow Mill Loch, Semblister, depth of water 20 cm., was completely colonised by *Eleocharis* (cover/abundance 7) and associated species, and had some 20 cm. of black reducing mud (percentage oxidised carbon = 39·9) on clay: here there were fourteen species, while the same total was recorded in a similar habitat by Lunga Water. It seems then that the plant can persist as a dominant in organic soils and (see p. 353) in marsh or fen conditions. Waters cover as wide a range of pH and alkalinity as *Littorella* and the species, like *Myriophyllum alterniflorum* and *Equisetum fluviatile,* grow in poor and rich waters. As with *Littorella* it is probable that those stands in poor to moderately rich waters are typified by *Juncus fluitans* while those in moderately rich to rich waters possess *P. filiformis* or *P. pectinatus*. In Zimmerman's water hardness classes (quoted by Curtis, 1959, p. 390) the distribution of *Eleocharis palustris* has no pronounced maximum.

Zonation. With increasing depth of water *Eleocharis* replaces a variety of swamp dominants although its maximum depth (55 cm.) falls considerably short of that reached by *Phragmites, Typha* or *Schoenoplectus.* Often the sole emergent species on exposed shores (see above), it is most frequently replaced in deeper water by *Littorella*, e.g. 6/7 examples given in Fig. 47, p. 322.

Open *Equisetum fluviatile* sociation (Table 49). This species predominates in two very different communities; in the first, like the *Eleocharis palustris* sociation, the only constant is *Littorella* (for the second, see p. 352). This community too, grades into open *Littorella—Lobelia* and is itself open, the dominant having a mean cover/abundance value of 5, the mean plant cover at soil surface being 26 per cent. while species density is 6 (Plate 51).

Again the community is typical of sandy substrates but it dominates in deeper water than *Eleocharis*, having a mean depth of water of 85 cm. and a range of from 40 to 150 cm. (West, 1910a, states 30–152 cm.). Thus the range of the *Eleocharis* and the *Equisetum* sociations on similar well submerged soils barely overlap. Both can give way to open *Littorella—Lobelia* or other related communities. One sample was taken adjoining an *Eleocharis* stand in a small inlet of Lunga Water, where species density is 14, plant cover 80 per cent. and both *Scorpidium* and *Sphagnum palustre* occurred. *Eleocharis palustris* and *Equisetum fluviatile* may occur abundantly in the same area in shallow swamp, or fen, soils (cf. Fig. 47).

Equisetum fluviatile and *Schoenoplectus lacustris* seem to be negatively associated. Only five quadrats with *Equisetum* also have *Schoenoplectus* out of fifty-eight quadrats having either species. As their range in depth, pH, and alkalinity of water overlap, soil difference may be involved. From the fact that *Equisetum fluviatile* is a constant of the *Littorella—J. fluitans* sociation (and often forms stands beside it) and from its often firm substrate (viz. Ba Ruaidhe), the *Equisetum fluviatile* sociation is found, perhaps like the *Eleocharis palustris* sociation, on mainly inorganic sandy soils, but this applies less generally to *Schoenoplectus.* The *Equisetum fluviatile* consocies in reedswamp in the English Lakes seems to occupy a more organic soil (60·9 per cent average organic content (Pearsall, 1918)).

Sparganium erectum society. Only four stands were studied in detail; none had more than six species and cover varied from 20 to 80 per cent., plant height from 44 to 130 cm. above the water, which reached a depth of 47 cm. The four lochs were rich (Carlingwark, Duddingston, Rescobie) and brackish (Wester, by Wick). As a dominant this species was not often observed although it is a widespread plant in the south and east of Scotland. Its uncommonness in the Highlands seems more likely to be determined by the low summer temperatures (see altitude "overlay" in *Atlas of the British Flora*) than by edaphic factors, since it can grow according to Cook (1962, quoting Olsen, 1950) in oligotrophic, and weakly saline, waters with low conductivities. Sturrock (1880) noted incidentally that the extensive stands at Rescobie were cut for litter.

Typha latifolia—Lemna minor sociation (Table 49). In five stands from open water (depth of water 60–0 cm.) *Typha* had one constant, *Lemna minor*, and mean water depth

19 cm. Species density was 5·6, mean cover at soil surface 42 per cent; this reached 85 per cent. where the water level was at the soil surface (here *Bidens cernua* and *Cicuta virosa* occurred). *T. latifolia* was sampled once in a closed stand, cover 95 per cent., having much *Pleurozium schreberi* and *Polytrichum commune* and the water table below the soil surface. The sample had, too, *Carex curta, C. echinata* and *C. nigra*; *Lemna* was absent.

The *Typha* stands were taken from three rich, one moderately rich and one poor loch. In the latter, Kinord, it is the only patch of *Typha* along the reedy west shore in which *Phragmites* and *Carex rostrata* predominate (Plate 53). There was 46 per cent. oxidised carbon, 1·6 per cent. N in this soil sample. The *Typha—Pleurozium* stand had a pH less than 6. Like *Phragmites* and *Eleocharis* the distribution of *Typha latifolia* has no pronounced maximum in relation to the water hardness classes of Zimmerman (in Curtis, 1958). Curtis cites *Lemna minor* as a prevalent species of *Typha* reedswamp in Wisconsin.

Typha angustifolia was only sampled at L. Lindores, Fife, where it is accompanied by *Ranunculus lingua* and *Lycopus europaeus* and muds are sandy (2·3 per cent. oxidised carbon) to highly organic (45 per cent. oxidised carbon) with pH from 5·30 to 6·28, the pH of open water being then 7·90.

Cladium mariscus—Myrica gale sociation (Table 49). *Cladium* is recorded from twenty-seven 10 km. squares in Scotland (*Atlas of the British Flora*), all but one example being coastal. Although this plant had been observed as a dominant in Raasay and South Uist it was only sampled in Wigtownshire, where it grows round several lochans in and near Anabaglish Moss. *Cladium* entirely surrounded one lochan excepting some 47 m. of *Phragmites* while *Phragmites* is always present as a subordinate species. Other constants are *Carex lasiocarpa* and *Sphagnum subsecundum* var. *auriculatum*. *Myrica gale, Hydrocotyle vulgaris* and *Drepanocladus revolvens* occur in 4/5 of the *Cladium* (and *Schoenus*) samples. *Cladium* reaches a height of 1·6 m., mean cover at soil surface is 45 per cent. and mean water depth is 1 cm. while the community extends from a water level of +28 cm. to —20 cm. One stand of *Schoenus nigricans* is included. This community was found on drier ground than the *Cladium—Myrica* sociation, but shares all its constant species. *Phragmites* is grazed here.

The lochs on Anabaglish lie in ground overlain by much blanket bog. The small affluents (in one of which *Hypericum elodes* grew) to the lochans were dry (September 1959) but the water levels in the lochans themselves were little lower than winter maxima; this and the clarity of the water suggested that the lochans were spring fed.

Zonation. From depths of water of 18 cm. to a level at the soil surface, *Cladium* (or *Phragmites*) reedswamp. Where the water table lies at the soil surface, to a water table at 20 cm., *Cladium—Myrica* or, locally, *Schoenus nigricans—Myrica*, fen. Landward of *Cladium—Myrica*, zonation is heterogenous and complicated by grazing; there is no carr and a variety of communities develop including *Myrica—Sphagnum* and *Myrica—Molinia—Calluna* stands. *Carex lasiocarpa* is a constant in the *Cladium—Myrica* sociation and the sequence parallels the *C. lasiocarpa—Myrica* sequence.

Relationships. In many parts of East Anglia the incidence of *Cladium* in shallow water of closed reedswamp marks the beginning of fen (Tansley, 1949, p. 653). Bushes may, or may not, invade down to this level. *Glyceria* and *Phalaris* probably replace *Cladium* in the Yare Valley fen. *Myrica gale* is listed as a characteristic associated species of Cladietum in the Bure Valley fen. *Cladium* has similar associates in Woodwalton fen (Poore, 1956).

Menyanthes trifoliata, Glyceria maxima, Potentilla palustris and, least commonly, *Phalaris arundinacea* form societies on permanently submerged soil. These species also form, like *Eleocharis palustris* and *Equisetum fluviatile*, fen sociations and are considered in that section (p. 350 *et seq.*), to which they more appropriately belong.

Phragmites communis sociations

Phragmites communis is one of the commonest dominants of swamp and fen in Scotland, and this description is based on information recorded in forty-five quadrats taken from Sutherland to Galloway. Through a combination of vegetation data such as total plant cover, number of accompanying species, and their cover contribution, with floristic data, namely the presence or absence of certain species, it has been possible to divide the stands into three main groups. These can be seen to correspond to different mean levels of summer water table.

Phragmites communis—Sparganium minimum and—Littorella open sociations (Table 50). These sociations occur in water with a mean depth of 56 cm. and a range of from 8 to more than 100 cm. There are no constants: *Sparganium* grows in five stands, *Littorella* in the other five and their distributions are mutually exclusive. Perhaps there are two types of pioneer *Phragmites* vegetation. The *Phragmites—Sparganium* stands contain much *N. alba* and/or *P. natans* and, therefore, carry more cover at the water surface than do the *Phragmites—Littorella* stands, which lack those species. The *Phragmites—Sparganium* stands occupy *Phragmites* peat or peat gyttja, frequently more than 50 cm. deep. This peat gyttja tends to have "sink-holes" and a submerged scarp or terrace where the *Phragmites* abuts on open water. The terrace may lie from water depths of 10 to 110 cm. Towards this open water, *Phragmites—Sparganium* usually gives way to floating-leaved vegetation, sometimes to *Schoenoplectus*. The *Phragmites—Littorella* stands occur in sandy bays, *Littorella* itself forming a sparse sward on the hard, often rippled, sand (Lurgainn, Lowes, Lindores (north shore), and an Daimh (Plate 54)). Indeed, this or *Eleocharis* constitutes typical reedswamp on shores of lochs where the finest material is sand and, since some degree of turbulence is implied, *Nymphaea* or *Nuphar* is not then found beyond the reeds; instead, *Schoenoplectus* and/or submerged linear- or rosette-leaved vegetation is found on a progressively shelving shore. Terracing is absent and *Phragmites* colonises along the substrate.

Phragmites communis society (pure stands) (Table 50). The mean depth of water is 13 cm. in this society (the range is from 50 cm. to a water table of less than 30 cm.). Here *Phragmites* reaches its greatest height above the soil surface: the mean is 252 cm. but figures of 345 cm. and 360 cm. were recorded (from L. Forfar in 1959 and 1960). Its areal cover is almost 100 per cent. while cover at soil or water surface is correspondingly negligible. Six was the maximum number of accompanying species noted.

Sometimes, as on the exposed north shore of L. Forfar, the soil is stony, but even this is overlaid by plant debris. Usually the soil is a *Phragmites* peat, the ground unoccupied by shoots being composed of dead leaves and stems which in samples above water form a loose mat up to 20 cm. thick. With water at the soil surface the soil is often too soft to bear a man's weight; when the soil is submerged it may be difficult to discern with, say, a probe any change in density between water and "soil".

These pure stands have been recorded from fifteen sites, including one near L. Eriboll in Sutherland, one at 329 m. in Perthshire and lowland sites in Fife and Galloway.

Phragmites communis—Galium palustre **sociation** (Table 50). Both the mean height of *Phragmites* and its areal cover have dropped from their peaks in the preceding society while the accompanying species have risen in cover and in number. The mean water level and most of the range now lies below the soil surface. *Galium palustre* (much being ssp. *elongatum*) is both constant and exclusive to this *Phragmites* sociation. *Mentha aquatica* and *Equisetum fluviatile* reach frequencies of almost 70 per cent. Two variants may be discerned within this sociation. The first, the *Ranunculus lingua—Cicuta virosa*, variant consists of four stands from lowland lochs (Duddingston, Carlingwark, Rescobie and Kilconquhar). The species named are exclusive to the variant while *Phalaris* and *Myosotis scorpioides* in addition to *Mentha* and *Equisetum* reach a frequency of 75 per cent. The second, the *Myrica gale—Carex demissa*, variant is represented by four stands (three ungrazed, one grazed) from Wester Ross and Glen Moriston; these stands contain species like *Erica tetralix*, *Drosera rotundifolia* and *Sphagnum recurvum*.

This sociation occupies peaty muds which may, or may not, be reducing and which may vary in texture from peat of *Sphagnum* or *Phragmites* itself to fine structured, apparently amorphous mud. In the ungrazed stands of the *Myrica* variant, *Phragmites* has a mean height of 108 cm. (cover 33 per cent.); its height in the R. *lingua* variant is 256 cm. (cover 50 per cent). The extent to which this may be an adaphic or climatic response is discussed later. Floristic data imply an edaphic difference between the variants associated with the rich or poor waters of the adjoining lochs.

Zonation. The sequence in which the *Phragmites* sociations have been described has a floristic basis and is also that of decreasing water level. It follows that the study of *Phragmites* beds in any locality where the species grows both in deep water and soil with a dry surface should reveal a sequence of vegetation and water table like that described in general terms. Frequently, of course, the sequences are incomplete, as where open water is absent and the *Phragmites* society and *P. communis—G. palustre* sociation, or the latter only, is found. There is also the pioneer, pure and mixed state of the dominant, with corresponding change in "performance" from the first to the last *Phragmites* sociation. Both these sets of facts imply plant succession. There is, however, no direct evidence of this except perhaps from Carlingwark and Lindores through comparisons with West's photographs (see p. 380).

The communities replacing *Phragmites* in deeper water have already been outlined. *Phragmites* is the predominant reedswamp species around smaller lowland lochs and also round a number of lochs in the Highlands, e.g. Gamhna. Consequently, as the water table drops to, and below, the soil surface, many different species may replace pure *Phragmites* or *Phragmites—Galium*. Thus, in the first eight zonation examples given in Fig. 49, *Phragmites* is displaced by *Glyceria maxima* (four times) and/or by *Phalaris* (six times); *Filipendula, Deschampsia cespitosa* and *Juncus effusus* also occur as dominant species. There is little *Salix*, less *Alnus*, in *Phragmites—Galium* stands but *Alnus* or *Salix* carr adjoins the reeds in several localities: its absence may frequently result from biotic activity. The next four samples lack *Phragmites* but are listed because on drier ground they possess *Filipendula* as a dominant and *Alnus*. These communities are irrigated by moderately rich to rich ground-water; incidentally, three of the localities support the *R. lingua—Cicuta virosa* variant.

A further six localities have recorded sequences involving *Phragmites* sociations (Gamhna, Uamha, lochan on Anabaglish Moss, and Lowes, Kinord and west end L. Garten; the last two are recorded in Fig. 47, p. 322). *Phragmites* alternates in shallow water with *Carex rostrata* and *Carex lasiocarpa* or with either of these species. As the water table drops, it is replaced by either of them, most frequently by *Carex lasiocarpa—Myrica*, and eventually by *Myrica* which may, or may not, have some development of either *Salix* or *Betula* carr, or of *Molinia* (see section on *C. lasiocarpa*). The lochs of which the water has been sampled are classed as poor. This accords with the view already expressed on the trophic status of the *Phragmites—Myrica—C. demissa* variant. All the twelve sequences irrigated by moderately rich to rich ground water lack *C. lasiocarpa* and all but one (Moraig) lack *Myrica*. Such divisions are seldom clear cut, however, so it should be noted that at the head of L. Avich *C. lasiocarpa—Myrica* and *Myrica—Molinia* sociations occur on black reducing mud, with such accompanying genera as *Angelica, Lythrum, Filipendula, Sonchus* and *Acrocladium*, in addition to *Juncus articulatus* and *C. vesicaria—V. scutellata* sociations. This ungrazed area contains *Alnus* amongst the *Salix* carr and, where the water table lies at the soil surface, *Phragmites—Galium* with *Typha*, and the *Carex paniculata* sociation (Plate 56).

The effects of grazing and cutting. There are data from five localities where *Phragmites* communities are confined to fenced areas: two, L. Avich and L. Eriboll, are illustrated in Plate 55 and Plate 56: the others are L. Forfar, L. Barhapple and Leac nan Saighead. On all these examples there is clear evidence in the unfenced ground (and just inside the fenced parts) that *Phragmites* is heavily cropped. In most cases the area has been fenced because of its higher water table and consequent danger to stock. Grazing, in so far as it eliminates *Phragmites*, may, therefore, accelerate the natural consequences of lowered water table. In unfenced, grazed areas a causal zonation factor is then the point where the water table is too near the surface to support stock. Further, in sequences which are apparently little disturbed all the dominants which can replace it occur above, or beside, the upper limits of *Phragmites*, i.e. *Glyceria maxima, Carex rostrata, C. nigra, J. effusus, J. articulatus*. The fence enclosing an

Y

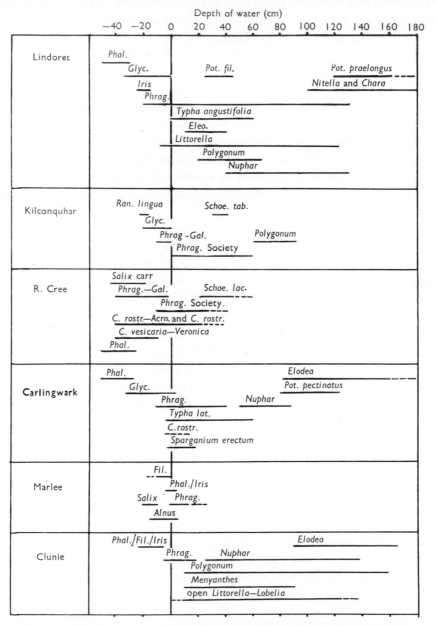

FIG. 49. Zonation data for 12 localities in relation to depth of water. They are examples mainly of swamps and associated fens and, except for Lindores and Carlingwark Lochs, do not claim to give a representative picture of zonation of the submerged communities. Even for swamps and fens the data may not apply to all parts of the given localities.

Depth of water (cm)

−40 −20 0 20 40 60 80 100 120 140 160 180

Park
- *Alnus* and *Desch. cesp.*
- *Alnus* and *Salix* and *Fil.*
- *Salix—Glyc.*
- *Salix—Equisetum*
- *Phrag.*
- *C. rostr.—Equisetum*
- *C. rostr.*

Lochend
- *Phal./Ag./Desch. cesp.*
- *C. rostr.—Potentilla pal.*
- *C. rostr.—Phrag.*
- *Phrag.*
- *Elodea*

Moraig
- *Fil.—Alnus*
- *Fil.—Acro.*
- *C. rostr.—Acro.*
- *C. rostr.—brown moss*   *Pot. natans*
- *C. rostr.— Menyanthes*
- *C. rostr.—Sphagnum*
- *C. rostr.—Myrica*
- *Myrica—Mol.*
- *Calluna*

Urquhart Bay
- *Alnus carr,* with *Phal./Ag./Fil./Salix*
- *Phal*
- *Alisma*
- *C. rostr.—Acro.*
- *C. rostr.—Menyanthes*

Meiklie
- *Alnus carr,* with *Fil. Desch. cesp.*
- *C. vesicaria*
- *C. rostr.—Menyanthes*   *Pot. natans*
- *Nymphaea*
- *Juncus fluitans*
- *. Littorella—Lobelia* (sands)

Rescobie Fen
- *S. atrocinerea* carr
- *Fil./C. nigra*
- *C. paniculata* or *C. rostr.*
- *Cicuta virosa*
- *Schoeno. lac.*

ungrazed area by Leac nan Saighead parallels the change in water table from open water to moorland. From water levels of +10 cm. to −20 cm., the grazed sequence is:—

Phragmites (20 cm. high)→*C. nigra—C. panicea* sward→(*Calluna*)—*Molinia*.

The ungrazed sequence is:—

Phragmites (80 cm. high)→*Phragmites—Myrica*→(*Calluna*)—*Myrica*.

Myrica and *Mentha aquatica* are also notably absent from the grazed area. *Carex nigra—C. panicea* swards are common on the shores of many lochs and are, clearly, biotically induced. Willis and Jefferies (1959) note *J. articulatus* and *Carex demissa* among those species that occur in grazed fen meadows and are rare in, or absent from, semi-natural fen field in the Gordano (Somerset) valley.

Environment and plant response. The maximum altitude at which a *Phragmites* stand was studied was 329 m. in Perthshire while general observation and reference to the *Atlas of the British Flora* suggest that the species is missing, in the central Highlands anyway, from most ground above 335-366 m. There are only three localities in Shetland and in none is there extensive *Phragmites* reedswamp. This distribution is instructive since Shetland near sea-level has summer temperatures more or less similar to those at 335 m. in the central Highlands (Spence, 1960). Some definition of climatic limits thus becomes possible.

In the absence of more refined measures of shoot diameter or leaf area and dry weight, height of flowering shoot was adopted as a sensitive enough measure of plant response for the present purposes while grazing and cutting effects were ignored. Fig. 50a (p. 342) indicates the existence of a positive correlation between height of flowering shoot of *Phragmites* and the mean temperature of the warmest month, as some measure of radiant energy during the growing season, from Sutherland to Wigtownshire. The estimated regression coefficient, b, of height of shoot (y) on temperature (x) is 15·479 cm.*

Phragmites ranges from poor to rich waters (as noted also by Zimmerman, in Curtis, 1959, p. 390) and its growth and development may vary widely in different localities in response to a number of edaphic factors. This is partly reflected in the spasmodic distribution of reedswamp (largely *Phragmites*) around Scottish lochs, a question discussed later in relation to factors governing the quality and distribution of substrates in these habitats. Differences in "performance" of *Phragmites* have already been noted in its *R. lingua—C. virosa* and *Myrica—C. demissa* variants. The modifying effect of soil within a given temperature regime is shown in Fig. 50b, plant height being correlated with percentage total nitrogen, and percentage metal-ion saturation, in the soil. The three Sutherland samples, the most northerly in the series, maintain the same order in Fig. 50c; the Eriboll sample is, perhaps, temperature-limited. The poorest

* Substituting in the formula $y = a+bx$, the fitted regression line $y = 15·479 x-653·38$. Since variation about the regression line is high, the standard deviation being 56·97 for distribution of mean height at any chosen value of temperature, the significance of b was tested. From the test for normally distributed estimates, b has a standard error of 6·49 which is significant at the 5 per cent. level. This is equivalent to 15·479±12·72 cm. or 2·76-28·20 cm. for a 95 per cent. confidence interval.

performance is given by *Phragmites* growing in sandy, metal-ion deficient soil in a poor water loch, L. nan Gobhar. (This probably applied also to shoot, and notably, flowering-shoot, density.) Some results of a germination experiment are pertinent here.

Seeds were sown out of doors at St. Andrews in November 1959, 36 per pot, each pot having silty sand or peat previously washed for 48 hours in its particular solution. Sets of pots of each type were placed with their soil surfaces at three levels with respect to the water surface (15 cm. above, 5 cm. above and 5 cm. below the water surface, in each of three types of water from distilled to hard (local tap water)). Establishment was consistently better on silty sand and best on the silty sand in hard water. Yield was also best on silty sand; on peat, in rain or distilled water, the surviving specimens were barely 0·82 cm. high after 18 months, at the conclusion of the experiment. These results are consistent with the field assessment just given of performance in relation at any rate to percentage metal-ion saturation. They also suggest that *Phragmites* may exist as a mature colony in conditions unsuitable for its establishment, a conclusion supported by another result of this experiment. In all waters and on both substrates there was no apparent germination under 5 cm. water. One seed germinated in three pots raised above the water level after 6 months. Mature *Phragmites* grows in as much as 1 m. water, where loch level is known to fluctuate little, when it may attain a far greater height than specimens on adjoining soil above water, and must colonise down the substratum.

A little has been said about factors governing the response of *Phragmites* to environment. Its relationship to the other common species, *Carex rostrata*, must also be considered. *Phragmites* is recorded once in thirty-eight *Carex rostrata* stands, although more objective stand selection might raise the value somewhat; while *Carex rostrata* occurs in all the *Phragmites* community-types with, however, a very small cover contribution and a maximum frequency of 55 per cent. in the *Phragmites—Galium* sociation, where both species density and cover of accompanying species is higher than in other *Phragmites* sociations. *C. rostrata* and *Phragmites* may, or may not, be significantly negatively associated, in terms of presence, in the manner of *C. rostrata* and *Glyceria maxima* (cf. p. 345). It is indeed likely that many swamp dominants known to occur in the same bodies of water are negatively associated, partly through the prevalence of vegetative reproduction amongst them.

Most swamp, floating-leaved and submerged dominants have means of vegetative spread and a tendency to form societies of more or less pure stands. It seems likely that fragmentation of a colony of any species will increase its chance of dispersal around a body of water and among interconnected bodies. Such colonisation must affect zonal relationships, as fragments of mature plants may exist initially, or indefinitely, in suboptimal conditions and hence make establishment possible in places where seedlings would fail, assuming that seeds and seedlings require a narrower range for establishment than viable fragments of mature plants. Thus *Phragmites* can grow successfully in 1 m. water but its seeds have failed to germinate in only 15 cm., while germination of *Carex rostrata*, as of many aquatic plants (Muenscher, 1936), is badly affected by dry storage of seeds for as little as two months (Thomson, unpublished). Yet the summer water table may be as much as 37 cm. below the soil surface of stands of the mature sedge and still well below zero in autumn. Seeds provide, it may be supposed, for the colonisation of new environments whether new river basins or loch systems. Human interference apart, colonisation by fragments plus different periods of time from establishment may account for the preponderance of *Phragmites* round one loch and of *C. rostrata* around an adjoining, similar one (and see Godwin, 1923).

FIG. 50. (a) The relationship between height of flowering shoot of *Phragmites communis* and mean temperature of the warmest month. The estimated regression coefficient, *b*, of height of shoot (y) on temperature (x) is 15·48 cm. The fitted regression line, $y = 15·48x - 653·38$; (b) plant height is correlated with percentage total nitrogen and (c) percentage total nitrogen is also correlated with percentage metal ion saturation in the soil. The modifying effect of soil within a given temperature regime is seen in the Sutherland samples.

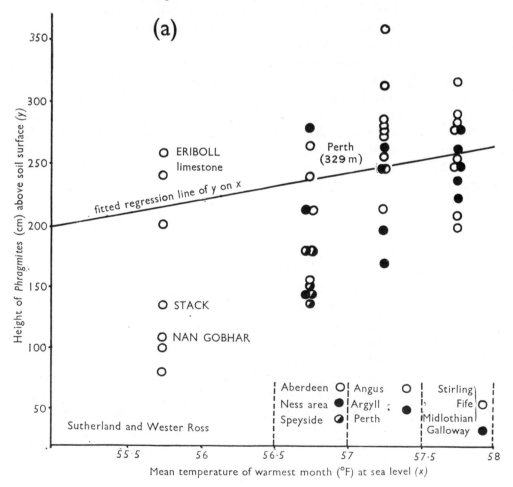

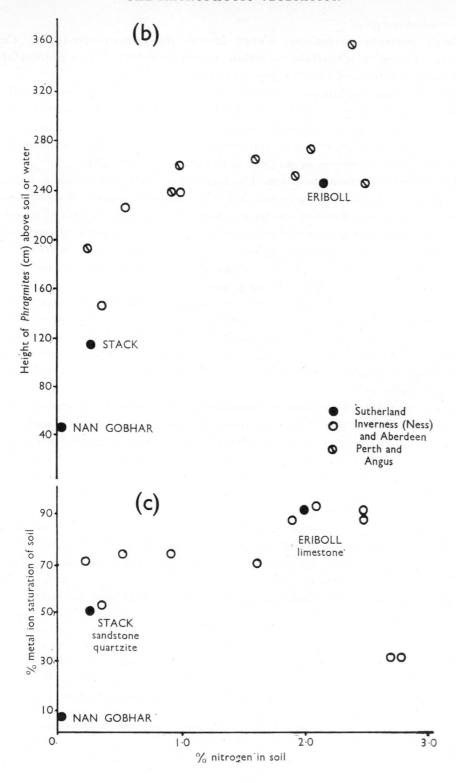

Carex community-types

   Carex rostrata sociations; *Carex lasiocarpa* community-types; *Carex vesicaria—Veronica scutellata* sociation; *Carex aquatilis*; *Carex paniculata—Angelica* sociation; and *Carex nigra* sociations.

   Carex rostrata sociations (Table 51). This description is based on data gathered in thirty-two quadrats from Shetland to Galloway. Through a combination of total plant cover, number of accompanying species and their cover contribution, and the presence or absence of certain species, three main community-types can be distinguished which correspond to different mean levels of the summer water table.

   Open *Carex rostrata* sociation. The total cover at the soil surface is not more than 50 per cent, the mean being 29 per cent. The maximum number of accompanying species is seven, their maximum and mean cover being respectively 16 and 6 percent. *Equisetum fluviatile* may be regarded as a constant species. Accompanying species range from *Cicuta virosa* in a swamp at Rescobie, Angus, to *Sparganium minimum* at L. Neldricken in the Stewartry. Water level ranges from 60 cm. to a water table of 6 cm. with a mean water level of 28 cm. (Plates 51 and 57).

   Seven soil samples under this sociation gave a mean of 13 per cent organic matter with a range from 5 to 29 per cent. Two samples analysed gave sand content of 80 and 71 per cent. but both looked like "black sandy muds". The sedges were here colonising inorganic soils and they were not forming root-rafts. Soils are protopedons or muds, notably lower in organic matter than the more developed *C. rostrata—Menyanthes* sociation of shallower water.

   Carex rostrata—Menyanthes sociation. *Menyanthes* is prominent in the preceding sociation and here it becomes constant. Mean cover at the soil surface rises to 61 per cent., the mean number of accompanying species to seven, their cover to 25 per cent while the mean water level decreases to 19 cm. (Plate 59). Plant cover is double that of the preceding community, water is somewhat shallower and the four available samples indicate fen peat formation, the mean percentage organic matter being 74·6 per cent. (cf. Pearsall's, 1920, figure of 89 per cent.).

   These stands may be distinguished from two stands, not listed here, from Rannoch Moor and Caithness, from which *Menyanthes* is absent and in which *Sphagnum cuspidatum* and *S. palustre* are prominent (Plate 58). They can be provisionally considered as a variant of this sociation.

   Carex rostrata—Acrocladium cordifolium/cuspidatum sociation. It is notable that either *A. cordifolium* or *A. cuspidatum* is always present and that together they may be classed as constant. *Potentilla palustris* is also a constant and prominent species. Indeed, taking the hundred (25 × 25 cm.) quadrats in all communities having both species, *Potentilla palustris* and *Acrocladium* are found to be significantly positively associated ($\chi^2 = 15\cdot32$, P.<0·001) and in an intensive study at Black Loch, Fife (Spence, unpublished)* *Potentilla* and *Acrocladium cordifolium* were found to be

   * For this and subsequent χ^2 tests, a 2×2 contingency table was used, the four cells containing respectively (*a*, *b*) quadrats in which either species was present without the other (*c*) quadrats in which both species occurred and (*d*) those containing neither species.

positively associated ($\chi^2 = 19\cdot25$, P.$<$0$\cdot$001). *Galium palustre* is a third constant, being sharply limited among the *Carex rostrata* communities to this sociation. Plant cover at the soil surface rises from 61 to 86 per cent., the mean number of accompanying species from 7 to 15, and their cover from 25 to 33 per cent. Water levels range from 3 cm. above, to 37 cm. below, the soil surface, with a mean of 5 cm. below.

The mean percentage oxidised carbon drops to 13$\cdot$5, but this figure is again based on only four, this time heterogeneous, samples. Certainly there is clear evidence of silting in a sample from Glen Urquhart, from a locality now sedimented which was open water in 1904 (p. 378); the remaining two samples are from swamps in rich-water areas. The development of the *Carex rostrata—Acrocladium* sociation is possibly connected with periodic silting whereas the *Carex rostrata—Sphagnum* stands were highly organic. There is a decrease in mean pH through the series but ranges are wide. Doubtless this decrease reflects the normal trend in moving from more or less open water to more concentrated solutions surrounding buffered muds in shallow water.

A possible unlisted variant is provided by a Caithness sample from which *Potentilla palustris* and *Acrocladium* are absent and in which *Sphagnum cuspidatum* is again prominent, with *Calluna, Empetrum, Erica tetralix, Myrica, Molinia, Narthecium ossifragum*, etc. *Agrostis canina* ssp. *canina, Veronica scutellata* and *Drepanocladus exannulatus* are common in, and among these three communities exclusive to, the *C. rostrata—Acrocladium* sociation and the latter, rich in pleurocarpous mosses, is related to the *Carex rostrata* brown moss mire or fen of Ratcliffe (p. 438).

All the *Carex rostrata* communities are recorded in, or adjoining, water of pH 6$\cdot$8 and of alkalinity 2$\cdot$8 to 89 p.p.m. $CaCO_3$. The species forms small stands at Kilconquhar, Carlingwark, Rescobie and many other rich-water lochs, although it does not form the main reedswamp in these places. This is composed of *Typha latifolia* or *T. angustifolia, Glyceria maxima* and *Phragmites communis*. From a study of all the relevant quadrats, *Glyceria maxima* and *Carex rostrata* appear to have a mutually exclusive distribution. Examination of their interrelationship at Black Loch (Fife) revealed the existence of a significant negative association between them (Spence, unpublished). *Typha latifolia* and *Carex rostrata* rarely occur together. The relationship of *Carex rostrata* to *Phragmites* has already been touched upon (p. 341). *Carex rostrata* penetrates to colder climates than *Phragmites*. Whilst the species may have the same range in water chemistry, this climatic distribution must reinforce the apparent tendency of *Carex rostrata* to occur more widely in poorer waters than *Phragmites*.

Zonation. Both *C. rostrata* and *C. lasiocarpa* form floating rafts in lochans with small outflows, in similar sheltered portions of larger lochs and by slow streams. On undisturbed shores in these places considerable zonal development may occur. The quiet north end of L. Moraig and swampy pools near L. Garten are two examples for *Carex rostrata* (see Fig. 49, p. 339). Data for these and other lochs show that landwards *C. rostrata* may either give way to *Sphagnum—J. bulbosus*, or it may blend with *Carex lasiocarpa* (q.v.) to give *C. rostrata+C. lasiocarpa→C. lasiocarpa→C. lasiocarpa+ Myrica*, or it may give *Filipendula, D. cespitosa, C. vesicaria* or *Phalaris*. It may overlap in the swamp zone occurring with most swamp dominants except *Schoenoplectus* which always stands in deeper water. Since it can grow in water up to 60 cm. deep, it may also overlap with floating-leaved species like *N. alba* or *Nuphar*, or *Potamogeton natans*. Though open *C. rostrata* does occur as a pioneer of submerged inorganic soils, it is atypical of the most exposed shores with coarse raw soils in which there is any pioneer reedswamp (cf. *Eleocharis* or *Equisetum fluviatile*) and on which open *Littorella—Lobelia* forms the shallowest submerged plant cover. It, therefore, does not often give way to *Littorella—J. fluitans* except where, unusually, that community grows in an organic soil. *Carex rostrata* and *Littorella—J. fluitans* thus tend to alternate along the shore as at Lochs Tarff, Garten and Kinord (north-east and west sides) (see Fig. 47, p. 322).

An example of known plant succession involving *C. rostrata* is provided at Urquhart Bay, L. Ness. West (1905, Fig. 19, reproduced here as Plate 67) photographed a bay on the delta to the south of the entry of the River Urquhart into L. Ness. Study of this area in August 1961 (Plate 66) showed that an open pool was by then almost silted up and that much vegetation had changed. The changes are summarised below:—

	1904			1961	
	Shallow open water			Shallow water	*C. rostrata* soc.
	Shallow water	*C. rostrata*		Water at soil surface	*C. rostrata—Acrocladium* soc.
Decreasing depth of water ↓		*C. rostrata*			*Alisma plantago-aquatica*
		Alisma			*Phalaris*
		Phalaris			*Phalaris* plus *Salix* carr

A number of documented examples show that the open *C. rostrata* sociation on the margin of lochs, and even floating rafts in sheltered pools, may not change at all in at least 57 years (see p. 379 and Plates 72, 73, 76 and 77).

Carex lasiocarpa community types (Table 51). There are too few samples to categorise the open *C. lasiocarpa* facies in which the water level, in four samples, ranges from +10 cm. to −20 cm. There are three constants in the *Carex lasiocarpa—Myrica* sociation, namely *Myrica* itself, *C. rostrata* and *Sphagnum subsecundum*. Plant cover reaches 50 per cent., the mean height of the dominant is 82 cm. and mean water table 1 cm. In *Myrica—C. lasiocarpa*, *Myrica* is dominant. Although there are only four samples they are consistent enough to show *C. lasiocarpa* as a constant with *Molinia* and *Sphagnum recurvum*. Plant cover is still high.

Soils under open *C. lasiocarpa* are either sandy raw soils typical of exposed shores (as for open *C. rostrata*) or, in sheltered localities, sedge peats composed of a frequently floating raft. The second and third communities have silty sedge peats.

As pointed out in discussing *Cladium mariscus* (p. 334) and *Phragmites communis* (p. 337), *Carex lasiocarpa* seems a typical dominant of ground in, or near, poor water and it is a typical "poor fen" indicator in Norway although some data of Gorham (1950) raise doubts as to what its presence indicates.

Zonation. Pure stands of *C. lasiocarpa* are a convenient starting point. These may, towards deeper water, be first mixed with, and then replaced by, *Phragmites* or *C. rostrata*. When *C. lasiocarpa* forms open stands on submerged sandy soil it is replaced in deeper water by open *Littorella—Lobelia* or *Littorella—J. fluitans*, etc. In very sheltered places where pure *C. lasiocarpa* forms a floating raft, as by the pools at the south end of L. na Ba Ruaidhe, considerable zonal development occurs. Landwards these pure stands merge into the *C. lasiocarpa—Myrica* sociation and *Sphagnum* spp. become prominent (cf. Fig. 47, p. 322).

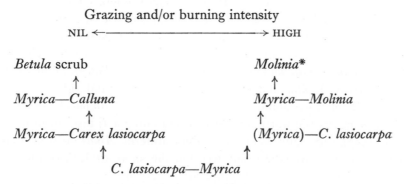

FIG. 51. The possible relationship between biotic factors and vegetation sequence involving *Carex lasiocarpa*.

Grazing and burning, or the absence of these factors, seems to determine the development of the vegetation thereafter since this is very variable. In most cases *Myrica* persists as a dominant, accompanied usually by *Molinia* and, alternatively, by *Calluna* or *Erica tetralix* as co-dominant or prominent species (cf. *Molinia—Myrica* mire type of Ratcliffe (p. 435). Sometimes, as at L. Ba, Rannoch Moor, *Myrica—Carex lasiocarpa* is only found on small ungrazed islands, *Myrica* itself being scarce on the grazed and/or burnt shore where *Molinia* is prominent. Two swamps near L. Garten have very undersized *Pinus* trees in the *Myrica—Calluna* sociation and little *Molinia* while these and several other stands of the sociation support young specimens of *Betula pubescens* and *Salix cinerea* ssp. *atrocinerea*. There is, usually, no further development of scrub vegetation in the fens behind the zones of *Carex lasiocarpa* communities, but the vegetation of part of a fen at the west end of L. an Choin, east of L. Ness, perhaps indicates the course of undisturbed development of the *Myrica—C. lasiocarpa* sociation.

* As Ratcliffe (p. 435) says, *Myrica* may always have been absent from some Molinieta and not necessarily eliminated from it by grazing and/or burning.

Here, partly isolated by wetter ground from the prevailing burnt or grazed *Calluna* and *Molinia* communities, is a thriving *Betula* scrub (Plates 59, 60, 61). *Myrica* bushes in the *Myrica—C. lasiocarpa* sociation are more than 1 m. high and there are many young *Betula* plants; *Molinia* is inconspicuous. Nearby, a *Myrica—Calluna* sociation is well developed, having an open to dense canopy of *Betula* trees: *C. lasiocarpa* is rare while *S. recurvum* remains prominent. As with *C. rostrata* there is direct evidence (p. 379) that the *C. lasiocarpa* and *C. lasiocarpa—Myrica* communities may be slow to change.

A similar sequence, involving concentric zones of *C. lasiocarpa* on a floating raft then, if undisturbed, *Sphagnum*-rich tall ericoid (open bog) communities and eventually scrub or forest vegetation, is described by Curtis (1959, p. 235) as typical of many small non-outlet lakes in northern Wisconsin. The rate of change in the Wisconsin *C. lasiocarpa* sequence is, like the Scottish ones, very slow.

C. vesicaria—Veronica scutellata sociation (Table 51). Six stands of *C. vesicaria* were studied. The species is not common, particularly as a dominant, in Scotland and almost none occurs north of the Great Glen. Unusually, it forms extensive pure stands in up to 40 cm. water in a bay at the south-east corner of L. Awe, south of Kilchurn Castle. In the five *C. vesicaria—V. scutellata* stands the mean water table is 10 cm. and there are, for a reedswamp community-type, a relatively large number of constants: *J. effusus*, *Galium palustre*, *Mentha aquatica*, *Potentilla palustris* and *Veronica scutellata*; *Juncus*, *Mentha* and *Veronica* are also differential. The soil varies from black reducing mud (of warp anmoor) to a purple brown alluvial clay-loam with a thin **L** layer. This suggests the warp-anmoor or dried-anmoor transition to mull described by Kubiëna (1953), especially where the sedges underlie *Alnus* on well drained soil as on the delta west of L. Meiklie (Plate 64). On the shore of L Awe there is a grazed *C. nigra—C. panicea* zone in which cropped *C. vesicaria* occurs. Passing from relatively dry to wetter ground, pure *C. vesicaria—V. scutellata* develops and then, in standing water, pure *C. vesicaria* with occasional *C. rostrata* which is normally the more abundant species. On the south-east shore of L. Lomond, above the entry of the Endrick Water, there is some development of a *Carex vesicaria* zone between open water and the grazed zone of *Agrostis canina*, *J. effusus* or *J. articulatus* communities. In bays the sedges give way to *Polygonum* or *Nuphar*. The more widespread *C. vesicaria—V. scutellata* sociation typically occupies ground towards the upper limit of the *C. rostrata* zones and is, indeed, replaced by this species as the soil becomes wetter. An example of this type, from Black Loch, Fife, is given when describing *C. nigra* sociations (p. 350); likewise, samples from Speyside and the Stewartry are further from open water. On swamps and fen south of L. Insch, Speyside, the sequence is: *Phalaris* (water table 20 cm.)→*C. aquatilis* or *C. vesicaria* (water table 5 cm.)→*C. rostrata* (water table 0 to water 2 cm. deep)→extensive *Equisetum—Acrocladium* (depth of water 3 cm.). On the swampy banks of the R. Cree above Newton Stewart, *Carex vesicaria* alternates, with a water table around 20 cm., with *Salix cinerea*, *Phragmites*, *Carex rostrata* or *Phalaris*: it is replaced in damper ground by *Phragmites* or *Carex rostrata*. Samples from both these areas contribute to the synoptic list for *C. vesicaria*.

Carex aquatilis is present in *C. vesicaria* stands from the River Cree and from the swamps at L. Insch, Speyside. It covers large areas of the latter swamp, less on the River Cree and at the entry of the River Ken into L. Ken. The species is only recorded from thirty-eight 10 km. squares in Scotland (*Atlas of the British Flora*), a quarter of these being on Speyside. West (1905) noted abundant *C. aquatilis* at the south end of L. Uanagan (Ness) but recent prolonged search revealed only *C. rostrata* and *C. lasiocarpa* in that reedswamp. Stands were recorded in the L. Insch, the River Cree and the River Ken localities but are not listed here. *C. vesicaria* contributes cover-abundance of 4–5 in each and the species list is, indeed, similar to that of the *C. vesicaria—V. scutellata* stands. *C. riparia* stands were only examined at Duddingston Loch, one of its few Scottish localities. *C. elata* swamp from one Scottish locality, Inchnacardoch Bay, L. Ness, is described and illustrated by West (1905). Possibly due to the late season when it was visited in 1960, only a few fruits of *C. elata* were gathered among the seemingly predominant C. rostrata. (No *C. elata* is recorded for Scotland in the *Atlas of the British Flora*!)

Carex paniculata—Angelica sociation (Table 51). Seven stands of the largest sedge in Scotland were examined in Speyside, Angus (Rescobie), Argyll (Avich) (Plates 62, 55 and 63 respectively) and Wigtownshire (Mochrum). Four were in carr, either under trees of *Betula, Salix* or *Fraxinus* or between them, in open swamp or by the shore of a loch (Mochrum), while soils varied from firm muds to, in the latter case, boulders. The tussock growth form makes very uneven ground so it is difficult to define the soil surface and hence water level in relation to soil surface. The tussocks themselves vary from 20 to 40 cm. in the height of the rhizome "trunk" to the base of the leaves and in leaf length also, from 70 to 186 cm., while some plants can reach a height of 230 cm. Spacing may be dense, with little or no colonisation between tussocks, or very open with diverse colonisation. The latter condition is illustrated in Plate 55, from ungrazed swamp and carr at the west end of L. Avich which, with carr at the north end of L. Rescobie, supports the finest specimens. With such diversity in habitat conditions, in terms of shade, of substrate texture and of moisture (from aquatic to epiphytic conditions), little floristic uniformity is to be expected. A list of fifty-six species in seven reedswamp stands is relatively high. *Angelica* is a possible constant. This combination of *Carex paniculata* and *Betula, Salix cinerea* ssp. *atrocinerea* or *Fraxinus* is similar to the swamp-carr of East Anglia described by Pallis (1911, in Tansley (1949)) where *Alnus* had developed on, and between, tussocks of *Carex paniculata, C. riparia*, etc.

Zonation. In ungrazed swamp-carr at Rescobie L.; *Filipendula* (water level at −5 cm.)→*C. nigra* (tussocks: water level −5 cm. to + 2 cm.)→*C. paniculata* and *C. rostrata* (water level +4 to +6 cm.). All these communities grew beneath a canopy of *Salix cinerea* ssp. *atrocinerea. Cicuta virosa* formed societies in open areas between the shrubs (water level −8 to +13 cm.). *Schoenoplectus lacustris* (water level +15 cm. or more) occurred in a pond in the middle of the carr.

Carex nigra sociations (Table 52). For a dominant that is fairly widespread, sampling has probably been inadequate. From the eight stands sampled a *C. nigra* society of open water and a short-turf, grazed *C. nigra—C. panicea* sociation have been discerned. The *C. nigra* society, observed several times on Speyside, had few accompanying species. The *C. nigra—C. panicea* sociation has *C. panicea*, *C. demissa*, *Eleocharis quinqueflora* and (possibly) *Drepanocladus revolvens* as constant and differential species. This latter community always bordered lochs on muds where the water level was more or less at the surface, giving way, with lowering of the water level, to *Agrostis* turf, to *J. effusus* or to a variety of grazed communities and, with raising of the water level, to open *Carex rostrata* or *C. vesicaria* or other swamp species. One stand was clearly a grazing conversion of *Phragmites—Galium* (p. 336). This community resembles the *Carex panicea—Campylium stellatum* mire (Ratcliffe, p. 437) of calcareous substrates, and two of the present quadrats were recorded in such ground. In the absence of grazing and/or trampling, and with a similar water table, *C. nigra* forms tussocks up to 1 m. (mean 65 cm.) high. This *C. nigra—Acrocladium* sociation entirely lacks the species that are constant in the previous community. It may, or may not, be part of the field layer in *Salix* or *Alnus* carr.

Zonation. At L. Awe, at entry of the River Tweely: *Alnus—J. articulatus* and *Molinia—Myrica→C. nigra—Acrocladium* and prominent *C. vesicaria→C. vesicaria* sociation→sparse *Equisetum fluviatile→*open water. At Black Loch, Fife: zone of *Filipendula* and/or *Phalaris→*narrow zone of *C. nigra—Acrocladium* and more limited *C. vesicaria—V. scutellata→C. rostrata—Acrocladium* (broad zone), etc.

Sociations dominated by partial hydrophytes, helophytes or hemicryptophytes

Phalaris arundinacea—Filipendula ulmaria sociation, Glyceria maxima— Iris pseudacorus sociation, Filipendula—Acrocladium cordifolium sociation, Potentilla palustris—Acrocladium cordifolium sociation (Table 53), **Equisetum fluviatile—Acrocladium sociation** (Table 49), **Juncus articulatus—Angelica sylvestris sociation** (Table 53), **and societies of Phalaris, Potentilla, Glyceria and Menyanthes trifoliata; Sphagnum subsecundum var. auriculatum—Juncus bulbosus sociation** (Table 54).

The dominants in these sociations are partial hydrophytes and/or helophytes or hemicryptophytes. *Potentilla palustris*, *Menyanthes trifoliata*, *Glyceria maxima* and, least commonly, *Phalaris arundinacea*, each form societies in permanently submerged soils, in depths of water of 20 cm. or more, at the margins of lochs or slow-moving rivers; *Menyanthes* indeed rarely predominates in any other way. Both *Potentilla* and *Glyceria*, however, form widespread sociations in soils having the summer water table below the soil surface. *Phalaris* occurs most commonly in such soils, while *Filipendula ulmaria* and *Juncus articulatus* are infrequent dominants elsewhere. *Phalaris—Filipendula*, *Filipendula—Acrocladium*, *Juncus articulatus—Angelica* and perhaps others are fen rather than swamp sociations but they are considered here because of their floristic and spatial connections with swamps. Zonation in all these communities is discussed after their description (cf. Fig. 49). Only *Glyceria maxima* communities have been studied in any detail. Too few stands were recorded of *Deschampsia cespitosa* and *Juncus effusus*, both important dominants of alluvial soils on margins of lochs, of the deltas at their ends (Plate 64), and of rivers. The soligenous mire community of *Juncus effusus*—*Sphagnum* is described by Ratcliffe (p. 436).

Phalaris—Filipendula **sociation** (Table 53). This sociation overlies soil with mean water table less than 30 cm. Along sequences of increasing height of water table, *Phalaris* only reappears as a dominant, and then infrequently, in permanently submerged soil. There the mean height of *Phalaris* was 164 cm., about 30 per cent. of the soil surface was uncolonised and species density was 12, although *Filipendula* was the only constant. Three of the samples formed the field layer to *Alnus*, *Fraxinus* or *Salix caprea*—*atrocinerea* carr. Soils varied from a black warp-anmoor, from 10 to more than 50 cm. deep, to purple-brown clay-loam with mull humus. Since the soil surface under this community is typically at some height above the summer water table, stands may not necessarily be subjected to annual flooding. This certainly applied to part of the stands observed, over four winters, at Lindores and Black Loch, Fife.

Stands were recorded from sites in Fife, Galloway and Speyside adjoining waters which are classed as moderately rich to rich. In view of the possible lack of winter flooding no close dependence on the trophic status of the water should be assumed but the species, although fairly widespread in Scotland, does have a denser distribution in the lowlands. It also has 75 per cent. presence in the eutrophic variant of the *Phragmites—Galium* sociation (p. 337). *Phalaris* is a typical fen dominant in Northern Ireland, East Anglia and the English Lake District, where it also forms reedswamp in the last two areas (Tansley, 1949).

Glyceria maxima—Iris **sociation** (Table 53). This sociation, in which *Iris* is constant and in which *P. amphibium* reaches 70 per cent., is found on the shores of a number of rich-water lowland lochs with a mean water table of less than 30 cm. The soil is usually black, reducing mud or warp-anmoor (as at Lindores) of varying depth (15 to more than 50 cm.) overlying mineral soil. At Lindores the sociation, unlike *Phalaris—Filipendula*, was flooded to a depth of 20 cm. or more during the winters 1957–62. *Glyceria maxima* grows vigorously, as high as *Phalaris*, and the previous season's dead leaves and stems seem to produce a loose medium unsuitable for associated species until this material has sunk to near the summer water table, when other plants do persist. A study of their relationship at Black Loch, Fife (Spence, unpublished), showed that *Carex rostrata*, *Acrocladium cordifolium* and *Potentilla palustris* are all significantly, negatively associated with *Glyceria*. Towards open water there may be a zone formed by other species but *Glyceria* itself frequently grows out continuously into the water, producing dense, pure reedswamp stands of 100 per cent. cover, from which *Iris* is quite absent. *Glyceria maxima* is often grazed by cattle, as Hubbard (1954) notes.

Pure and mixed stands of *Glyceria maxima* have been sampled from localities in Aberdeenshire down to the Stewartry: every loch containing *Glyceria* stands is a kettle-hole in fluvio-glacial clays (p. 375) with rich water. The species is almost absent from the Highlands (*Atlas of the British Flora*) and this implies a closer dependence on rich water than is indicated by *Phalaris*, for instance, which indeed, is not necessarily flooded in winter.

Glyceria is a typical fen dominant in East Anglia.

Filipendula Acrocladium sociation (Table 53). *Filipendula* is a constant in the *Phalaris—Filipendula* sociation. Here, with a slightly higher mean water table, at 14 cm., than that sociation, it becomes dominant while *Phalaris* dwindles. Although only four stands were listed in detail, they share three constants: *Alnus*, *Galium palustre* and *Acrocladium* (*cordifolium* or *cuspidatum*). A canopy of *Alnus* or *Salix cinerea* is recorded in three stands: this applied to four out of a further five stands observed but not listed in detail. Soils noted include several black reducing, or non-reducing, damp warp-anmoors and a number of brown earths, the latter particularly under mature *Alnus* wood, as on the delta at the River Urquhart's entry into L. Ness. While certainly higher than under normal *Phalaris—Filipendula*, the level of the water table varied between stands, sometimes rising above the soil surface, so that the sociation is liable to seasonal or constant flooding. The adjoining water varies from moderately rich to rich. Although it may be a widespread species in Scotland the distribution of this sociation is primarily lowland but it does occur, if undisturbed, by rich water lochs in the Highlands, such as the limestone L. Moraig or L. Croispol. In the former it predominates on a few small islands surrounded by *C. rostrata* swamp and inaccessible to stock. Its intolerance of grazing and/or burning is seen in its abundance on the shores of some ungrazed islands in freshwater lochs in Shetland and its total absence from the grazed shore of the lochs (Spence, 1960). Willis and Jefferies (1959) note its similar intolerance of grazing in the fens of the Gordano Valley, Somerset.

Potentilla—Acrocladium cordifolium sociation (Table 53). With a slightly higher mean water table than the *Filipendula—Acrocladium*, this sociation has two constants, *Carex rostrata* and *Acrocladium*, there being a significant positive association between them and *Potentilla* itself. *Phalaris* and *Filipendula* are rare. Under *Potentilla—Acrocladium* is a loose structure formed of the intertwined stems of *Potentilla* in the top of which *Acrocladium* creates a moss mat. The level at which this mat forms, or indeed whether it forms at all, is clearly related to the height of the summer water table. In several localities (and not only in this community) where the soil is slightly submerged in summer, the presence of a log or stump has allowed moss cover to develop on its surface where otherwise there is no emergent bryophyte colonisation at all. The *Potentilla—Acrocladium* stands at Lindores and Black Loch were submerged during three consecutive winters' observations. *Potentilla* can form unstable rafts in open water. The community adjoins lochs with moderately rich to rich waters. The absence of both *Potentilla* and *Acrocladium* from the *Carex rostrata—Sphagnum palustre* community should be noted.

Equisetum fluviatile—Acrocladium cordifolium sociation (Table 49). Four stands of the community reveal three, perhaps four, constants, *Potentilla palustris Acrocladium cordifolium*, *Galium palustre* and *Menyanthes trifoliata*. Plant cover is typically 85 per cent., the water table 2 cm., and *Equisetum* itself has a mean height of

94 cm. (compared with 139 cm. in the open community) and a cover-abundance value of 7.

At Black Loch, L. of Park and extensively at L. Eader da Bhaile on Raasay, the community occurs between or under the bushes in *Salix cinerea* ssp. *atrocinerea* carr. In one stand *Utricularia intermedia* was very abundant on red oxidising mud; in another, *Sphagnum squarrosum* was well developed, the soil being probably a warp-anmoor. Any successional relationship between the open and closed communities has not been studied.

A complex interrelationship of *Equisetum* with various common fen dominants was noted in a mesotrophic fen and carr at L. Eader da Bhaile. Apart from its dominance in the nearby swamp (alkalinity of water 84·3 p.p.m. $CaCO_3$), *Equisetum* occurred as a constant in four closed community-types:—*Filipendula*—*Acrocladium* sociation (p. 352): *Eleocharis*, with *Galium palustre* constant: and *Menyanthes*, and *Caltha*, each with *Eleocharis* constant.

***Juncus articulatus*—*Angelica* community** (Table 53). Although four possible constants have emerged, this community is certainly undersampled, particularly since it is prominent in grazed swamps and fens like those by the Spey, west of L. Insch, and in the zones adjoining swamps by many lochs. It is undoubtedly favoured by grazing, being far commoner on grazed sides of fenced areas than on the ungrazed sides (see p. 337). However, its relationships with biotically influenced communities like *Agrostis canina* ssp. *canina*, *Holcus*, *Juncus effusus*, etc. have not been studied. There are too few samples of this and of Ratcliffe's *Juncus acutiflorus*—*Acrocladium* mire (p. 437) to judge their affinities.

***Sphagnum subsecundum*—*Juncus bulbosus* sociation** (Table 54). The *Juncus fluitans*—*Lobelia dortmanna* association is typical of submerged soils in poor to, more rarely, moderately rich waters. *J. fluitans* is dominant in two of the sociations, *J. fluitans*—*Utricularia vulgaris* and *J. fluitans*—*S. subsecundum*: these are separated floristically and occupy progressively shallower water. A third sociation in this sequence (but not in the same association) is *Sphagnum subsecundum* var. *auriculatum*—*J. bulbosus*, of which five stands from Shetland to Galloway contain no less than eight constants, two of these being further *Sphagnum* species. The pH of the soil ranged from 3·25–4·58 and the adjoining lochans contained poor water. Floristically this community is of interest, together with the *J. fluitans*—*Sphagnum subsecundum* sociation, in being the richest in bryophytes of those studied. Bryophytes may predominate spasmodically in other aquatic communities in Scotland, viz. *S. squarrosum* in an *Equisetum fluviatile*— *Acrocladium* stand or *Acrocladium cordifolium* in a *Potentilla*—*Acrocladium* stand, but neither there nor, more strikingly, in submerged habitats do they approach in abundance the bryophytes of the *Sphagnum subsecundum*—*J. bulbosus* sociation of margins, and of *J. fluitans*—*Sphagnum subsecundum* below the water surface in small pools of peat bogs, or the calm shallows of lochans with poor water. (The two sociations do not in fact often occur side by side.) This community is related to, and is possibly a damper facies of, the sub-alpine *Carex*—*Sphagnum* mire type of Ratcliffe (p. 436). *Sphagnum*

z

subsecundum—J. bulbosus is normally grazed; a lightly grazed sequence (Flatpunds) ran: *Sphagnum—J. bulbosus→C. rostrata—Acrocladium→C. rostrata—Menyanthes.* The usual sequence (in Applecross) is: *Eriophorum—Sphagnum→Carex nigra—C. panicea→ Sphagnum—J. bulbosus >J. fluitans—Sphagnum→Sparganium minimum* (open water).

TABLE 38

Community sequences at the named localities in relation to a gradient in water-table, from below to above the soil surface, in each locality.

Alnus carr

Salix carr

	marsh or		fen				fen or swamp					swamp		
Vegetation types / Lochs	A			B				C					D		
	D. cespitosa society	*J. articulatus*	*Filipendula—Acrocladium*	*Phalaris—Filipendula*	*Filipendula—Acrocladium*	*J. articulatus—Angelica*	*J. effusus* society	*Glyceria—Iris*	*Potentilla—Acrocladium*	*Equisetum—Acrocladium*	*C. rostrata—Acrocladium*	*C. vesicaria—V. scutellata*	*Phragmites* society	*Carex rostrata* society	*C. vesicaria* society
Lindores	+	...	...	+	...	...	...	+	...	...	...	...	+	...	...
Black Loch	...	...	...	+	+	...	...	+	+	+	+	...	...	+	...
Rescobie	+	...	...	+	...	+	+	...	...	...	...	...	+	+	...
Clunie	...	...	...	+	+	...	...	+	...	...	...	...	+	...	...
Carlingwark	...	...	...	+	...	...	...	+	...	...	...	...	+	...	...
Lomond (north end)	+	+	...	+	...	+	...	+	...	...	...	...	...	+	...
Gartochcraggan	+	...	...	+	...	+	+	...	...	+	...	...	...	...	...
Lochend	+	...	...	+	...	...	...	...	+	...	...	...	+	+	...
Meiklie	+	...	+	...	+	...	...	...	...	...	...	+	...	+	+
Insch-swamp	+	...	...	+	...	...	...	...	...	...	+	+	...	+	+
Urquhart	...	...	...	+	+	...	...	...	...	...	+	...	...	+	...

Dry land ————————————→ Permanently submerged soil

Increasing height of water-table

Zonation. Excepting the *Sphagnum—J. bulbosus* sociation, two or more of these sociations are always found together, so their zonation is treated similarly and is summarised for twelve localities in Table 38. The actual depth of the water has been ignored, attention being confined to the vegetation sequence in each locality from dry land (left) to permanently submerged soil (right). *Deschampsia cespitosa* always occurs on the driest ground (A); *Phalaris—Filipendula* sociation comes next in 9/11 cases (B); then

Glyceria—Iris or *Potentilla—Acrocladium* (C); and finally, with, or without, pure stands of *Glyceria* or *Potentilla*, true reedswamp (D). Alder carr occurs in (A) and possibly in (B), while willow carr occurs in (A), (B) and, locally, in (C).

Stands dominated by *Phragmites* (or *Carex rostrata* or *J. fluitans*) have been separated into sociations by vegetational criteria which follow gradients in water depth. In Table 38, the community sequences at different localities are listed in relation to increasing mean level of the water at any one locality and the sequences conform to a general pattern. On a smaller scale, Griffiths (1932) notes in his account of vegetation of Butterby Marsh that while the number of species per station and their vertical range vary, the vertical sequence of the dominants does not.

A note on mean and range in water levels of aquatic, swamp and fen vegetation

When drawing up synoptic tables the mean level of the water table or depth of water for each stand of a particular community was noted and the values were then averaged to give a mean for that community-type. Forty-nine community-types of aquatic vegetation as a whole for which means and ranges of water levels are available are classified in Table 39 according to their dominant species as emergent, rosette, floating-leaved, submerged linear-leaved and submerged broad-leaved. It should be noted that this depth distribution is based on mean values and that these are derived from samples of different sizes (p. 357).

The communities classified as reedswamp, rich and poor fen

Swamp and fen community-types dominated by widespread species like *Phragmites*, or by other less common species, are partly differentiated by depth of water. It may be said, to generalise, that species-poor, or pure, reedswamp of permanently, or seasonally, submerged soils (aquatic reedswamp) may be followed, on seasonally submerged soils, by herb- and moss-rich fens (amphibious reedswamp of Af Rantzien, 1951); on seasonally, or spasmodically, submerged soils this is replaced by, or intergrades with, fen or marsh dominated by helophytes or hemicryptophytes.

This idea may be developed further by first subtracting from the list of swamp and fen communities all those dominated by habitual helophytes or hemicryptophytes. This eliminates *Deschampsia cespitosa*, *Filipendula—Acrocladium*, *J. articulatus* (and *J. effusus*) and much *Alnus* and *Salix* carr. Next, all moss- and herb-rich communities can be extracted in which one or more of the following species are constant: *Acrocladium cordifolium*, *A. cuspidatum*, *Angelica sylvatica*, *Galium palustre*, *Mentha aquatica*, *Sphagnum recurvum* and *Veronica scutellata*. From some knowledge of the chemistry of the adjoining or inundating waters the following sociations can be said to comprise moderately rich to rich fen:

Phragmites—Galium, the *Ranunculus lingua—Cicuta virosa* variant being one representative of rich fen; conspicuous accompanying *Filipendula* may constitute another.
Carex rostrata—Acrocladium spp.
C. vesicaria—V. scutellata

C. nigra—Acrocladium spp.
C. paniculata—Angelica
Phalaris—Filipendula
Glyceria maxima—Iris pseudacorus
Equisetum fluviatile—Acrocladium (with *Sphagnum squarrosum*)
Eleocharis palustris—Acrocladium spp.
Potentilla—Acrocladium spp.

Where there has been no obvious interference, drier ground in areas bearing these communities carries carr of *Alnus*, *Fraxinus* and of *Salix caprea*, *S. cinerea* ssp. *atrocinerea* and *S. aurita*. These sociations of moderately rich to rich fen are provisionally grouped in a **Phragmitio—Acrocladion Alliance**.

The following may be classed as poor fen:
Phragmites—Myrica—C. demissa variant
Myrica—C. lasiocarpa—Sphagnum recurvum (*Angelica*, *Filipendula*, etc. absent)
Cladium mariscus—Myrica
C. rostrata—Sphagnum palustre
Sphagnum auriculatum—J. bulbosus

Occasionally undisturbed zones on drier ground than these communities bear *Salix cinerea/aurita—Betula pubescens* carr. The vegetation types of poor fen are provisionally placed in a **Myrico—Caricion lasiocarpae Alliance**. They are related to the "Leuco—Scheuchzerion alliance" (Nordhagen, 1943) of oligotrophic and strongly acidiphilous mires with permanently high water tables.

The remaining communities, consisting of societies and species-poor sociations, comprise reedswamp.

Equisetum fluviatile—Littorella
Eleocharis—Littorella
Schoenoplectus lacustris—J. fluitans
Typha latifolia—Lemna minor
Phragmites—Sparganium and *Phragmites—Littorella*
Societies of all these dominants with societies of *Carex vesicaria*, *C. nigra*, *Cladium*, *Glyceria maxima* and *Phalaris arundinacea*

The sedge communities are equivalent to the "species-poor Magnocaricion elatae" of Scandinavian ecologists, e.g. Koch, from which such species as *Cicuta virosa*, *Galium palustre* ssp. *elongatum*, *Lycopus europaeus*, *Solanum dulcamara*, *Utricularia intermedia* and *Acrocladium giganteum* are specifically mentioned as absent (Af Rantzien, 1951). The swamp community-types are provisionally grouped in a **Schoenoplecto—Magnocaricion Alliance**.

TABLE 39

The mean and range of depth of water in which 49 community-types occur together with the classification of their predominant species into one of 5 growth-form groups (e = emergent, r = rosette, fl = floating-leaved, sl = submerged linear-leaved, sb = submerged broad-leaved). Six pondweed societies are included for each of which there are less than 3 sets of depth data (*). For depth of water, — indicates that this lies below the soil surface.

	Sociation (binomial) or Society	Mean	Range	
e	Phalaris—Filipendula	−30	...	
	Filipendula—Acrocladium	−14	−30 to	1
e	Glyceria maxima—Iris	−25	−30 to	−11
	Potentilla—Acrocladium	−8	−25 to	8
e	Phragmites—Galium	−10	−40 to	2
e	Carex vesicaria—V. scutellata	−10	−30 to	40
e	C. rostrata—Acrocladium	−5	−37 to	10
e	Equisetum fluviatile—Acrocladium	−2	−7 to	3
e	Glyceria maxima	−1	−12 to	9
e	C. lasiocarpa—Myrica and Myrica—C. lasiocarpa	0	0 to	7
e	C. lasiocarpa	0	−20 to	10
e	Carex paniculata—Angelica	0	−50 to	36
	(C. nigra)	0	−15 to	12
sl	Sphagnum—J. bulbosus	0	−5 to	5
e	Cladium mariscus	1	−19 to	28
sl	J. fluitans—Sphagnum	11	5 to	25
e	Phragmites	13	−30 to	50
e	Typha latifolia—Lemna	19	0 to	60
e	C. rostrata—Menyanthes	19	3 to	43
e	Open C. rostrata	28	6 to	60
r	Littorella—Lobelia	29	30 to	60
sl	Pot. filiformis—Chara	30	15 to	70
e	Eleocharis—Littorella	28	8 to	55
sl	Pot. filiformis—Littorella	44	5 to	107
r	Lobelia—J. fluitans	50	15 to	150
r	Littorella—J. fluitans	53	0 to	125
e	Phragmites—Sparganium	56	8 to	110
r	Isoetes	66	3 to	250
sl	Pot. pusillus *	60	...	
f	Nymphaea "occidentalis"	67	20 to	125
sl	J. fluitans—Utricularia	71	28 to	170
sl	Pot. pusillus *	85	60 to	120
e	Equisetum fluviatile—Littorella	85	40 to	150
e	Schoenoplectus lacustris—J. fluitans	88	30 to	150
sl	Chara—Myriophyllum	89	40 to	250
sb	Pot. gramineus	100	40 to	260
f	Polygonum amphibium	100	30 to	200
f	Nymphaea alba	103	20 to	195
f	Nuphar lutea	102	20 to	150
f	Pot. natans	102	12 to	260
sb	Pot. alpinus *	120	...	
sb	Pot. × nitens *	125	80 to	170
sb	Elodea canadensis	179	50 to	200
sl	Pot. obtusifolius *	180	110 to	350
sb	Pot. lucens *	185	...	
sl	Fontinalis	190	80 to	300
sb	Pot. × zizii	200	160 to	250
sl	Nitella opaca	200	100 to	400
sb	Pot. perfoliatus	206	100 to	300
sb	Pot. praelongus	220	150 to	300

The classification adopted for descriptive purposes in the present account is based for convenience upon dominant species, sociations being distinguished on floristic grounds by use of constant and/or differential species. However, a classification of the type outlined above emphasises causal relationships, particularly those involving the level of the water and its nutrient status. The sociations thus grouped should readily fit into the phytosociological classifications of, for example, Nordhagen (1943), Duvigneaud (1949) and Oberdorfer (1954).

FACTORS CONTROLLING DISTRIBUTION OF VEGETATION

Distribution of vegetation and soils in and around given lochs

Swamp distribution. It is the conspicuousness of *Phragmites* or *Nymphaea* or *Nuphar* on a loch that makes them noticed when travelling over Scotland. Since they can be seen so easily from a passing car, or when walking on the shore, it is easy to realise how spasmodic their occurrences are. For example, in a journey along 36 km. of L. Ness, reedswamp occurs but twice, in Inchnacardoch Bay and in various parts of the delta where the River Urquhart enters the loch. Only three patches of reedswamp were noted on L. Lurgainn, Sutherland. These occur in sandy inlets on the north shore. Both north and south shores are rocky, the loch itself being a true rock basin in Torridonian sandstone (Murray and Pullar, Vol. II, Pt. 1, 1910, p. 190). Reedswamp and floating-leaved vegetation occurs in a sandy and muddy bay at the south end of L. Clunie; most of the eastern shore is stony. Lunga water in Shetland has a rocky shore quite devoid of emergent and floating-leaved plants. There are, however, two small inlets on the north side cut off from the main body of water. These shallow inlets are filled with mud which bears much emergent and floating-leaved vegetation. L. Gamhna is almost surrounded by reedswamp except for its north and north-west shores which are rocky or stony. Duddingston Loch, too, has reedswamp on all but its north and north-west shores, these shores forming a steep rocky continuation of the scarp above them. In contrast to all these examples Kilconquhar, Black Loch (Fife) and White Loch (Anabaglish Moss) are all ringed by more or less continuous reedswamp and, in part, by floating-leaved plants.

What accounts for these differences? The distribution of reedswamp seems to be related to the distribution of certain substrates. The largest lochs, like Ness or Lurgainn, with the stoniest shores have the most limited reedswamp, this being confined to a few sandy bays or detrital fans. Apart from climatic or chemical considerations the physical difficulty of colonising piles of stones or boulders must be great.

These differences result partly from the origin and subsequent history of the lake basin. Duddingston provides an example of this. The steep escarpment on its north-west side continues underwater and according to Peach and Horne (1910, p. 495) is part of an unmodified rock basin; this shore could not be colonised by reedswamp. On the other hand the loch is ponded by blown sand from the 30·5 m. raised beach along most of the rest of its shore and this bears thick reedswamp.

The extent of reedswamp around any body of water is also connected with its volume, area and depth. A series of lochs is enumerated in Table 40, from L. Ness with the greatest volume and mean depth of Scottish lochs, down to two of the smaller lochs, Duddingston and Black Loch. Provided that the basin is not almost unmodified rock it may be suggested that volume of water is, very roughly, inversely proportional to the area of reedswamp. The smaller the body of water, the greater the chance of finding a more or less continuous reedswamp. Since volume, or some function of volume, will

TABLE 40

Volume and some dimensions of 9 Scottish lochs; data mainly from Bathymetrical Survey (1910). *Ness:* valley rock basin; *Lurgainn:* true rock basin; *Lunga Water:* rock basin; *Lindores:* kettle-hole in fluvio-glacial deposits; *Kilconquhar:* kettle-hole in 30·5 m. raised beach; *Gamhna:* kettle-hole in fluvio-glacial deposits; *Duddingston:* part true rock basin, ponded by sand of 30·5 m. raised beach; *Black Loch:* kettle-hole in fluvio-glacial deposits.

Loch	Volume million cu. ft.	Area square miles	Max. depth ft.	Mean depth ft.
Ness	263,162	21·78	754	433
Lurgainn . . .	2,140	1·26	156	60.9
Clunie	170	0·21	69	29·1
Lunga Water . .	...	0·20	...	...
Lindores . . .	24	0·17	10	5
Kilconquhar . .	16	0·15	6	3·9
Gamhna . . .	10	0·04	41	9·5
Duddingston . .	...	0·03	10	5·1
Black (Fife) . . .	...	0·01	10	...

determine, under given climatic conditions, the degree of turbulence (a connection studied in more detail on p. 364), it seems likely that turbulence affects the distribution of reedswamp either directly, or through its effect on substrate distribution.

These tentative findings are next applied to aquatic vegetation as a whole, primarily by study of examples of horizontal and vertical community distribution in given lochs.

Distribution of aquatic vegetation in given lochs in relation to water depth and substrate. The vegetation of the west shore of Corby L., Aberdeenshire (Fig. 52a), shows a familiar sequence of growth forms from dry land to permanently submerged soils. Starting in a *Phragmites—Galium* stand with a water table of 4 cm., a transect crosses a stand of pure, taller *Phragmites* with a water level of +3 cm., and drops over a peat scarp into 40 cm. water overlying soft black mud, the surface of which slopes gently. Here *Nuphar lutea* is dominant, accompanied by a number of submerged species. From a depth of about 110 cm., and into deeper water, the *Nuphar* sociation is replaced by a linear-leaved submerged sociation in which *Callitriche hermaphroditica* and tall (105 cm.) *Potamogeton obtusifolius* are co-dominant. The soil is soft mud (gyttja) and colonisation is continuous from the edge of the west shore. On the west shore of Hempriggs, however, colonisation is scanty on the sandy, then rocky, substrate until a depth of 260 cm. when bottom muds

(a) LOCH CORBY

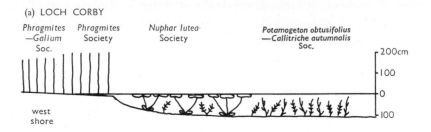

(b) LOCH MABERRY

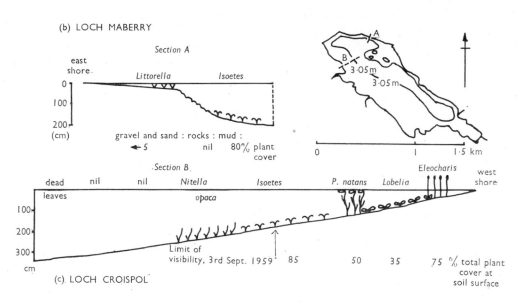

(c) LOCH CROISPOL

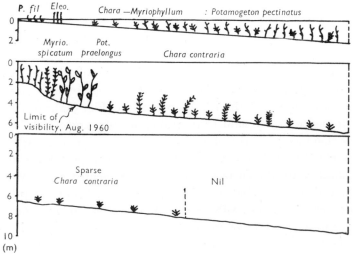

Fig. 52.

are reached which, as at L. Corby, are black and densely colonised, this time by *Fontinalis*.

In a transect across the long axis of L. Maberry in the Stewartry (Fig. 52b) the south-west facing shore only supports open *Littorella—Lobelia*, with cover of less than 5 per cent., on a gentle slope of coarse sand that gives way, at a water depth of 30 cm., to steep, uncolonised boulders. These boulders merge at a depth of 150 cm. into bottom muds supporting *Isoetes* with cover up to 80 per cent. On the opposite shore, which has an unbroken sandy and muddy slope, there is with increasing depth of water a growth-form sequence of, and almost continuous colonisation by, emergent, rosette, floating-leaved, rosette and linear-leaved vegetation.

The transect and sketch map of the south end of L. Croispol, Durness (Fig. 52c), shows rich vegetation which changes as water deepens and soils vary as follows: sociations of *P. filiformis*, *Eleocharis* (sands), *Chara aspera* and/or *Potamogeton pectinatus* (sandy marls or marls), *Myriophyllum spicatum*, *Potamogeton praelongus* and, finally, *Chara contraria* (marl with more organic matter). Substrate, then, seems to vary with vegetation type and, when very coarse, to prevent colonisation.

The shallow water of headlands and bays of L. Neldricken covers rocks or discontinuous open *Littorella—Lobelia* on sand. Fine sediments covered by various communities deepen as the water deepens (Fig. 53), except that two outlets bear deep mud in shallow water. The possible effects of water depth and soil type upon vegetation may, therefore, be compared. An example of the former effect is the replacement of *Equisetum fluviatile* on deep muds in shallow water by *Carex rostrata*, the maximum recorded water depths for these species being 150 cm. and 60 cm. respectively (L. na Ba Ruaidhe). This *Carex rostrata* community on soft mud itself contrasts with open *Littorella—Lobelia* of sands in similar shallow water. On L. Tarff the shallow channel between a wooded island and the shore is covered by open *Carex rostrata* (Plate 57) on soft mud with 6·3 per cent. oxidised carbon, while the open shore nearby bears sparse *Littorella—Lobelia* on sand (p. 362). Numerous examples may be seen, in Fig. 47 (p. 322) of the different communities on firm sands and on soft muds in shallow water in the same loch. An example of precise change in composition of soil with depth is provided by data for the mechanical analyses of aquatic soils in the north-west corner of L. Kinord (Fig. 54a, p. 363). The total amount of sand falls, that of silt and clay rises, with increase in depth of water.

FIG. 52. (a) West-east sketch transect across one-quarter of Loch Corby, Aberdeenshire, showing reedswamp and *Phragmites*-peat scarp leading down to floating-leaved and submerged linear-leaved communities on black silty mud (gyttja).

(b) Two sketch transects, on the east and west shores of Loch Maberry, Wigtownshire. Section A has accurate scales. Section B has an accurate vertical scale but the horizontal scale is reduced by a factor of about 7 (i.e. 1 cm. = 7 m. horizontal, = 1 m. vertical). Compare section A on exposed shore with section B on sheltered shore.

(c) Sketch transect (the horizontal scale being approximate only) northwards from middle of south shore of L. Croispol, on Durness, Sutherland, limestone. *Chara* spp. in the *Chara—Myriophyllum* soc. are listed in Table 45, p. 397.

Influence of substrate on degree of colonisation within given lochs. The total lack of reedswamp from stony or gravelly soils has already been remarked: likewise, the absence of all but *Eleocharis palustris* swamp from many sandy shores. Many submerged sands also arc devoid, or nearly devoid, of vegetation, e.g. a huge sandy area of L. Tulla less than 80 cm. deep, where the Tulla Water enters, and much of the shallow shore on the south-west corner of L. Lomond, below Balmaha. These are examples where plant colonisation is more or less prevented. Perhaps where there is plant cover some correlation exists within the photic zone between the type of soil and the amount of plant cover developed; low cover being taken here to imply some limit on colonisation.

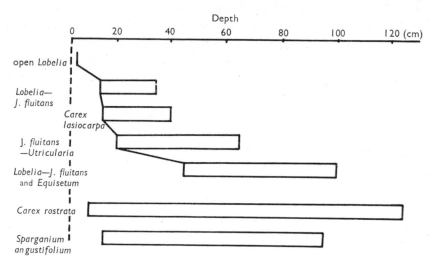

Fig. 53. Depth of deposits (over firm substrate) under named community-types and minimum depth of water in which they occur in L. Neldricken. Open *Lobelia* community is discontinuous on sandy bays and headlands all round loch. The last two communities are confined to shallows of the south-west corner and of the outlet of the loch.

The material for Fig. 54b was gathered at the open, south-east end of L. Kinardochy where substrates at a given depth appear very uniform. As the soil becomes finer with increasing depth, so does total plant cover increase, which suggests that factors controlling the distribution of soil-type also control the degree of plant cover. This is demonstrated more precisely with data from L. Tarff (Fig. 54c). Beneath the shallow water of an open bay on the south shore is firm, uncolonised, strongly rippled sand. To a depth of 120 cm. the proportion, by weight, of sand decreases while percentage plant cover increases, and three fairly distinct vegetation zones are crossed, the last being a *Littorella—J. fluitans* "turf" of about 90 per cent. cover on shallow mud. In deeper water, again, there is an *Isoetes* community with lower percentage cover and higher percentage sand in the soil.

The vegetation sequence with increasing depth of water in the shallow east end of L. Watten is: open *Eleocharis*→*P. filiformis*→open *Chara aspera*→80 per cent. cover at 140 cm. The soil in the shallow water is firm and comprises well packed, mainly small,

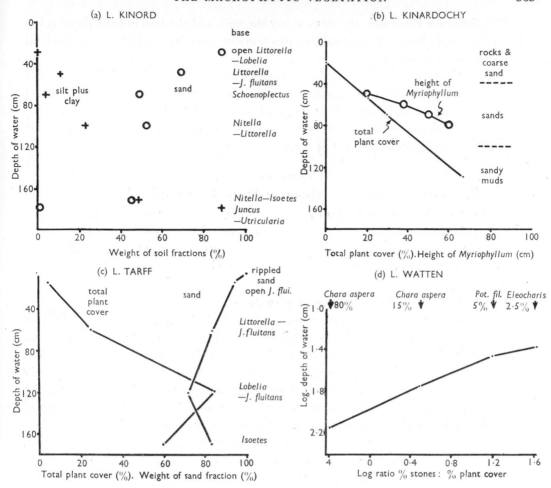

FIG. 54. (a) Decrease by weight in coarse, and increase in fine, fractions with increasing depth of water, at north-west end of L. Kinord, Aberdeenshire. Zonation is shown by predominant species above each soil sample.

(b) Effect of substrate on degree of colonisation. Data for (b) were gathered at the open south-east corner of L. Kinardochy; substrates appear uniform at a given depth. As soil becomes finer with increasing depth of water so does plant cover increase. The figure also shows that the height of *Myriophyllum* shoots increases with depth (cf. p. 364).

(c) Data gathered in shallow open bay on south shore of L. Tarff. To a depth of 120 cm., proportion by weight of sand decreases while percentage plant cover increases, and three fairly distinct vegetation zones are crossed.

(d) Data from the shallow east end of L. Watten, Caithness. Both "stones" and total plant cover were estimated as percentage of sample area (1 m²). The figures by the arrows indicate percentage plant cover at the given depths of water. Area covered by plants is correlated, at least in shallow water, with area covered by stones.

stones with sand between. At a water depth of 140 cm. the soil is softer and has few stones on the surface. In Fig 54d both "stones" and the plant cover are estimated as

percentage sample area. The four readings suggest:—$\log \dfrac{\%\ \text{stones}}{\%\ \text{plant cover}} \propto \log$ depth of water.

The shallower the water, the more stony the soil, and the less ground there is for plant colonisation. It may be inferred that this is not an open habitat but one in which all available space is colonised.

One of the ways in which plants themselves may be affected in shallow water is shown by some height data for *Equisetum fluviatile* on a gently sloping sandy beach at the northern end of L. Hacoin. The height of shoots above the water surface is proportional to the depth of water in the three available samples (and see, also, figures for height of *Myriophyllum* shoots in Fig. 54c).

TABLE 41

Equisetum shoot height in relation to depth of water at L. Hacoin

Shoot height above water (cm.)	.	.	45		18·6		c.5
Depth of water (cm.)	.	.	150		50		15
Ratio	.	.	.	.	.	0·30	0·37	0·33
Loch bottom material	.	.	mud			gravels	

Study of factors controlling distribution in given lochs

Turbulence and elutriation. Horizontal and vertical changes in aquatic vegetation have been noted; so have limits to colonisation in shallow and deep water. Causal factors responsible are now described, considering first those which influence the distribution of vegetation in shallow water well within the photic zone. Evidence already given (p. 359) suggests that, at a given depth and part of a particular loch within the photic zone, a single factor influences both fineness of material and the possible degree of plant colonisation, and that this factor is turbulence or wave action. As soon as a lake basin fills with water three processes begin: (a) erosion by turbulence of the shore line, (b) deposition of incoming sediment and, (c) colonisation by rooted and floating plants. A submerged shore line is out of harmony with its environment although, where the shore is more or less vertical, there will be little erosion. Otherwise, whatever the physical composition of the shore line, some erosion will start by a process of wave cutting and fragmentation. A beach is cut out of the existing shore and the eroded material is graded by a process of elutriation. The heaviest eroded material, such as gravel or sand, settles more or less *in situ*, or is only transported for very short distances; sandy shores may be presumed to have developed from material on the lake shore. Finer materials like silts or clays are carried back from the shore to be deposited at some depth, the finest material lying under the deepest water. This explanation fits the phenomena noted in the present account, none of which however, occurred in water more than 2 m. deep. In lochs as a whole it is found that brown muds tend to occur in deeper water than clays, with sand in the shallows. Full documentation of these trends are found in Caspari (1910), West (1910b) and Slack (1954).

In terrace formation, the sand cut from the beach is deposited on the gently sloping littoral shelf which is continuous with the beach but composed of transported material. This most frequently supports open *Littorella—Lobelia* (viz. L. Maberry, and p. 321).

The shelf stops abruptly at a steep slope which in Scottish lochs is most often composed of coarse fragments, from 5 cm. diameter up to 30 cm. or more, which may be transported material and/or the boulders of glacial deposits from which the clay has been washed out. This steep, almost always uncolonised, slope merges eventually with the bottom muds of the basin floor. Further examples of terracing are given by Pearsall (1918, 1920) for the English Lakes.

Terracing is really an extreme manifestation of the sorting effect of waves. All submerged shore lines are eroded but elutriation effects, of course, occur without the development of marked terracing, as was shown earlier for smooth, gentle slopes of uniform topography, e.g. at L. Watten, L. Kinardochy and L. Tarff.

From what will be said, in the next section, on the relationship of turbulence, area and depth, terracing may be expected to be most continuous around the largest, deepest lochs and more or less absent from small, shallow lochs.

Turbulence in relation to area and depth of water. Wedderburn (1910) first showed, from a study of vertical temperature distribution at various points along the axis of a loch, that a wind blowing in one direction for some time over a thermally stratified lake moved warm surface water to the lee side. This deepened the epilimnion there and tilted the isotherms in the thermocline. When the wind dropped the tilt became unstable and the isotherms moved back to the horizontal. If they swung past the horizontal they set up a series of oscillations or temperature seiches, or standing waves (Ruttner, 1953). Mortimer (1942, p. 176) showed that a relationship exists between the dimensions of a lake basin, its exposure to wind, and the mean eddy diffusion coefficient, (A), in the hypolimnion. In other words, wind-generated displacement of surfaces of equal density can induce temperature seiches of sufficient magnitude in the hypolimnion to produce the observed degree of turbulence. For eleven lakes Mortimer shows that the degree of turbulence, or coefficient (A), is proportional to depth and area.

This supports, at least for larger bodies of water, the supposition made earlier that volume of water, or some function of volume, influences, through its effect on turbulence and hence soils, the distribution of reedswamp around lochs. Since shallow bodies of water lack thermal stratification, turbulence will be more or less independent of depth but it will still depend on area, as the height of waves seems to vary with the square root of the "fetch" of the waves. Two consequences of the relationship between turbulence and area and depth are, firstly, that as the area and depth of lakes increase so does the depth to which wave action penetrates; secondly, thermal stratification and its possible biological consequences are lessened, particularly in deep lochs like Morar where turbulence remains too great throughout the year for marked seasonal development of thermal stratification (see p. 369).

Aspect. Whenever a body of water is large enough for strong development of turbulence, the aspect of any part of a shore line will become important, for it may determine whether, and what, plants will colonise that area. This has already been exemplified by brief reference to swamp development in sheltered bays or inlets of large bodies of water like Lunga Water or L. Clunie or L. Ness (p. 359). The different soil and vegetation types on the various headlands and bays of L. Neldricken (p. 361) and L. Tarff (p. 322), or the east and west sides of L. Maberry (p. 360) may also be interpreted in terms of exposure or shelter. L. Clunie may now be considered in slightly more detail.

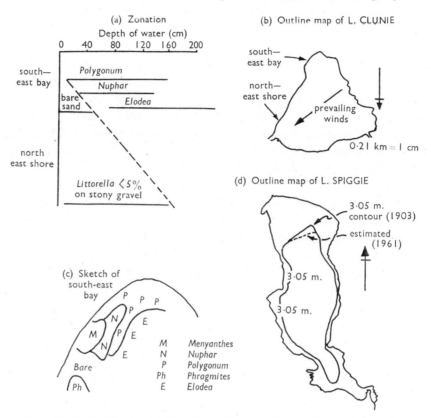

FIG. 55. Loch Clunie. (a) Zonation with depth in south-east bay and on the north-east shore. Showing the qualitative effect of aspect and turbulence on the distribution of soils and vegetation; (b) outline map; and (c) sketch of south-east bay.

(d) Loch Spiggie. Outline map, showing 10 ft. contour line, from Bathymetrical Survey (1910). The water to the north of this line covers a deposit of shell sand which slopes gently to a depth of 1 m. and then very steeply to the 3·05 m. (10 ft.) contour. The shell sand and deeper lying black mud at 3·05 m. bears vegetation like limestone (viz. Durness) lochs. The southern end supports reedswamp, floating-leaved and submerged sociations absent from the exposed north shore.

This loch in Perthshire has a surface area of about 52 hectares shaped like a rough equilateral triangle with one point to the south (Fig. 55a, b, c). Most of the soil of the shallow bay in the south-west corner is colonised to a depth of more than 2 m. There are some small areas of bare sand from o to 50 cm. depth. At the north-east corner of the loch fully exposed for the length of the loch from the west and south-west, substrate particles are larger, being gravel or stones, and reach a depth of 1·5 m., with less than 5 per cent.

plant cover provided by open *Littorella—Lobelia*. This example shows the qualitative effect of aspect and degree of turbulence upon the distribution of vegetation, directly and through its effect on soil distribution.

The second detailed example is L. Spiggie in south Shetland. Almost one-quarter of the surface of L. Spiggie comprises a shell-sand deposit in less than 100 cm. depth of water; beyond that contour the deposit slopes abruptly to deeper water (Fig. 55d). The loch is impounded by a barrier composed of this sand which continues northwards for some 40 m. to the Bay of Scousburgh and north-west for about 10 m., also to the sea. This sandy shelf is mainly occupied from below depths of water of 50 cm. to the beginning of a sharp dip at a depth of 1 m. by the *Chara aspera—Myriophyllum* sociation. Near the shore there are local communities of *Potamogeton filiformis* and *P. pectinatus*. The only emergent vegetation is *Eleocharis palustris*. In deeper water, around 150–300 cm., the soil is soft, black mud colonised mainly by *Fontinalis*. This end of the loch is like a Durness limestone loch (cf. Croispol, p. 360). The rest of the loch overlies a shallow valley and is floored by boulder clay. Its southern end is narrower and is entered by the Burn of Hillwell, draining hill land. This part of the loch (some 1/10 of the area just described) possesses a number of reedswamp and submerged societies of which the species are quite absent from the exposed shell-sand deposits of the north end, e.g. *Carex rostrata, Equisetum fluviatile, Phalaris, Potamogeton natans—J. fluitans*. These communities with a number of dominants common to both ends form a mosaic on coarse sandy, to organic, soils. *P. filiformis* and *Chara—Myriophyllum* sociations occur on very limited sand in shallow water.

The contrast then lies between submerged sociations of open *Littorella—Lobelia* or *P. filiformis*, on sandy shores—shore of elutriation, and floating-leaved and varied submerged vegetation on less inorganic soils—soils rather of deposition. This in part reflects the existence in a given loch of coarser sediments at the top of an exposed shore than of a sheltered shore; it may also reflect the inability of certain species to become established and to grow under turbulent condition.

Changes in growth-form and limits on vegetation with depth. In this account stands dominated by widespread species like *Phragmites, Carex rostrata* and *Juncus fluitans* are divided on floristic bases into community-types that follow gradients in depth of water. Certain sequences of swamp and fen sociations of various species showed a tendency to recur along gradients of depth of water in different localities. Finally, species-poor swamp, and moss- and herb-rich fen, are partly differentiated on a basis of depth of water. All these facts imply a causal connection between the depth of the water and its correlated factors, and the distribution of emergent aquatic and other community-types.

To extend the inquiry to floating-leaved and submerged community-types, the data on depth of water for all community-types presented in Table 39 (p. 357) could be used, but this depth distribution is based on mean values, themselves derived from samples of various sizes. Instead, the distribution, in even-sized classes for depth of water, of 382 quadrats classified by growth form of the predominant species together with twenty samples for which depth data alone are known (Fig. 56a), may be considered. The sample distribution is then seen to be strongly biased in favour of seasonally waterlogged soils and submerged soils of shallow water. More than half the quadrats occur with water levels from −40 cm. to +40 cm. and most of them are dominated by

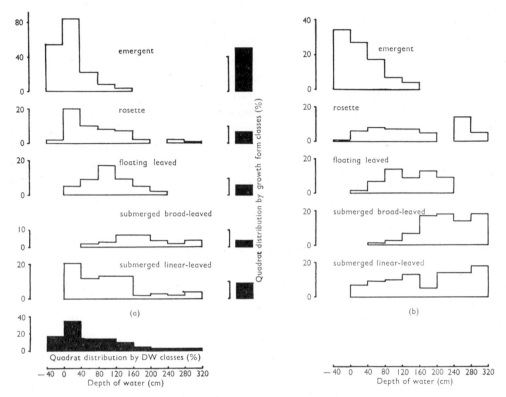

FIG. 56. (a) The distribution in (40 cm.) depth of water classes of 382 quadrats grouped by the predominant species into five growth-form classes (a sixth, helophytes, is excluded) (see Table 39). Since emergent aquatics account for 47 per cent. (with helophytes 51 per cent.) of the quadrats, the frequency scale of this group is halved in the histogram. Also given are the quadrat distribution by growth form classes and by depth of water (DW) classes.

(b) Quadrats grouped by growth forms of predominant species and arranged in proportional depth of water classes which corrects the bias towards shallow water. (It cannot overcome the largely subjective choice of sample area of predominant species). Assuming parity of sampling by depth of water classes, there is an emergent, floating-leaved and submerged broad-leaved sequence. Rosette-types occur as dominants at all depths while submerged linear-leaved dominants are slightly more abundant in deep water.

emergent aquatics which themselves total nearly 50 per cent of all quadrats. About one-fifth of the quadrats occur in water more than 1·2 m. deep and they are fairly evenly divided among growth-form classes. The peaks and distributions of the frequency of the emergent, floating-leaved and submerged, broad-leaved groups maintain that order in relation to increasing depth of water, but those of the rosette and linear-leaved

PLATE 50. *Chara* beds, with some emergent *Eleocharis palustris*, at the south end of L. Croispol on the Durness limestone (August, 1961). The clarity of this loch is exceptional for Scotland.

PLATE 51. Emergent and floating-leaved vegetation in the north-east corner of L. an Ordain. *Carex rostrata* and *Equisetum fluviatile* with *Sparganium angustifolium* (floating-leaves) and beyond, some *Potamogeton natans* (September 1960).

PLATE 52. Reedswamp and floating-leaved vegetation on L. an Loin, Wester Ross. Upper half of loch covered by *Nymphaea alba* (with some *Schoenoplectus lacustris*) its near margin marked by dark, smooth water. Scattered *Schoenoplectus* (from *J. fluitans*—*Utricularia*) in foreground.

PLATE 53. Loch Kinord, Aberdeenshire, showing part of reed-swamp on the west shore consisting here mainly of *C. rostrata*—*Menyanthes* with the only clump of *Typha latifolia* in the left fore-ground and a belt of flowering *Phragmites communis* in the middle distance (September 1960).

PLATE 55. Part of ungrazed reedswamp and carr at L. Avich, Argyll (note grazed slope behind). Three tussocks of *Carex paniculata*, 1·5 to 2 m. high with *Salix caprea* and *S. aurita* behind and the latter in foreground. *Phragmites, Equisetum fluviatile, Filipendula* and *Lythrum salicaria* are in front. The water-table is at the soil surface. This ungrazed area is poor in *J. articulatus* which predominates in the adjoining grazed area from which *Carex paniculata* and *Phragmites* are absent (see Plate 56) (July, 1959).

PLATE 54. *Phragmites—Littorella* sociation on sandy soil at L. an Daimh.

PLATE 58. Loch na h'Achlaise, Rannoch Moor (a poor water loch), shallow, ponded by drift lying on schist and granite. Open *Carex rostrata* sociation in shallow water on dark brown sandy soil with 10 per cent. C. In even shallower water this is replaced by a *C. rostrata—Sphagnum cuspidatum, S. palustre*, community (September, 1961).

PLATE 59. L. an Choin, Inverness-shire. General view of *Betula* carr (cf. Plate 60, 61) developed at the west end of the loch. The foreground and the shore is occupied by a dense belt of *Carex rostrata—Menyanthes* with a *Menyanthes* society crossing into a dense *Nymphaea alba* zone (see zonation data in Fig. 47, p. 322) (September, 1960).

PLATE 60

L. an Choin, Inverness-shire. *Carex lasiocarpa* and tall *Myrica* in the shoreward part of the *Betula* scrub.

PLATE 61. L. an Choin, Inverness-shire. *Myrica—Calluna* sociation with scattered *Betula* and occasional *Carex lasiocarpa* (landward of Plate 59).

PLATE 62

L. Avich. Tussock of *Carex paniculata* with scattered *Phragmites*, in front of *Salix caprea* and *Salix cinerea* ssp. *atrocinerea* with foreground of *Lychnis, Sonchus, Filipendula* (cf. Plates 59 and 64).

PLATE 63. *Carex paniculata* tussock, 2 m. high, with young epipytic specimen of *Betula pubescens*: *Athyrium filix-femina Filipendula* and *Phragmites*. Ungrazed carr at West end of L. Avich, Argyll (August, 1959).

PLATE 64

Alder-wood on alluvium at west end of L. Meiklie with extensive
meadow of *Deschampsia cespitosa* (Table 38, p. 358), and some
Carex vesicaria in foreground on slightly damper soil (September
1960).

PLATE 65. General view of L. an Ordain, Inverness-shire, a kettle-hole in fluvio-glacial clays. This is a poor-water loch (September, 1960).

PLATE 66. View south across part of delta formed by entry of R. Urquhart into L. Ness (1960). Growth of shrubs to right of picture prevented photograph being taken at West's exact site, identified by persistence of one of the few colonies of *Alisma plantago-aquatica* on this bay. The spit in the middle distance of West's photograph is now wooded while the pool in the foreground is now *Carex rostrata—Acrocladium* and *C. rostrata—Menyanthes*. *Alisma* is much restricted. The pool is filled with sandy sediment, with only 6·1 per cent. C, 0·1 per cent. N (cf. with West's Fig. 19, Plate 67).

TE 67. West, G., Fig. 19, *Proc. roy. soc. Edinb.*, **25**, (1904–05). rsh scene at Urquhart Bay, looking out towards L. Ness. *nyanthes trifoliata* in foreground. *Phalaris arundinacea* on right left. Groups of *Alisma plantago* in centre, on the left of them, *ex rostrata. Alnus glutinosa* on both sides; same again in middle ance, with *Equisetum limosum*. Dead tree washed up on the re. Cultivated land on opposite side of bay.

PLATE 68. L. Uanagan (1960). A stream enters the loch at left foreground and a detrital fan extends out to the *Schoenoplectus* stand. This has developed considerably in 56 years, as has the open *Carex rostrata* sociation nearer the shore. The stream entry too has become silted up. (This photograph is more restricted than West's, cf. his Fig. 35, Plate 69).

PLATE 69. West, G., Fig. 35, *Proc. roy. soc. Edinb.*, **25**, (1904–05). L. Uanagan. View south-west to north-east, showing the various zones of vegetation described in the text.

PLATE 70. L. Uanagan (1960). View taken from north of Plate 68, the stream entering beyond the right foreground. Further from this stream than the previous area, there is little development of *Schoenoplectus lacustris*, while the marginal open *Carex rostrata* stand in the foreground has not developed at all (cf. with West's Fig. 33, Plate 71).

PLATE 71. West, G., Fig. 33, *Proc. roy. soc. Edinb.*, **25**, (1904–05). West end of L. Uanagan, with *Scirpus lacustris* growing out in water. *Eriophorum angustifolium, Carex* and other marsh plants in the foreground.

PLATE 72. L. a'Mheig (1960). At an altitude of 1200 ft., this loch receives drainage from a peat-covered granite plateau. As far as the farther end of the flat island the water is shallow and turbid, beyond, the water is deeper. A small stream enters from the left and drains to the right. The islands comprise *Carex lasiocarpa—Myrica*, the shallows between bearing open *Carex rostrata*, etc. The crescent beyond the sedges is *Potamogeton natans*. There appears to have been no change in 54 years, except that the "carr" on the big island is moribund (cf. with West's Fig. 52, Plate 73).

PLATE 73
West, G., Fig. 52, *Proc. roy. soc. Edinb.*, **25**, (1904-05). Loch a'Mheig. *Carex rostrata* advancing into the loch in crescent formation.

PLATE 74. L. na Ba Ruaidhe (1960). This loch lacks any large affluent. The foreground mainly contains open *Carex rostrata* sociation, while the crescent in middle distance comprises *Nymphaea alba* with *Equisetum fluviatile* in shallower water on its right (and submerged broad-leaved pondweeds in deeper water at left). Emergent and floating-leaved vegetation has not changed in 54 years and some of the carr has died (cf. with West's Fig. 71, Plate 75).

PLATE 75. West, G., Fig. 71, *Proc. roy. soc. Edinb.*, **25**, (1904–05). L. na Ba Ruaidhe. View of a western bay, showing *Carex rostrata*, *Phragmites communis*, *Equisetum limosum* and *Nymphaea alba* encroaching on the water in crescent formation. Islands with dwarf birch and alder.

PLATE 76. L. Tarff (1960). The small effluent from this loch leaves in right foreground. The open *Carex rostrata* there and in the sheltered area behind the island (seen in detail in Plate 57) has not developed at all in 54 years (cf. with West's Fig. 94, Plate 77).

PLATE 77. West, G., Fig. 94, *Proc. roy. soc. Edinb.*, **25**, (1904–05). A general view of L. Tarff, looking north-east, showing wooded islands and *Carex* associations in shallow places.

groups do not. Their high frequencies in shallow water may partly reflect the sampling method, one bias of which can be removed by multiplying or dividing the samples to produce equal proportions in each class of water depth (Fig. 56b), although this does not, of course, overcome the largely subjective choice of the sample areas for predominant species. In this histogram the emergent, floating-leaved and submerged, broad-leaved sequence is again evident, while rosette forms now occur uniformly at all water depths. Submerged, linear-leaved types occur, perhaps, slightly more abundantly in water more than 2 m. deep, but only twenty-four, or 6 per cent., of all quadrats were recorded here. It seems probable that the rosette form is not causally connected with depth of water or accompanying factors while the linear-leaved groups, a collection of bryophytes, Characeae, *Potamogeton* species and *Juncus fluitans* is perhaps too heterogenous to have any adaptive meaning. The data of both Fig. 56a and Fig. 56b show that the submerged broad-leaved group, all *Potamogeton* species, occur most abundantly as dominants of deeper water which suggests a correlation between this growth form and factors such as diminished turbulence or light.

From the zonation data of Figs. 47 and 49 (pp. 322, 338) it can be seen that more than 90 per cent. of the lochs have communities in which there is overlap in the range of depth of water in which they occur. In shallow water there may be, say, seven communities; in deep water there is one. From very different depths in different lochs but at a more or less consistent depth, so far as could be judged, within a given loch a single species eventually predominates. Thus, for example, in discussing the communities formed by *Fontinalis* spp., *Isoetes lacustris*, etc. (p. 325), it was noted that stands in the most deeply colonised zones tended most often to be composed of one of these species and that, where limits of colonisation are known to have been reached, these are always pure stands.

Temperature decreases with depth but it may be questioned whether it is ever likely, in Scotland, to limit vegetation before a factor such as light does. Some effects of thermal stratification may be studied by comparing temperature data collected during the Bathymetrical Survey from L. Baile a Ghobhainn, Lismore, a limestone loch of moderate size like L. Croispol, and L. Morar, the deepest and third largest loch in Scotland. L. Baile is 1·13 km. long and 13·5 hectares in extent with a mean depth of 11·89 m. and a maximum depth of 26·84m. Serial temperature readings over the deepest soundings, on 12th August 1904, showed a range from surface to bottom of 8·3°C. The full set of readings indicate a thermocline below 3·05 m. and a temperature of 12·1°C. at 12·2 m. Vegetation, often dense and formed solely by *Fontinalis*, occurs to this depth of 12·2 m. which is the maximum colonised depth recorded for Scotland by West (1910b). In other words, even in a loch supporting rooted plants at the greatest depth of any in Scotland, temperature seems unlikely to limit the downward penetration of vegetation.

A series of temperatures were taken on L. Morar from the surface to the bottom at 310·18 m. on 29th April, 3rd September 1887: in July 1902 and in March and October 1903. Before the onset of stratification, the temperature range in April over 310·18 m. was about 8°C., the same range reached over 26·84 m. in the smaller L. Baile. L. Morar

2 A

has brown water typical of lochs in the palaeogenic Highlands, in which vegetation may, as at L. Ness, penetrate to a depth of 7·62 m. There is also, in L. Morar, compared with L. Baile, a more gradual change in temperature with depth from 3·2°C. at the surface in July. Temperature seems, therefore, even less likely to limit the downward penetration of rooted plants in this far commoner type of loch. Pearsall (1920, p. 169) concludes from a similar type of evidence that temperature does not limit downward penetration of water plants in the English Lakes.

The relationship has already been discussed earlier (p. 316) between stratification, trophic status of water, and the orthograde and clinograde curve of oxygen concentration with increasing depth of water. The present study adds no new facts to this and it can only be repeated here that shallow, rich-water lakes readily produce black reducing muds which may, due to the presence of dense plankton and other plant growth, to intense oxidation, and to oxygen depletion at the mud surface, develop into iron sulphide muds. This perhaps explains the absence of rooted aquatic plants in certain black muds within the photic or littoral zone, viz. Rescobie and Carlingwark lochs. The sparse colonisation of some brown muds in sheltered areas of poor water lochs possibly results from accumulation of allochthonous organic matter under conditions which, on the mud surface at least, are more or less permanently oxidised and deficient in available nutrients.

Light decreases with depth of water and this may account for the accompanying, consistent decrease in the number of community-types and species until the limits of colonisation are eventually reached. No attempt was made to measure underwater light intensity during the present survey since most lochs were only visited once and because of its wide variation between lochs in the quality and intensity of light, as deduced from considering those lochs in Table 35 (p. 324) where colonisation has not reached their maximum depth. The clear limestone lochs Baile and Croispol are colonised to the greatest depth, brown water (poor to moderately rich) lochs show shallower limits, while rich water (plankton-rich) lochs have the shallowest limits to colonisation. There is also seasonal variations in the quality and intensity of light at any given depth in many lochs while FeS muds develop, within photic limits, in stagnant, shallow rich-water lochs. It may at least be concluded that light is more likely than temperature to impose limits on vegetation with depth. Factors controlling changes in community-types and growth-forms with increasing depth of water, as distinct from the absolute limits of all rooted vegetation, include changes in quality and decreasing intensity of light, with decreasing turbulence and soil particle size. These are discussed in the next section.

Discussion and conclusions

The *P. filiformis—Chara* association is typical of water of far higher alkalinity than that in which the *Lobelia—J. fluitans* association is found. Sociations of both groups were only seen in two of the lochs studied, and only over a very small area of one of these lochs (p. 325) did *P. filiformis* and *J. fluitans* occur together. Then *P. praelongus* is apparently typical of water rich in electrolytes while *Subularia*, for example, is the opposite. If it be assumed that between water and soil a dynamic equilibrium more or less always exists despite known instances of wide annual fluctuations in the composition of the water, the first conclusion is that the chemistry of the water of a particular loch determines whether a species can grow in it, if seeds and suitable space are available. A loch is a single habitat in this respect ecologically, except that under conditions of a limiting supply in the water of a particular anion or cation, a silt might become critically more important than a sand (see p. 311).

The frequently high variation in water chemistry in a given body of water, already alluded to, may partly explain the fact that few aquatic species can be categorised as calcicole or calcifuge, although more refined water analyses may eventually reveal other causal factors. Thus, through the use of a compositional index of stands (the value of each stand being the product of the relative frequency of each species and its joint occurrence index number), Swindale and Curtis (1957) showed distinct correlations with conductivity, content of nitrate ions, etc. Stands with high indices have high conductivities, high nitrate content and a high pH while stands with low indices show the converse.

Provided that both the nutrient status of the water is suitable for a given species and that disseminules and space are available, the factors controlling species or community distribution within any single body of water may next be considered. In their survey of aquatic vegetation in Wisconsin, Swindale and Curtis (Curtis, 1959, p. 396) were unable to correlate light measurements with community distribution, even in a single lake. Curtis, none-the-less, considered the depth factor important in submerged aquatic communities almost entirely because of its relationship to light intensity. Pearsall (1920, p. 168) considered that light conditions did not determine the distribution of the vegetation except by imposing limits on the downward extension of water plants. From several direct and indirect lines of evidence he concluded that the silting factor underlay the distribution of all types of aquatic vegetation found in the English Lakes: "the distribution of aquatic plants in the English Lakes is primarily governed by the nature of the substrate."

To consider further the relative importance of substrate, hydrophytes themselves must be studied. Hydrophytes of all types share a plentiful supply of aerenchyma, presumably in response to low oxygen levels in the water in which they are wholly, or partly, submerged (but see Williams and Barber, 1961). A distinction must next be made between emergent and submerged aquatics in that it is mainly the root system of the emergent aquatic that is submerged, not the whole plant. Accordingly, of other structural features ascribed to hydrophytes in general (see, for example, Arber (1921), Strasburger (1930), Weaver and Clements (1929), Daubenmire (1953), Sinnot (1960)), only those features are considered here which are held to be typical of submerged aquatics and submerged parts of floating-leaved aquatics. These are (1) absence of cuticle from stem and leaves; (2) highest concentration of chloroplasts in the epidermal layer, and chlorenchyma of shade, or sponge, type; (3) leaves generally thin, a few cells thick and/or much dissected; (4) small amount of water-conducting tissue; particularly noticeable, in stems and petioles, in relation to the size of the cortical region; (5) small size of roots:

"rudimentary development of a root system" (Steward and Sutcliffe, 1959, p. 434) and absence of root hairs (Daubenmire, 1953, p. 148) except in mud (Weaver and Clements, 1929, p. 338); or total absence of roots.

The first three features must ensure maximum rate of photosynthesis in diffuse light and maximum rate of respiration at low oxygen levels. The facts of free absorption of ions from, and discharge of ions to, solutions by the leaves or shoots of submerged plants have, of course, been utilised for many years in the study of salt uptake (e.g. *Elodea*, *Vallisneria*, etc.) and may have led some authors (e.g. Sutcliffe, 1962, p. 21) to maintain that submerged aquatics obtain most of their mineral requirements from the surrounding water through their leaves. The last two generalisations mentioned above, small size of water conducting tissue and of root system, might appear to support this contention. Concerning water conducting tissue Haberlandt (1914), for example, showed that the fused xylem strands in *Elodea*, *Zannichellia* and *Najas* were reduced to a central intercellular passage surrounded by phloem (see also Arber, 1920, p. 208). However, by comparing the stem anatomy of plants of a species of *Achyranthes* which were rooted in soil, with their shoots in water-deficient, and water-saturated, atmospheres, but not in liquid water, Eberhart (in Sinnott, 1960, p. 330) demonstrated that excess atmospheric water increased the size of cortex and pith and reduced the development of xylem and parenchyma. Thus the stem xylem of rooted aquatics may be reduced when the shoots are grown in either liquid, or excess atmospheric, water. Since the plants with their shoots in the water-saturated atmosphere must still obtain salts via their roots, there is not necessarily any connection between reduced xylem and route of salt entry.

Apart from the fact that some submerged and floating-leaved aquatics entirely lack roots there seems to be little evidence that most remaining aquatics have "reduced" roots. The roots of small plants of exposed soils in shallow water may even be larger than those of bigger less exposed plants. The claim that they lack root-hairs may also be dubious; Pearsall (1918, p. 82) lists eighteen aquatics on which he (or Pond) has observed root-hairs and Arber (1920) gives further examples, while the present author has observed their extensive development on *Potamogeton × schweinfurthii* in Uganda. Aquatics are also said to have reduced leaves (Weaver and Clements, p. 339) but the leaves of *Potamogeton lucens* or *P. praelongus* can reach 20×6 and $18 \times 4 \cdot 5$ cm. while the stems can exceed 2–5 m. in length. These two broad-leaved species occur in deep and, therefore, less turbulent water, and dissected or linear-leaves may be considered to have surface areas that are reduced in response to mechanical stress, just as plants of *Myriophyllum alterniflorum* may become shorter, in a given loch, as the substrate enters shallower and more exposed water (p. 363). It has already been noted, however, that many linear-leaved species occur in both deep and shallow water.

The evidence for salt uptake by roots of submerged aquatics is now examined. The question of the existence (Arber, 1920), or not (Crafts, *et al.*, 1947), of a transpiration stream in submerged, rooted aquatics is largely irrelevant in the matter of salt uptake since root pressure could presumably achieve this. There is some experimental evidence, albeit indirect, of root uptake by such plants. Titcomb (1924, in Weaver and Clements,

1929) and Snell and Pond (1907, 1905, in Pearsall, 1918, p. 82) showed that aquatic plants growing in the same water developed better when rooted in "rich humus-filled soil" than when they grew in sand; Pearsall (1918, p. 82) listing six such species. Many species, including *Elodea*, have been shown in experiments to acquire sufficient nutrients for normal growth only when rooted in the substratum (Brown, 1913, Pond, 1905, in Weaver and Clements, 1929; Misra, 1938, p. 411). Without precise specification of waters and substrates, however, no general conclusion can be drawn from such results, although some of them imply that the plants depend ultimately on ions derived from the substrate rather than from the water around their shoots and leaves.

Where there has been a positive response, as in the case of plants rooted in "rich humus-filled" soil, some explanation is possible in terms of the Jenny-Lips contact exchange theory. The roots of a plant growing in this "rich humus-filled" soil (i.e. a soil having colloids with a high degree of metal ion saturation) are able, by exchange at the root surface, to utilise adsorbed reserves on the soil micelle which may not be available to the surrounding water, especially where there is even in summer, as in unstratified lakes, an interposed layer of oxidised mud. A substrate might thus supply to a plant an ion which is no longer present in the water during the height of the growing season. Anions, except when they constitute (as suggested) ions in seasonally short supply, may as readily enter by shoot or leaves. It is, however, possible that cations, being often relatively insoluble, enter mainly through the roots so that a soil rich in colloids with some degree of metal ion saturation possesses, even under normal conditions, advantages not found in, say, a sand. So the nature of colonisable soil (such as percentage silt or clay) may be important in any one water regime.

I return now to Pearsall's (1921, p. 267) conclusions "that the distribution of submerged aquatics in the (English) Lakes depends on the character of the substrate rather than upon the variation in the composition of the lake waters or in the physical conditions of the habitat." Although no alkalinity data are given by Tansley (1949), comparison of the "hardness" classes of the English Lakes and East Anglian Broads indicates that the waters of the richest lake, Esthwaite, are just "moderately rich". In other words, the variation in composition of the water over submerged soils in the English Lakes is far less than that in the Scottish lochs examined in the present study. For, where soils were taken from a number of different lochs, soil properties measured under any species did not differ significantly from those under any other. Thus, to paraphrase an earlier discussion (p. 311); there is a greater chance in lakes with fairly similar water chemistry, that the mean values of soil features under two species, such as fineness of texture or cation-exchange capacity, will differ significantly, than there is for similar features in lakes with different water chemistry. The English Lakes may, in this respect, approximate to a single water regime.

A case has been made for the importance of certain substrates within one water regime, and substrate unquestionably influences the distribution of rooted aquatic vegetation in particular lochs insofar as it determines, through their size, a particle limit above which colonisation is not possible. However, soil particle size, turbulence and light decrease with depth and vegetation, which varies with depth, may be said to vary with all these factors. Likewise, in shallow water soil texture and turbulence vary simultaneously so that, while vegetation may change with either, they cannot *a priori* be separated. Provided that there are particles of a suitable size to be colonised, the presence or absence of rooted vegetation in a loch may be determined as much by the effect of turbulence on establishment, or subsequent development, as by the texture of the particles and their chemical properties. For example, amongst submerged species, the association of *Fontinalis* with rocks in shallow water and with soft muds in deep water, may rather reflect the abundance of free CO_2 in these two zones (p. 326) than the nature of the substrate, while *Nitella opaca* is associated with soft mud and with the low light intensity found in the calm, deeper water where such mud accumulates. The growth at considerable depths of large, submerged species with long shoots and broad leaves may partly result from decreased turbulence. Linear-leaved pondweeds as a group cover a wide range of depths and so, of the broader-leaved types, does *P. gramineus* although it tends to nanism in shallow water. Broad-leaved species like *P. ×zizii* or *P. praelongus* seem unable to predominate in water less than 150 cm. deep and their association with a particular soil type may reflect the connection of fine mud and tall plants with decreased turbulence and low light intensity.

The interrelationship between these factors and possible plant response are summarised in the following figure (Fig. 57):—

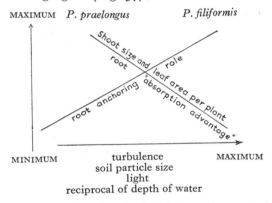

FIG. 57. Inter-relationships between various environmental factors and the possible response of two species of *Potamogeton* (*P. praelongus* and *P. filiformis*).

Boulders and other coarse substrates apart, soil may not be deduced with certainty to be the limiting, or controlling, factor in the distribution of any emergent species. *Equisetum fluviatile* and *Schoenoplectus lacustris* are a species pair of similar depth range and, often, of water chemistry. Their negative association may be attributed either to requirements for different soils or to competition, similar to that which determines the predominance of *Schoenoplectus* or *J. fluitans* in a particular area. However, *Equisetum fluviatile* and *Eleocharis palustris* both occupy submerged, sandy, exposed shores with almost mutually exclusive depth ranges while *Carex rostrata* and *Equisetum fluviatile* may both grow in submerged deep mud (at Neldricken), the former reaching depths of water up to 60 cm., the latter to 150 cm. Causal explanations of the type of zonation displayed at, for example, L. Maberry (Fig. 52b), Spiggie (Fig. 55d), Clunie (Fig. 55c, d), etc., are, therefore, bound to be tentative.

The distribution of vegetation and limits to its colonisation, within given lochs, appear to be controlled by:—

1. Turbulence and elutriation which when extreme may both prevent colonisation and produce (2).
2. Coarse substrata.
3. Turbidity limiting the photic zone through plankton and organic and inorganic sediments.
4. Depth of water (linked to (2)).
5. Steepness of slope, often linked to (1).
6. Highly reducing muds and, according to Pearsall (1920) and Misra (1938), certain highly organic, but not necessarily reducing, muds also inhibit colonisation.

It may be concluded that in many lochs shallow water communities are diverse because soils and turbulence, as determined by aspect and volume of water, vary. In deep water, soils and vegetation become more uniform with a diminished range in turbulence and as light becomes progressively more limiting. Moreover the water chemistry of any loch usually determines whether a species can grow in it; thereafter, since particle-size, turbulence, light and vegetation may all vary together, and since hydrophytes may obtain nutrients by root or shoot, substrate can rarely be deduced as the primary factor governing distribution.

Scottish lochs: the general environment

The lochs described in the present account have almost all originated as the result of glacial activity. These lochs fall into two groups, those formed in glacial rock basins and in drift basins. Many examples in the first category are listed by Peach and Horne (1910) as true rock basins but a number of these, following Hutchinson's (1957) classification, may be further distinguished as fjord lakes, typically having oversteepened sides, e.g. L. Stack, L. Morar, and as ice-scour lakes, on shattered or jointed mature surfaces, e.g. lochans on the Torridonian sandstone, Applecross. The glacial rock basin group is predominantly Highland and, since it includes the deepest and most of the large lochs in the country, must contain by far the greater volume of fresh water in Scotland. The principal drift basin type studied is the kettle-hole (Peach and Horne) or kettle (Hutchinson) lake formed in cavities left by melting outwash, or fluvio-glacial material, discharged from pre-existing valleys. These lochs occur in the Highlands, e.g. Calder, Gamhna, Watten, an Ordain (Plate 65), and the lowlands, e.g. Lochs Leven, Lindores, Rescobie, but their vegetation does not, of course, exhibit a corresponding "highland" or "lowland" character. Of the remaining smaller categories in which the present lochs can be classified, mention need only be made of the solution lakes represented by the Durness limestone lochs (Plate 50): the other types, i.e. lake associated with shore lines, etc., belong biologically to the larger categories, so far as rooted aquatics are concerned.

A rock basin may, or may not, have a deposit of glacial drift or alluvium. Drift may be continuous or it may be confined to the lower part of the basin which, once the basin is filled, comes to lie below the limits of extreme turbulence. Rock-basin lakes tend, therefore, to possess little or no drift and hence colloidal inorganic material for redistribution, compared with basins in the other categories which are either drift-basins or else, for other reasons, have surfaces in which particles of small size predominate.

The size range of incoming particles will depend on the geology of the catchment area and to some extent on the volume and rate of flow of incoming water. Since the basin became filled upon the retreat of the ice, it is unlikely that, away from the deltas, particles much larger than those of 2 mm. diameter will have been transported any distance within the loch. In regions of soft sedimentary rock, such as calciferous sand-stones, or of glacial drift, the incoming sediment must consist mainly of clays and silts. In hard rock regions, as over much of the Highlands, incoming sediment must be largely organic, either in the form of plant debris or of colloidal, or dissolved, matter. Material added to that existing on the substrate of the original rock basin and in its water tends, therefore, except in the case of agriculturally improved land, to perpetuate the original properties. An ice-scour lake starts with no available sediment and particles must be produced by waves cutting the bedrock. The inflow may drain similarly scoured country bearing, in all probability, scattered bog vegetation and is itself, therefore, largely organic and nutrient-poor. Much the same could be said for many fjord lakes. By contrast a lake basin in a kettle-hole in fluvio-glacial drift of calciferous sandstone origin will at once provide readily transportable fine material and soluble matter to the water filling it. To this is added, in the inflow, similar material.

The materials on which waves act in the process of erosion vary from silts and clays to bare jointed rock surfaces. Action on the latter produces large rock fragments, such as are commonly found on the shores of most rock basins. As the area and depth of lakes increase so does the depth to which wave action, elutriation and coarse substrata penetrate. In large rock basins, therefore, strong turbulence will tend to remove any fine drift material to considerable depths and coarse sand will provide the smallest particles. These may be limited, as at Lurgainn, to sheltered bays, while boulders and stone fragments with no infilling are a common feature at, or below, the waterline of such lochs.

In fact, the coarsest material exhibited on the shoreline of a particular loch, down to the limits of the photic zone, will be an expression of the geological history of that loch. In the Highlands this material is composed predominantly of sands, gravels, or boulders, the result of the action of large volumes of water upon substrates consisting originally of rock or coarse drift with scant subsequent inwashing of finer particles. Recalling what was said earlier about turbulence and elutriation and about the principal loch types, it follows that the most widespread substrate within the photic zone in Scottish lochs is likely to consist of coarse, uncolonisable rock fragments, arranged along the shore as a more or less continuous terrace. Above this there is variable development of a sparsely colonised, sandy protopedon on a littoral shelf below which lies a narrow strip of variously colonised brown mud. It was previously concluded (p. 314) that the greatest area of shoreline in Scotland lay beneath poor waters, of from 1 to 15 p.p.m. $CaCO_3$. Drift basins and others comprise a smaller category in which the nutrient status of the water varies from poor to rich and in which colonisation within the photic zone tends to be less fragmentary and substrates finer.

With all the available evidence it is now possible to predict within broad limits the likely extent of plant colonisation on the floors of Scottish lochs. It has already been established that the greatest aggregate length of shoreline in Scotland is rock-margined, dropping steeply to deep water beyond photic limits. How much of the floor of these lochs, the most extensive type, is colonised? The only places in L. Ness where aquatic plants are abundant are Urquhart Bay, Inchnacardoch Bay and Borlum. Generally the limits of the photic zone at water depths of 9·15 m. (the depth to which *N. opaca* may penetrate) are reached very close to the shore (West, 1905). The Bathymetrical Survey (Vol. II, p. 387) calculates that 13 per cent. of the water surface overlies 0–30·5 m. water; from sections provided on the map about 4·8 per cent. of the surface overlies 0–9·15 m. water. Apart from the bays, however, which comprise less than 0·1 per cent. of the total area, most of the shore at, and from immediately below, the water line is too rocky for colonisation. It is doubtful if plants cover as much as 5 per cent. of the area between 0 and 9·15 m. In other words, less than 0·24 per cent. of the surface area of L. Ness is likely to be colonised by higher plants.

This is perhaps an extreme, since gradients of more than 1:1 are frequent on the shore of L. Ness; indeed the two deeper zones of 18·3–21·3 m. and 21·3–24·4 m. are each larger than any shallower zone. For L. Morar with 42 per cent. of its surface (Bathymetrical Survey, Vol. II, p. 199) between 0 and 30·5 m., one may calculate an equivalent figure of 0·7 per cent for the colonisable area; with steeper shores, the figures for L. Tay and L. Ericht are less. Steepness, of course, is no sure guide since much shallower water in these larger lochs may overlie the finest elutriated material remaining— sand. Thus 67 per cent. of the surface of L. Lomond overlies water 0–30·5 m. deep, most of this figure being contributed by the shallow south basin of which large tracts, at least in the south-east corner, comprise uncolonised, rippled sand. Here colonisation in 0–9·15 m. water amounts to less than 1 per cent. of the area. Even if as much as 20 per cent. of the loch's surface overlies 0–9·15 m. water, less than 1 per cent. of the whole surface is likely to be colonised.

Lochs like Croispol have already been remarked as being exceptional in clarity, in the area fully colonised by plants, and in the depth to which plants penetrate. Shallow drift-basin lochs like Watten, an Choin, na Uala, Hempriggs, Grasswater (from 1·5 to 2·5 m. deep) are fully colonised but their contribution to the total surface area of Scottish lochs is small; while a number of drift-basins like Rescobie or Carlingwark apparently have colonisation in shallow water limited by reducing muds. It may, therefore, be concluded that most of the floors of most Scottish lochs are very sparsely colonised.

Stability and change in aquatic vegetation

A familiar picture of aquatic and swamp vegetation is a series of zones parallel to the water's edge, dominated by different species and life-forms. As stated in the introduction to this chapter it is perhaps too readily assumed in those habitats that both the spatial sequence of communities in relation to gradually decreasing depth of water, for example, represents plant succession or change with time, and that such change is rapid. In order to study rates of change a number of sites which were photographed by George West fifty years ago for his work on the Bathymetrical Survey of Scotland, were re-photographed in 1959 or 1960. In addition, the positions shown on recent maps of parts of the margins of some lochs have been compared with their recorded positions on the maps of the Bathymetrical Survey. These investigations are of a preliminary nature.

L. Kinord, in Aberdeenshire, is bounded on its western margin by reedswamp (Plate 53). There is some evidence that up to 20 cm. of sediment has accumulated on parts of the floor of the north-west corner of the loch during the past fifty-seven years but the reedswamp itself has apparently advanced no whit during that time. The margin of the north shore of L. Spiggie has not changed in fifty-eight years, although in the loch itself the 3·05 m. contour, formed by the edge of the submerged sand, does seem to have advanced in places a few tens of centimetres. L. Meiklie in Glen Urquhart has an unchanged margin except for the delta at its western end. The river has cut a new channel through the delta and a small "strath" loch has been formed, with some additional sedimentation on the margin of the main loch in that locality. The vegetation at this end of the loch does not tally with West's (1905) description; this may result partly from plant succession following an evident build-up of the shallower soil by incoming sediment over fifty-seven years. This quantity of incoming sediment must considerably exceed that entering L. Kinord per unit time since the shore of Kinord, just mentioned, has no detectable inflow, one marked in the 1903 map being omitted in the 1955 edition. However, the fact that underwater and marginal succession may proceed rapidly in delta sites is well illustrated by Pearsall's maps, made in 1914–15 and 1929 (in Tansley, 1949) of the vegetation at the entry of the Black Beck into Esthwaite Water, in the English Lakes.

On the delta where the River Urquhart enters L. Ness, in Urquhart Bay, there is photographic (and probably cartographic) evidence of fairly rapid change in reedswamp vegetation during the past fifty years. Comparison of Plate 66 with West's 1905 photograph (Plate 67) shows that sediment has filled in the bay in the middle distance, the spit in the middle distance is now wooded and the pool in the foreground is now *Carex rostrata* (actually *C. rostrata—Acrocladium*) swamp, having soil with 6·1 per cent. oxidised carbon, 0·1 per cent. nitrogen and the once abundant *Alisma* is very restricted. This succession is associated with rapid silting (silt being water-borne sediment).

Rapid vegetation change has also occurred on the high shingle beach with swamp behind, at Borlum at the south end of L. Ness. West's (1905) photograph, which was taken landward from the ridge, shows open water then reedswamp. Fifty-seven years later this open water had been colonised by swamp and fen vegetation (the ridge itself being too densely covered by shrubs to make photography possible).

A narrow stream flows through a swamp into the south-west corner of L. Uanagan, Plate 68, or Plate 69, and this has produced a broad, level, detrital fan of which the outer zone is marked by a belt of *Schoenoplectus lacustris*. Apart from the gravel margin colonised by open *Littorella—Lobelia*, the intervening soil below a depth of about 50 cm. of water is more or less covered by *J. fluitans—Utricularia* and *P. × zizii* sociations. Comparison with West's photographs (Plates 70, 71) reveal two features. In fifty years, the *Schoenoplectus* belt has expanded and there has been an almost complete lack of change in the marginal open *Carex rostrata* stand at the north-west corner of the loch (left side in the plate), at some distance that is from inflow currents. Once again silting may be deduced as having caused changes whereas there seems to have been none in its absence. West (1905) recorded abundant *Chara* beds, apparently in the areas presently covered by *J. fluitans—Utricularia*, etc., in up to 2·1 m. water and, beyond that, *P. lucens* (which may be an error for *P. praelongus*) dominant at that depth.

L. a Mheig lies at an altitude of 366 m. in the peat covered, granite plateau above the north-west shore of L. Ness. As far as the further end of the flat island shown in Plate 72, the water is shallow and turbid, overlying soft dark sediment with about 20 per cent. oxidised carbon, 1·28 per cent. nitrogen. Beyond that the water is deeper; a small stream enters from the west (i.e. left), draining to the east. The islands comprise swamps of *Carex lasiocarpa—Myrica*, with moribund *Betula—Salix* on one, the intervening shallows bearing open *C. rostrata* or open *Carex lasiocarpa* and *Equisetum fluviatile*. The "crescent" consists of *P. natans*. The absence of succession in fifty-seven years is striking, both on the margin of the loch and on the reedswamp island, and in the floating-leaved vegetation (cf. Plate 73).

L. na Ba Ruaidhe, too, lacks any large affluent (Plate 74) and here, once again, floating-leaved reedswamp, and even carr, vegetation has remained static. Indeed there is more change in the moorland (cf. Plate 75), particularly in the spread of trees, than in the so-called hydrosere! An additional pair of samples are provided by Plate 76, and West's comparison photograph, of L. Tarff, a poor-water loch (Plate 77). At the L. Tarff effluent, neither the margin nor even the open *Carex rostrata* (seen in more detail in Plate 57) has developed in fifty-four years. Curtis (1959, p. 235) notes that a characteristic feature of many of the small "non-outlet" lakes in North Wisconsin is a band of vegetation that floats out over the water around the shore of the lake bed. The prisere progresses from the *Carex lasiocarpa* raft edging open water, via ericoid-rich *Sphagnum* bog to conifer swamp and mesic hardwood forest. From the age of trees along such radial lines the rate of advance of mat and forest seems to be about 30 cm. per year. Curtis' plates (25 and 26) of Devil's Track Lake show considerable forest growth in seventeen years but, like the situation at L. an Mheig, no advance by the sedge mat.

What accounts for these different rates of change and which is the commoner situation in Scotland? The demonstrable difference over half a century between Mheig and Ba Ruaidhe, on the one hand, and Urquhart Bay, on the other, is that the marginal or colonisable soil in the first two lochs has not risen while it has in the delta of Urquhart Bay. Likewise, change has taken place on the submerged detrital fan of L. Uanagan but not on the marginal soils out of direct contact with it.

Superficially, the dark muds bearing these marginal open communities at Uanagan, a Mheig (or Tarff) look organic, and highly organic mud may inhibit colonisation presumably, in poor waters, because of its high hydrogen-ion saturation (Pearsall, 1920). However, samples from Uanagan, a Mheig and Tarff have respectively 4·8, 20·4 and 6·2 per cent oxidised carbon while the Ba Ruaidhe soil is light in colour with only 2·1 per cent. oxidised carbon.

The difference must lie in the rate at which net accumulation of sediment (say, per annum) takes place, but what sort of sediment accumulates? This depends on the original nutrient status of the inflow water. Absence of inwashed finer fractions (silt plus clay) may be expected in most lochs in the palaeogenic Highlands. Change must then result from net accumulation of organic, or inorganic, residues that are too large to be moved once deposited by water currents. Even in sheltered reedswamp, however, little accumulation of organic matter may take place. A small lochan on Anabaglish Moss, Wigtownshire, illustrates this; comparison with West's Fig. 64 (1910a), indicated that the complete circle of *Cladium mariscus* reedswamp had hardly advanced, if at all, into the open water in fifty years. This clear, spring-fed lochan on sandstone had little silting or turbulence and the *Cladium* must have provided organic matter suitable for autogenic succession, yet change was negligible. Absence of change must here be associated with absence of additional nutrients for development of vegetation. Likewise, the open and other reedswamp sociations in the shallows of poor waters may have failed to change in fifty-eight years because of insufficiently available nutrients to support more than the existing biomass; they represent, in this context, an edaphic climax. It may be suggested that, even where turbulence is slight, autogenic factors have little effect on plant succession in the absence of finer fractions in the inwashed sediments of poor to moderately rich waters. Change is brought about primarily by an allogenic factor, the net accumulation of inorganic sediments. Pearsall (1918, 1920, 1921) reached the same general conclusions from his study of the vegetation of English Lakes (also producing evidence, for which I have nothing comparable, that submerged communities occur in definite successions controlled likewise by the rate of inorganic sedimentation).

In the least turbulent parts of lochs like Lindores or Carlingwark, which are kettle-holes in fluvio-glacial clays, comparison with West's (1910a) photographs indicates accumulation during the past fifty years of silt, clay and dead plant material, i.e. warp anmoor and fen peat, with consequent rapid allogenic-autogenic successions of the East Anglian fen pattern; although this vegetation change has still to be accurately recorded.

These rich water lochs on fluvio-glacial clays are, however, in the minority. All the evidence led indicates that in most Scottish lochs, i.e. those in the palaeogenic Highlands, rate of change in marginal reedswamp and floating-leaved vegetation is normally very slow. This is obvious in steep rocky shores which represent the prevailing condition but it seems to apply even in those few places where change in soil level is gradual from above, to well below, water level. Urquhart Bay then, seems likely to be the exception over most of Scotland.

Varying rates of change over fifty years have been shown in marginal and aquatic vegetation of Highland lochs. It is concluded that these variations must have resulted from net accumulation rate of inorganic sediment, that there has been no change in the absence of this allogenic factor, and that the rate of change is normally very slow. In certain rich water kettle-holes there is evidence of rapid autogenic-allogenic succession.

ACKNOWLEDGEMENTS

I acknowledge with thanks the help of the following specialists in checking most, and correcting a number of, my identifications of species in the named plant groups: Dr A. J. Brook (*Characeae*), Mr. J. E. Dandy (*Potamogeton*), Miss Ursula Duncan (*Sphagnum* mainly), Dr. Edward Lodge (*Drepanocladus* mainly). This work was carried out whilst I was on the staff of the Botany Department, St. Salvator's College, University of St. Andrews, and my thanks are due to Mr. J. B. Kenworthy and Mr. R. L. A. Oliver for doing most of the soil analyses reported in the present work; Mr. Oliver helped in numerous other ways. Mr. A. V. Holden kindly permitted me to use some of his unpublished data on pH and alkalinity of Scottish lochs. The transport, running costs and aquatic equipment were provided by a grant from the Carnegie Trust for the Scottish Universities. I should like to acknowledge the Trust's support, without which this work would not have been done, and to thank the former Secretary, Mr. T. A. F. Noble, for his help.

REFERENCES

AF RANTZIEN, HENNING HORN   1951   Macrophyte vegetation in lakes and temporary pools of the alvar of Oland, South Sweden I. The alvar and its amphibious vegetation II. The aquatic vegetation. *Svensk bot. tidskr.*, **45**, 72–120, 484–497.

ARBER, A.   1920   *Water Plants*. Cambridge.

Atlas of the British Flora   1962   Ed. Perring, F. H. and Walters, S. M. London.

BROWN, W. H.   1913   The relation of the substratum to the growth of *Elodea*. *Philip. J. sci., ser. C., Botany*, **8**, 1–20.

CASPARI, W. A.   1910   The deposits of the Scottish freshwater lochs. In, Murray, J. and Pullar, L., *Bathymetrical Survey of the Scottish Freshwater Lochs*, Vol. I, 261–274. Edinburgh.

CLAPHAM, A. R., TUTIN, T. G. and WARBURG, E. F.   1962   *Flora of the British Isles*. 2nd edn. Cambridge.

COOK, C. D. K.   1962   *Sparganium erectum*. Account for *Biological Flora of the British Isles, J. Ecol.*, **50**, 247–255.

CRAFTS, A. S., CURRIER, H. B. and STOCKING, C. R.   1949   *Water in the Physiology of Plants*. Waltham, Mass.

CURTIS, J. T.   1959   *The Vegetation of Wisconsin, an Ordination of Plant Communities*. Madison, Wisconsin.

DAUBENMIRE, R. F.   1953   *Plants and environment*. London.

DUVIGNEAUD, P.   1949   Classification phytosociologique des tourbières de l'Europe. *Bull. bot. soc. Belg.*, **81**, 58–129.

FASSETT, N. C.   1940   *A manual of aquatic plants.* Madison, Wisconsin.

GLÜCK, H.   1936   *Pteridophyten und Phanerogamen.* Heft 15 of *Die Süsswasser-Flora Mitteleuropas* ed. Pascher, A. Jena, Germany.

GODWIN, H.   1923   Dispersal of pond floras. *J. Ecol.,* **11,** 160–164.

GORHAM, E.   1950   Variations in some chemical conditions along the borders of a *Carex lasiocarpa* fen community. *Oikos,* **2,** 217–240.

                            1957   The chemical composition of some natural waters in the Cairngorm-Strath Spey district of Scotland. *Limnology and Oceanography,* **2,** 143–154.

                            1958   The influence and importance of daily weather conditions on the supply of chloride, sulphate and other ions to freshwater from atmospheric precipitation. *Phil. trans. Roy. Soc., Lond.,* **B241,** 147–178.

GRIFFITHS, B. M.   1932   The ecology of Butterby Marsh, Durham. *J. Ecol.,* **20,** 105–127.

HARRISON, Y. HESLOP   1955   *Nuphar* Sm. Account for *Biological Flora of the British Isles, J. Ecol.,* **43,** 342–364.

                            1955   *Nymphaea* L. Account for *Biological Flora of the British Isles, J. Ecol.,* **43,** 719–734.

HOLDEN, A. V.   1961   Concentration of chloride in freshwaters and rain water. *Nature, Lond.,* **192,** 961.

HUBBARD, C. E.   1954   *British grasses.* London.

HUTCHINSON, G. E.   1957   *A Treatise on Limnology* I. New York.

JACKSON, M. L.   1958   *Soil chemical analysis.* London.

KUBIENA, W. L.   1953   *The soils of Europe.* Madrid and London.

LIVINGSTONE, D. A.   1963   Chemical composition of rivers and lakes. U.S. Geological Survey Professional Paper 440 G. *Data of Geochemistry.* Sixth edn., Washington.

MATTHEWS, J. R.   1914   The White Moss Loch: a study in biotic succession. *New Phytol.,* **13,** 134–148.

MISRA, R. D.   1938   Edaphic factors in the distribution of aquatic plants in the English Lakes. *J. Ecol.,* **26,** 411–451.

MORTIMER, C. H.   1941   The exchange of dissolved substances between mud and water in lakes. I and II. *J. Ecol.,* **29,** 280–329.

                            1942   The exchange of dissolved substances between mud and water in lakes. III and IV. *J. Ecol.,* **30,** 147–201.

                            1949   Underwater "soils", a review of lake sediments. *J. Soil Sci.,* **1,** 63–73.

MUENSCHER, W. C.   1936   Storage and germination of seeds of aquatic plants. *Cornell Univ. Agri. exp. sta. Bull.,* **652,** 1–17.

MURRAY, J. and   1910   *Bathymetrical Survey of the Scottish Freshwater Lochs.* Vols.
    PULLAR, L.   I to VI. Edinburgh.

NORDHAGEN, R.   1943   Sikilsdalen og Norges Fjellbeiter, en Plantesosiologisk Monografi. *Bergens Mus Skr.,* **22.**

OBERDORFER, E.   1954   *Süddeutsche Pflanzengesellschaften.* Jena.

OLSEN, S.   1950   Aquatic plants and hydrospheric factors. *Svensk bot. tidskr.,* **44,** 1–32; 332–373.

PEACH, B. N. and   1910   The Scottish lakes in relation to the geological features of
    HORNE, J.   the country. In, Murray, J. and Pullar, L., *Bathymetrical Survey of the Scottish Freshwater Lochs.* Vol. I, 439–513. Edinburgh.

PEARSALL, W. H.   1918   On the classification of aquatic plant communities. *J. Ecol.,* **6,** 75–84.

                            1920   The aquatic vegetation of the English lakes. *J. Ecol.,* **8,** 163–201.

PEARSALL, W. H.   1921   The development of vegetation in the English Lakes, considered in relation to the general evolution of glacial lakes and rock-basins. *Proc. Roy. Soc.*, **B92**, 259–284.

PERRING, F. H.   1961   Report of field meeting to the Isle of Lewis and Harris, 1959. *Proc. bot. soc. Brit. Isles*, **4**, 204.

POND, R. H.   1905   The biological relation of aquatic plants to the substratum. *U.S. Com. Fish & Fisheries Rep.* 1903, 485–526.

POORE, M. E. D.   1957   The ecology of Woodwalton Fen. *J. Ecol.*, **44**, 455–492.

PYEFINCH, K. A.   1960   *Trout in Scotland*. Edinburgh.

RAUNKIAER, C.   1937   *Plant Life Forms*. Oxford.

RUTTNER, F.   1953   *Fundamentals of Limnology*. Trans. Frey, D. G. and Fry, F. E. J. Toronto.

SINNOTT, E. W.   1960   *Plant morphogenesis*. London.

SLACK, H. D.   1954   The bottom deposits of Loch Lomond. *Proc. Roy. Soc. Edinb.*, **B65**, 213–238.

SPENCE, D. H. N.   1960   Studies on the vegetation of Shetland. III. Scrub in Shetland and in South Uist, Outer Hebrides. *J. Ecol.*, **48**, 73–95.

STEWARD, F. C. and SUTCLIFFE, J. F.   1959   Plants in relation to inorganic salts. In, *Plant Physiology, A Treatise*, (Ed. F. C. Steward). Vol. 2, 253–478. New York.

STRASBURGER, E.   1930   *Text-Book of Botany*. 6th English ed. trans. Lang, W. H. London.

STURROCK, A.   1880   A botanical report from the Loch of Rescobie. *Scot. nat.*, 1880, **5**, 347–351.

SUTCLIFFE, J. F.   1962   *Mineral Salt absorption in plants*. London.

SWINDALE, D. N. and CURTIS, J. T.   1957   Phytosociology of the larger submerged plants in Wisconsin lakes. *Ecology*, **38**, 397–407.

TANSLEY, A. G.   1949   *The British Islands and their Vegetation*. Cambridge.

THOMSON, C. M.   1962   *Factors influencing the germination and establishment of* Carex rostrata *Stokes*. Unpublished Honours thesis, University of St. Andrews.

TITCOMB, J. W.   1924   Aquatic plants in pond culture. *Rep. U.S. com. fish.* 1923, app. **2**, 1–24.

WEAVER, J. E. and CLEMENTS, F. E.   1929   *Plant Ecology*. New York.

WEDDERBURN, E. M.   1910   Temperature of Scottish lakes. Murray, J. and Pullar, L. *Bathymetrical Survey of Scottish Freshwater Lochs*. Vol. I, 91–144. Edinburgh.

WEST, G.   1905   A comparative study of the dominant phanerogamic and higher cryptogamic flora of aquatic habit in three lake areas of Scotland. *Proc. Roy. Soc. Edinb.*, **25**, 967–1023.

   1910a   A further contribution to a comparative study of the dominant phanerogamic and higher cryptogamic flora of aquatic habit in Scottish lakes. *Proc. Roy. Soc. Edinb.*, **30**, 65–181.

   1910b   An epitome of a comparative study of the dominant phanerogamic and higher cryptogamic flora of aquatic habit, in seven lake areas in Scotland. In, Murray, J. and Pullar, L. *Bathymetrical Survey of the Scottish Freshwater Lochs*. Vol. I, 156–260. Edinburgh.

WILLIS, A. J. and JEFFERIES, R. L.   1959   The plant ecology of Gordano Valley. *Proc. Bristol nat. soc.*, **29**, 469–490.

WILLIAMS, W. T. and BARBER, D. A.   1961   The functional significance of aerenchyma in plants. *Symp. Soc. Exp. Biol.*, **15**, 132–144.

TABLE 42

List of lochs and/or swamps of which some plant-communities were studied during the survey, arranged in alphabetical order of counties, together with the samples (+) of community-

	Submerged-leaved community-types											Floating-leaved community-types				
	Linear-leaved and rosette								Broad-leaved							
	Eldea society	Fontinalis society	Isoetes society	Juncus fluitans—Lobelia association	Myriophyllum spp.—societies sp =spicatum	Nitella spp. societies	Potamogeton filiformis—Chara association	Linear-leaved pondweed societies (synopsis, p. 319)	P. gramineus society	P. praelongus society	Other pondweed societies p. 327	Nymphaea alba society	Nuphar lutea society	Polygonum amphibium society	Potamogeton natans—J. fluitans sociation	Sparganium spp. societies
	1	2	3	4	5	6	7	8	9	10	11	12	13	14	15	16
ABERDEEN																
Corby	...	...	...	...	...	...	...	+	...	...	...	...	+	...	...	...
Kinord	...	*	+	+	...	+	...	...	...	...	+	...	*	*	...	...
Loirston	...	*	...	+	...	...	...	*	...	...	...	...	...	...	...	...
Park	...	...	...	...	...	...	...	...	...	...	...	...	...	...	...	...
ANGUS																
Forfar	...	...	...	...	...	...	+	...	...	...	...	...	...	...	...	...
Rescobie	+	...	...	...	...	...	+	...	...	...	...	...	...	...	...	...
Restenneth	...	...	...	...	...	...	...	...	...	...	...	...	...	...	...	...
ARGYLL																
Avich	...	...	...	...	...	...	...	...	...	...	...	*	...	...	+	...
Gealach	...	...	...	...	...	...	...	...	...	...	...	*	...	...	...	...
h'Achlaise	...	...	*	+	...	...	...	...	...	...	...	...	...	...	...	...
Awe	...	...	+	+	...	...	...	...	...	...	...	...	...	...	...	*
CAITHNESS																
Calder	...	...	...	...	...	+	+	+	+	...	...	...	...	...	+	...
Hempriggs	...	+	...	...	...	...	+	...	...	...	+	...	...	...	...	...
Hollistan	...	...	...	...	...	...	...	...	...	...	...	...	...	...	...	...
Sarclett	...	+	...	...	...	...	...	...	...	...	+	...	...	...	...	...
Watten	...	...	...	...	+sp	...	+	+	...	...	...	...	...	...	...	...
Wester	...	...	...	...	...	...	...	+	...	...	...	...	...	...	...	...
Yarhouse	...	...	+	...	...	...	+	...	+	...	...	...	...	...	+	...
FIFE																
Black	...	...	...	...	...	+	...	*	...	...	...	+	+	...	...	...
Leven	...	...	...	...	...	...	+	...	...	...	...	...	...	...	...	...
Lindores	...	...	...	...	*	...	+	*	*	+	*	...	+	+	...	...
Kilconquhar	...	...	...	...	...	...	...	...	...	...	...	...	...	...	...	...
MIDLOTHIAN																
Duddingston	...	...	...	...	...	...	...	...	...	...	...	...	...	...	...	...
INVERNESS: (NESS)																
Ba Ruaidhe	...	...	...	*	...	...	...	...	+	+	...	+	...	...	...	...
Ceon Ghlas	...	...	...	*	...	...	...	...	...	+	...	...	...	...	...	...
an Choin	...	+	...	...	...	...	...	...	...	...	...	+	...	...	*	...

types in each which form the basis of the synoptic tables. This table shows the distribution of samples, not of community-types. * denotes stands observed, or used for depth or soil data, but not recorded in detail. s denotes *C. rostrata—Sphagnum cuspidatum.*

Swamp and fen community-types

	1	2	3	4	5	6	7	8	9	10	11	12	13	14	15	16	17	18	19	20	21	22	23	24
1	...	...	...	...	...	...	...	...	...	...	...	...	...	...	...	...	...	+	+	...	*	...	...	...
2	...	...	...	...	*	*	...	...	...	...	...	...	...	...	...	...	...	*	...	...	...	...	+	+
3	...	...	...	...	...	...	...	...	...	...	+	+	+	...	...	...	...	...	+	...	...	...	...	...
4	...	...	+	+	+	...	...	...	...	...	...	...	+	...	...	+	+	+	+	...	...	...	...	...
5	...	...	+	+	...	...	...	...	...	...	...	*	*	...	...	...	...	+	+	+	*	*	...	...
6	...	...	+	+	...	...	...	...	...	...	...	*	...	*	...	...	...	+	...	...	...	...	...	...
7	+	...	...	+	...	*	+	...	...	...	...	...	...	+	...	...	...	*	+	...	...	...	...	...
8	+	...	...	...	...	...	...	...	...	...	...	...	...	...	...	...	*	...	...	...	...	...	...	...
9	...	...	...	...	+s	...	...	...	...	...	...	...	...	...	...	...	...	...	...	...	...	...	...	...
10	...	...	+	...	...	*	+	...	...	...	...	...	...	+	...	...	...	*	*	...	+	...	...	...
11	...	*	...	...	...	...	...	...	+	...	...	...	...	*	...	...	...	...	...	...	...	...	...	...
12	...	...	...	...	+s sp.	...	...	...	...	...	...	...	...	*	...	...	...	...	...	...	...	...	...	...
13	...	...	...	...	...	...	...	...	+	...	...	...	...	...	...	...	...	...	...	...	...	...	+	...
14	...	...	...	...	...	...	...	...	+	+	...	...	...	...	...	...	...	...	...	...	...	...	...	...
15	...	...	...	*	...	...	...	...	+	...	...	...	...	...	...	...	...	...	...	...	...	...	...	...
16	...	...	+	...	...	+	*	...	*	+	+	+	+	...	...	*	...	...	...	+	...	...	...	*
17	...	...	...	...	...	...	...	...	...	+	...	*	+	...	...	*	+	+	+	+	...	...	...	...
18	...	...	...	...	...	...	...	...	...	...	...	...	+	...	...	*	...	...	...	...	...	...	...	...
19	...	...	...	...	...	...	...	...	...	...	...	...	*	...	...	*	...	+	+	...	*	*	...	+
20	+	+	...	...	+	...	...	...	...	+	...	...	...	...	+	...	...	...	...	...	...	...	...	...
21	...	...	...	...	*	...	...	...	...	...	...	...	...	...	...	...	...	...	...	...	...	...	...	...
22	+	...	...	...	+	...	...	...	*	...	...	...	...	...	+	...	...	...	...	...	...	...	...	...

Column headings:

1. *Carex lasiocarpa* and *C.l.—Myrica*
2. *C. nigra—C. demissa*
3. *C. nigra—Acrocladium*
4. *C. paniculata—Angelica*
5. *C. rostrata* and *C. rostrata—Menyanthes*
6. *C. rostrata—Acrocladium*
7. *C. vesicaria* and *C. vesicaria—V. scutellata*
8. *Cladium mariscus—Myrica*
9. *Eleocharis palustris—Littorella*
10. *Equisetum fluviatile—Littorella*
11. *E. fluviatile—Acrocladium*
12. *Filipendula—Acrocladium*
13. *Glyceria* and *Glyceria—Iris*
14. *Juncus articulatus—Angelica*
15. *Myrica—C. lasiocarpa*
16. *Phalaris* and *Phalaris—Filipendula*
17. *Phragmites—Sparganium* and *P. comm.—Littorella*
18. *Phragmites* society
19. *Phragmites—Galium*
20. *Potentilla—Acrocladium*
21. *Schoenoplectus—J. fluitans*
22. *Sparganium erectum*
23. *Sphagnum subsecundum—J. bulbosus*
24. *Typha latifolia—Lemna minor*

2 B

TABLE 42—*continued*

	Submerged-leaved community types											Floating-leaved community-types				
	Linear-leaved and rosette								Broad-leaved							
	Elodea society	*Fontinalis* society	*Isoetes* society	*Juncus fluitans—Lobelia* association	*Myriophyllum* spp.—societies sp=*spicatum*	*Nitella* spp. societies	*Potamogeton filiformis—Chara* association	Linear-leaved pondweed societies (synopsis, p. 319)	*P. gramineus* society	*P. praelongus* society	Other pondweed societies p. 327	*Nymphaea alba* society	*Nuphar lutea* society	*Polygonum amphibium* society	*Potamogeton natans—J. fluitans* sociation	*Sparganium* spp. societies
	1	2	3	4	5	6	7	8	9	10	11	12	13	14	15	16
INVERNESS: (NESS)—continued																
Glen Moriston	...	...	...	...	...	...	...	...	...	...	...	...	...	...	...	...
Lochend	+	...	...	...	...	...	...	...	...	...	...	...	...	...	...	...
Meiklie	...	...	...	+	...	...	...	...	...	...	...	...	+	...	+	...
a'Mheig	...	...	...	+	...	...	...	...	...	...	...	...	...	...	*	...
Ness: Borlum	...	...	...	...	...	...	...	...	...	...	...	...	...	...	...	...
Inchnacardoch	...	...	...	...	...	...	...	...	...	...	...	...	...	...	...	...
Urquhart	...	...	...	*	...	...	...	...	...	...	...	...	...	+	...	...
Oich	...	...	...	+	+	...	...	...	...	...	...	...	...	...	...	+
an Ordain	+	...	...	*	+	...	...	...	...	...	+	...	...	...	+	+
Tarff	...	...	*	+	+	...	...	...	...	...	...	...	...	...	...	...
Uanagan	...	...	...	...	...	...	...	...	...	...	...	...	...	...	...	...
INVERNESS: (SPEY)																
Swamp nr Aundarroch	...	...	...	...	...	...	...	...	...	...	...	...	...	...	...	...
Garten	...	...	...	+	...	+	...	+	+	...	...	+	...	...	+	...
Mor	...	...	...	...	+	*	...	*	...	...	...	...	...	...	...	...
Gamhna	...	...	...	+	...	+	...	+	+	...	...	...	...	...	...	...
na Uamha	...	...	...	...	...	...	...	...	...	...	...	...	...	...	...	*
Uath lochan	...	...	...	...	...	...	...	...	...	...	...	...	...	...	...	...
Mallachie	...	...	...	+	...	...	...	...	...	...	...	+	...	...	...	...
Swamp, Insch	...	...	...	...	...	...	...	...	...	...	...	...	...	...	...	...
Insch	...	...	...	*	...	...	...	...	...	...	...	...	...	...	...	+
PERTH																
Clunie	+	...	...	...	...	...	...	...	...	...	...	...	+	+	...	...
Kinardochy	...	...	...	+	+	...	...	...	+	*	...	...	...	...	...	...
Lowes	...	...	...	+	...	+	...	+	+	...	...	...	+	...	...	...
Marlee	...	...	...	...	...	...	...	...	...	...	...	...	...	...	...	...
Moraig	...	...	...	...	...	...	+	...	+	...	...	...	...	...	+	...
an Daimh	...	...	...	+	...	...	...	...	+	...	...	...	...	...	...	...
W. Ross																
an Loin	...	...	...	+	+	...	...	+	...	+	...	+	...	...	+	...
Dhugaill	...	...	...	+	...	...	...	...	...	...	...	...	...	...	+	...
Applecross	...	...	...	+	...	...	...	...	...	...	...	...	...	...	...	...
R. Torridon	...	...	...	+	...	...	...	...	...	...	...	...	...	...	...	*
nan Saighead	...	...	...	...	...	...	...	...	...	...	...	...	...	...	...	...
SHETLAND																
nr Flatpunds	...	...	...	+	+	...	...	...	...	...	...	...	...	...	+	...
Garderhouse	...	...	...	...	...	...	...	...	...	...	...	...	...	...	...	...
Grasswater	...	...	...	+	+	...	...	...	...	+	...	...	...	...	...	+
Lunga Water	...	...	...	...	...	...	...	...	...	...	...	...	...	...	...	...
Mill L, Semblister	...	...	...	+	...	...	...	...	...	...	...	...	...	...	...	...
Sandy Water	...	...	...	...	...	...	...	...	...	...	...	...	...	...	...	...

Swamp and fen community-types

	Carex lasiocarpa and C.l.—Myrica	C. nigra—C. demissa	C. nigra—Acrocladium	C. paniculata—Angelica	C. rostrata and C. rostrata—Menyanthes	C. rostrata—Acrocladium	C. vesicaria and C. vesicaria—V. scutellata	Cladium mariscus—Myrica	Eleocharis palustris—Littorella	Equisetum fluviatile—Littorella	E. fluviatile—Acrocladium	Filipendula—Acrocladium	Glyceria and Glyceria—Iris	Juncus articulatus—Angelica	Myrica—C. lasiocarpa	Phalaris and Phalaris—Filipendula	Phragmites—Sparganium and P. comm.—Littorella	Phragmites society	Phragmites—Galium	Potentilla—Acrocladium	Schoenoplectus—J. fluitans	Sparganium erectum	Sphagnum subsecundum—J. bulbosus	Typha latifolia—Lemna minor
	1	2	3	4	5	6	7	8	9	10	11	12	13	14	15	16	17	18	19	20	21	22	23	24
	...	...	...	...	...	...	...	...	...	...	...	...	...	...	...	...	...	+	...	...	...	...	...	...
	...	...	...	...	*	+	...	...	...	...	...	...	...	...	...	*	+	...	...	...	...	...	...	...
	*	...	...	...	+	...	+	...	+	...	...	*	...	...	*	...	...	...	...	...	...	...	...	...
	...	...	...	...	+	...	...	...	...	*	...	...	...	...	*	...	...	...	...	...	...	...	...	...
	...	...	...	...	*	...	+	...	...	...	...	...	...	...	...	*	...	...	...	*	...	...	...	...
	...	...	...	...	*	...	+	...	...	...	...	*	*	...	...	*	...	*	*	...	...	...	...	...
	*	...	...	...	*	...	...	...	...	+	...	...	...	...	*	...	...	...	...	...	...	...	...	...
	+	...	...	...	+	...	...	...	...	...	...	...	...	...	+	...	...	...	...	+	...	...	...	...
	+	...	...	+	*	...	...	...	...	...	...	...	...	...	+	...	...	...	...	...	...	...	...	...
	+	+	...	...	...	...	...	...	*	*	...	...	...	...	...	...	+	...	...	...	*	...	...	+
	...	...	*	...	...	...	...	...	...	...	...	...	...	...	...	...	+	...	...	...	...	...	...	...
	+	...	...	...	...	...	...	...	...	...	...	...	...	...	...	...	*	...	+	...	...	...	...	...
	+	...	...	...	+	...	...	...	...	...	...	...	...	...	...	...	+	...	+	...	...	...	...	...
	...	...	...	...	...	+	+	...	...	+	...	...	...	...	...	+	...	...	...	...	...	...	...	...
	...	...	...	...	...	...	...	...	...	...	...	...	...	...	...	...	...	...	...	...	...	...	...	...
	...	...	...	...	...	...	...	...	...	...	...	*	...	...	*	...	...	...	...	...	...	...	...	...
	+	...	...	...	*	...	...	...	...	+	...	...	...	...	...	...	+	+	...	...	...	...	...	...
	...	...	...	...	...	...	...	...	...	...	...	+	...	...	...	*	...	+	*	...	...	...	...	...
	...	...	...	...	*	+	...	...	...	...	...	+	...	...	...	...	...	+	...	...	...	...	...	...
	...	...	...	...	...	...	...	...	...	...	...	...	...	...	...	...	*	+	...	...	...	...	...	...
	...	+	...	...	+	...	...	...	...	...	...	...	...	...	...	...	...	...	...	...	+	...	...	...
	...	...	...	...	...	...	...	...	+	...	...	...	...	...	...	...	...	...	...	...	*	...	...	...
	...	...	...	...	*	...	...	...	...	...	...	...	...	...	...	...	...	...	...	...	...	...	+	...
	...	+	...	...	...	...	...	...	...	...	...	...	...	...	...	...	+	...	+	...	...	...	...	...
	...	...	...	...	+	+	...	...	...	...	...	...	...	...	...	...	...	...	...	...	...	...	+	...
	...	...	...	...	+	...	...	...	...	...	...	...	...	...	...	...	...	...	...	...	+	...	+	...
	...	...	...	...	...	...	...	...	+	+	...	...	...	...	...	...	...	...	...	...	...	...	+	...
	...	...	...	...	...	...	...	...	+	...	...	...	...	...	...	...	...	...	...	...	*	...	...	...

TABLE 42—*continued*

	Submerged-leaved community types											Floating-leaved community-types				
	Linear-leaved and rosette								Broad-leaved							
	Elodea society	Fontinalis society	Isoetes society	Juncus fluitans—Lobelia association	Myriophyllum spp.—societies sp=spicatum	Nitella spp. societies	Potamogeton filiformis—Chara association	Linear-leaved pondweed societies (synopsis, p. 319)	P. gramineus society	P. praelongus society	Other pondweed societies p. 327	Nymphaea alba society	Nuphar lutea society	Polygonum amphibium society	Potamogeton natans—J. fluitans sociation	Sparganium spp. societies
	I	2	3	4	5	6	7	8	9	10	11	12	13	14	15	16
SHETLAND—continued																
Spiggie	...	+	...	+	+	+	+	+	+	...	...	...	...	...	...	...
Stanevatsoe	...	...	...	...	+	...	...	...	+	...	...	+	...	...	+	+
STEWARTRY (Kirkcudbright)																
Carlingwark	+	...	...	...	...	...	...	+		...	...	...	+	...	...	...
Cree, R.	...	...	...	...	...	...	...	...		...	...	...	...	...	...	...
Ken	...	...	+	+	...	...	...	...		...	...	...	+	...	...	...
Maberry	...	...	+	+	...	+	...	...		...	...	...	*	...	+	...
Neldricken	...	...	...	+	...	...	...	...		...	...	...	...	...	...	+
Valley	...	...	...	+	...	...	...	...		...	...	...	...	...	...	...
STIRLING																
Lomond	...	...	*	+	...	...	...	...		...	...	...	*	+	...	...
Dubh	...	...	...	*	...	...	...	...		...	...	...	*	...	...	...
Gartochcraggan	...	...	...	...	...	...	...	...		...	...	...	...	...	...	...
SUTHERLAND																
An Aigeil	...	...	...	...	*	...	+	+	...	...	+	+	...	*	...	...
Calladail	...	...	...	...	+	...	+	...	*	...	...	...	...	...	*	...
Croispol	...	...	...	...	+sp	...	+	+	...	+	...	...	...	...	...	...
Lanish	...	...	...	...	+sp	...	+	...	...	+	...	...	...	...	...	...
Beg	...	...	...	+	...	...	...	...	...	...	...	...	...	...	...	...
Creagach	...	...	...	...	+	...	...	...	+	...	...	...	...	...	...	...
nr Creagach	...	...	...	...	...	...	...	...	+	...	...	...	...	...	...	...
nr Eriboll	...	...	...	...	...	...	...	...	+	...	...	...	...	...	...	...
nan Gobhar	...	...	...	...	...	...	...	...	...	...	...	...	...	...	...	...
Hacoin	...	...	...	+	...	...	...	...	...	...	...	+	...	...	...	...
nr Hacoin	...	...	...	...	...	...	...	...	...	...	...	...	...	...	...	...
Hope	...	...	*	+	...	...	...	...	...	...	...	...	...	...	...	...
Lurgainn	...	...	*	*	...	...	...	...	...	...	...	...	...	...	...	...
Merkland	...	...	+	+	*	...	...	...	...	...	...	...	...	+	...	...
Maiden	...	...	+	+	...	...	...	...	+	...	...	...	...	...	...	...
Mhor	...	...	*	*	+	...	...	...	...	...	...	...	...	...	...	...
an Ordain	...	...	...	*	...	...	...	...	...	...	...	+	...	...	...	...
Stack	...	...	*	+	*	...	...	...	...	...	...	+	...	...	...	...
nr Stack	...	...	...	...	...	...	...	...	...	...	...	...	...	...	+	...
Tarbach Mor	...	...	*	*	...	...	...	...	...	...	...	...	...	...	...	...
na-Uala	...	...	...	+	...	...	...	...	...	...	...	*	...	...	...	...
WIGTOWN																
Barhapple	...	...	...	...	...	...	...	...	...	...	...	...	...	...	...	...
Black	...	...	...	...	...	...	...	...	...	...	...	...	+	...	...	...
Dernaglar	...	...	...	...	...	...	...	...	...	...	...	*	...	+	...	...
Magillie	...	...	+	+	...	...	...	...	...	...	...	...	...	...	...	...
Mochrum	...	...	+	*	...	...	...	...	...	...	...	...	+	...	...	...
White, Anabaglish	...	...	...	...	...	...	...	...	...	...	...	...	...	...	...	...
White, Castle Kennedy	...	...	...	...	...	...	...	...	...	...	+	...	...	...	...	...

Swamp and fen community-types

	Carex lasiocarpa and C.f.—Myrica	C. nigra—C. demissa	C. nigra—Acrocladium	C. paniculata—Angelica	C. rostrata and C. rostrata—Menyanthes	C. rostrata—Acrocladium	C. vesicaria and C. vesicaria—V. scutellata	Cladium mariscus—Myrica	Eleocharis palustris—Littorella	Equisetum fluviatile—Littorella	E. fluviatile—Acrocladium	Filipendula—Acrocladium	Glyceria and Glyceria—Iris	Juncus articulatus—Angelica	Myrica—C. lasiocarpa	Phalaris and Phalaris—Filipendula	Phragmites—Sparganium and P. comm.—Littorella	Phragmites society	Phragmites—Galium	Potentilla—Acrocladium	Schoenoplectus—J. fluitans	Sparganium erectum	Sphagnum subsecundum—J. bulbosus	Typha latifolia—Lemna minor
	1	2	3	4	5	6	7	8	9	10	11	12	13	14	15	16	17	18	19	20	21	22	23	24
	…	…	…	…	+	…	…	…	*	*	…	…	…	…	…	+	…	…	…	…	…	…	…	…
	…	…	…	…	+	…	…	…	…	…	…	…	…	…	…	…	…	…	…	…	…	…	…	…
	…	…	…	…	…	*	…	…	…	…	…	…	+	…	…	…	+	*	+	…	+	…	…	…
	…	…	…	…	+	…	+	…	…	…	…	…	…	…	…	…	…	*	+	…	*	…	…	…
	…	…	…	…	…	…	…	…	…	…	…	…	…	…	…	+	…	…	…	…	…	…	…	…
	+	…	…	…	+	…	…	…	+	…	…	…	…	…	…	+	…	…	…	…	…	…	…	…
	…	…	…	…	…	…	…	…	…	+	…	…	…	…	…	…	…	…	…	…	…	…	…	…
	…	…	…	…	…	…	…	…	…	…	…	…	…	…	…	…	…	…	…	…	…	…	+	…
	…	…	…	…	…	…	+	…	*	…	…	…	…	*	…	*	…	…	…	…	*	…	…	…
	+	…	…	…	*	…	+	…	+	…	…	…	…	…	…	…	+	…	…	…	…	…	…	…
	…	…	…	…	…	…	…	…	…	…	…	…	…	…	…	+	…	…	…	…	…	…	…	…
	…	*	…	…	…	…	…	…	…	…	…	…	…	…	…	…	*	…	…	…	*	…	…	…
	…	…	…	…	…	…	…	…	+	…	…	…	…	…	…	…	…	…	…	…	…	…	…	…
	…	…	…	…	…	…	…	…	+	…	…	+	…	…	…	…	…	…	…	…	…	…	…	…
	…	…	…	…	…	…	…	…	*	…	…	…	…	…	…	…	…	…	…	…	…	…	…	…
	…	…	…	…	…	…	…	…	*	*	…	…	…	…	…	…	…	…	…	…	…	…	…	…
	…	…	…	…	…	…	…	…	*	…	…	…	…	…	…	…	…	…	…	…	…	…	…	…
	…	…	…	…	…	…	…	…	…	…	…	…	…	…	…	…	…	+	+	…	+	…	…	…
	…	…	…	…	…	…	…	…	…	…	…	…	…	…	…	…	…	+	+	…	…	…	…	…
	…	…	…	…	*	…	…	…	*	*	…	…	…	…	…	…	…	…	…	…	*	…	…	…
	…	…	…	…	…	…	…	…	…	…	+	…	…	…	…	…	…	…	…	…	…	…	…	…
	…	…	…	…	…	…	…	…	…	…	…	…	…	…	…	…	+	…	…	…	…	…	…	…
	…	…	…	…	…	…	…	…	…	…	…	…	…	…	…	…	*	…	…	…	…	…	…	…
	+	…	…	…	…	…	…	…	…	…	…	…	…	*	…	+	…	…	…	…	…	…	…	…
	*	…	…	…	…	…	…	…	*	…	…	…	…	…	…	…	…	…	…	…	+	…	…	…
	…	…	…	…	…	…	+	…	…	…	…	…	…	…	…	…	…	+	+	…	…	…	…	…
	+	…	…	…	…	…	+	…	…	…	…	…	…	…	…	…	…	…	…	…	…	…	+	+
	…	…	…	…	…	…	…	…	*	…	…	…	…	…	…	…	*	…	…	…	…	…	…	…
	*	…	…	+	…	*	…	…	…	+	…	…	…	…	…	…	*	…	…	…	…	…	…	…
	…	…	…	…	…	…	…	+	…	…	…	…	…	…	…	…	…	…	…	…	…	…	…	…
	…	…	…	…	…	…	…	…	…	…	…	…	…	…	…	…	…	…	…	…	…	…	…	…

TABLE 43

List of lochs and/or swamps of which some plant communities were studied during the survey from 1958–61. Water analysis data are also given (for soil data see Table 44).

LOCALITY	COUNTY	WATER ANALYSES		
		pH	Alkalinity p.p.m. CaCO$_3$	Conductivity (μmhos)
Achlaise L. na h'	Argyll	6·61	...	...
Aigeil, L. an; Stoer	Sutherland	8·60	157·0	375
Applecross, lochans at Pass of	Ross	6·64	<0·05	43
Aundarroch, swamp at; Spey	Inverness	...	...	...
Avich, swamp at L.	Argyll	...	...	...
Awe, L.	Argyll	...	...	...
Barhapple, L.	Wigtown	...	...	...
Beg, L.	Sutherland	...	...	...
Black L., Castle Kennedy	Wigtown	6·60	...	...
Black L.	Fife	...	...	...
Calder, L.	Caithness	7·70	44·4	...
Calladail, L.: Durness	Sutherland	8·70	117·6	...
Carlingwark, L.	Stewartry	8·50	...	...
Ceon Ghlas, L.; Ness	Inverness	...	...	...
Chadha Charnaich, L. na; Raasay	Inverness	7·20	23·5	...
Choin, L. an; Ness	Inverness	6·38	3·75	71
Clousta, L.	Shetland	7·61	44·8	216
Clunie, L.	Perth	7·20	16·4	...
Corby, L.	Aberdeen	...	...	...
Creagach, L.; nr. Eriboll	Sutherland	...	...	...
Cree, R.	Stewartry	...	...	...
Croispol, L.; Durness	Sutherland	8·70	135·4	302
Dernaglar, L.	Wigtown	...	...	...
Dhughaill, L.	Ross	...	...	...
Dubh, L.; Lomond	Stirling	...	...	...
Duddingston, L.	Midlothian	...	...	...
Eader na Bhaile, swamp by L.; Raasay	Inverness	8·40	83·1	...
Eriboll, swamp nr. L.	Sutherland	...	...	...
Flatpunds, lochan nr. L.	Shetland	7·30	...	...
Forfar, L.	Angus	9·60	106·0	...
Gamhna, L.; Speyside	Inverness	7·00	9·2	...
Garderhouse, lochan nr.	Shetland	...	...	...
Garten, L.; Speyside	Inverness	6·90	7·8	...
Gealach, L. an; Lorne	Argyll	...	...	...
Gobhar, L. nan	Sutherland	...	...	...
Grasswater	Shetland	...	...	...
Hacoin, L.; and lochan nr.	Sutherland	6·83	20·0	191
Hempriggs, L.	Caithness	8·90	59·2	...
Hollistan, L.	Caithness	...	...	...
Hope, L.	Sutherland	...	...	...
Insch, L. and swamp; Speyside	Inverness	6·90	13·2	...
Ken, L.	Stewartry	7·20	...	...
Kilconquhar, L.	Fife	8·10	...	...
Kinardochy, L.	Perth	7·20	20·0	...
Kinord, L.	Aberdeen	6·64	0·09	44
Lanish, L.; Durness	Sutherland	8·70	77·6	...
Leven, L.	Fife	...	...	...
Lindores, L.	Fife	7·90	52	...
Lochend, L.; Ness	Inverness	...	...	...

TABLE 43—*continued*

| LOCALITY | COUNTY | WATER ANALYSES | | |
		pH	Alkalinity p.p.m. CaCO₃	Conductivity (μmhos)
Loirston, L.	Aberdeen	...	...	...
Loin, L. an	Ross	7·99	57·0	121
Lomond, L.	Stirling	6·50	5·0	...
Lowes, L. of	Perth	7·00	13·6	...
Lunga Water	Shetland	6·95	...	...
Lurgainn, L.	Sutherland	6·75	...	...
Maberry, L.	Stewartry	...	...	...
Magillie, L.	Wigtown	[4·81]	...	...
Maiden, L.	Sutherland	7·24	15·0	131
Mallachie, L.; Speyside	Inverness	7·20	...	...
Marlee, L.	Perth	7·10	20·8	...
Meiklie, L.; Ness	Inverness	...	...	...
Merkland, L.	Sutherland	6·80	...	...
Mheig, L. a'; Ness	Inverness	...	...	...
Mhor, L.	Sutherland	6·80	5·2	...
Mill, L. Semblister	Shetland	6·00	...	...
Mochrum, L.	Wigtown	7·30	...	...
Mor, L.; Speyside	Inverness	...	...	...
Moraig, L.	Perth	8·20	69·6	...
Moriston, swamp in Glen	Inverness	...	...	...
Neldricken, L.	Stewartry	6·80	...	...
Ness, L.; Borlum, Inchnacardoch, Urquhart	Inverness	...	...	...
Oich, L.; Ness	Inverness	...	...	...
Ordain, L. an; Ness	Inverness	7·06	12·5	84
Ordain, L. an	Sutherland	...	...	...
Park, L. of	Aberdeen	...	...	...
Rescobie, L.	Angus	8·70	89·6	...
Restenneth, swamp at	Angus	...	...	...
Rothiemurchus, swamp in	Inverness	...	...	...
Ruaidhe, L. na Ba; Ness	Inverness	7·20	...	...
Sarclett, L.	Caithness	9·50	75·8	...
Saighead, Leac nan	Ross	...	...	...
Sandy Water (Lang Kames)	Shetland	7·11	30·1	164
Soulseat, L.	Wigtown	7·40	...	...
Spiggie, L.	Shetland	7·80	37·0	415
Stack, L.	Sutherland	6·70	2·8	...
Stanevatsoe, L.	Shetland	7·08	25·2	194
Tarff, L.; Ness	Inverness	6·88	10·0	67
Torridon, R.	Ross	...	...	...
Uala, L. na	Sutherland	6·73	10·0	79
Uamha, L. na; Speyside	Inverness	...	...	...
Uanagan, L.; Ness	Inverness	7·28	37·5	107
Uath lochan; Speyside	Inverness	...	...	...
Valley L.	Stewartry	...	...	...
Vidlin, lochan near	Shetland	...	...	...
Watten, L.	Caithness	9·30	61·2	...
Wester, Wick	Caithness	...	...	...
White L., Anabaglish	Wigtown	6·65	...	...
White L., Castle Kennedy	Wigtown	8·45	...	...
Yarhouse L.	Caithness	...	...	...

TABLE 44

Soil properties measured under the named community-types, together with localities.

Locality	Sand			Oxidised carbon % C	% organic matter (2 × % C)	% silt plus clay	pH	% N	C/N
	% fine	% coarse	total						
(1) Carex lasiocarpa sociation									
Uanagan	4·7	0·7	5·4	30·3	60·6	34·0	6·11	...	...
an Ordain (Ness)	0·3	0	0·3	32·7	65·4	34·3	4·92	...	...
Stack	...	...	...	34·5	69·0	...	5·44	0·92	39
Ba Ruaidhe	...	...	...	0·9	1·8	...	6·81	0·01	89
Ba Ruaidhe	...	...	...	38·6	77·2	...	5·73	0·97	39
(2) Open Carex rostrata soc. (I), Carex rostrata—Menyanthes (II), C. rostrata—Sphagnum (IIb), C. rostrata—Acrocladium (III)									
II Grasswater	2·1	1·2	3·3	38·0	76·0	20·7	5·88	...	...
II Flatpunds	0·1	0	0·1	38·7	77·4	22·5	5·73	...	...
IIb h'Achlaise	19·1	37·5	56·6	16·2	32·4	11·0	5·71	...	...
I Uanagan	36·0	44·5	80·5	4·8	9·6	9·9	5·61	...	...
II an Choin	0·8	0·2	1·0	39·3	78·6	20·4	...	...	...
I Tarff	60·5	11·1	71·6	9·9	19·8	8·6	5·69	...	...
I Tarff	...	...	...	2·5	5·0	...	6·39	...	...
I Ness	...	...	...	13·5	27·0	...	5·52	0·73	18
III Ness	...	...	...	6·1	12·2	...	5·58	0·1	60
I a' Mheig	...	...	...	2·6	5·2	...	5·86	1·07	15
I Ba Ruaidhe	...	...	...	2·2	4·4	...	6·76	0·20	11
I Meiklie	...	...	...	14·5	29·0	...	5·53	0·40	36
III Lochend	...	...	...	22·9	45·8	...	5·55	0·44	52
I Rescobie	...	...	...	1·9	3·8	...	6·54	...	...
IIb Hollistan	...	...	...	43·2	86·4	...	5·69	0·27	160
III Restenneth	...	...	...	8·8	17·5	...	6·65	2·43	3·6
II Rescobie	...	...	...	16·3	32·6	...	6·40	0·36	45
II Park	...	...	...	34·2	68·4	...	...	2·04	17
	...	...	...	16·4	32·8	...	...	0·53	33
(8) Nymphaea alba soc.									
an Ordain	6·1	1·5	7·6	30·0	60·0	32·4	6·18	...	...
an Aigeil	10·6	74·5	85·1	3·9	7·8	7·1	8·09	...	...
na Uala	28·2	30·5	58·7	21·0	42·0	0	6·32	...	...
an Loin	55·9	13·2	69·1	5·7	11·4	19·9	6·55	...	...
an Ordain (Ness)	1·1	10·3	11·4	39·6	79·2	21·2	5·38	...	...
an Choin	17·7	0·7	18·4	26·7	53·4	27·4	5·59	...	...
Stanevatsoe	6·5	0·5	7·0	40·5	81·0	12·0	6·31	...	...

								⋮	
								⋮	
(6) J. fluitans—Utricularia (U), J. fluitans—Sphagnum subsecundum (S) sociations									
U na' Uala	36·5	8·2	44·7	19·7	39·4	15·9	⋮	6·19
U an Loin	33·2	7·0	40·2	21·1	42·2	17·6	⋮	6·89
S Applecross	36·5	59·4	95·9	1·2	2·4	1·7	⋮	5·92
S Applecross	16·3	0·7	17·0	33·0	66·0	17·0	⋮	5·82
S Applecross	14·2	3·8	18·0	28·0	56·0	26·0	⋮	5·39
S Applecross	2·5	2·9	5·4	41·4	82·8	11·8	⋮	5·82
U Merkland	71·8	16·5	88·3	1·0	2·0	91·7	⋮	5·82
U Uanagan	10·5	3·4	13·9	38·4	76·8	9·3	⋮	6·38
S Meiklie	5·2	0·4	5·6	22·2	44·4	35·3	⋮	5·38
U Grasswater	12·1	2·9	15·0	29·9	59·8	55·1	⋮	5·99
U Flatpunds	3·2	0·5	3·7	43·2	86·4	61·6	⋮	6·12
U Kinord	0	0	0	5·2	10·4	89·6	⋮	5·62
S a Mheig	...	...	...	20·4	40·8	...	⋮	5·81
(7) Littorella—J. fluitans and Nitella—Littorella (N)									
Grasswater	3·0	8·9	11·9	42·3	84·6	3·5	⋮	5·75
Applecross	13·9	29·9	43·8	12·9	25·8	30·4	⋮	6·00
Tarff	44·3	39·8	84·1	1·1	2·2	13·7	⋮	6·59
Tarff	70·1	2·1	72·2	1·8	3·6	24·2	⋮	5·89
Kinord	20·8	48·6	69·4	9·7	19·4	11·2	⋮	6·42
N Kinord	47·5	7·2	54·8	11·3	22·6	22·6	⋮	5·80
(5) Isoetes and Nitella—Isoetes (N)									
Merkland	81·5	14·0	95·5	0·1	0·2	4·3	⋮	6·16
Tarff	81·4	2·1	83·5	2·7	5·4	11·1	⋮	6·92
N Kinord	20·0	26·0	46·0	3·0	6·0	48·0	⋮	6·18
(10) Schoenoplectus—Littorella soc.									
an Loin	17·7	6·5	24·2	8·1	16·2	59·6	⋮	6·38
Sandy Water	20·0	61·4	81·4	5·9	11·8	6·8	⋮	6·81
Uanagan	25·1	1·5	26·6	25·5	51·0	22·4	⋮	5·61
Kinord	43·2	7·8	50·8	22·3	44·6	4·6	⋮	5·68
(11) Miscellaneous samples									
Fontinalis; an Choin	15·7	1·0	16·7	28·8	57·6	23·7	⋮	5·25
P. natans; Vidlin	10·0	1·3	11·3	39·9	79·8	8·9	⋮	6·22
P. × zizii; Uanagan	5·2	0·4	5·6	22·2	44·4	9·3	⋮	5·38
Lobelia; Lurgainn	18·5	77·4	95·9	0·6	1·2	2·9	⋮	...
Phragmites; Lurgainn	14·1	81·8	95·9	0·4	0·8	3·3	⋮	6·38
Phragmites; Dubh	8·6	46·3	54·9	5·1	10·2	34·9	⋮	...

[An additional set of 14 *Phragmites* samples are represented graphically in Fig. 50c, p. 343.]

TABLE 45

Synoptic Table of Sociations in the *Potamogeton filiformis-Chara* association (p. 320) and the *Juncus fluitans—Lobelia dortmanna* association (p. 321).

Association	Potamogeton filiformis—Chara			Juncus fluitans—Lobelia dortmanna				
Sociation	P. filiformis—Chara	Littorella—P. filiformis	Chara—Myriophyllum alterniflorum	Open Littorella—Lobelia	Lobelia—Littorella	Littorella—Juncus	Juncus—Utricularia	Juncus—Sphagnum
Number of stands	8	5	9	5	9	15	15	10
Plot size (sq. m.)*	2·5	2·6	...	3	2	3·3	3	1·5
Soil type	sandy protopedon	sandy protopedon	sandy marl-marl	protopedon	protopedon-brown mud	protopedon brown mud	brown mud	brown mud
Water level, cm. above soil surface — Mean	30	44	89	29	50	53	71	11
Water level — Range	15 to 70	5 to 107	40 to 250+	30 to 60	15 to 150	0 to 125	28 to 170	5 to 25
pH water: range	7·7 to 9·6	7·8 to 7·9	7·8 to 9·3	6·7 to 8·0	6·8	4·8 to 8·0	6·7 to 8·0	6·6 6·8
Alkalinity (p.p.m. CaCO₃) Range	35 to 157	35 to 136	35 to 135	28 to 57	28 to 95	1 to 57	1 to 57	0 to 5
Alkalinity — Mean	80	70	83	...	5	14	17	...
Total vegetation cover at water surface (%)	<5	8	<5	<5	12	<5	10	10
Total vegetation cover at soil surface (%)	46	57	78	30	60	53	88	82
Species density	5·7	5·2	6·4	6·0	6·3	8·2	9·7	7·5
Equisetum fluviatile	12 ++†	40 +	...	60 1	56 3	33 +	40 +	10 +
Isoetes lacustris	...	...	...	20 +	22 +	40 1	13 +	10 ++
Agrostis temuis	...	...	...	...	...	...	...	10 ++
Carex echinata	...	...	...	...	...	...	...	10 +
C. lasiocarpa	...	...	...	...	11 +	13 +	...	...
C. nigra	...	...	...	...	...	13 ++	13 +	10 +
C. rostrata	...	...	...	...	...	6 +	...	...
Eleocharis multicaulis	12 +	20 +	11 +	**80 2**	11 +	20 +	20 +	30 +
E. palustris	...	...	...	20 +	...	...	...	...
E. quinqueflora								

Species	1	2	3	4	5	6	7	8
Eleogiton fluitans		7 +	6 +					
Eriophorum angustifolium	20 1		6 +					
Glyceria fluitans			87 3				20 + (20 +)	12 +
Juncus fluitans	100 8	100 8		100 2	100 2			
Phragmites communis		20 2	13 +					
Schoenoplectus lacustris								
Sparganium angustifolium								
S. emersum	10 +	} 40 +						
S. minimum								
Potamogeton alpinus								12 +
Potamogeton filiformis							80 1	100 7
P. gramineus		33 +	20 +	22 +		44 +		12 +
P. natans	70 2	73 +	20 +			22 +		
P. ×nitens						11 +		12 +
P. obtusifolius		13 +	6 4			11 +	40 1	
P. pectinatus						33 +		37 +
P. perfoliatus						33 +		25 +
P. polygonifolius		13 +				11 +		
P. praelongus	10 +					11 +		
Potamogeton pusillus		7 +				11 +		12 +
P. ×zizii		7 +						12 +
Zannichellia palustris								37 1
Apium inundatum								12 +
Callitriche hermaphroditica	30 1	33 +	13 +					
C. intermedia		7 +	20 +					
C. stagnalis		7 +	6 +				20 +	
Caltha palustris ssp. radicans			6 +					
Elatine hexandra			6 +					
Hippuris vulgaris			6 +					
Hydrocotyle vulgaris				11 +				
Littorella uniflora	30 +	67 2	100 7	100 3	100 5	88 2	100 7	75 1
Lobelia dortmanna	20 +	60 3	87 2	100 6	100 5			
Menyanthes trifoliata		27 +	6 +					
Myriophyllum alterniflorum		87 3	53 2	22 +	60 1	86 2	40 1	
M. spicatum	40 +					11 +		
Nuphar pumila			6 +					12 +
Nymphaea alba								12 +
N. "occidentalis"								
Polygonum amphibium		20 +						12 +

TABLE 45—*continued*

Association	Potamogeton filiformis—Chara			Juncus fluitans—Lobelia dortmanna				
Sociation	*P. filiformis —Chara*	*Littorella —P. filiformis*	*Chara— Myrio-phyllum alterniflorum*	*Open Littorella Lobelia*	*Lobelia— Littorella*	*Littorella— Juncus*	*Juncus— Utricularia*	*Juncus— Sphagnum*
Ramunculus aquatilis	12 +	...	11 +	...	11 +	6 +	...	...
R. baudotii	...	...	...	...	...	...	...	...
R. trichophyllus	12 +	...	...	40 1	11 +	27 +	20 +	**80** 3
R. flammula	...	...	...	20 +	...	27 3	20 +	20 +
Subularia aquatica	...	...	...	...	...	13 +	**94** +	30 +
Utricularia vulgaris	12 +	...	...	...	11 +	13 +	...	...
Acrocladium cuspidatum	...	...	11 +	...	...	13 +	...	...
Bryum pallens	...	...	11 +	...	...	...	...	...
Cinclidotus fontinaloides	12 +	...	11 +	...	...	...	...	...
Drepanocladus aduncus	...	...	11 +	...	...	13 +	7 +	20 +
D. lycopodioides	...	...	...	...	...	...	...	10 +
D. exannulatus	...	...	...	...	22 +	...	...	...
D. revolvens	...	...	...	...	...	6 +	...	...
Fissidens adianthoides	...	...	...	...	...	13 +	33 +	...
Fontinalis antipyretica	12 +	40 +	11 +	20 +	...	...	...	...
Hygroamblystegium irriguum	...	...	...	...	...	...	...	...
Tayloria lingulata?	...	...	...	...	...	...	7 +	20 +
Scorpidium scorpioides	...	...	...	...	...	...	13 +	10 +
Sphagnum cuspidatum	...	...	...	...	...	...	...	...

	C1		C2		C3		C4		C5		C6		C7		C8	
S. palustre	…	…	…	…	…	…	…	…	…	…	…	…	…	…	10	+
S. plumulosum	…	…	…	…	…	…	…	…	…	…	…	…	…	…	10	+
Sphagnum subsecundum var. **auriculatum**	…	…	…	…	…	…	…	…	33	+	…	…	20	+	**100**	**4**
Jungermannia tristis	…	…	…	…	…	…	…	…	…	…	6	+	…	…	…	…
Marsupella aquatica	…	…	…	…	…	…	…	…	…	…	…	…	7	+	…	…
Pellia neesiana	…	…	…	…	…	…	…	…	…	…	…	…	7	+	…	…
Riccardia multifida	…	…	…	…	…	…	…	…	…	…	…	…	…	…	10	+
Scapania undulata	…	…	…	…	…	…	…	…	11	+	…	…	…	…	10	+
Chara aspera	75	1	40	1	**100**	**7**	…	…	…	…	…	…	…	…	…	…
Chara aspera var. lacustris	25	1	20	+	…	…	20	+	11	+	6	+	…	…	…	…
C. delicatula var. annulata	…	…	20	+	33	2	…	…	…	…	…	…	…	…	…	…
C. delicatula var. barbata	…	…	…	…	…	…	…	…	…	…	…	…	13	+	…	…
C. globularis	…	…	…	…	11	+	…	…	…	…	…	…	…	…	…	…
C. papillosum	…	…	…	…	44	1	…	…	…	…	…	…	…	…	…	…
C. rudis	…	…	…	…	11	+	…	…	…	…	…	…	…	…	…	…
Nitella flexilis	…	…	…	…	…	…	…	…	…	…	…	…	…	…	…	…
N. opaca	…	…	20	+	11	+	…	…	11	+	40	++	20	++	10	+
N. translucens	…	…	…	…	…	…	…	…	…	…	13	+	13	+	…	…
Batrachospermum moniliforme	12	1	…	…	…	…	…	…	…	…	…	…	…	…	…	…
Sponge, Spongilla lacustris	…	…	…	…	…	…	…	…	33	+	13	1	…	…	…	…

(In column C1 the values for *Chara aspera* (75 1) and *Chara aspera* var. *lacustris* (25 1) are braced together as 87.)

* In all synoptic tables in this chapter, plot size, the total vegetation cover and height of vegetation are mean values.

† In all synoptic tables in this chapter the quantitative data for species are shown as per cent. presence in the first column and mean cover-abundance (Domin scale) in the second, under each community type. A species having a presence of 80 per cent. or more (75 per cent. or more in some species-poor sociations) is regarded as a constant and shown in bold, as are dominant species.

TABLE 46

Synoptic table of some linear- and rosette-leaved Societies (p. 325) with *Potamogeton gramineus* sociations (p. 327) and individual quadrats of stands of linear-leaved *Potamogeton* species (other than *P. filiformis*, p. 320). (Cols. 1 and 4 record % presence only.)

Society	(1) Fontinalis anti-pyretica	(2) Elodea canadensis	(3) Isoetes lacustris	(4) Nitella opaca / N. opaca var. brachyclema / N. translucens	(5) Potamogeton gramineus	Quadrats of Potamogeton species*							
						Watten	Carlingwark	Croispol	Calder	an Loin	Lowes	Corby	Spiggie
Number of stands	3	5	7	8	12								
Water level cm. above soil surface — Mean	190	179	66	200	100	28	80	90	55	32	250	110	60
— Range	80 to 300	50 to 200	3 to 250	100 to 400	40 to 260	±8	±20	±30	±20	±8	±100		
Total vegetation cover at soil surface (%)	?90	75	66	?90	...	25 sand	100	100 mud	100	80 sand		100 mud	80
Species density	3	5	5·7	4·5	6·3	4	4	8	6	4	5	6	11
Equisetum fluviatile					8 +								
Isoetes echinospora				12	8 +								
I. lacustris			**100 7**	25	8 +								
Elodea canadensis		**100 7**	28 +	12	24 +		3						
Juncus fluitans		20 +	57 +		16 +								
Sparganium angustifolium													
S. minimum			14 +										
Potamogeton alpinus	33	40 4		12	8 +								
P. berchtoldii				25	8 +				9	7	2		
P. crispus													
P. filiformis		20 +		25	8 +			1		7	2	4	6
P. gramineus					**100 7**								
P. lucens					8 +								
P. natans		20 +			66 1			2	1				
P. × nitens					16 +								
P. obtusifolius				12	8 +			9				6	
P. pectinatus					8 +	4	7				8		4
P. perfoliatus	33	40 +		37	24 +				2				2

Species	1	2	3	4	5	6	7	8	9	10	11	12	13
P. praelongus													
P. pusillus	33	40 +		25	8 +								7
P. × sparganifolius				12									
P. × zizii										1			
Apium inundatum													
Callitriche hermaphroditica			11 +	12	16 +				1			8	2
C. intermedia			28 ++	12								2	
C. stagnalis			28 ++						1				
Elatine hexandra			28 +	12									
Littorella uniflora		40 4	42 1		25 +	2		1		1	1		1
Lobelia dortmanna			56 1		16 ++								
Myriophyllum alterniflorum				37	33 +								3
M. spicatum							5	+					
Nuphar lutea		20 1	42 1								1	3	
Ranunculus aquatilis					8 ++								+
R. trichophyllus	33	20 +	28 ++	12	8 +								
Subularia aquatica			14 ++										
Utricularia vulgaris					8 +								3
Fontinalis antipyretica	dominant		14 ++	37									
Tayloria lingulata			14 ++										
Chara aspera	33				50 +	1		3					
C. contraria				25									+
C. delicatula					8 ++								
C. delicatula var. annulata var. barbata					24 +	3		3					
C. globularis	33												
C. papillosum								4					
C. rudis					8 +								
Nitella flexilis									6				
N. opaca		40 +		dt. twice	58 ++							5	
N. opaca var. brachyclema				dt. thrice	8 ++								+
N. translucens				dt. thrice	8 ++					4			
Spongilla lacustris			70 1		16 ++								

* Columns of individual quadrats in Tables 46, 47, 52 and 54 record cover-abundance on Domin's scale. Dominant and constant species and their cover-abundance are printed in bold type.

TABLE 47

Individual quadrats of various broad-leaved *Potamogeton* spp. communities (p. 327).

Loch	Hemp-riggs	Sarclett	Kinord	Ceon Ghlas	Lanish	White	an Loin	Uanagan	Ordain (Ness)
Total vegetation cover at soil surface (%)	?100	...	to 100	100	100	?100	100	80	90
Soil type	black mud	mud	brown mud	mud	grey marl	mud	grey mud	brown mud	brown mud
Water level, cm. above soil surface	285 ±15	205 ±45	130 ±30	190 ±30	200 ±50	185 ±75	190 ±10	210 ±40	120
pH	8·9	9·5	7·0	?	8·7	8·5	8·0	7·3	7
Alkalinity (p.p.m. CaCO$_3$)	59	76	2	?	78	?	57	37	12
Isoetes lacustris			1	+					
Juncus fluitans									+
Sparganium minimum				+				4	
Potamogeton alpinus							+		7
P. berchtoldii			2						
P. crispus			2				1		
P. gramineus					4				
P. perfoliatus	8	8	9				9	6	
P. × zizii								+	
P. lucens				8	8	7			
P. praelongus			5				1		+
P. natans									
P. obtusifolius									
P. pectinatus		+							
Ceratophyllum demersum						+			
Elodea canadensis									+
Littorella uniflora				+				+	+
Lobelia dortmanna			+	+				+	+
Myriophyllum alternifolium									+
M. spicatum					2	4			
Ramunculus baudotii			+				1		
Utricularia vulgaris									
Fontinalis antipyretica	+	+	+						
Chara aspera	+			+	+				
C. globularis									
Nitella opaca			5					+	
N. translucens									+

TABLE 48

Synoptic table of floating-leaved communities (pages 329 to 331).

Society	(1) ssp. occidentalis	(2) ssp. alba	(3) Nuphar lutea	(4) Potamogeton natans	(5) Polygonum amphibium
	(1) (2) Nymphaea alba				
Number of stands . .	4	8	11	13	5
Plot size (sq. m.) . .	45	3	3	3	3
Soil type	brown mud	sand, brown mud, black mud	brown or black mud	sand, brown mud	sand or brown mud
Water level, cm above Mean	67	103	102	102	100
soil surface Range	20–125	20–195	20–150	12–260	30–200
pH mean	7·2		7·2	7·5	...
range . . .	6·4 to 8·6		6·6 to 7·9	6·8 to 9·4	...
Alkalinity (p.p.m. CaCO₃) .	2·5 to 157		2·5 to 52	5·2 to 57(117)	...
Total vegetation cover water surface (%)	55	80	41	55	c. 55
Total vegetation cover soil surface (%)	64	44	43	55	c. 50
Species density . . .	10	6	5	6	7
Equisetum fluviatile . .	50 1	25 1	18 +	7 +	40 +
Isoetes lacustris . .	...	...	...	7 +	...
Alisma plantago-aquatica .	...	12 +	...	...	20 +
Carex rostrata . . .	...	25 1	...	...	...
Eleocharis multicaulis . .	25 +	12 +	...	7 +	...
E. palustris . . .	25 +	...	...	7 +	20 +
Eleogiton fluitans . .	25 +	...	...	...	...
Elodea canadensis . .	...	...	27 1	7 +	40 4
Glyceria fluitans . .	...	...	...	7 +	...
Lemna minor . . .	...	...	9 +	...	...
L. trisulca	...	...	9 +	...	...
J. articulatus . . .	12 +	...	...	...	...
Juncus fluitans . . .	**75 3**	37 1	36 +	**78 1**	20 +
Phragmites communis . .	25 +	...	9 +	...	...
Schoenoplectus lacustris .	...	...	...	14 1	...
Sparganium angustifolium .	...	12 +	9 +	28 +⎫	...
S. emersum . . .	25 +	...	...	... ⎬77+	...
S. minimum . . .	25 +	...	18 +	49 +⎭	...
S. erectum	...	...	9 +	...	...
Potamogeton alpinus . .	...	12 +	...	7 +	...
P. berchtoldii . . .	...	50 1	18 +	7 +	20 +
P. crispus . . .	...	...	9 +	...	20 1
P. filiformis . . .	...	12 +	...	...	...
P. gramineus . . .	25 +	25 +	18 +	7 +	40 +
P. × lintonii . . .	...	...	9 +	...	...
P. natans	50 2	37 1	27 +	**100 7**	40 4

TABLE 48—*continued*

Society	(1) *Nymphaea alba* ssp. occidentalis	(2) *Nymphaea alba* ssp. alba	(3) *Nuphar lutea*	(4) *Potamogeton natans*	(5) *Polygonum amphibium*
P. obtusifolius . . .	...	12 +	54 1	...	40 +
P. perfoliatus . . .	...	12 +	...	14 +	40 +
P. pusillus . . .	25 +	...	9 +	...	...
Potamogeton × sparganifolius .	...	12 +	...	7 +	...
P. × zizii	...	12 +	18 +	7 +	40 1
Apium inundatum . .	...	...	9 +	...	...
Callitriche hermaphroditica .	...	...	9 +	...	20 +
C. intermedia . . .	...	...	...	7 +	...
C. stagnalis . . .	...	...	...	...	...
Hippuris vulgaris . .	...	12 +	9 +	...	...
Hydrocotyle vulgaris . .	...	...	...	...	...
Littorella uniflora . .	...	...	36 1	21 +	40 +
Lobelia dortmanna . .	...	25 +	9 +	28 +	...
Menyanthes trifoliata . .	...	...	...	7 +	...
Myriophyllum alterniflorum .	...	...	9 +	57 1	20 +
M. spicatum . . .	...	...	9 +	...	...
Nuphar lutea . . .	...	12 +	**100 7**	7 +	60 2
Nymphaea alba . . .	...	**100 7**	...	...	...
N. alba ssp. occidentalis	**100 7**	...	...	14 +	...
Polygonum amphibium .	...	...	...	...	**100 6**
Ranunculus aquatilis . .	...	...	9 +	...	20 +
R. flammula . . .	...	...	...	7 +	...
R. trichophyllus . .	...	...	9 +	...	20 +
Utricularia vulgaris . .	...	12 +	...	14 +	...
Acrocladium cuspidatum .	25 +	...	...	...	...
Drepanocladus exannulatus .	25 +	...	...	...	...
Fontinalis antipyretica . .	50 3	12 2	...	...	20 +
F. antipyretica f. gracile .	25 +	...	...	...	...
Mnium punctatum . .	25 +	...	...	...	...
Scorpidium scorpioides . .	50 +	...	...	...	...
Sphagnum subsecundum var. auriculatum	25 +	...	...	...	...
Jungermannia tristis . .	25 +	...	...	...	...
Chara aspera var. lacustris .	...	...	...	7 +	...
C. delicatula . . .	25 +	...	...	7 +	40 +
C. globularis . . .	...	...	...	...	...
Nitella flexilis . . .	...	...	...	...	...
N. opaca	...	...	...	7 +	...
var. brachyclema . .	...	25 +	...	...	...
N. translucens . . .	50 1	25 4	...	...	...
Spongilla lacustris . .	...	12 +	9 +	7 +	...

TABLE 49

Synoptic table of: (1) *Schoenoplectus lacustris—Juncus fluitans* sociation, (2) *Equisetum fluviatile—Littorella* sociation, (3) *Eleocharis palustris—Littorella* sociation, (4) *Typha latifolia—Lemna minor* sociation, (5) *Equisetum fluviatile—Acrocladium* sociation and (6) *Cladium mariscus—Myrica gale* sociation.

Sociation	(1) *Schoenoplectus lacustris— Juncus fluitans*	(2) *Equisetum fluviatile— Littorella*	(3) *Eleocharis palustris— Littorella*	(4) *Typha latifolia— Lemna minor*	(5) *Equisetum fluviatile— Acrocladium*	(6) *Cladium mariscus— Myrica gale*
Page no.	331	333	332	333	352	334
Number of stands	8	6	11	5	4	4
Plot size (sq. m.)	3	3	2	3	3	3
Soil	1 clay, 3 peat-gyttja, 3 silty sand, 1 sand	sand or sandy mud	sand in nine	sedge-peat	sedge-peat	mud
Mean height (cm.)	128	54	18	196	94	145
Water level, cm. above, or below (−), Mean	88	85	28	19	−2	1
Range	150 to 30	150 to 40	55 to 8	60 to 0	3 to −7	28 to −19
Total vegetation cover at water surface (%)	15	14	24	42	85	...
Total vegetation cover at soil surface (%)	52	26	43	...	...	40
Species density	6·4	6	8·3	5·6	15	12·5
Fraxinus excelsior	...	...	...	...	...	...
Myrica gale	...	...	...	...	...	**100 3**
Salix cinerea ssp. atrocinerea	...	...	...	...	25 2	...
S. aurita	...	...	...	...	25 2	...
Equisetum arvense	...	...	...	...	25 +	...
Equisetum fluviatile	12 +	**100 5**	55 +	40 +	**100 7**	...
Isoetes lacustris	12 5	...	...	...	...	...
Agrostis canina ssp. canina	...	...	...	...	25 +	50 1
Deschampsia cespitosa	...	...	...	...	...	...
Glyceria fluitans	...	...	18 +	...	25 +	...
Glyceria maxima	...	...	...	...	25 +	...
Molinia caerulea	...	...	...	...	...	50 1
Phalaris arundinacea	...	...	...	20 +	...	...
Phragmites communis	...	17 +	...	...	...	**100 2**

Species	1	2	3	4	5	6
Carex aquatilis	·	·	·	20 +	·	·
Carex curta	·	·	·	·	·	25 +
C. demissa	·	·	·	·	25 +	·
C. echinata	·	·	·	·	·	25 +
C. lasiocarpa	·	·	·	·	·	**100 2**
C. nigra	·	·	18 +	·	25 2	25 +
C. panicea	25 1	·	9 +	20 +	25 +	·
C. rostrata	·	17 +	·	40 1	50 2	·
C. vesicaria	·	·	·	·	·	·
Cladium mariscus	·	·	·	·	·	**100 8**
Eriophorum angustifolium	25 +	·	·	·	25 +	·
Eleocharis multicaulis	·	·	·	20 +	·	25 +
E. palustris	12 +	·	**100 5**	·	25 1	·
Eleogiton fluitans	12 +	·	·	·	·	·
Elodea canadensis	·	·	·	·	·	·
Juncus articulatus	·	·	27 +	·	25 ++	·
J. effusus	·	·	·	·	25 ++	·
J. fluitans	**87 1**	33 +	45 1	**80 4**	25 ++	·
Lemna minor	12 +	·	·	·	·	·
Potamogeton crispus	·	·	·	·	·	·
P. filiformis	·	33 1	9 +	·	·	·
P. gramineus	50 1	50 2	·	·	·	·
P. natans	12 +	·	36 1	·	·	·
P. obtusifolius	·	·	9 ++	·	·	·
P. pectinatus	·	·	·	·	·	25 +
P. polygonifolius	·	·	18 ++	·	·	·
P. ×zizii	25 2	·	·	·	·	·
Schoenoplectus lacustris	**100 5**	·	·	**100 7**	·	·
Sparganium erectum	75 +	·	·	·	·	·
Sparganium minimum	·	·	·	·	·	·
Typha latifolia	·	·	·	·	·	·
Angelica sylvestris	·	·	·	20 +	25 1	·
Bidens cernua	12 +	·	·	·	·	·
Callitriche stagnalis	·	·	9 +	·	·	·
Caltha palustris	·	·	9 ++	·	·	·
Cardamina amara	·	·	18 ++	20 +	50 1	·
Cicuta virosa	12 +	·	·	20 +	·	·
Elatine hexandra	·	·	·	·	·	·
Epilobium palustre	12 +	·	·	20 +	50 1	·

TABLE 49—continued

Sociation	(1) Schoenoplectus lacustris—Juncus fluitans	(2) Equisetum fluviatile—Littorella	(3) Eleocharis palustris—Littorella	(4) Typha latifolia—Lemna minor	(5) Equisetum fluviatile—Acrocladium	(6) Cladium mariscus—Myrica gale
Filipendula ulmaria	...	...	...	...	50 2	...
Galium palustre	...	...	...	20 +	75 **1**	25 +
Hippuris vulgaris	...	...	...	...	...	75 **1**
Hydrocotyle vulgaris	37 1	75 1	...	...	...	...
Littorella uniflora	25 +	33 +	72 **3**	...	...	...
Lobelia dortmanna	...	...	27 1	...	...	25 +
Mentha aquatica	...	17 +	9 +	20 +	25 +	25 +
Menyanthes trifoliata	12 +	...	...	20 +	75 **2**	...
Myosotis caespitosa	...	50 1	36 +	...	25 +	...
Myriophyllum alterniflorum	...	17 1	...	...	...	...
Nymphaea alba	...	17 +	9 +	...	...	...
N. alba ssp. occidentalis	...	...	...	...	...	...
Nuphar lutea	12 +	...	...	20 +	...	...
Pedicularis palustris	...	...	...	...	25 +	...
Polygonum amphibium	...	...	9 +	...	25 +	...
Potentilla palustris	...	...	9 +	20 +	100 **4**	...
Ranunculus acris	...	...	9 ++	...	25 +	...
R. flammula	...	...	27 ++	...	25 +	25 +
Rorippa nasturtium-aquaticum	...	...	9 +	...	...	...
Rumex hydrolapathum	...	...	...	20 +	25 +	...
Scutellaria galericulata	...	...	...	...	25 +	...
Stellaria alsine	...	...	...	...	...	...
Subularia aquatica	12 +	...	...	...	...	...
Succisa pratensis	...	...	...	...	25 +	...
Utricularia intermedia	...	17 +	...	...	25 1	50 1
U. vulgaris	12 +	...	18 +	...	...	...
U. minor	...	...	...	...	...	...

Species	1	2	3	4	5	6	7
Valeriana officinalis		25 +					
Veronica scutellata		50 +					
Acrocladium cordifolium		75 2					
A. cuspidatum	25 +			9 +			
A. stramineum	25 +						
Aulacomnium palustre							
Brachythecium rivulare			40 +				
Campylium stellatum	50 +			18 +		12 +	
Drepanocladus revolvens	75 1	25 +					
Eurhynchium praelongum							
Fissidens adianthoides	25 +			27 +	25 +		
Fontinalis antipyretica							
Mnium hornum							
M. punctatum		25 +		27 3	25 +	12 +	
Scorpidium scorpioides	75 1	25 +		9 +	25 +		
Sphagnum palustre							
S. papillosum	25 1						
S. plumulosum	25 1						
S. subsecundum var auriculatum	75 1	25 1		18 +			
S. squarrosum		25 +					
Chiloscyphus pallescens		25 +					
Lophocolea bidentata	50 +	25					
Riccardia multifida	25 +						
R. pinguis							
Chara aspera				9 +		12 +	
C. contraria				18 1			
C. delicatula				9 +		12 +	
C. delicatula var. barbata				18 +	25 +		
Nitella flexilis				18 +	25 +		
N. opaca				27 +		25 +	

TABLE 50

Phragmites communis sociations: I *P. communis—Sparganium minimum* and *P. communis—Littorella* open sociations; II *P. communis* society; III *P. communis—Galium palustre* sociation and variants: *Ranunculus lingua—Cicuta virosa* IIIa, and *Myrica gale—C. demissa* IIIb.

	Phragmites— Sparganium I	Phragmites communis II	Phragmites— Galium III	Phragmites— R. lingua IIIa	Phragmites— Myrica IIIb
Page no.	*335*	*335*	*336*	*336*	*336*
Number of stands . .	10	15	20	4	4
Plot size (sq. m.) . . .	3·2	7	3·6	4·6	3·5
Soil type	sandy protopedon, peat and peat gyttja	fen peat	fen peat	fen peat	fen or Sphagnum peat
Water level above, or {Mean	56	13	−10	−22	−4
below (−), soil surface {Range	110 to 8	50 to −30	2 to −40	...	...
pH	6·3	5·7	5·8	6·3	...
Total vegetation cover at water surface (%)	41	32	...	...	...
Total vegetation cover at soil surface (%)	55	30	68	74	86
Cover of dead leaves, at soil surface (%)	33	69	...	...	28
Height of vegetation (cm.) .	137	255	204	256	86
Alnus glutinosa . . .	...	...	5 +	...	...
Calluna vulgaris . .	...	...	10 +	...	50 1
Erica tetralix . . .	...	...	10 +	...	50 1
Myrica gale . . .	...	7 +	25 1	...	**100 3**
Salix cinerea ssp. *atrocinerea* .	...	7 +	10 +	...	...
S. aurita	...	...	5 +	...	...
Dryopteris filix-mas . .	...	...	5 +	...	...
E. fluviatile . . .	40 +	20 +	50 1	75 1	...
Agrostis canina ssp. *canina* .	...	...	40 1	...	50 1
A. stolonifera . . .	...	...	16 +	50 +	...
Glyceria maxima . . .	...	...	15 +	25 1	...
Molinia caerulea . .	...	...	25 1	...	**100 3**
Phragmites communis . .	**100 6**	**100 9**	**100 7**	**100 8**	**100 6**
Phalaris arundinacea .	...	...	20 +	75 1	...
Poa pratensis . . .	...	...	20 +	...	...
Carex curta . . .	...	...	5 +	...	25 1
C. demissa	...	...	...	...	50 +
C. dioica	...	...	...	...	25 +
C. lasiocarpa . . .	20 1	7 +	20 +	...	...
C. nigra	...	...	20 +	...	50 1
C. panicea	...	...	20 +	...	**100 2**
C. paniculata . . .	...	...	25 1	...	...
C. pulicaris . . .	...	...	...	...	25 +
C. riparia	...	7 +	5 +	...	...
C. rostrata . . .	10 +	20 1	55 2	25 +	...
C. echinata . . .	...	...	10 +	...	50 1
C. vesicaria . . .	...	...	10 +	...	...
Eleocharis palustris .	20 +	...	...	...	...

TABLE 50—*continued*

	Phragmites—Sparganium I	Phragmites communis II	Phragmites—Galium III	Phragmites—R. lingua IIIa	Phragmites—Myrica IIIb
E. quinqueflora	...	...	5 +	...	25 +
Eleogiton fluitans	10 1	...	...	...	...
Elodea canadensis	10 +	7 +	...	...	...
Eriophorum angustifolium	...	...	10 +	...	25 +
Juncus articulatus	...	...	10 +	...	...
J. bulbosus	50 2	...	10 +	...	50 1
J. conglomeratus	...	...	5 +	...	...
J. effusus	...	...	5 +	...	...
Rhychnospora alba	...	...	5 +	...	25 1
Alisma plantago-aquatica	10 +	...	...	...	...
Iris pseudacorus	...	...	15 +	50 1	...
Lemna minor	10 +	20 1	10 +	25 +	...
Hypericum elodes	...	13 +	...	...	...
Narthecium ossifragum	...	...	5 +	...	25 +
Nuphar lutea	...	7 +	...	...	...
Nymphaea alba	30 1	...	...	...	...
N. alba ssp. occidentalis	10 1	...	...	...	...
Potamogeton natans	30 1	...	...	...	...
Potamogeton alpinus	20 +	...	...	...	...
P. polygonifolius	10 1	7 +	...	...	...
Sparganium erectum	...	7 +	5 +	25 +	...
S. minimum	50 1	...	...	...	...
Typha angustifolia	10 +	...	...	...	...
T. latifolia	...	...	10 +	25 +	...
Achillea ptarmica	...	...	5 +	...	...
Angelica sylvestris	...	7 +	15 +	...	...
Aster ad lanceolatum	...	...	5 +	25 +	...
Caltha palustris	...	13 +	25 +	50 +	...
Cardamine amara	...	7 +	15 +	50 1	...
C. pratensis	...	...	10 +	...	...
Cicuta virosa	...	7 +	10 +	50 1	...
Drosera longifolia	...	...	10 +	50 +	...
D. rotundifolia	...	...	5 +	...	25 +
Epilobium obscurum	...	...	30 +	50 +	...
E. palustre	...	7 +	15 +	...	...
Filipendula ulmaria	...	...	30 +	...	...
Galium palustre *	...	...	**85 1**	...	50 1
G. uliginosum	...	...	5 +	...	...
Heracleum sphondylium	...	...	5 +	...	...
Hydrocotyle vulgaris	10 +	...	25 1	...	25 1
Littorella uniflora	50 2	...	...	...	...
Lobelia dortmanna	40 1	...	...	...	...
Lotus uliginosus	...	...	5 +	...	...
Lycopus europaeus	...	...	5 +	...	...
Lythrum salicaria	...	...	10 +	...	...
Mimulus guttatus	...	...	5 +	25 1	...

* 33% ssp. *elongatum.*

TABLE 50—*concluded*

	Phragmites—Sparganium I	Phragmites—communis II	Phragmites—Galium III	Phragmites—R. lingua IIIa	Phragmites—Myrica IIIb
Mentha aquatica	10 +	13 +	65 2	**75 2**	50 1
M. × verticillata	...	...	20 +	50 1	...
Menyanthes trifoliata	20 +	7 +	30 +	25 +	...
Myosotis caespitosa	...	...	5 +	25 +	...
M. scorpioides	...	...	35 1	**75 1**	...
Oenanthe crocata	...	...	5 +	...	...
Pedicularis palustris	...	...	10 +	...	...
Polygonum amphibium	10 +	...	...	...	...
P. hydropiper	...	...	10 +	...	...
Potentilla erecta	...	...	5 +	...	25 +
P. palustris	...	13 +	...	...	35 1
Ranunculus flammula	10 +	...	5 +	...	25 1
Rorippa nasturtium-aquaticum	10 +	7 +	5 +	25 1	...
Rumex conglomeratus	...	...	10 +	50 +	...
R. hydrolapathum	...	...	10 +	25 +	...
Scutellaria galericulata	...	7 +	25 1	25 +	...
Senecio aquatica	...	...	5 +	...	...
Solanum dulcamara	...	7 +	10 1	...	...
Stachys palustris	...	...	...	25 +	...
Stellaria alsine	...	...	15 1	...	...
Succisa pratensis	...	...	10 +	...	25 +
Utricularia intermedia	...	...	10 1	...	...
U. vulgaris	40 +	...	5 +	...	25 +
Valeriana officinalis	...	...	5 +	...	...
Viola palustris	...	...	...	...	25 +
Veronica scutellata	...	...	20 +	...	25 +
Acrocladium cordifolium	...	13 +	40 1	50 1	...
A. cuspidatum	7 +	...	30 +	25 +	...
A. sarmentosum	...	...	5 +	...	...
A. stramineum	...	...	5 +	...	25 1
Aulacomnium palustre	...	...	5 +	...	...
Brachythecium rutabulum	...	...	15 +	...	...
Drepanocladus exannulatus	...	...	5 +	...	50 1
D. revolvens	...	...	10 +	...	...
Eurhynchium praelongum	...	...	25 +	...	...
Hylocomium splendens	...	...	5 +	...	...
Pottia sp.	...	...	5 +	...	25 1
Sphagnum recurvum	...	...	5 +	...	25 +
S. rubellum	...	...	5 +	...	...
S. squarrosum	...	...	5 +	...	...
S. subsecundum var. *inundatum*	...	...	5 +	...	25 1
S. subsecundum var. *auriculatum*	...	...	5 +	...	25 +
Scapania undulata	...	...	...	...	...
Chara aspera	10 +	...	...	...	...
Nitella opaca	10 +	...	...	...	...

TABLE 51

Synoptic table of *Carex rostrata*, *C. lasiocarpa*, *C. vesicaria* and *C. paniculata* community-types.

Sociation	Carex rostrata sociations			Carex lasiocarpa community-types			C. vesicaria—Veronica scutellata	C. paniculata—Angelica sylvestris
	open C. rostrata	C. rostrata—Menyanthes	C. rostrata—Acrocladium	open C. lasiocarpa facies	C. lasiocarpa—Myrica	Myrica—C. lasiocarpa		
Page no.	344	344	344	346	346	346	348	349
Number of stands	11	8	11	4	11	4	6	7
Plot size (sq. m.)	3	2·3	3·3	2	2	2·5	2	4
Soil type	sandy protopedon	sedge peat	...	raw, or sedge peat	silty sedge peat	silty sedge peat	warp-anmoor to clay-loam	...
% C.	6·1	37·5	13·5	16·8	36	30	...	...
Water level, cm. above (+) or below (−), the soil surface — Mean	+28	+19	−5	0	−1	0	−10	0
Range	+60 to +6	+42 to +3	+10 to −37	+10 to −20	+5 to 0	+7 to 0	+40 to −30	+36 to −50
pH (mud) mean	5·94	5·92	5·58	6·50	5·39	6·11	...	...
Total vegetation cover at water surface (%)	23	67	...	41	...	...	...	...
Total vegetation cover at soil surface (%)	29	61	86	...	90	90	65	45
Mean height (cm.) of dominant above soil or water (the higher)	62	72	69	68	82	72	85	153
Alnus glutinosa	...	...	9 +	...	9 +	25 +	...	56 2
Betula pubescens	...	...	...	...	9 +	25 1	...	...
Erica tetralix	...	12 +	...	...	24 +	...	...	...
Myrica gale	9 +	...	18 +	...	**90 3**	**100 8**	20 +	42 1
Salix cinerea ssp. atrocinerea	...	...	9 +	...	18 +	...	...	...
S. aurita	...	...	...	...	...	...	...	14 +
Vaccinium uliginosum	...	...	...	...	...	...	...	14 +
Equisetum fluviatile	**72 1**	37 2	45 1	25 +	27 1	25 +	60 1	14 +
Athyrium filix-femina	...	...	...	...	...	...	...	14 1
Dryopteris filix-mas	...	...	...	...	...	...	...	14 ++
D. borreri	...	...	...	...	...	...	...	14 ++

Species	1	2	3	4	5	6	7	8
Agrostis canina	28 1	40 1	50 1	72 1		63 2	12 +	
A. tenuis	28 +						14 +	
Deschampsia cespitosa		20 1						
Festuca ovina		20 +				18 +		
F. rubra			25 1	18 +	25 +		18 +	
Glyceria fluitans						9 +		9 +
G. maxima				9 +		9 +	9 +	
Holcus lanatus	28 +		75 4	63 2		9 +	9 +	9 +
Molinia caerulea		28 +		9 +				
Nardus stricta						9 +		
Phalaris arundinacea						9 +		
Phragmites communis	14 +			27 +	50 1	18 +	18 +	
Carex aquatilis		40 1	25 +	36 1				
Carex curta				9 +	25 +			
C. demissa								
Carex elata			25 +	36 1		9 +		
C. echinata			100 4	100 8				
C. lasiocarpa	14 +	20 +		54 1	100 7	9 +	24 +	9 +
C. nigra				27 +			12 +	
C. panicea								9 +
C. paniculata	100 9		9 +	81 2		100 8	100 8	
C. pulicaris			50 1			9 +	12 +	9 +
C. rostrata	42 1	40 1		27 +	50 1			100 6
C. utricularia						9 +	12 +	9 +
C. vesicaria		100 8		9 +	25 1	12 +	12 +	
Eleocharis quinqueflora				9 +		18 +	24 +	
Eriophorum angustifolium						27 1	37 1	
Eleogiton fluitans		20 +		27 +		36 +		
Juncus articulatus					50 1			9 +
J. fluitans								45 1
J. effusus	42 1	80 2						9 +
J. conglomeratus								
Alisma plantago-aquatica								
Dactylorchis fuchsii								
Lemna minor	14 +			9 +				18 +
Potamogeton natans	14 1		25 +	9 +	25 +		12 1	18 +
P. polygonifolius			25 +		25 1		37 1	9 +
Sparganium minimum								

TABLE 51—continued

Sociation	Carex rostrata sociations			Carex lasiocarpa community-types			C. vesicaria —Veronica scutellata	C. paniculata —Angelica sylvestris
	open C. rostrata	C. rostrata— Menyanthes	C. rostrata— Acrocladium	open C. lasiocarpa facies	C. lasiocarpa —Myrica	Myrica— C. lasiocarpa		
	I	IIa	IIIa	I	II	III		
Sparganium emersum	...	12 +	...	25 +	...	...	...	...
Triglochin palustre	...	...	...	...	...	...	...	...
Achillea ptarmica	...	...	...	...	9 +	25 1	40 1	20 +
Angelica sylvestris	...	...	9 +	...	...	...	...	**84 2**
Callitriche hermaphroditica	...	...	36 +	...	9 +	...	20 +	42 +
Cardamine pratensis	9 +	...	...	...	...	...	...	14 +
Cicuta virosa	...	...	9 +	25 1	9 +	...	...	...
Cirsium heterophyllum	...	...	...	...	9 +	25 1	...	...
Drosera rotundifolia	...	...	...	...	9 +	25 +	...	...
D. longifolia	...	...	...	...	...	...	...	...
Epilobium obscurum	...	...	27 +	...	18 +	...	20 1	28 1
E. palustre	...	12 +	9 +	...	9 +	25 +	60 2	70 2
Filipendula ulmaria	...	...	27 +	...	...	...	...	...
Hippuris vulgaris	...	...	9 +	...	...	...	...	...
Galium palustre	...	...	**90 2**	...	54 1	50 1	**100 2**	56 1
G. uliginosum	9 +	12 +	9 +	25 1	27 +	...	40 +	14 +
Hydrocotyle vulgaris	18 1	...	27 1	...	...	...	...	14 +
Hypericum elodes	18 +	...	9 +	...	...	...	...	...
Littorella uniflora	...	...	...	...	...	...	20 +	...
Lobelia dortmanna	...	...	...	...	9 +	20 +	...	14 +
Lotus uliginosus	...	...	...	...	...	...	...	...
Lychnis flos-cuculi	...	...	...	...	...	...	...	14 +
Lycopus europaeus	9 +	...	...	...	...	...	...	28 1
Lysimachia nemorum	...	...	...	...	...	...	40 1	28 +
Lythrum salicaria	...	...	18 +	...	9 +	...	...	14 +
Mentha aquatica	9 +	...	9 +	...	18 +	...	**80 2**	...
M. ×verticillata	45 1	...	63 1	50 1	45 1	50 2	...	28 1
Menyanthes trifoliata	9 +	**87 4**	18 +	...	...	...	...	...
Montia fontana ssp. fontana	...	...	9 +	...	...	...	20 +	...
Myosotis scorpioides	...	...	...	...	...	...	...	...

Species	1	2	3	4	5	6	7	8
Myosotis caespitosa						9 +		18 +
Myriophyllum alterniflorum							27 1	
Nuphar lutea			25 +	9 +	25 +		12 +	
Nuphar pumila					25 +			
Nymphaea alba							12 1	9 +
N. alba ssp. occidentalis				27 +				
Pedicularis palustris								
Polygonum amphibium						9 +		
Potentilla erecta	14 +			9 +		9 +		
P. palustris	56 1	**100 2**	75 2	45 1	50 1	90 3	25 1	18 +
Ranunculus acris	14 1	40 1	25 +	18 +				9 +
R. flammula		20 +		36 +		45 1	37 1	
R. repens	14 +	20 +						
Rubus fruticosus agg.	14 +							
Rumex acetosa	28 1	40 +				9 +	12 +	
Scutellaria galericulata	14 1	20 +						
Sonchus sp.	14 +	20 +						
Succisa pratensis	14 +		25 1	18 +		9 +		
Trientalis europaeus				9 +				
Trollius europaeus	14 +		25 +	9 +		9 +		9 +
Utricularia intermedia							12 1	9 +
Utricularia vulgaris	14 +				50 1		12 ±	
Valeriana officinalis		40 1	25 +	18 +		63 +		
Veronica scutellata	28 +	**100 1**		36 1		9 +		
Viola palustris								
Acrocladium cordifolium	**84 1**	20 +	50 1	9 +		45 1 ⎱ 36 1 ⎰ **81.2**		
A. cuspidatum			25 +	27 1		9 +	12 +	
A. sarmentosum				9 +	25 +			
A. stramineum	14 +		50 1	9 +		27 +		
Aulacomnium palustre				18 +		27 +		
Brachythecium rutabulum	14 +	20 +		9 +		9 +		
Bryum pseudotriquetrum		20 +		18 +		9 +		
Campylium stellatum	28 +		50 1	9 +		9 +		
C. polygamum				9 +				
Climacium dendroides						9 +		
Cratoneuron commutatum var. falcatum	28 +							
Ctenidium molluscum		25 1						
Dicranum scoparium	14 1							

TABLE 51—*continued*

Sociation	Carex rostrata sociations			Carex lasiocarpa community-types			C. vesicaria—Veronica scutellata	C. paniculata—Angelica sylvestris
	open C. rostrata	C. rostrata—Menyanthes	C. rostrata—Acrocladium	open C. lasiocarpa facies	C. lasiocarpa—Myrica	Myrica—C. lasiocarpa		
	I	IIa	IIIa	I	II	III		
Drepanocladus aduncus	...	...	...	...	...	25 1	...	...
D. exannulatus	...	...	54 1	25 1	36 +	25 +	20 +	...
D. revolvens	...	...	...	...	18 +	...	60 1	28 1
Eurhynchium praelongum	...	...	9 +	...	9 +	...	...	...
Fissidens adianthoides	...	12 +	9 +	...	...	...	...	...
Fontinalis antipyretica	...	...	9 +	...	...	50 +	...	14 +
Leptodictyum riparium	...	...	...	...	...	...	...	...
Philonotis seriata	...	...	...	...	...	...	...	...
Pseudoscleropodium purum	...	...	...	...	9 +	25 +	...	...
Pleurozium schreberi	...	...	...	...	9 +	25 1	...	...
Rhytidiadelphus squarrosus	...	...	...	...	...	25 +	...	...
Scorpidium scorpioides	...	...	18 +	25 1	36 +	...	...	...
Sphagnum cuspidatum	...	12 1	18 +	...	36 +	25 1	...	...
S. palustre	...	12 1	18 +	...	27 1	...	...	...
S. papillosum	...	...	...	...	...	...	...	...
S. plumulosum	...	...	...	...	...	...	...	...
S. recurvum	...	...	9 +	...	} 90 3	75 2	20 +	...
S. subsecundum var. **auriculatum**	18 +	37 1	18 1	50 1	}	25 +	...	...
S. subsecundum var. **inundatum**	...	...	27 1	...	...	...	...	...
S. squarrosum	...	...	18 1	...	...	...	...	...
Thuidium tamariscinum	...	...	...	...	9 +	...	...	...
Jungermannia tristis	...	...	...	...	...	...	...	...
Marchantia polymorpha	...	...	9 +	...	...	...	...	...
Pellia epiphylla	...	...	18 +	...	27 +	25 +	...	...
P. neesiana	...	...	18 +	...	...	...	...	...
Riccardia multifida	...	...	9 +	...	9 +	50 1	...	...
R. pinguis	...	...	9 +	...	17 +	50 1	...	...
Scapania dentata	...	...	9 +	...	18 +	25 +	...	...
Chara aspera	9 +	...	...	...	...	...	...	...

TABLE 52

Quadrats of *Carex nigra* sociations (p. 349).

Locality		*C. nigra—C. panicea* sociation			*C. nigra—Acrocladium* sociation			
	Mor	an Loin	nan Saighead	ba Ruaidhe	Restenneth	Rescobie	Awe	Black, Fife
Height (cm.)	...	15	...	6±2	45±5	85±15	...	55
Total vegetation cover (%)	...	60	90	90	80	70	90	80
Water level, cm. above, or below (−), soil surface	12±2	0	0	3±1	−4±1	−2±3	−15	1
		grazed sward			ungrazed, under or by carr			
Alnus glutinosa	.	.	.	.	.	.	2	.
Myrica gale	.	.	.	.	.	.	1	.
Equisetum fluviatile	3	.	.	.	1	2	2	+
Agrostis canina ssp. canina	.	.	1	.	.	1	1	.
Agrostis stolonifera	.	.	1	2	4	.	.	2
Molinia caerulea	.	.	.	.	.	.	.	.
Nardus stricta	.	.	3	2	.	.	.	.
Phragmites communis	.	.	.	.	.	.	.	.
Carex curta	1	1	1	1	.	.	.	.
C. demissa	.	.	2	2	.	.	.	.
C. dioica	.	.	.	.	.	.	.	.
C. lasiocarpa	.	.	.	5	3	.	.	.
C. nigra	7	6	5	5	7	7	8	7
C. panicea	.	+	4	2	.	.	.	.
C. pulicaris	.	.	.	.	.	5	2	.
C. rostrata	4	+	.	3	2	5	4	4
C. vesicaria	.	.	.	.	.	.	.	.
Eleocharis quinqueflora	+	2	1	.	.	.	.	.
Eriophorum angustifolium	+	.	.	.	.	.	.	.

Species	1	2	3	4	5	6	7	8
Juncus articulatus				2			2	2
J. bulbosus	1			1	2			
J. effusus		3				3		
Lemna minor			2					
Potamogeton natans								2
Angelica sylvestris				1				
Caltha palustris		1		1				
Cardamine pratensis			1	1				
Cicuta virosa								
Drosera longifolia								
Epilobium palustre	1		3	1	1			
Filipendula ulmaria	2							+
Galium palustre	3	2	2	3		2		
G. uliginosum				3				3
Hydrocotyle vulgaris		2				3		
Mentha aquatica			2	2		1		
Menyanthes trifoliata								
Myosotis palustris		1			1		1	
Pedicularis palustris		1	1	1	1			
Parnassia palustris		1						2
Potentilla palustris	3	2	6		2	3		
Ranunculus flammula		2			1	2		
Sagina nodosa					4	1		
Utricularia intermedia					1			
Veronica scutellata					1			
Acrocladium cordifolium	6	1						
A. cuspidatum		2	3	3		2	+	
Campylium stellatum				4	3			
Climacium dendroides								
Drepanocladus revolvens					1			
Mnium hornum		1	2					
Rhytidiadelphus squarrosus								
Sphagnum subsecundum var. *auriculatum*						1		
S. squarrosum		4	5			4		
Scorpidium scorpioides		3			1	(+)		

TABLE 53

Synoptic table of (1) *Glyceria maxima* society, (2) *Potentilla palustris—Acrocladium* soc., (3) *Glyceria maxima—Iris pseudacorus* soc., (4) *Juncus articulatus—Angelica* community, (5) *Filipendula ulmaria—Acrocladium* soc. (6) *Phalaris—Filipendula ulmaria* soc.

		(1) Glyceria maxima society	(2) Potentilla palustris— Acrocladium soc.	(3) Glyceria maxima—Iris pseudacorus soc.	(4) Juncus articulatus— Angelica community	(5) Filipendula ulmaria— Acrocladium soc.	(6) Phalaris— Filipendula ulmaria soc.
Page no.		351	352	351	353	352	351
Number of stands		7	8	7	4	4	5
Plot size (sq. m.)		5	4	7	4	4	4
Water level, cm. above (+), or below (−), soil surface	Mean	−1	−8	−25	−10	−14	−20
	Range	+9 to −10	+8 to −26	−11 to +30	...	+1 to −30	...
Total vegetation of cover at soil surface (%)		68	73	78	85	74	70
Species density		3·5	6·4	13·6	24	16·5	12
Mean height (cm.)		161	38	153	65	107	164
Alnus glutinosa		...	...	...	50 1	75 2	20 4
Fraxinus excelsior		...	...	...	...	...	20 3
Myrica gale		...	...	...	...	25 1	...
Salix cinerea ssp. *atrocinerea*		...	12 +	14 +	25 +	25 2	20 +
Athyrium filix-femina		...	...	...	...	25 +	...
Dryopteris filix-mas		...	...	...	...	...	20 ++
Equisetum fluviatile		...	12 +	14 +	25 +	25 +	20 ++
Agrostis canina ssp. *canina*		...	25 +	14 +	75 1	50 2	60 1
Deschampsia cespitosa		...	...	...	...	25 +	20 +

Species	1	2	3	4	5	6
Dactylis glomerata						
F. vivipara	⋮ +	25 +	50 +	14 +	12 +	
Glyceria maxima	20 +	50 2	⋮ +	**100 8**	37 1	**100 9**
Molinia caerulea	20 +		25 +			
Phalaris arundinacea	**100 8**	50 1		42 +	12 +	
Phragmites communis		25 +	25 +	14 +		
Poa sp.		25 +		14 +		
Alisma plantago-aquatica				14 +		
Carex aquatilis	20 +					
C. lasiocarpa	20 +	25 +	50 1			
C. nigra	20 +	50 2	25 +	14 +		33 +
C. rostrata	20 3		25 +	28 1	**75 3**	16 +
C. vesicaria		25 +				
Corallorhiza trifida	20 +					
Eleocharis palustris		25 1	25 +			
Iris pseudacorus				**85 1**	50 1	
Juncus acutiflorus		25 +	**100 8**	14 +		
J. articulatus	40 +		50 1			
J. effusus		25 +				33 +
Lemna minor				28 +	12 +	
Sparganium erectum	20 3					
Angelica sylvestris	20 +	25 1	100 2	14 +		
Aster ad. lanceolatus	40 +		50 +	28 +		
Cardamine amara		25 +		14 +		
C. pratensis		25 1	100 1		12 +	
Centaurea nigra		25 +				
Chamaenerion angustifolium		50 1				16 +
Chrysosplenium oppositifolium		25 +		28 +	12 +	
Cicuta virosa				14 +		
Cirsium heterophyllum		25 +	50 +	14 +		
Convolvulus arvensis				14 +		
Epilobium obscurum	20 +			28 +		

TABLE 53—continued

	(1) Glyceria maxima society	(2) Potentilla palustris—Acrocladium soc.	(3) Glyceria maxima—Iris pseudocorus soc.	(4) Juncus articulatus—Angelica community	(5) Filipendula ulmaria—Acrocladium soc.	(6) Phalaris—Filipendula ulmaria soc.
E. palustre	...	...	42 1	50 1	25 +	...
Epilobium sp.	16 +	12 +	14 +	75 4	...	...
Filipendula ulmaria	...	...	28 +	75 2	**100 8**	**100 1**
Galium aparine	...	...	14 +	25 +	**100 2**	60 +
Galium palustre	...	50 1	57 1	...	...	...
G. uliginosum	...	...	...	...	25 1	...
Geranium pratense	...	...	...	...	...	...
G. robertianum	...	...	14 +	...	...	...
Geum rivale	...	...	14 +	...	...	...
Hydrocotyle vulgaris	...	12 +	...	25 +	25 1	20 +
Lathyrus pratensis	...	...	28 +	50 4	...	...
Lycopus europaeus	...	...	14 +	25 1	...	...
Lysimachia vulgaris	...	...	42 +	...	...	...
Lythrum salicaria	...	...	...	25 +	50 1	40 +
Lychnis flos-cuculi	...	...	...	25 +	25 1	40 1
Mentha aquatica	...	12 +	57 +	50 +	25 +	...
M. ×verticillata	...	...	...	...	...	...
Menyanthes trifoliata	...	12 +	...	...	...	20 +
Myosotis scorpioides	...	25 +	28 +	...	50 1	...
Myosotis caespitosa	...	...	14 4	...	...	20 +
Oenanthe crocata	...	...	14 +	25 +	...	...
Pedicularis sylvatica	...	25 +	14 +	...	...	...
Polygonum amphibium	16 +	...	71 1	...	...	...
Potentilla palustris	33 +	**100 8**	42 1	25 +	25 1	20 +
Ranunculus acris	...	...	...	...	...	...

R. aquatilis	16 +	...	...	...	...	20 +
R. flammula	...	12 +	...	25 +	...	...
R. lingua	16 +	...	14 +	...	25 +	...
R. repens	...	...	14 +	...	...	20 +
Rorippa nasturtium-aquaticum	...	...	14 +	...	...	...
Rumex acetosa	...	...	14 +	...	...	...
Rumex conglomeratus	...	...	14 ++	...	...	...
R. hydrolapathum	16 +	...	14 ++	...	...	20 +
Senecio aquatica	16 +	...	14 +	50 1	...	20 +
Scutellaria galericulata	...	...	...	25 +	...	20 +
Succisa pratensis	...	...	14 +	...	...	...
Trifolium repens	...	...	...	25 1	25 +	20 +
Valeriana officinalis	...	...	14 ++	...	...	20 ++
Veronica beccabunga	...	...	14 +	...	...	20 +
Veronica scutellata	...	...	42 +	...	25 1	...
Vicia cracca	...	...	...	...	25 +	20 +
Viola palustris	...	...	...	50 +	...	20 +
Urtica dioica	16 +	16 +	14 +	...	...	20 +
Acrocladium cordifolium	16 +	**75 3**	28 1	75 2	**75 3**	...
A. cuspidatum	...	...	...	25 +	25 1	20 +
Brachythecium rivulare	...	...	...	100 1	25 1	...
Eurhynchium praelongum	33 +	12 +	57 1	25 +	50 2	20 +++
Fissidens adianthoides	...	...	...	...	...	20 +
Mnium hornum	...	...	...	14 +	50 1	20 ++
M. punctatum	...	...	...	...	...	20 +
M. undulatum	...	...	...	50 +	25 1	20 +
Rhytidiadelphus squarrosus	...	...	...	50 1	25 1	...
Sphagnum palustre	...	...	...	50 1	...	...
S. subsecundum var. auriculatum	...	...	...	25 4	...	...
Chiloscyphus sp.	...	...	...	...	25 1	...

The following species also occurred in the *Juncus* community:
Lotus uliginosus (50 +), *Parnassia palustris* (25 +), *Trollius europaeus* (25 +), *Drepanocladus exannulatus* (50 +), and *Pleurozium schreberi* (50 +).

TABLE 54

Quadrats of *Sphagnum subsecundum* var *auriculatum—Juncus bulbosus* soc. with two *Potamogeton polygonifolius* stands (p. 353).

Locality	I					II		I
	Apple-cross	Flat-punds	Mill	Garder-house	Apple-cross	Valley	Mill	Synoptic
Sample area (sq. m.) .	1	1	1	1	1	1	1	...
Type of mire . .			topogenous			soligenous		...
Water level, cm. above (+) or below (−) soil surface	+4	−5	0	−1	+5	0	+1	0±5
pH mud . . .	...	4·50	4·58	3·25	...	...	5·80	...
% cover at soil surface .	90	100	100	100	100	75	70	100
Height (cm.) . . .	...	25	20	10	4	...	10	15
Calluna vulgaris . .	...	...	...	...	...	1	...	...
Myrica gale . . .	...	...	...	...	...	1	...	...
Carex demissa . .	...	1	2	...	...	3	1	50 1
C. nigra . . .	2	...	1	2	...	...	2	50 1
C. panicea . . .	...	...	5	2	...	4	2	50 2
C. pulicaris . . .	...	1	2	...	...	...	...	50 1
C. rostrata . . .	...	1	...	...	...	...	...	25 +
C. echinata . . .	2	1	3	1	3	...	1	100 2
Eleocharis quinqueflora .	...	4	2	...	...	...	4	50 2
Eriophorum angustifolium	4	2	3	...	1	2	4	75 2
Trichophorum cespitosum	...	...	...	...	...	1	...	...
Agrostis canina . .	...	...	...	...	...	1	...	...
A. stolonifera . . .	...	...	...	?	...	...	...	...
A. tenuis . . .	3	3	2	2	4	...	...	100 3
Festuca vivipara . .	...	2	+	...	...	2	...	50 1
Holcus lanatus . .	...	1	...	...	...	...	...	25 +
Molinia caerulea . .	...	...	...	...	...	2	...	...
Nardus stricta . .	...	1	2	...	...	...	...	50 1
Juncus articulatus . .	...	3	3	4	...	3	3	75 3
J. bulbosus . . .	8	4	4	3	4	...	3	100 4
Luzula campestris .	...	2	...	...	...	...	...	25 1
Narthecium ossifragum .	...	...	...	...	...	2	...	...
Potamogeton poly-gonifolius	+	4	4	2	+	7	8	100 3
Callitriche hermaphroditica	...	...	...	+	...	...	...	25 +
Cardamine pratensis .	...	1	...	...	...	...	...	25 +
Drosera rotundifolia .	...	...	...	...	...	1	...	...
Epilobium palustre . .	...	3	...	...	3	...	...	50 2
Hydrocotyle vulgaris .	...	3	...	...	...	...	...	25 1
Menyanthes trifoliata .	...	2	...	...	...	...	...	25 1
Montia fontana ssp. *fontana*	...	2	...	...	...	...	...	25 1
Pinguicula vulgaris . .	...	...	...	...	...	1	...	...
Potentilla palustris . .	...	3	...	...	...	...	...	25 1

TABLE 54—*continued*

Locality	I					II		I
	Apple-cross	Flat-punds	Mill	Garder-house	Apple-cross	Valley	Mill	Synoptic
P. erecta . . .	...	...	1	...	...	...	...	25 +
Ranunculus flammula .	**1**	**4**	**2**	**1**	**3**	...	...	**100 3**
Stellaria alsine . .	...	...	...	...	2	...	...	25 1
Veronica scutellata . .	...	2	...	...	...	...	...	25 1
Viola palustris . .	...	1	1	...	2	...	...	75 1
Acrocladium cuspidatum .	...	+	...	...	...	...	...	25 +
A. sarmentosum . .	...	...	...	...	...	1	...	...
Aulacomnium palustre .	...	1	1	...	...	...	...	50 1
Cratoneuron commutatum var. *falcatum*	...	3	...	...	...	...	...	25 1
Drepanocladus exannu-latus	**1**	**1***	**3**	**3***	+	...	...	**100 2**
D. revolvens . . .	1	...	...	...	...	2	...	...
Polytrichum sp. . .	...	...	...	+	...	...	...	25 +
Pottia sp. . . .	...	...	...	+	...	...	...	25 +
Sphagnum cuspidatum .	**2**	**2**	**2**	**5**	+	...	...	**100 2**
S. palustre . .	**2**	**2**	...	...	**1**	...	...	} **100 3**
S. papillosum . .	...	...	6	1	...	1	...	
S. plumulosum . .	+	...	4	...	4	1	...	50 2
S. subsecundum var. *auriculatum*	**6**	**8**	**6**	**7**	**7**	**6**	...	**100 7**
Pellia neesiana . .	...	3	...	...	...	...	...	25 1
Riccardia multifida . .	...	...	1	...	...	1	...	25 +
R. pinguis . . .	...	3	2	...	+	2	...	75 1
Scapania gracilis . .	...	...	...	1	+	...	...	50 +

* var. *rotae*.

CHAPTER 10

MIRES AND BOGS

D. A. RATCLIFFE

Wherever free water accumulates in such quantity as to form a *water-table* near, at, or above the ground surface, there is vegetation of another large class, here termed *aquatic*, although the term "wetland" has come into use recently to cover this broad class of habitat. The plants of such habitats are adapted to more or less continuous waterlogging of the substratum (and therefore the root systems) and the anaerobic conditions which result are unfavourable to decomposition of dead plant remains, so that there is commonly an accumulation of these as peat. Aquatic conditions are governed by several factors, such as rainfall/evaporation and porosity of the substratum, but slope and configuration of the ground may be regarded as the master determining factors.

Within the broad class of aquatic vegetation, a primary subdivision may be made according to the height of the water-table in relation to ground surface, and life form of the associated vegetation. First there are bodies of free water, either more or less stagnant, as in ponds and lakes or moving as in rivers, which possess a very open type of vegetation, composed of true hydrophytes (including both floating and submerged plants). Second, are swamps where the ground is permanently or seasonally submerged but a relatively dense growth of vegetation (total or partial hydrophytes) appears above the water surface. Thirdly there are drier swamps where the water-table only occasionally, if ever, appears above ground surface, although it seldom falls far below. The vegetation usually forms a completely closed cover over the substratum and is composed largely of helophytes or hemicryptophytes.

These three phases may be successively related, as in the classical concept of the hydrosere, thus marking stages of increasing maturity of development in habitat and vegetation. However, even where two or more phases occur together in a spatial gradient, they do not necessarily stand in this temporal relationship; and when one phase occurs alone it does not follow that it has either developed from a more immature phase or will develop into a more mature phase.

Lakes and ponds often show a characteristic sequence or zonation which includes all three phases in passing along the water-table gradient from open water to surrounding dry land. Such aquatic vegetation complexes are determined largely by topography (topogenous) in that they lie in basins, hollows, channels or other sites where the high and relatively stagnant water-table depends on the shape of the land. The ground or peat surface is, therefore, level or imperceptibly sloping and lateral movement of water is usually much impeded. Swamp vegetation of both types (as defined above) is traditionally known as *fen* in Britain, but depending on the nutrient content of the water, and therefore of the peat, there are separations into "poor" and "rich" fen.

There are, however, other types of swamp vegetation which are determined by different conditions of waterlogging. Sites where wetness of the ground is maintained by gravitational lateral seepage of water are common in hill country, in channels and hollows or where slopes flatten out, especially in valley floors, and have been called "valley bogs" or "flush bogs". While topography is again the main controlling factor, the ground usually has at least some slope and the water-table is maintained by a flow of water through the substratum. Such examples are said to be *soligenous*. The depth of peat at the site is usually less than in most fens, but there may be considerable affinity between the two groups both in types of peat and floristics, and since the water supply again varies widely in chemical content, soligenous bogs also range from "poor" to "rich". To simplify terminology the word *mire* is here used as a synonym for soligenous bog, although Continental ecologists use it in a wider sense.

Another group of aquatic habitats, springs, rills and flushes, is best included here although it does not really belong to any of the categories so far mentioned. It is perhaps not correct to speak of a water-table in connection with these habitats, but all involve a rapid and localised flow of drainage water at or just below the ground surface. Some examples are intermittent, drying up seasonally, and all are strongly subject to variation in volume of water and rate of flow according to rainfall fluctuations. The amount of humus accumulation varies widely and is sometimes quite low, true peats occurring seldom, and there is again a wide range in nutrient status of water and substratum. This group is also best represented in hill country.

There remains an important group of aquatic vegetation which could be included by definition within the second and (more particularly) third main subdivisions as swamp. The high and stagnant water-table depends not only on the ground being level or only gently inclined, but also on a high rainfall and low evaporation rate. The water supply to the living vegetation is in fact derived almost entirely from the atmosphere and not from drainage water seepage from other ground. Topography is still the master factor, but the difference is between its retarding run-off of water at the site and concentrating water from other sites. For this reason, atmospheric moisture is regarded as the effective controlling condition and the term *ombrogenous* is used to describe this type of aquatic vegetation. The dependence of the vegetation on rain water ensures a consistently low nutrient status of the substratum, which in turn favours the accumulation of peat. Ombrogenous bog sometimes develops on lowland sites such as plains, valleys or basins which originally held topogenous fen but where the living surface has grown above the influence of drainage water. Such examples often grow most rapidly in their centres, giving a slightly convex surface overall, and are then known as *raised bogs*. Some ecologists (e.g. Tansley, 1949) prefer to regard raised bog as a topogenous type, but the contrary view is taken here.

The typical situation of ombrogenous bogs is, however, on gently contoured uplands where the rainfall is high (over 127 cm.), but in the extremely humid north-west of Britain they are equally characteristic of low-lying land. From the way in which they smother all but the steep ground in a layer of peat, they have appropriately been named *blanket bogs*. Both raised and blanket bogs often develop surface systems of pools, but these are best treated as part of the same vegetation complex rather than with the lake and pond group of aquatic habitats. The term *bog* has been adopted here as a convenient abbreviation for all classes of ombrogenous bog.

The criteria used in making a working subdivision of aquatic vegetation are thus varied. Height of water-table, source of water and its nutrient content, relation to topography and life form of the plants themselves, are all used in producing the above classification. Some peatland ecologists prefer a simpler initial separation into *minerotrophic* types (topogenous fens, soligenous mires, springs, rills and flushes) depending on a terrestrial and therefore nutrient-enriched water supply, and *ombrotrophic* types (raised and blanket bogs) depending solely on nutrient-deficient atmospheric moisture and wind-borne particles. These two classes of peatland correspond to the two main categories proposed by Fraser (1954) in a classification of peat deposits, namely, Azonal and Intrazonal (minerotrophic) determined largely by topography and drainage, and Climatic or Zonal (ombrotrophic) depending on high rainfall in cool-temperate regions. Even then, however, further subdivision according to other criteria is necessary, and there is no provision for open water habitats.

In practice, after a preliminary separation of groups of aquatic vegetation according to habitat, phytosociological criteria are needed to subdivide and define these groups and thus enable any particular stand to be assigned to a suitable position in the classification. Moreover, in some localities, there are complexes of aquatic vegetation in which bog, mire and fen communities may all be recognised. Good examples on Rannoch Moor and in Abernethy Forest have been described by McVean and Ratcliffe (1962). Here, topography is relatively uniform, and it is vegetational change which gives the key to the controlling change in drainage conditions.

Whatever the criteria used for classification, it is found that while the different groups of aquatic vegetation so distinguished may be distinct and well defined in places, on examining the whole of Scotland there are found intermediates which emphasise that variation is continuous throughout the whole range.

An attempt is made in Fig. 58 (which should be looked at in conjunction with the accompanying map, Fig. 59) to summarise the principal types of mire, bog, spring and flush vegetation together with some indication of their distribution and range, and the fertility of their soils (pp. 430 and 431; descriptions of some of these vegetation types are deferred until Chapter 15).

Mires

The term "mire" was defined on p. 427 as the synonym for all soligenous wetland, i.e. peat and associated vegetation depending on lateral flow of water. The affinities with fen were also indicated, these being sometimes so close that separation can only be made on arbitrary floristic grounds, and differences between fen and mire are far less clear-cut than between fen and bog. Again, the poorer types of mire intergrade with bog, so that mire can be regarded as an intermediate category.

Mires are essentially determined by physiography. They depend on a topography and geological structure which give a localised concentration of gravitational seepage water close to or at ground surface during at least part of the year. Such sites are thus absent from summits and watersheds and appear lower down the slopes, in hollows, channels and beside streams, being especially well developed where steep slopes flatten out into the floor of a valley. Sometimes mires occur where the ground appears superficially to be no different from that immediately adjacent, but they are often associated with the change from colluvium to glacial drift, evidently in response to alteration in drainage conditions, since drift tends to be the less permeable type of substratum. Mires also sometimes develop as recolonisation stages in the erosion channels or "haggs" of blanket bogs. The ground surface usually has some slope, however slight, but some level swamps in small basins among the hills are better regarded as mire than fen on floristic grounds. Height of the water-table varies greatly, and is permanently at the surface in some examples, but subject to considerable fluctuations in level, or even seasonal absence, in others. As the amount of water seepage falls off spatially there are transitions to damper types of grassland or heath, and intermediate communities are sometimes difficult to classify.

Depending on the permanence of waterlogging, mire peats and soils are more or less anaerobic and reducing. The basal mineral horizons are usually strongly gleyed, though where waterlogging is seasonal and intermittent or fluctuates in level, the characteristic greyish colour is replaced by a red mottle. Depth of the peat horizon (where this is distinct) or humus content (where mineral and peat horizons are not distinct) also varies according to degree of waterlogging, and is naturally greatest where the ground is wettest. Humus content also depends on acidity, for rate of decomposition increases as pH rises, and in calcareous areas the less permanently waterlogged mires often have muddy peats with an intimate mixture of humus and mineral particles, whereas mires of comparable wetness in non-calcareous areas show a separation into mineral and humus horizons. This may be partly due to the greater activity of the soil fauna in calcareous sites, where animals such as earthworms are commonly present and help to mix the different soil components. Depending on situation, too, periodic flooding of the mire surface may result in intermittent deposition of mineral particles and sometimes their incorporation in definite layers in the peat (see p. 435).

As in fens, the mineral ion content of seepage water affecting mires varies greatly, but mainly according to chemical composition of the parent material both in the

FIG. 58. The main types of bog, mire, spring and flush vegetation are listed in the systematic order of the text, and two widespread facies with well-marked distribution patterns are included.

The total altitudinal range over the whole of Scotland is given for each type, but the normal range, or the range in any one district, may be a good deal less.

The terms oligotrophic (O), mesotrophic (M) and eutrophic (E) are defined as criteria of soil fertility on p. 432. Each vegetation type is allotted to its appropriate range according to the chemical soil data at present available.

The geographical regions 1–9 are shown in Fig. 59 and the known distribution of each vegetation type given accordingly. Where a vegetation type is extensi in a region it is indicated by a dash, but where t occurrence is limited, a dot is used. These term extensive and limited, have only relative meaning wh comparing the main groups of vegetation, i.e. extensive occurrence of any spring or flush vegetati covers a far smaller area than a limited occurrence any bog, while mires are intermediate between the ot two groups in this respect. Although the method do not indicate any localised distributions *within* region it will be clear that certain vegetation types ha markedly western or eastern distributions, and that

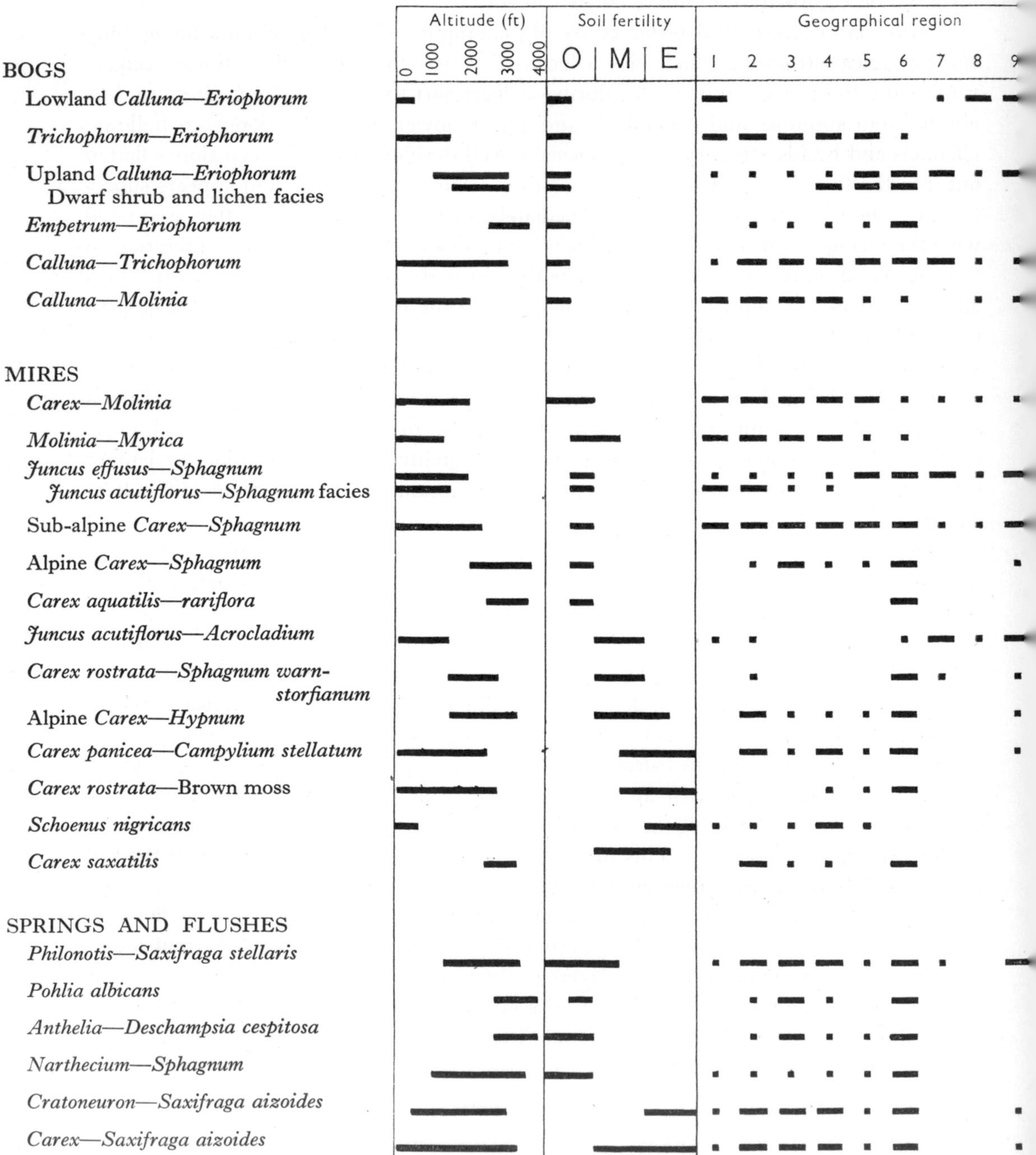

	Altitude (ft)	Soil fertility	Geographical region
	0 1000 2000 3000 4000	O M E	1 2 3 4 5 6 7 8 9

BOGS

Lowland *Calluna—Eriophorum*

Trichophorum—Eriophorum

Upland *Calluna—Eriophorum*
    Dwarf shrub and lichen facies

Empetrum—Eriophorum

Calluna—Trichophorum

Calluna—Molinia

MIRES

Carex—Molinia

Molinia—Myrica

Juncus effusus—Sphagnum
    Juncus acutiflorus—Sphagnum facies

Sub-alpine *Carex—Sphagnum*

Alpine *Carex—Sphagnum*

Carex aquatilis—rariflora

Juncus acutiflorus—Acrocladium

Carex rostrata—Sphagnum warn-
              storfianum

Alpine *Carex—Hypnum*

Carex panicea—Campylium stellatum

Carex rostrata—Brown moss

Schoenus nigricans

Carex saxatilis

SPRINGS AND FLUSHES

Philonotis—Saxifraga stellaris

Pohlia albicans

Anthelia—Deschampsia cespitosa

Narthecium—Sphagnum

Cratoneuron—Saxifraga aizoides

Carex—Saxifraga aizoides

w are northern, central or southern. Types with regular geographical distributions are usually mesophic or eutrophic, following the irregular distribution of calcareous rocks. Similarly, the montane types which need high altitude are confined to regions with the highest mountains. Region 8 is generally lowland and so has only a limited range of habitats.

From the figure it is possible to glean information about the vegetational inter-relationships, and to see which types could be expected to occur in any particular area. It is evident, for instance, that *Empetrum—Eriophorum* bog is likely to be the high level counterpart upland *Calluna—Eriophorum* bog, since they both occur in the same region, under similar soil conditions, but over a different range of elevation. Again, by similar reasoning, Alpine *Carex—Hypnum* mire evidently replaces Alpine *Carex—Sphagnum* mire when soil base-status rises, and both could be expected to occur in an area with both acidic and calcareous rocks. Where the figure indicates that two types occur under the same range of altitude and soil fertility, and in the same region (e.g. *Trichophorum—Eriophorum* and *Calluna—Molinia* bog, or *Juncus effusus—Sphagnum* and Sub-alpine *Carex—Sphagnum* mire) it is probable that some other edaphic condition, such as degree of waterlogging, is the differentiating factor.

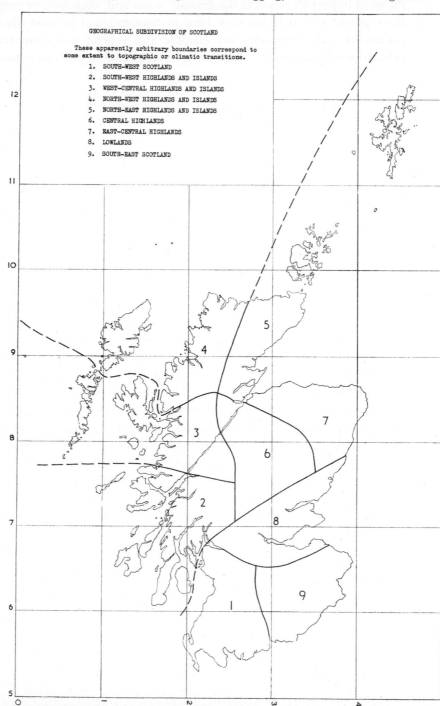

GEOGRAPHICAL SUBDIVISION OF SCOTLAND

These apparently arbitrary boundaries correspond to some extent to topographic or climatic transitions.

1. SOUTH-WEST SCOTLAND
2. SOUTH-WEST HIGHLANDS AND ISLANDS
3. WEST-CENTRAL HIGHLANDS AND ISLANDS
4. NORTH-WEST HIGHLANDS AND ISLANDS
5. NORTH-EAST HIGHLANDS AND ISLANDS
6. CENTRAL HIGHLANDS
7. EAST-CENTRAL HIGHLANDS
8. LOWLANDS
9. SOUTH-EAST SCOTLAND

FIG. 59. Map of nine geographical regions recognised in connection with the distribution of bogs, mires, springs and flushes illustrated in Fig. 58.

superficial deposits and underlying bedrock. Where blanket bog is extensive, it too has an influence on the chemical composition of drainage water. The presence of free calcium carbonate is the most important petrological feature in this respect, although rocks rich in less readily available calcium, e.g. calcium silicates, as in hornblende, may also give a calcareous drainage water. The pH of mire peats or soils depends largely on content of exchangeable calcium, which is closely related to that of the irrigation water. On non-calcareous basic rocks such as serpentine and peridotite, magnesium replaces calcium as the most important cation in the drainage water and, therefore, in irrigated substrata but these parent materials are very local in Scotland and in most districts the extent of calcareous rock determines the edaphic and vegetational character of mires. Non-calcareous siliceous rocks may be rich in other cations such as potassium but these are

TABLE 55

Characteristics of the three types of mires recognised in this account

Fertility level	Soil		Water	
	Exchangeable Calcium (mg./100 gm.)	pH	Calcium (mg./litre)	pH
Oligotrophic . .	< 30	< 5·0	< 4	< 5·7
Mesotrophic . .	30–300	5·0–6·0	4–10	5·7–6·5
Eutrophic . . .	> 300	> 6·0	> 10	> 6·5

largely unavailable and produce acidic, nutrient-deficient substrata. Pearsall (1950) has pointed out that moderately acidic flushed soils are usually rich in iron which, under the anaerobic reducing conditions, is readily transported in the ferrous state.

It has been found convenient to subdivide mires into the three broad classes, oligotrophic, mesotrophic and eutrophic. In the literature there appears to be a certain confusion about the meaning of these terms, and for the present purpose they are defined according to exchangeable calcium content, which shows so wide a range of variation in the substrata and drainage waters of mires. Subject to occasional discrepancies, there is a fairly close correlation between exchangeable calcium level and pH, and the corresponding pH ranges are given in the table above. Since calcareous rocks are local in Scotland, occurring mainly in the Breadalbane-Clova region, eutrophic mires are the least common type, and oligotrophic mires are the most widespread and extensive.

This treatment obviously gives an arrangement of floristic groups according to richness in calcifuge or calcicole species. It is, however, probable that floristic variation in mire vegetation may be due to differences in concentration of other ions besides calcium. Pearsall (1950) believes that some species are associated with a high content of iron in the substratum; and in the north and west of Scotland, a number of species which elsewhere are associated with high calcium status grow in iron-rich wet habitats. Pearsall (1956) and Gorham (1956, 1961) have shown that bog, mire and fen waters vary widely in content of other ions such as sodium and chloride.

It is also true that some of the plant species which reach dominance in mire vegetation have a very wide range of tolerance for calcium status and pH. Although these are important in the physiognomy of the communities they dominate, they are of no value to the above method of floristic arrangement according to calcium or acidity requirements, or as indicators of soil conditions. For such purposes, the subordinate species have to be used. Tolerant species include several sedges, *Carex rostrata, C. nigra, C. panicea, C. saxatilis;* rushes such as *Juncus acutiflorus* and *J. squarrosus;* grasses such as *Nardus stricta, Agrostis tenuis* and *Molinia caerulea;* and a variety of other species of wet ground such as *Phragmites communis, Myrica gale, Eriophorum angustifolium, Trichophorum cespitosum, Erica tetralix* and *Schoenus nigricans.* The range of tolerance varies, and some of these plants do not grow under markedly eutrophic conditions, while others attain dominance only at one end of the scale or the other. Again, some species change in their nutrient tolerance requirement in different parts of their geographical range, with the general tendency to become more exacting and calcicolous towards their limits: this is especially true of western plants, such as *Schoenus* and *Myrica*, which become rare or local in the east.

Calcium status and acidity in mires are perhaps best indicated by the bryophyte component of the vegetation. In oligotrophic types this is usually dominated by Sphagna which have a low base tolerance, though in mesotrophic mires there may be an abundance of other species of *Sphagnum* which do not grow in the poorest waters. Sphagna are absent from eutrophic mires and here, as in many mesotrophic types, mosses of the sub-class Bryales dominate the bryophyte component; the so-called "brown mosses" which include large pleurocarpous species, mainly of the former genus *Hypnum*, are especially well represented. Mesotrophic and eutrophic mires also typically contain an abundance of dicotyledonous herbs, whereas in oligotrophic mires, monocotyledons form a larger proportion of the vascular flora.

Variation in mire floristics is related to other edaphic factors, such as height of water-table and seasonal fluctuations in level, rate of water-flow and aeration of water. Climatic variation on both local and regional scales is important too: there is an altitudinal separation into lowland (or forest-zone) and montane mires, while certain types have a well-defined geographical distribution, eastern-western or northern-southern, corresponding to the main gradients of climatic wetness and temperature.

Mires are perhaps less affected by human disturbance than bogs, since their vegetation is not so easily burned, and the water-table is usually less readily lowered. As mires are far less extensive than bogs, there is also a lesser incentive to reclamation, though in these days of mechanical ditching, an increasing number are being converted to damp grassland merely by the cutting of drains. The mesotrophic and eutrophic types provide valuable grazing when thus treated. Soil or peat erosion in mires is rare,

2 E

but occasionally, during heavy rain, the ground becomes so charged with water that a landslip takes place, and both vegetation and surface soil layers are deposited farther down the slope. Many of the mires described below differ from Scandinavian counterparts largely in the absence of trees or shrubs, and it is clear that the difference is due to the elimination of woody growth by felling and grazing in the Scottish examples. Lowland mires probably once formed part of alderwood (*Alnus glutinosa*) or willow scrub (*Salix cinerea* ssp. *atrocinerea*, *S. caprea* and *S. aurita*), while montane types would support growths of northern willows such as *Salix lapponum* and *S. phylicifolia*. In some cases there may have been further floristic changes under the influences of grazing, treading and manuring by domestic animals, such as the rise to dominance of the rushes, *Juncus effusus* and *J. acutiflorus*. Some of the very high level mires may, however, be in a more or less original state.

VEGETATION TYPES

Oligotrophic mires

   Carex—Molinia mire (Table 56, col. 1). In this type of mire, *Calluna vulgaris* and *Erica tetralix* are both constant, but the latter has a slightly higher cover: few other shrubs are present. The other constants include *Molinia caerulea*, *Carex echinata*, *C. panicea*, *Eriophorum angustifolium*, *Narthecium ossifragum*, *Drosera rotundifolia* and *Potentilla erecta*. Sphagna have a moderate cover on average and the lists include a wide variety of grasses, sedges, mosses and other plants which in bogs are associated with some degree of water movement or mineral enrichment, e.g. *Selaginella selaginoides*, *Festuca ovina* agg., *Nardus stricta*, *Carex nigra*, *Juncus kochii*, *Succisa pratensis*, *Aulacomnium palustre* and *Sphagnum recurvum*.

   This mire shares six constants with the *Trichophorum—Eriophorum* blanket bog described later (p. 462 and Table 57, col. 2), and it was regarded by McVean and Ratcliffe (1962) as a facies of that bog type—Trichophoreto—Eriophoretum caricetosum. There is often a close spatial relationship between the two, the mire occurring in seepage areas, depressions and channels within the bog, or on steeper adjacent ground where the bog gives way to a general cover of *Trichophorum—Calluna* or *Molinia—Calluna* communities. There are floristic similarities also to *Molinia—Myrica* and sub-alpine *Sphagnum* dominated mires. A distinctive facies is dominated by *Erica tetralix*, *Molinia*, and sometimes *Trichophorum*, and has a wide selection of basiphilous species, though these usually have a low cover.

   Carex—Molinia mires are most common in western Scotland, but they occur in many eastern districts which are too dry to support *Trichophorum—Eriophorum* bog, and seem there to be even more strongly associated with irrigation than in the west. The altitudinal range is rather greater in the east, reaching an upper limit of 610 m. (2000 ft.), whereas in the west most occurrences are below 457 m. (1500 ft.). The facies with basiphilous species has a decidedly eastern distribution and is often found in association with calcareous flushes or mires, occupying a transitional position between these and oligotrophic vegetation on non-irrigated soils, but sometimes forming hummocks within the flushes. The area occupied by individual stands seldom exceeds a few hundred square metres, and is usually much less, though, in the aggregate, *Carex—Molinia* mires are extensive in some places.

Carex—Molinia mires usually occur on fairly shallow peats overlying gley mineral soils, but the peat varies a good deal in depth and humification. Peats have shown pH values from 4·0 to 4·4 and water samples from 4·3 to 4·8. A single silty peat sample from beneath the facies with basiphilous species gave a pH value of 6·0, agreeing with field observations on soil preferences.

Similar mire communities occur in parts of the English Lake District and North Wales, and more widely in western Ireland.

Molinia—Myrica mire (Table 56, col. 2). In this mire, *Molinia caerulea* and *Myrica gale* are co-dominant, though in varying proportions, and their growth is usually so dense and tall that there are few other associated species, *Potentilla erecta* being the only other constant. There is some floristic variation, however, from species-poor stands to those with a variety of basiphilous plants. The typical community has little *Sphagnum*, but examples with a high cover of Sphagna may be found locally and are perhaps best regarded as transitional to other *Sphagnum*-dominated mires.

Molinia—Myrica mires are most frequent and extensive in western Scotland, and occur on periodically flooded ground alongside watercourses of all sizes, and where there is water seepage on gentle slopes, or amongst low-level blanket bogs. They are more local in the eastern Highlands and do not occur in the eastern half of the Southern Uplands. Eastern examples show, like the *Carex—Molinia* mires, a more decided restriction to richer irrigated soils than those in the west, and *Myrica* becomes more prominent than *Molinia* towards the east. Individual stands reach an area of a hectare or more and are locally extensive in the aggregate. *Molinia—Myrica* mires occur almost from sea level up to 366 m. (1200 ft.).

The peats are well humified and sometimes pseudofibrous, and there is usually a good deal of alluvial sediment, either generally distributed through the deposit or in intercalated layers, while eastern examples are often humus rich silts rather than peats. This peat overlies a gleyed mineral soil which is often alluvial in origin. Soil acidity varies widely, as the range of floristics indicates, and pH measurements range from 3·8 to 6·1.

From the altitudinal range, this type of mire clearly belongs to the forest zone, and though most occurrences are in treeless country, it is sometimes found in open pine or birchwood. *Molinia—Myrica* communities are thus evidently anthropogenic and have probably been derived in many places from such woods, or more particularly from alder-wood and willow scrub. Some stands still contain a good deal of willow. Repeated burning and heavy grazing reduces the amount of *Myrica* and some nearly pure *Molinia* grasslands may have been derived from this type of mire, although *Myrica* has rather a discontinuous distribution and may always have been missing from some Molinieta which appear to be in favourable situations for its growth. There are transitions to a variety of other mire communities especially those with abundant *Juncus acutiflorus*.

Molinia—Myrica mires are found locally in the English Lake District and North Wales, and widely in western Ireland.

Juncus effusus—Sphagnum mire (Table 56, col. 3). This is an easily recognisable type of mire with *Juncus effusus* as physiognomic dominant, but the true dominants in terms of cover are *Sphagnum recurvum*, *S. palustre* or *Polytrichum commune*, either singly or as a mixture. The other constants are *Carex nigra*, *Galium saxatile* and *Potentilla erecta*. There is a moderate variety of grasses, dicotyledonous herbs and mosses which are associated with some slight degree of enrichment of the substratum. Besides the two dominant species, there are other Sphagna such as *S. robustum*, *S. girgensohnii*, *S. teres* and *S. squarrosum*, which depend on water movement in the substratum.

Juncus effusus—Sphagnum mires are widespread in the eastern Scottish uplands but local in the west, where they tend to be replaced by a type which differs mainly in having *Juncus acutiflorus* in place of *J. effusus*. They are sometimes extensive with stands up to two hectares in size, and in the drier eastern districts are often quite sharply delimited from the adjoining dry heather moor or grassland. They occur up to 610 m. (2000 ft.) on gentle slopes in valleys, and in hollows or channels which concentrate seepage water.

The soils are somewhat variable, ranging from gley podsols to deep peaty gleys, according to the degree of waterlogging. The drier gley podsols usually have *Polytrichum commune* as the moss dominant, whereas the peaty gleys are *Sphagnum* dominated. Water samples show a pH range of 4·4 to 5·0 but the peats and soils have not been studied. The *Juncus acutiflorus—Sphagnum* mires, which occur extensively in parts of the western Highlands and Galloway, are associated with wet peaty gleys, and probably show a range of acidity similar to other oligotrophic *Sphagnum* mires.

This is another biotically derived kind of vegetation which probably supported willow scrub and perhaps alder- or birchwood in former times. *Juncus effusus* appears to be a plant especially associated with disturbance and this mire may well be a completely artificial type.

Juncus effusus—Sphagnum mire is one of the most widespread upland types of vegetation in the British Isles, occurring with great floristic uniformity in many parts of northern England, Wales, south-west England and Ireland.

Sub-alpine Carex—Sphagnum mire (Table 56, col. 4). *Sphagnum* is dominant, with *S. recurvum*, *S. palustre*, *S. papillosum* and *S. subsecundum* var. *auriculatum* occurring separately or in various mixtures, only the first species being constantly present. The vascular plant layer usually has *Carex echinata* and *C. nigra* as dominants, and the other constants are *Eriophorum angustifolium* and *Potentilla erecta*. In floristics there is a strong resemblance to *Juncus effusus—Sphagnum* mire, and two other closely related types differ largely in replacement of the two dominant Carices by *Juncus squarrosus* and *Carex rostrata* respectively, the *Sphagnum* layer and other associates remaining much the same.

Carex—Sphagnum mire is widely distributed in Scotland, occurring in most hill areas, though its stands are mostly small, varying from a few to 200 sq. m. in size. It is found from low elevations (around 91 m. (300 ft.)) up to the tree limit, but at higher levels (above 732 m. (2400 ft.)) its floristics change sufficiently to warrant the separation of an alpine *Carex—Sphagnum* mire (p. 536). There is thus a good deal of altitudinal overlap with the *Juncus effusus* and *J. acutiflorus* oligotrophic mires, although the present type extends to much higher levels. The reasons for its separation from these other types and from the *Juncus squarrosus* and *Carex rostrata—Sphagnum* mires are not clear, although differences in rate of water movement and aeration may be involved. The values of pH for water samples show a similar pH range, 4·5–5·7, to those for the *Juncus effusus—Sphagnum* mires.

Similar communities occur in various upland areas of northern England, Wales and Ireland.

Mesotrophic and eutrophic mires

Juncus acutiflorus—Acrocladium cuspidatum mire (Table 56, col. 5). On base-rich soils the equivalent to *Juncus effusus—Sphagnum* mire is dominated by *Juncus acutiflorus*, with a mixed bryophyte layer in which *Acrocladium cuspidatum* is usually present. The vegetation contains many mildly basiphilous species, such as *Holcus lanatus, Carex panicea, Achillea ptarmica, Crepis paludosa, Epilobium palustre, Prunella vulgaris, Ranunculus acris* and *Bryum pseudotriquetrum*. If Sphagna occur, they are species associated with nutrient-rich water.

Rich *Juncus acutiflorus* mires occur mainly in the south and east of the Highlands and in the eastern half of the Southern Uplands, and are locally extensive in some districts, with individual stands of up to two or more hectares. In the west they are largely replaced by oligotrophic *Juncus acutiflorus* mires, though on damp base-rich soils in coastal parts of the western Highlands there is a similar species-rich mire in which the dominant is a presumed hybrid between *J. acutiflorus* and *J. articulatus*. The altitudinal range is from near sea level to 366 m. (1200 ft.) and the sites are exactly comparable to those of oligotrophic *Juncus effusus* mire. As well as intergrading with other oligotrophic *Juncus* mires, the *Juncus acutiflorus—Acrocladium* type shows transitions to *Molinia—Myrica* mire, which replaces it to the north and west, there being a zone of overlap with mixtures of the two communities.

The soils are usually strongly gleyed, with a surface layer of base-rich peat varying in humification and mineral content. The water-table is usually high but subject to some seasonal fluctuation. Peat samples showed a pH range of 5·2–5·5 whereas waters varied from 5·7 to 6·4 and are mesotrophic rather than eutrophic. The associated species give a better indication of soil conditions than the dominant, which has a very wide tolerance of soil base-status.

Rich *Juncus acutiflorus* mires occur widely on the hills of northern England and north Wales. Like *Juncus effusus*, this rush probably indicates disturbance when dominant, and *Juncus acutiflorus* mire is best regarded as an anthropogenic type of vegetation.

Carex panicea—Campylium stellatum mire (Table 56, col. 6). This is a eutrophic, species-rich type of mire dominated by a mixture of sedges or sometimes by one species in particular, and containing a wide range of basiphilous herbs and bryophytes. The sedges are *Carex demissa, C. dioica, C. echinata, C. flacca, C. nigra, C. panicea* and *C. pulicaris*. Characteristic basiphiles include *Eleocharis quinqueflora, Selaginella selaginoides, Juncus articulatus, Linum catharticum, Prunella vulgaris, Campylium stellatum, Cratoneuron commutatum, Drepanocladus revolvens* var. *intermedius, Ctenidium molluscum, Fissidens adianthoides, Bryum pseudotriquetrum* and *Scorpidium scorpioides*. The mosses do not usually have a high cover, but sometimes one species attains dominance. There are close relationships to other eutrophic mires, notably the Alpine *Carex—Hypnum* and *Carex rostrata*—brown moss types, and to the richer kinds of damp grassland, such as the *Agrostis—Festuca* communities containing *Saxifraga aizoides*.

Although some stands contain montane plants such as *Tofieldia pusilla, Saxifraga aizoides* and *Juncus triglumis*, the majority lie between 30 m. (100 ft.) and 610 m. (2000 ft.) and so belong to the potential Forest Zone. On Morrone at Braemar, Aberdeenshire, this kind of mire occurs extensively with calcareous flushes in parts of the birch-juniper wood. Occasional examples may be found up to 838 m. (2800 ft.) but without differing markedly in floristics from those at lower levels. *Carex panicea—Campylium stellatum* mires are found alongside calcareous springs, flushes and rills, or in places where the seepage water is not canalised. In area they vary from a few to several hundred square metres, but are usually small.

This type of vegetation is confined to strongly calcareous substrata and is best represented on the band of Dalradian limestone and calcareous mica-schist extending from Breadalbane to Clova, though there are occurrences throughout the Scottish uplands. The soils are wet, silty muds with varying amounts of humus, but pure peat horizons are unusual. Their pH ranges from 5·9 to 6·3 and exchangeable calcium content from 372 to 992 mg. per 100 gm. of air dried soil.

Similar mires occur on limestone and other calcareous rocks in northern England.

Carex rostrata—brown moss mire (Table 56, col. 7). Although eutrophic, this type of mire is rather uniform and floristically poor, with *Carex rostrata* as physiognomic dominant, and several other sedges more sparingly represented. There are few herbs and the cover of vascular plants is usually rather open. Pleurocarpous "brown mosses" form a complete cover and include *Campylium stellatum, Cratoneuron commutatum, Drepanocladus revolvens* var. *intermedius* and *Scorpidium scorpioides*, which may grow mixed or with one species locally dominant.

This is quite a rare type of vegetation, though examples have been found in widely scattered parts of Scotland. It appears to depend on a highly calcareous but virtually stagnant drainage water, as in a hollow or basin, and such conditions are extremely local, even in areas of lime-bearing rocks. The altitudinal range is fairly wide, from 30–793 m. (100–2600 ft.) so that some examples occur well above the forest limit, but floristically they do not differ greatly from low-lying stands. Because of the topogenous rather than soligenous conditions in some sites, and the affinity with brown moss communities of eutrophic lowland fens, the *Carex rostrata*—brown moss mire could also be regarded as fen. The stands are, however, usually small, from a few to several hundred square metres in area, and so approximate in size to many other types of mire.

The substratum is a waterlogged brown moss peat, containing little or no mineral matter, and with a pH range of 5·5–5·8. It corresponds to the *Hypnum* peat moor of Kubiëna (1953). Water samples show pH values of 6·5–6·8.

Similar vegetation occurs very locally among fen swamps in northern England, mostly where drainage is from Carboniferous limestone.

Schoenus nigricans mire (Table 56, col. 8). This is another floristically poor but strongly eutrophic mire, with *Schoenus nigricans* completely dominant in dense tussocks. Other monocotyledons such as *Eriophorum angustifolium* are usually present, but herbs are few and mosses less important than in many mires, although *Campylium stellatum* is constant.

Schoenus nigricans mires are very local and apparently confined to western Scotland where they occur in waterlogged hollows receiving drainage from limestone, ultra-basic igneous rocks or blown shell sand. The stands are usually less than 300 sq. m. and have not been found above 183 m. (600 ft.). The soils are calcareous peats or marls with a high pH (8·0 in one sample), though from their proximity to the sea, some appear to be saline as well.

Schoenus mires could also be regarded as fen, both from their situation and from their affinity to certain lowland fen communities containing an abundance of *Schoenus*. In western Scotland, similar vegetation with a more open growth of *Schoenus* occurs in flushes, and where base-rich water emerges amongst blanket bogs. Although this type of mire has a more western distribution than the *Carex rostrata*—brown moss type, the two occur together at Bettyhill in Sutherland.

Similar *Schoenus* dominated vegetation occurs in lowland fens in various parts of England, in the "valley bogs" of the New Forest and Dorset heaths, and in western Ireland, but is not necessarily associated with eutrophic conditions.

BOGS

The great extent of bog-land of one kind or another is a striking feature of the Scottish landscape. This is a reflection of the general wetness of climate, the prevailing bog being dependent on moisture originating as precipitation (see p. 427). Over most of the western half of the country the climate is so humid that there is a pronounced tendency to peat formation wherever slope of the land lies below about 15°, since ground moisture there remains almost continuously in excess of that lost by evaporation. Not only are soil conditions generally anaerobic, but the rain water has a low content of mineral elements, giving high acidity. Such conditions, under a cool climate, ensure a low rate of microbial activity and thus favour the accumulation of plant remains as peat.

The subdivision of ombrogenous (or ombrotrophic) bog into raised bog and blanket bog has already been made on p. 428, and it was noted that this separation is based on relationships to topography.

Raised bogs

Raised bogs occur on more or less flat ground in low-lying country, on alluvial plains in broad river valleys or on marine sediment which has become raised above sea-level. Smaller examples sometimes occupy glacial drift hollows and "kettle-holes". The absence of slope is thus largely responsible for waterlogging of the ground in such situations. Raised bog is a decidedly local type in Scotland and the bulk of the extensive peatlands are blanket bog. The distribution of raised bogs is complementary to that of blanket bog since it is less restricted climatically and well developed in areas with a rainfall as low as 75 cm. (30 ins.) a year. It might perhaps be regarded as the lowland equivalent or extension of blanket bog, occurring on level ground where the necessary degree of wetness is maintained by complete absence of slope. Raised bogs occur mainly in the Solway region, the Central Lowlands, and locally in a few places along both the east and west coast lowlands.

Examination of the peat stratigraphy of raised bogs has shown that they usually originated as minerotrophic fen, which formed the basal peat layers, sometimes over lake sediments. Pollen analysis has revealed that some of the lake muds belong to early Late-glacial times, and that the deposits under the present raised bog began to form under sub-arctic conditions very different from those of the present day. Later, when the Post-glacial Period was well advanced, a pronounced vegetational change took place, as shown by the transition from fen peat to bog peat. Either in response to increasing wetness of climate or as the result of the living surface growing above the influence of mineral-rich seepage water, an oligotrophic vegetation gradually took the place of the original fen swamps. Bog plants which tolerate or need acidic, base-deficient waters became dominant. Among them were the Sphagna, some of which are believed to have the power of increasing the acidity of their habitat. Once established, these oligotrophic conditions have persisted ever since, for the rising bog surface becomes increasingly independent of water supplied by lateral drainage and ever more dependent on that derived from the atmosphere. The upper peat laid down since the vegetational change-over shows a good deal of variation in humification and composition, but is relatively uniform chemically, with a low pH and low content of available chemical elements (cf. Godwin and Conway, 1939). Raised bog may thus have originated from topogenous fen, but the bog part of the vegetational sequence must be regarded as ombrogenous, or at least ombrotrophic.

Raised bogs may extend an unbroken surface over considerable areas (up to approx. 10 sq. km. (4 sq. miles) on East Flanders Moss) but the plains on which they lie are naturally broken up by rivers and subsidiary streams, or surface irregularities, and ultimately pass into higher, sloping ground. There is therefore a limit to the extent of a particular bog, and in the original state the boundary would seem commonly to consist of a lower-lying fen-type swamp or carr ("lagg") influenced by minerotrophic water and sometimes carrying a stream. Water flows into this marginal drainage system from the bog edge, and sometimes from mineral soils on the other side, as well as from ground farther up the catchment. In some cases the marginal swamps and streams are occupying their original positions, which imposed the limits to the spread of bog, while in others, the centrifugally expanding bog may have pushed them in front of it. Whichever the case, the spread of bog is checked by a flow of enriched ground water. In other situations the limitation may be merely that of increasing slope and run-off and marginal fen or stream vegetation is then lacking, there being a gradual transition to mineral soils with woodland in the natural state.

Whatever conditions limit the lateral spread of a raised bog, there is usually a decrease in depth of peat from the centre towards the edges, and this may become more sudden at the actual perimeter, giving a marked slope down to the level of the laggs. Such a marginal bank is called a "rand". In vertical section, a typical raised bog is convex, hence the name, and this reflects the differential rate of growth (i.e. peat formation) from the centre outwards. Some bogs have evidently spread centrifugally, so that the shallower edges are younger than the deeper centre. The convexity may be regarded as the effect of varying rate of peat formation in response to a hydrological gradient, from the stagnant, base-deficient, anaerobic water of the bog centre to the moving, base-enriched, aerated water of the laggs. The convexity is, however, only relative, bearing in mind that a raised bog may be 3·2 km. (2 miles) or more in diameter but only 9 m. (30 ft.) deep in the centre.

Where a plain is traversed by several streams, there may be separate patches of raised bog, or one patch may have various arms and projections, the whole forming a dissected complex. This is true of West Flanders Moss in the Central Lowlands of Perthshire and Stirling, and Lochar Moss on the Solway Plain in Dumfriesshire. Claish Moss in Sunart, Argyll, is a fine series of raised bogs lying in a string along the south side of Loch Shiel, each patch being separated from its neighbours by lagg streams which drain into the loch from the slopes above (Plate 78). Moine Mhor, near the Crinan Canal, Argyll, is another comparable but more disturbed group of raised bogs. Individual raised bogs occur in several parts of the Solway region, such as Moss of Cree in Wigtownshire, Kirkconnell Flow in Kirkcudbrightshire and Nutberry Moss in Dumfriesshire. East Flanders Moss in Perthshire is a single raised bog and there is an isolated example, Corpach Moss, at Fort William in Inverness-shire. All these examples lie at very low levels, less than 30 m. (100 ft.) above mean sea level, and most would seem to lie on former marine alluvium.

From their position in fertile lowlands, at least in southern Scotland, raised bogs are mostly surrounded by agricultural land. In many instances there has been obvious encroachment of farmland on to the original bog, due to reclamation by draining, removal of peat and the addition of fertilisers, so that the margins are no longer natural. The laggs have often disappeared and been replaced by artificial ditches, while the bog edges are commonly grown with birch or pine. Sometimes cut faces of peat form an abrupt boundary to the bog, and the cutting of fuel peat has left numerous depressions, which often show secondary colonisation to form wet *Sphagnum* bog again. Less complete reclamation leads to the appearance of poor *Juncus effusus* and *Molinia* grown pastures which grade into the true bog vegetation, and this itself shows all degrees of modification in a general process of drying out. It would seem that some raised bogs of olden times have completely disappeared and the extent of others has been greatly reduced as a result of expanding agriculture, especially in the Solway region, and the Central Plain. Even the remaining raised bogs are now under attack, chiefly by the development of local moss-litter extraction, during which the surface is completely drained and largely cut away (see p. 546).

Blanket bogs

Blanket bog, in contrast to raised bog, depends on high precipitation and is absent from the drier parts of Scotland, although it is by far the more extensive type of the two in the country as a whole. Since precipitation is partly related to altitude, blanket bog is characteristic of uplands but descends to sea level in the humid west and north of Scotland. The very apt name describes how this type of bog smothers the gentler slopes and level ground in an unbroken mantle of peat.

Rate (and therefore depth) of peat formation depend on a resultant of factors, for precipitation/evaporation ratio interacts with slope and porosity of substratum in determining wetness of ground. It is, for instance, obvious in theory that under uniform climate, rate of peat formation will vary according to slope of the ground, or that on sites of uniform gradient, there will be variations according to differences in climatic wetness. While blanket bog thus becomes an increasingly conspicuous component of vegetation in an east to west direction across Scotland, its actual extent in any district depends a great deal upon topography. It is far more extensive on the elevated mountain plateaux of such eastern areas as Clova, Atholl and the Monadhliath than in precipitous western hill country such as Knoydart, Kintail and Glen Coe, even though these are far wetter areas than the others. But the biggest blanket bogs of all are on the vast undulating moorlands and plains of Sutherland and Caithness. In this district, a continuous area of approximately 2500 sq. km. (1000 sq. miles) is mostly covered with blanket bog.

Probably in all Britain there are no scenes more impressive in their barren desolation than the enormous "flowes" (level bogs) which lie between Strath Naver and Strath Halladale, and thence stretch away eastwards almost to the coast of Caithness. Towards the western limits of this great tract, high and rugged mountains such as Ben Loyal, Ben Hope and Ben Klibreck rise singly and suddenly from the bogland, but there is no better vantage point for viewing the flowe country than the centrally placed Ben Griam More or Ben Griam Beag near Forsinard. From these twin hills, blanket bog stretches away mile upon mile in every direction, the flat or gently undulating surface broken only by a few lochs of medium size and more numerous dubh lochans (black tarns). The Moor of Rannoch on the borders of Perthshire and Argyll is a blanket bog occupying a large basin surrounded by high mountains. Here, however, as on the extensive blanket bogs of west Sutherland and the Outer Hebridean Isles of Lewis, Benbecula, North Uist and South Uist, the bog surface is broken by very numerous projections of moraine or bedrock, and honeycombed by a multitude of lochans.

Since blanket bog occurs on sloping as well as flat ground, it is less clearly delimited from the vegetation of drier ground than in the case of raised bog. On the contrary, it is quite usual for blanket bog to show a gradual transition to non-peaty vegetation and soils, through intermediate "wet heaths" or "wet grasslands" with peat podsols or gley podsols. If there is a sudden steepening of slope, with consequent improvement in drainage, the blanket bog may show a fairly sharp boundary, with rapid spatial change from deep peat to largely mineral soil. This transition zone would correspond to the rand of a typical raised bog. More usually, peat of intermediate depth occupies larger areas, but its extent obviously depends on slope and drainage. In steep sided hill country, intermediate types may be far more extensive than true blanket bog, as in many parts of the western Highlands.

In deciding when an organic soil is deep enough to qualify as a "peat" as distinct from a peaty mineral soil, it has become conventional (e.g. Fraser, 1954) to take 30–50 cm. as a minimum depth. This arbitrary limit to the term is useful and could be applied as a definition of "bog" also, but it then agrees less well with limits drawn according to floristic criteria. For the purposes of the present account, a much wider interpretation of the term blanket bog is taken, based on floristics rather than peat characteristics, and includes certain types of wet heath on peaty mineral soils.

Stratigraphical studies (e.g. Durno, 1961) have shown that blanket bogs mostly originated at the onset of the Atlantic Period, in response to the marked increase in wetness of climate at that time. Instead of replacing earlier swamp vegetation, as did the raised bogs, the blanket bogs usually developed on once dry ground occupied by forest. The presence of a layer of tree remains at the junction of the basal peat and the underlying mineral soil is very characteristic and is to be seen in numerous sites where erosion has exposed the stumps and roots. Once oligotrophic bog was formed, it continued to grow and lay down peat during the remainder of the Post-glacial Period. In vegetational history and stratigraphy, deep blanket bog shows a general similarity to the ombrogenous phase of raised bog: Sphagna are prominent, and with ericoid shrubs and monocotyledons (chiefly Cyperaceae) have formed the bulk of the peat, which varies in degree of humification at different depths, indicating periods of change in vegetation composition and rate of peat formation. Blanket bogs show signs of drying in both surface peat layer and living vegetation, but this would appear to be an effect of human disturbance rather than increasing dryness of climate.

Like raised bogs, blanket bogs have been reduced in area locally by conversion to agricultural land, although from their occurrence in places where both climate and underlying mineral soil are unfavourable to farming, they are not a particularly attractive proposition for reclamation schemes. More often they have merely become converted into drier types of moorland, with vegetation which forms peat very slowly if at all. In contrast to raised bogs, which in Britain are exclusively lowland, blanket bogs occur at all altitudes up to 1067 m. (3500 ft.), although peat formation above this level would appear to be limited by the extreme severity of climate. The higher-lying examples fall within the montane zone and are considered separately from those which lie within the potential forest limits (Chapter 15, p. 536). Probably because of their occurrence under more extreme climatic conditions, as well as on sloping ground, blanket bogs are much more susceptible to erosion than raised bogs, and many are now in a highly degenerate state (p. 454 and Plate 79).

Intermediate bogs

The categories of raised bog and blanket bog may be regarded as the two end points of a cline, for they are linked by a complete series of intermediates. While many examples may, from their clearly defined topographic features, be assigned without hesitation to one category or the other, there are some bogs which just as obviously cannot be classified in this way, since they combine the features of both categories. The usefulness of the distinction then breaks down and it becomes simpler to think in terms of a single large class of ombrotrophic bog.

These intermediate bogs usually lie at fairly low levels, (i.e. 30–304 m. (100–1000 ft.)) and in only moderately wet districts, so that they occur under a range of environments intermediate between that of typical raised bog and blanket bog. Their surface is usually flat, or with an exceedingly gentle slope, and there may sometimes be a tendency towards the convexity of the true raised bog. The marginal features of raised bog such as rand and laggs are usually lacking, however, or present along parts of the bog edge, and there is often a gradual transition to wet heath and then dry heath at the bog margin. Examples of this type occur in Wigtownshire, around Mochrum and Glenluce, and in Lanarkshire to the east of Wishaw. Other examples of intermediate bog occur in basins or channels in glacial drift country. These basin and channel bogs are rather small in area and their surface is usually flat or nearly so, while the edges are usually without rand or lagg, although there may be diffuse seepage areas ("soaks") or even a central patch of open water within the bog. There are very good examples of this type in Abernethy Forest, Inverness-shire (see Plate 80). In such examples, the bog probably originated as topogenous fen, which was later replaced by ombrotrophic peat, as in the classical sequence of raised bog development.

Again, on some extensive areas of undoubted blanket bog, just south of the Scottish border, it has been shown (S. B. Chapman pers. comm.) that the underlying drift contains hollows which originally held fen when the surrounding land was dry. These swampy hollows became nuclei for bog development during the Atlantic Period and blanket bog later spread over the whole area. The vegetation of the original hollows is sometimes represented by the persistence of fen plants such as *Phragmites communis* in the present living bog vegetation, but these hollows are often quite undetectable from the present uniformity of the surface in relief and floristics. The vegetational history of these pockets corresponds to that of raised bog, and at a transitional period, before peat had spread over the surrounding land, they may even have appeared as raised bogs. This picture is probably equally true of many Scottish blanket bogs. Blanket and raised bogs are thus not always separable in a time sequence.

The lack of clear distinction between the two types is perhaps best illustrated by a chain of bogs, collectively known as the Silver Flowe, along a broad valley of the Kirkcudbrightshire hills. The lowest bog has all the appearances of a typical raised bog, with oval outline, convex relief and well developed laggs and rand. Passing up the valley, each succeeding bog bears a diminishing resemblance to true raised bog, there being a disappearance of convexity (to give the so-called "flat" raised bog), laggs and finally the rand, until the bog patches at the head of the valley are true blanket bog (Fig. 60). Moreover, stratigraphical examination of the two lowest bogs disclosed (Ratcliffe and Walker, 1957) that there is no underlying fen peat and the deposits did not begin to form until the Atlantic Period, i.e. although raised bogs in appearance they have the characteristic history of blanket bog, and appear to be wholly ombrogenous.

In conclusion, then, the subdivision into raised bog and blanket bog is a useful one in many cases, but becomes artificial when bogs over the whole of Scotland are considered.

Features of bogs in general

Some features are common to all bogs, whether raised, blanket or intermediate between these, while certain trends in floristics and surface pattern found over Scotland as a whole are geographical and climatic rather than related to these topographic categories.

Relations to climate. The difference in geographical distribution of raised bog and blanket bog in Scotland is both topographic and climatic. Although most raised bogs occur in the lowlands where rainfall is low, they do not depend on relative dryness of climate, as is shown by the development of Claish Moss under the extremely humid climate of Western Argyll. Their scarcity in mountain country with heavy rainfall is largely due to the unsuitability of the terrain, whilst on suitable ground in wet districts such as Sutherland their identity is lost in the general cover of blanket bog. On the other hand, blanket bog needs a more humid climate than raised bog before it can begin to develop and its distribution has more definite geographical limits.

In stating that blanket bog is confined to the wetter districts of Scotland, the problem of defining "wetness" arises. As Tansley (1949) pointed out, rainfall is the least useful of the various indices of climatic wetness for attempting a correlation with the distribution of blanket bog. McVean and Ratcliffe (1962) found that the meteorological category of the "wet day" (a day with 1 mm. (0·04 in.) or more of rain) was the most satisfactory of the available indices to use in relating certain vegetational distribution patterns to the controlling wetness of climate. This index takes into account the annual distribution as well as the amount of rainfall and so gives a better idea of overall wetness. A map of wet days (op. cit., p. 146) shows, for instance, that the flowe country of east Sutherland and Caithness is considerably wetter than the area around Perth and Dunkeld, although the range of rainfall in the two areas is the same.

Potential evapotranspiration has been discussed in Chapter 2 and is likely to be the best of all indices of wetness for making correlations with vegetational distribution, as the map on p. 32 suggests. It is a measure of the effective humidity impinging on

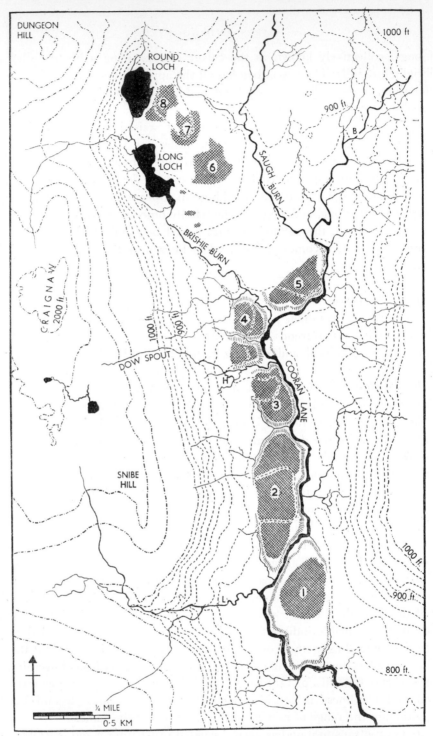

FIG. 60. The Silver Flowe bogs. This map shows the distribution of individual patches of hummock-hollow bog (cross-hatching) in the valley of Cooran Lane, Kirkcudbrightshire. They are seen to occupy the flattest parts of the valley floor, but their relation to topography changes from south to north. The southerly bogs have well-marked "rands" (shown by hachures) and marginal "lagg" streams, giving slightly convex central areas, as in a typical raised bog. The rands gradually become less marked and the most northerly patches are differentiated from the general expanse of blanket-bog only by their hummock-hollow surface structure. The steeper slopes above are covered mainly with shallow *Calluna—Molina* bog.

vegetation and controlling the wetness of the ground, and so has a direct relationship to peat formation.

It is clear that, despite considerable regional variation in climate, the whole of Scotland, except for a few small areas on the east coast, is wet enough to allow the development of ombrogenous bog. Blanket bog is the type associated with more extreme oceanicity, whereas raised bog is especially characteristic of climates with intermediate humidity, and so occurs in Continental districts. In areas of similar topography there is a strong correlation between wetness of climate and extent of bogland or depth of peat in any particular situation. In the northern hemisphere generally, the distribution of ombrogenous bog is related more to coldness of climate than to high precipitation and atmospheric humidity. Low temperature favours peat accumulation by reducing rates of evaporation and microbial decomposition. There are probably few parts of the world, however, where peat occurs so extensively on sloping ground as in western and northern parts of the British Isles.

The relationships between floristic trends and climatic gradients in Scotland are discussed in the accounts of the different vegetation types.

Peat. One common characteristic is that the peat of ombrogenous bog is invariably acidic and base deficient. Acidity varies with degree of oxidation and humification, the drier, more humified peats usually having the lower pH values, as was pointed out by Pearsall (1938). The values for pH range from 3·4 to 4·6, there being some slight seasonal variations at any one site. Shrinkage of peat on drying is so great that measurements of exchangeable ions based on dry weight are meaningless when compared with those for soils of low humus content. Such determinations are more suitably made on equal *volumes* of peat, which have comparative meaning with mineral soils, if similar volume measurements of these are made. As an alternative, measurements of the ion content of bog waters may be made, although these vary at the same site according to dilution by rain, and samples are best collected after a standard drought period.

The low nutrient status of bog peats is a direct consequence of their dependence on the atmosphere for a supply of chemical elements. The only other possible source of supply to the living surface is from decomposition of the underlying peat, and upward diffusion from below. Little is known about either of these possibilities, and in particular whether the underlying mineral soil can influence the surface of supposedly ombrogenous bog. In the north-west Highlands it has been noted (McVean and Ratcliffe, 1962, p. 105) that the shallow peat of *Calluna—Trichophorum* wet heaths on Cambrian quartzite gives way to relatively deep blanket bog with *Calluna* and *Eriophorum vaginatum* on the smaller areas of calcareous mudstones and grits. The implication here is that the higher nutrient content of the underlying calcareous rocks has led to a higher rate of plant production and peat formation than on the quartzite, although the peat itself is acidic and base-deficient on both types of rock. There is, however, a possibility that the two substrata differ in porosity. On the whole blanket bog appears to be indifferent to the chemical composition of the underlying rock and occurs on calcareous and non-calcareous rocks alike.

The historical study of Scottish peat deposits has lagged behind that in England although, before the days of pollen analysis, Lewis (1905–07, 1911) made an extensive survey of Scottish bogs and published copious data on their stratigraphy. Recent work by Durno (1961) suggests that the Quaternary history of Scottish vegetation may be regarded as a more northern and montane version of the summarised picture given by Godwin (1956) for England and Wales.

A characteristic feature of blanket peat is the presence of a basal layer with tree remains, mostly of pine, birch, oak or juniper which evidently grew on the underlying mineral soil. Tree remains are less consistently found at the base of the ombrogenous peat in raised bogs, but they may occur also in the underlying topogenous fen peat, and there represent a stage of carr woodland. It is generally believed that the growth of wet bogs was responsible for the death and swamping of these forests, but the story may not be quite so simple as a mere drowning of the woodlands. Certainly, trees are able to grow moderately well, or at least reach seed-producing age, in quite wet bogs, as may be seen in the pine-grown bogs of Abernethy Forest, although tree growth is inhibited when the water-table is really high. Durno and McVean (1959) record that in blanket peat on Beinn Eighe in Wester Ross there are charred stumps representing at least three successive pine forests destroyed by fire in Boreal and Atlantic times. These authors found frequent traces of charcoal in peats of more recent age and McVean (pers. comm.) has found similar evidence of widespread influence of fire in blanket peat of varying age in several parts of the Highlands.

Nearly all the ombrogenous peat deposits which have been examined show variations in rate of growth through their history, the changes being revealed by a stratification of the peat into layers of different composition and humification. The so-called humified "retardation layers" lying above and below fresh unhumified peat are often held to mark a temporary drying of the climate with reduced rate of peat formation; the overlying "recurrence surface" indicates the return to wetter conditions and rapid bog growth. In some blanket bogs a second buried tree layer is present at an intermediate depth, on top of a humified stratum, and is believed to correspond to the beginning of the wetter Sub-atlantic Period which followed the relatively dry Sub-boreal. Even basal tree remains in hill peat, particularly the shallower deposits, are not necessarily Boreal in age and some are quite recent. The shallower and drier bogs and wet heaths with peaty soils may have carried an intermittent tree cover right through Post-glacial times up to the recent period of intensive human disturbance.

Vegetation. It follows that the vegetation of bogs is composed of plants which have a low mineral nutrient requirement and can tolerate fairly high acidity. Most species, notably the Sphagna, are decidedly calcifuge and grow only under oligotrophic conditions but a few, such as *Calluna* and *Myrica* can tolerate a wider range of soil base-status. Moreover, McVean (1959) has shown that on the poorest quartzite soils even the oligotrophic Sphagna show increased growth after the addition of phosphate. Some Sphagna reputedly have the power of acidifying their habitat, thus ensuring the permanence of oligotrophic conditions in bogs where they are abundant or dominant.

One result of this edaphic situation is that bog is invariably land of low productivity for grazing animals. The apparently closed cycle involving small amounts of nutrients leads to a low rate and amount of plant growth, and the plant tissues themselves have poor feeding value. Improvement of such ground necessarily involves increasing the nutrient turnover, either by introducing an extraneous supply to the surface in the form of fertiliser or by accelerating the rate of release from the underlying peat, or both (see p. 457).

The prominence of Sphagna in all types of bog has already been indicated. When dominant these plants occupy a unique position, for they form a living surface to the peat and are themselves part of the substratum for the vascular plants. As the apices of *Sphagnum* stems grow upwards the lower parts die and become peat, although it is not easy to determine the depth at which death of the *Sphagnum* cells occurs. Dominant *Sphagnum* forms a continuous carpet which grows upwards fairly rapidly, thereby raising the whole surface, whereas growth of the vascular plants is more irregular and localised. The Sphagna are therefore the most rapid peat-formers among bog plants, although different species have different rates of growth. The robust carpet and hummock formers such as *Sphagnum papillosum*, *S. magellanicum*, but more particularly *S. rubellum*, *S. fuscum* and *S. imbricatum* appear to grow most rapidly, and rise well above the water-table; while others such as *S. cuspidatum* and *S. auriculatum* do not rise far above the water-table, and are evidently less important as peat formers. The *Sphagnum* carpet usually contains a selection of small mosses and liverworts, but these occupy a subsidiary position and are insignificant as peat formers.

The abundance of *Sphagnum* is itself related primarily to the wetness of the ground. On flat ground with a high water-table, conditions for *Sphagnum* growth are optimal and there is usually a more or less complete carpet. The vascular plants then occupy a subordinate position, with an incomplete cover and usually non-tussocky habit, rooted in the *Sphagnum* carpet and upper peat, and forming a separate open community. *Sphagnum* dominated bog is thus essentially a two-layered type of vegetation. The upper layer of vascular plants is a mixture mainly of dwarf shrubs and monocotyledons, and it is a peculiarity of bog vegetation that dicotyledonous herbs are poorly represented.

Surface patterns and their relation to bog growth. Most of the species present are more or less hydrophilous but, taking the whole bog flora, there is a considerable range of variation in tolerance to, or dependence on, aquatic conditions. This is shown mainly as a vertical zonation of species in relation to the water-table, a phenomenon most marked in bogs which have an uneven surface.

Although from a distance, some bogs appear to be completely flat, closer examination nearly always shows a considerable irregularity of surface on a small scale. The ground surface, consisting either of living *Sphagnum* or dead peat, is usually undulating, with numerous slight elevations or hummocks and corresponding depressions or hollows. An average amplitude of change in elevation between hummock and hollow is about 30 cm., but on some bogs the tallest hummock may reach 70–80 cm. above the mean level of the bog surface and the hollows may attain a depth of 100 cm. or even more below.

2 F

The deeper hollows lie below the water-table and then appear as distinct water-filled pools. In places the bog surface lacks this micro-relief, and such areas may be termed "flats"; they also form an intermediate zone vertically and horizontally between hummock and hollow, and then correspond to a "mean surface level". On bogs where the surface as a whole is level or only gently inclined, the water-table is usually at, or just below, mean surface level. On the Silver Flowe in Galloway it has been found that the water-table in such a bog fluctuates according to weather and season. The fluctuation is in relation to the surface, and the water level moves up and down in the natural pools or pits dug into the surface peat. On these bogs there is no tendency for the surface as a whole to move up and down due to a swelling in volume of the peat after heavy rainfall, although this may possibly happen on other bogs.

While it is difficult to establish a datum for measurement, the surface of a hummock and hollow bog obviously experiences a varying degree of wetness according to vertical level at any one time. This is complicated by vertical movements of the water-table over a period, but the general amplitude is reflected in the vertical zonation of bog plants.

The spatial sequence (described on p. 460) is similar over the whole of Scotland, although some species have a local geographical distribution. It allows us to distinguish "hollow" or "pool" and "hummock" species, though some have a wide range of moisture tolerance, and a few are restricted largely to a narrow intermediate zone. Stratigraphical evidence suggests that this vegetational gradient represents also a true, though small-scale, succession in time, i.e. the process of upward growth in hummock and hollow bogs. The pool Sphagna form a carpet to the hollow and by upward growth gradually raise its level until other less extreme hydrophilous Sphagna and vascular plants can colonise the surface. The pool thus grows up level with the bog "flats" to become part of this stage, and the open water disappears. The "flat" may then be invaded by hummock building Sphagna which raise the surface still higher above the water-table, and impart to it a convexity. As the surface rises, the vascular plants become more tussocky and luxuriant, and they may reduce the area of *Sphagnum*. In any case, upward growth of a *Sphagnum* hummock is eventually checked by increasing dryness at the surface. The tallest and driest hummocks thus tend to have a capping of vascular plants and other mosses instead of *Sphagnum*, and there often appear species which are unable to grow closer to the water-table. The sequence represents a typical growth process, starting slowly, then accelerating to the rapid median phase and ending in senescence.

There seems no doubt that this micro-succession does occur in places, but it is not an inevitable process, and it does not follow that all hollows will develop into flats and hummocks, or that flats and hummocks have necessarily developed from hollows. Even more controversial is the further sequence of changes once the change from hollow to hummock has occurred. Tansley (1949) has given a good account of Osvald's Regeneration Complex theory, in which the upward growth of hollows into hummocks results in older senescent hummocks being overtopped by the more active surrounding surface; these senescent hummocks eventually become the loci of new hollows, and the process is repeated, so that any particular point on the bog shows one or more complete cycles of change over a period. This idea is perhaps too facile, and has not so far been borne out by careful stratigraphical examination of the peat in the well-developed hummock-hollow system of the Silver Flowe in Galloway (see Ratcliffe and Walker, 1958).

More often it appears that the upward growth of hummock and hollow bogs is an irregular process and that while on some bogs some hollows have become converted into flats and hummocks, on others they are persistent features which have occupied exactly the same places for a long time. On the Silver Flowe the hummock-hollow system is a relatively recent feature but on some bogs it appears to be a long established feature. The whole subject of bog growth is so open to conjecture that further discussion would seem profitless until a really thorough investigation has been made.

Equally puzzling is the actual arrangement of hollows on the bog surface. When this type of bog is viewed from the air or surrounding higher land, it is usually strikingly obvious that the hollows are arranged in a definite pattern. The hollows are usually elongated in outline and water-filled, so that they show up very clearly as pools, and they lie with their long axes parallel to the general surface contours of the bog or, conversely, at right angles to the direction of slope (see Plates 78 and 82). This parallel alignment is lacking only when the bog surface has no slope, and the hollows then have a more random arrangement and are often less elongated. Bogs with these aligned hollow systems are widespread over the Boreal zone and have been described from many parts of Scandinavia and Canada (see Sjörs, 1961). In Scotland they are widespread in the west and north but, apart from the Galloway uplands, are confined to the Highlands. Finely developed examples occur on the Silver Flowe in Galloway, Claish Moss in Sunart, and in many places on the great "flowe" country of east Sutherland and Caithness, as around the Strathy River, Strath Halladale, Strathmore and Badenloch. Aligned hollows also occur in the forest bogs of Abernethy in Inverness-shire.

Such surface patterns are most usual on the lower lying blanket bogs, and are not usual on the high level plateau bogs, but they also occur on raised bog (Claish Moss) and the intermediate bogs (Abernethy). They do not occur on the raised bogs of the Solway region or Central Lowlands, although these have smaller and unaligned hollows in places, or larger, more rounded and less distinct depressions. This distribution does not seem to correspond entirely with high rainfall and atmospheric humidity, since Abernethy is a relatively dry area and aligned hollow systems are characteristic of bogs in many continental regions elsewhere in the world. Even so the best examples are situated in very wet parts of Scotland. Since they occur also in the valley bogs of the New Forest and Dorset heaths in southern England, these aligned hummock-hollow systems are not restricted to the cooler parts of Britain, as would otherwise seem to be the case.

The mode of development of aligned hummock-hollow systems is also a matter of conjecture and disagreement. Pearsall (1956) has suggested two possible interpretations of the system on a bog near the Strathy River in Sutherland. One theory is that the surface skin of the bog has furrowed due to shrinkage of the underlying peat during a period of desiccation, while the other is that "pressure-folding" has taken place due to the weight of the semi-fluid mass of peat tending to move down the slope. Sjörs (1961), on the other hand, has pointed out that downhill movement or soil-creep explanations are not consistent with the facts, since "flarks" (i.e. hollows or pools) are absent from steep bog slopes and best developed on slopes too gentle to allow peat-flow at all. While offering no alternative explanation, Sjörs remarks that "flarks" are primarily dependent on the water flow across the peatland. From the strong superficial resemblance in aerial view (cf. Plate 78) of these aligned hummock-hollow systems to solifluction terracing and furrowing in lava flows and glaciers, it is very tempting to believe that some form of pressure due to gravity is responsible. Certainly, when the overall surface slope is steep, a pool sometimes appears to be pushing forward on the downslope side and forcing up a bank between it and the next pool. It may be that these systems are absent from steeper bog slopes because run-off is too rapid and the water-table too low to allow their formation. Hummock and hollow systems seem always to be associated with a water-table close to or at the bog surface, and any fall in water-table is usually followed by their degeneration.

Enough has been said to indicate that the processes of bog growth are still very imperfectly understood, and that there are some intriguing problems in need of attention by those versed in hydrodynamics as well as plant ecology.

Recent changes in bog vegetation. Whatever the growth processes of bogs, there is no doubt that the last few hundred years have seen a general slowing down or complete cessation of bog regeneration. Bog surfaces have dried out and become covered with vegetation which forms peat very slowly, and many have been affected by erosion which at times results in complete destruction of the bog. This change involves increasing desiccation, certainly as an effect, if not as a cause. The process of drying is so general that it would almost seem to be climatically induced especially as bog stratigraphy so often shows "retardation layers" or "*Grenz* horizons" (i.e. peat strata representing reduced rate of bog growth) which are held to mark periods of greater climatic dryness in earlier times. However, it would seem unwise to invoke climatic change in the absence of reliable supporting evidence, and there are no strong grounds for believing that the climate of Britain has become appreciably drier during the last few hundred years. It is likely in theory that any increase in warmth (for which there is better evidence) might have led to a slightly drier climate by increasing evaporation.

On the other hand, there is every sign that human disturbance has become so widespread as to be almost universal over the boglands of Britain during recent times, and this influence has had the general effect of lowering water-tables. Moor burning has become standard practice over virtually all unenclosed land except woodland in Scotland, provided that the vegetation is combustible. Despite the wetness of the ground, bog vegetation suffers a good deal from this activity and during a dry period, when the water-table falls slightly below the surface, fires can creep over a *Sphagnum* dominated bog, scorching and killing the moss. The dominant species, notably *S. papillosum*, *S. magellanicum* and *S. rubellum* seem particularly sensitive to fire, and though they may eventually recover after a single fire, repeated burning at short intervals rapidly causes a drastic and apparently irreversible reduction in their cover. The vascular plants suffer less, for while their aerial parts may be burned, their roots usually lie deep enough to be unaffected; and when growth is renewed they appear more luxuriant and clumped or tussocky than before. The improved performance is partly due to the direct effects of surface drying, but the increased aeration and death of *Sphagnum* may lead to more rapid decomposition of the surface peat and a greater release of nutrients. It is noticeable particularly on those Solway and Central Lowland raised bogs which are already largely dried out, that in the spring and early summer following a further fire, *Eriophorum vaginatum* is often stimulated to such profuse flowering that the ground appears as if covered with snow. Increased flowering in *Molinia* after burning has been shown to be due to the higher temperature at the growing apices resulting from removal of the insulating layer of litter (H.F.R.O. Report, 1961). The same is probably true with *Eriophorum vaginatum*, though there is the possibility of a kind of "top-dressing" effect of the ash from the burned vegetation.

The general effect of burning is therefore to cause a drying out of bog surfaces. Sphagna are reduced while the vascular component of the vegetation becomes more prominent, and finally completely dominant. Drying bogs usually show a co-dominance of ericoids, chiefly *Calluna* and *Erica tetralix*, and monocotyledons such as *Eriophorum vaginatum* and *Trichophorum cespitosum*. Repeated burning, especially when combined with grazing, tends to suppress the ericoids, at least temporarily, and bogs may then become completely dominated by the more resistant *Eriophorum* or *Trichophorum* to form a fire climax. In dry districts, however, the last stage in desiccation is the complete dominance of *Calluna* on peat which has become too dry to support even mildly hydrophilous plants. In western and northern districts, where atmospheric humidity is high, drying of the bogs is usually marked by a great increase in *Rhacomitrium lanuginosum* which forms dense hummocks and carpets (Plate 84, see also Gimingham *et al*, 1961).

The peat surface undergoes parallel changes, becoming dry, oxidised and encrusted. During recolonisation a high proportion of the peat is left bare of cover, so that the drying process is accelerated. The original Sphagna dwindle but other species, notably *S. compactum* and *S. tenellum*, often favour the bare, burnt peat and become abundant, and an algal skin frequently develops on the peat, reducing percolation of rain water and increasing run-off, and rendering the surface biologically inactive.

The series of floristic changes which mark the drying-out of bogs is somewhat similar to the natural vegetational gradient reflecting permanent differences in wetness of ground. In other words, it is only possible to judge from the underlying peat whether a community intermediate between wet *Sphagnum* bog and dry heath has been derived from a wetter type of vegetation, or whether it is in a more or less original state.

Besides fire, human influence includes the draining of bogs with the deliberate intention of lowering the water-table, and the cutting of peat, which has similar effects. Surface draining by shallow ditches has long been practised as a means of drying bog lands and improving them for grazing animals. Nowadays, with increased mechanical efficiency available, formerly undisturbed, remote or high-lying bog areas are being drained.

Peat cutting has been equally widespread, but until recently has been on a small scale, by the local inhabitants, and as a source of fuel. The shallower bogs and the edges of the deeper bogs have been most affected, since their compacted and well humified peats are more satisfactory fuel than the quick-burning "fresh" *Sphagnum* peats. This local cutting of peat has helped to tap the margins of some bogs and may have contributed to the drying-out process, but it has affected mainly low-lying bogs, since peat was less easily transported from the higher levels. The method of removal often leaves water-filled shallow depressions, a metre or so deep, and these are gradually colonised by Sphagna, especially *S. recurvum* and *S. cuspidatum*, and other bog plants, so that pockets of wet bog eventually regenerate. On some severely disturbed bogs these overgrown peat workings are the only remaining *Sphagnum* dominated and actively growing sites.

In more recent years, bogs have been subjected to large scale, commercial exploitation for their peat, and this usually leads to the complete destruction of the original vegetation. This topic is dealt with more fully later, but it again affects mainly the lower-lying and more accessible bog lands. Forest clearance is yet another activity which has probably had a profound effect on bog hydrology. It is reasonable to suppose that, before human influence became so widespread, the edges of most bogs, and even the actual surfaces of the less wet bogs, were at least partly wooded, up to the altitudinal tree limit.

Some indication of this state is given by the forest bogs of Abernethy in Inverness-shire. Here, the continuous cover of pinewood is broken by wet, bog-filled hollows in channels and hollows of the glacial drift, though the change from one type of vegetation to the other is usually gradual. There is a decrease in stature of the trees as the ground becomes wetter, and even on spongy Sphagnetum there is often an open growth of stunted pines, many being scarcely a metre high though quite old (Plate 80). These "checked" trees eventually die, but there is no shortage of seedlings to replace them. Some of the shallower bogs have a fairly complete tree cover, and only in the very wettest sites are pines quite absent. There is a very strong resemblance to the pine and spruce forest bogs which are so widespread in Scandinavia (cf. Sjörs, 1948), and it is likely that the treeless nature of most of our boglands below the tree limit is unnatural. Locally, especially on lowland raised bogs, there is a good deal of colonisation of drying areas and margins by *Betula pubescens*, and patches of birchwood may replace the original bog vegetation.

Peat erosion. Drying-out may be accompanied by erosion in a general process of bog deterioration. Wastage of peat occurs either by sheet erosion, giving a denudation of the surface layers, or by "hagging" whereby a ramifying system of gullies eats back ever more widely from the bog edges and cuts down to the mineral substratum (see Plate 79). Both types of erosion may occur together, especially at high altitudes. Bogs with margins which give way to increasingly steep downhill slopes (as do many plateau blanket bogs) are particularly susceptible to gully erosion, since run-off is rapid at their edges. Lowland raised bogs and intermediate bogs often show no appreciable erosion, no matter how dry they may become. Flat hummock and hollow bogs show a very characteristic form of erosion by the enlargement of their hollows, which become very sharply defined pools, with bare peat edges, often undercut and with a bare deepened floor. Such pools usually have little or no *Sphagnum*, although they may contain more robust growths of *Menyanthes trifoliata* and *Eriophorum angustifolium* than the unfilled *Sphagnum* hollows. Their shape often tends to become oval instead of elongated, and intervening hummocks and ridges may break down to give an anastomosing network. Such eroded pool systems are very distinct in aerial view and at first accentuate the concentric pattern of alignment (see Plate 78), although more complete erosion leads to breakdown of the pattern and dissection of the surface into an irregular assortment of haggs and ridges.

It is obvious, as Osvald (1949) has pointed out in a survey of bog erosion all over the British Isles, that wind, water and frost are the chief agents of erosion. As soon as bare peat is exposed, it is acted upon by the elements, and unless rapidly colonised by some form of plant life (such as lichens or algae), will soon begin to break down. A loose peat surface is unfavourable to all plant growth, and once formed will usually continue to erode; wind removes particles rapidly, water washes them away and frost accelerates the loosening process. Gullying is a rapid form of water erosion whereby peat is removed in a moving current, and may originate as a subterranean channelling. Once the surface is broken, the bare, sloping sides of the gullies are exposed to the other forces of erosion. Pool enlargement takes place as a result of marginal scouring by wind-agitated water in a manner analogous to the formation of salt marsh pans.

The initial *causes* of erosion are, by contrast, far from obvious and are not yet properly understood. There are three main views on the subject. One is that bog erosion is due to climatic change, though even here there is disagreement on whether the change is towards wetness or dryness. A second idea is that bogs, by their very mode of growth, contain the seeds of their own destruction, and that their upward expansion gives an increasingly unstable system which is vulnerable to the various agents of erosion; it has been suggested that some bogs outgrow their water-table. The final view is that human disturbance, in one form or another, is the responsible factor.

While it could be that all three explanations are at least partly true, there is certainly most evidence in favour of the third. It has been shown above that, as a result of human activities, there has been a lowering of water-tables in bogs all over Scotland, leading to increased dryness of the surface. Burning, in particular, exposes the peat surface and would be likely to lead to sheet erosion, while both burning and marginal disturbance by forest clearance could lead to the initiation of gullying at the bog edges. Considerable denudation of mineral soils and shallow peat has been caused by moor fires, and the effects are particularly harmful in the deforested moraine country of the western Highlands. On the other hand, the severely eroded blanket bogs of the Clova-Caenlochan plateau lie well above the present potential forest limit.

Utilisation of peatlands

Peat has long been valued as a fuel, but only during recent years has it been considered and tried as a commercial and industrial source of power. The Scottish Peat Committee was appointed in 1949 to carry out a survey of Scottish peat deposits and to explore the practicability of exploiting these commercially, especially for production of electric power. As part of this scheme, an experimental peat-burning gas turbine generating station was set up at Altnabreac in Caithness in the heart of the enormous expanse of blanket bog which covers the north-eastern tip of Scotland.

The Scottish Peat Committee published their second report in 1962 and some of their reported findings are summarised below. Scotland has an estimated total area of 1,700,000 acres of peat two feet or more deep of which probably about 1,000,000 acres are capable of improvement for agricultural production or forestry. Over 100,000 acres of deep peat have been surveyed in detail, including the major deposits. Large scale exploitation of peat for industrial purposes, mainly as electricity and fuel, has been found to be technically feasible. But to do so at competitive prices, under the present fuel situation, would need a substantial subsidy. This might be worth doing in the Highlands and Islands for the sake of employment and social benefits, for the economics of the area, and for the ultimate benefits to agriculture. Even so, the Committee stated that, "Leaving aside such special cases, however, we have reached the conclusion that the prospect of large-scale exploitation of peat for fuel in the foreseeable future is so slight as to be inconsiderable." It was suggested that there is more promise in the development of Scottish peatland for agriculture, forestry and horticultural purposes. The Altnabreac plant was closed in 1960, and large scale peat working is now confined to southern Scotland, where one or two lowland raised bogs are being exploited for "moss litter".

Moss litter is the name given to unhumified ("fresh") *Sphagnum* peat laid down in the most actively growing bogs. The peat is cut by hand in large trenches to a depth of 1·2–1·9 m. (4–6 ft.), stacked for air drying, broken up, and packed into bales for transporting. The original use as a litter for domestic animals has now been replaced to some extent by its use in horticulture, as a soil conditioner, for composts, for making absorbent pots, and as a constituent in compound fertilisers. The exploitation of peat for these purposes could be increased greatly by the introduction of mechanical cutting and by using peats of highest humification which, in the light of recent research, seem likely to be as valuable as the fresh peats. "Fortified peats" with added chemical fertiliser are being developed and may become valuable in both horticulture and agriculture. There are a few other limited industrial uses of peat, including the production of wax and activated carbon, and as a preventive against pitting of castings in iron founding. Although living *Sphagnum* was extensively collected and dried for use as a surgical dressing in the First World War, it is no longer used for this purpose, but has a certain value in horticulture, as a packing material and in making wreaths.

In the past, utilisation of peat land for agriculture has been concerned largely with removal of the peat and cultivation of the underlying mineral soil. On shallow deposits, ploughing and addition of fertiliser have led to the incorporation of the peat with the

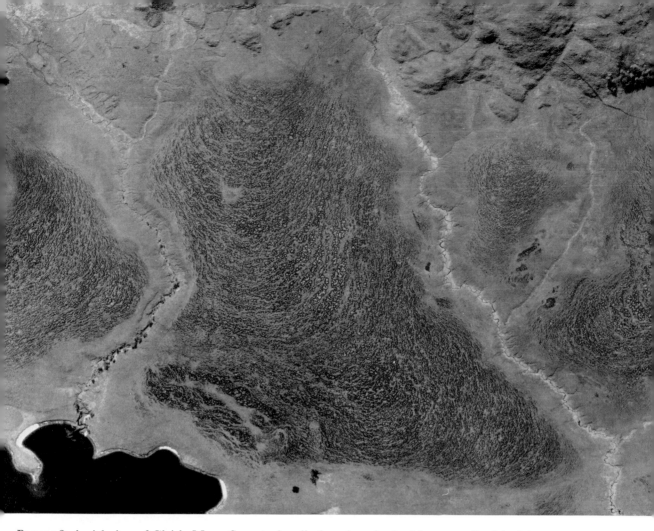

PLATE 78. Aerial view of Claish Moss, Sunart, Argyll. A series of raised bogs on alluvial plains beside L. Shiel. The raised patches of hummock-hollow complex are separated by "lagg" streams with Molinietum, and transitional sloping "rands". The distinctive pattern of pool arrangement, with long axes parallel to the surface contours, is strikingly shown; particularly, as many pools are enlarged by erosion, giving sharp edges and converting many hummocks into islands. R.A.F. photograph, Crown Copyright reserved.

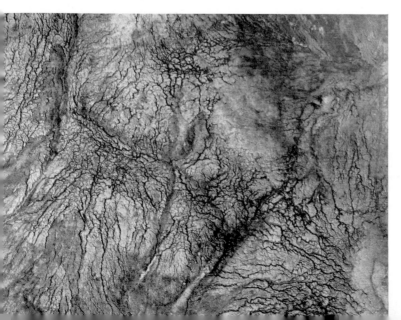

PLATE 79
Aerial view of blanket bogs on Ben Wyvis, Ross-shire. An area of upland *Calluna—Eriophorum* blanket bog severely dissected by gully erosion. The ramifying system of "haggs" is cutting back to tap the whole area of bog and there are signs of complete breakdown, with incipient sheet erosion. R.A.F. photograph, Crown Copyright reserved.

PLATE 80. Channel bog in Abernethy Forest, Inverness-shire. A *Sphagnum*-rich *Calluna—Trichophorum* "intermediate" bog occupying a glacial drift channel in the pinewoods near L. Garten. There are numerous stunted pines which are held "in check" by the high water-table. On other parts of this bog system there are well developed *Sphagnum* hollows and the local emergence of minerotrophic water is marked by the presence of both poor and rich mire communities.

PLATE 81. Hummock-hollow complex on the Silver Flowe, Galloway. I. The hollows are overgrown with *Sphagnum* and appear to be growing upwards into "flats" and perhaps hummocks. The hummocks are crowned with a more luxuriant growth of vascular plants. This state is regarded as typical of undisturbed, actively-growing humock-hollow bogs.

PLATE 82. Hummock-hollow complex on the Silver Flowe, Galloway. II. The hollows have less *Sphagnum* and so appear as distinct pools and there are signs that their edges are eating back into the adjacent "flats" and hummocks. The pools have their long axes parallel to each other and at right angles to the direction of surface slope. This part of the Silver Flowe (Snibe Bog) approaches raised bog in topography, but the patches at the foot of the farther rocky hill are undoubted blanket bog.

PLATE 83. Hummock-hollow complex on the Silver Flowe, Galloway. III. This shows incipient degeneration, with enlarged pools linking up and giving rise to island hummocks. The pools have only a sparse *Sphagnum* growth, although algae are abundant and *Menyanthes trifoliata* is well represented. This condition is associated with more marked fluctuations in water-table than that shown in Plate 82.

PLATE 84. *Rhacomitrium* hummocks on Claish Moss, Sunart, Argyll. A degenerate patch of low-level, hummock-hollow raised bog beside L. Shiel. The pools are enlarged and sparsely vegetated, and often have steep, bare margins, while the flats and hummocks have largely dried out and numerous mounds of *Rhacomitrium lanuginosum* take the place of *Sphagnum* hummocks. A marked drop in water-table has accompanied these changes.

soil. In the lowlands it is probable that a good deal of former peat-clad alluvial land has been converted into rich farmland. The blanket bogs of the uplands mostly overlie strongly leached drift soils and reclamation has been more local. At present much attention is being given to the conversion of bog into farmland by addition of mineral fertiliser to the surface, followed by the sowing of grass seed mixtures. It has been shown that even with no other preparation of the bog surface, a promising growth of grass can soon be obtained, and the original vegetation disappears, particularly on shallow peat. If the bog surface is treated further, by draining and rotovation, the results are considerably improved. Good grass crops for hay and grass-meal may be grown and there is promise that the converted surface peat would in time become a substratum of sufficient quality to allow the cultivation of cereal and root crops. Many private schemes of this kind have been established, and in crofting communities it is ancient practice to cultivate boglands by the addition of such natural fertilisers as seaweed and shell-sand. Various organisations are concerned in research and demonstration in this field, notably the Macaulay Institute for Soil Research, the Hill Farming Research Organisation, and the Scottish Agricultural Colleges.

The oases of green in the midst of dark, barren peatlands are certainly impressive, and show convincingly the potentialities for improvement. The economics of the matter are, however, the limiting factor at present. It is clear that provided adequate treatment and sufficient quantity of fertiliser is added to bog peat, a radical improvement in productivity can be induced. Repeated applications of fertilisers at suitable intervals are evidently necessary to sustain the improved soil conditions, floristic composition and plant production, but the effects may be to some extent cumulative. When the water-table remains high, there is a close similarity to hydroponic growth of crops, since the plants are deriving their nourishment from a mineral-rich surface layer of water.

Both methods of improvement, the complete removal of peat as well as fertilisation of the bog surface, may be combined, especially where the cut peat has other uses, and the enriched surface layer is deposited on top of the underlying mineral substratum. Even if the bog surface is not deliberately lowered by cutting, a gradual shrinkage down-wards might be expected (as in the case of the Fenland peats) by the more rapid oxidation and wind removal of peat caused by cultivation of the surface.

The Forestry Commission have successfully afforested some areas of deep peat in recent years, although wet bog is not a particularly favourable type of ground for growing trees. Surface draining is essential as a first step, and this is now possible even on *Sphagnum* dominated bogs by the use of light, tracked machines towing ploughs. The seedling trees are planted in the upturned peat ridges from the furrows, and ground mineral phosphate is applied to each. The chief tree grown on deep peat is *Pinus contorta*, though the growth of this species may prepare the ground for others such as Scots Pine and Sitka Spruce. Examples of deep afforested bogs are to be seen at Lon Mor near Fort William and around Clatteringshaws Loch in Kirkcudbrightshire. Shallow peat has been used extensively for afforestation, particularly in western Scotland, and the wet heaths of *Trichophorum* and *Molinia* with *Calluna* give good growths of the above three species. As with agricultural improvement, altitude soon limits the possibilities of using boglands for timber production, and planting much above 305 m. (1000 ft.) is not usual.

The Second Report of the Scottish Peat Committee, from which much of the information in this section has been drawn, gives a full and valuable account of the whole subject of peat utilisation, together with a detailed appraisal of its economics. For further details the reader should consult this work, and the Reports of the above-mentioned bodies who work in this field.

Conservation

From an economic viewpoint, bogland is virtually a desert, covering about one-tenth of the total land surface of Scotland. Unproductive land is not tolerated in a country where the population has outgrown its food resources and, whatever the prospect of using peat as a source of power and heat, there is a growing pressure for the large-scale development of Scottish boglands for agriculture and forestry. The potentialities for such improvement are now well known and, where the climate is suitable, more and more bogland will probably be replaced by pasture, arable land or forest. Lowland bogs, especially in southern Scotland, might well disappear entirely, although the bogs of the higher moorlands and mountains will probably remain as long as the traditional use of uplands as sheep walk, grouse moor and deer forest is continued.

Already, however, most bogs have suffered some damage from human activities, as indicated on p. 452. Few have escaped burning at some time and many are now in a highly modified state. Only a very few could be said to be still in a "natural" or original condition. To most people this may seem quite unimportant, but to the naturalist, and especially the ecologist interested in the dynamics of vegetation, bogs in their primitive state have a particular interest. Only a few species of bog plant, such as *Scheuchzeria palustris*, appear to owe their survival to lack of disturbance, but some would become much rarer or even disappear locally if the remaining lowland bogs dried out completely. Burning of hill blanket bogs has probably greatly increased the rarity of some dwarf shrubs such as *Betula nana*, and the great decrease in abundance of *Sphagnum imbricatum* is often attributed to disturbance. The same is true of certain animals, vertebrate and invertebrate, which live on bogs. Yet the unique character of bogs lies in the fact that they are, to some extent, the creators of their own environment. The substratum is laid down by the plants themselves and by its very nature carries up the water-table. The peat surface itself is a living layer, at least in *Sphagnum* bogs, and growth of one part may alter conditions at both that site and adjacent parts of the bog. The mode of growth often produces surface undulations and associated with this vertical irregularity are mosaic patterns in vegetation. The way in which these surface patterns arise is not yet understood, and the process poses a fascinating but difficult problem for future study.

Bogs thus have a twofold interest to the biologist, as the habitats for a variety of plants and animals, and as complete living systems with a unique growth process. In recognition of their importance, the Nature Conservancy has established a series of

Scottish bogs as National Nature Reserves. Here, under protection from further human disturbance, examples of various bog types will be preserved in a state as close as possible to the original condition.

Kirkconnell Flow, on the estuary of the River Nith near Dumfries, has been chosen as an example of a lowland raised bog. It is thickly grown with Scots pine and birch, and the surface is now in a far from original condition, but the prevention of burning and further draining may promote recovery of the vegetation. Farther inland in Galloway, the Silver Flowe Nature Reserve represents a series from raised bog to blanket bog and shows one of the least disturbed and best developed of the aligned hummock-hollow systems in the country. A Perthshire portion of Rannoch Moor has been set aside as an example of *Trichophorum—Eriophorum* low level blanket bog, with complexes of soligenous mire and poor fen. In north Sutherland, a patch of hummock-hollow bog alongside the Strathy River is preserved as a remaining example of the original *Sphagnum*-dominated blanket bog which must once have occupied great areas of the Sutherland-Caithness flowe country. Other Nature Reserves in upland country contain examples of blanket bog, such as the Clova-Caenlochan, Rhum, Beinn Eighe, Inverpolly, Inchnadamph and Hermaness Reserves. Still further examples of bogs have been scheduled by the Nature Conservancy as Sites of Special Scientific Interest, although this does not confer any power of protection.

Conservation of this kind seeks to preserve for posterity "museum-piece" examples of types of undisturbed habitat which are fast disappearing in Britain. The Reserves are created for the use of all who have an interest in natural history, however simple or recondite this may be. It is now recognised too, that boglands in the hills have an important part in the lives of the population as a whole, in that they act as reservoirs, soaking up water during a wet period and releasing it gradually during ensuing drought. This stabilising effect of blanket bogs on river flow is under investigation in the Pennines, where Conway and Millar (1960) have found that eroded and artificially drained *Calluna—Eriophorum vaginatum* bog lacks the water storage capacity of the unbroken surfaces of peat. The conservation of hill peatlands thus has a wider significance in the field of hydrology, particularly as water supply in urban and industrial areas is an ever-growing problem.

VEGETATION TYPES

Lowland *Calluna—Eriophorum* bog (Table 57, col. 1). The typical vegetation of lowland raised bogs has *Calluna vulgaris* and *Eriophorum vaginatum* as co-dominants, but it differs considerably in associated species from the upland *Calluna—Eriophorum* blanket bogs. Since the surface of a raised bog is flat or only very gently inclined, the water-table is high and the undisturbed parts consist of a *Sphagnum* carpet, usually dominated by *S. magellanicum*. Towards the better drained edges, Sphagna are probably reduced in proportion to vascular plants, even in the undisturbed state. The majority of raised bogs are now completely covered with a vegetational mosaic which reflects a varying degree of drying according to disturbance, mainly by draining and fire.

The least disturbed Sphagnetum has a rather open growth of *Calluna vulgaris*, *Erica tetralix*, *Eriophorum vaginatum*, *E. angustifolium*, *Narthecium ossifragum* and *Drosera rotundifolia*, as constants. *Trichophorum cespitosum* is less constant and abundant on the whole, though on parts of West Flanders Moss it replaces *Eriophorum vaginatum* as a co-dominant with *Calluna* on the drying bog. Two of the most characteristic species of Scottish raised bogs are the dwarf shrubs *Andromeda polifolia* and *Vaccinium oxycoccos*, which occur plentifully and constantly in most of the main examples. Both species have a southern distribution in Scotland and *Andromeda* does not occur north of the Highland line. While both occur very locally in blanket bog, they may be regarded as good differential species between this and raised bog, as far as the floristic analyses are concerned (Table 57). On East Flanders Moss, one of its very few British stations, *Ledum groenlandicum* occurs in this community.

The *Sphagnum* carpet sometimes contains a good deal of *S. rubellum*, which tends to form hummocks, and there are occasional hummocks of *S. fuscum* and *S. imbricatum*. *S. papillosum* is not usually abundant except in disturbed sites. Pools or infilled hollows are less usual on raised bogs south of the Highlands and tend to be small and shallow. They are usually grown with *S. cuspidatum* and, very locally, *S. pulchrum*. Both hollows and *Sphagnum* flats close to the water-table have a local abundance of *Rhynchospora alba* and *Drosera anglica*. The *Sphagnum* carpet supports a growth of liverworts, such as *Mylia anomala*, *Odontoschisma sphagni*, and less plentifully of *Cephalozia media*, *C. macrostachya*, *C. connivens*, *Cladopodiella fluitans*, *Riccardia latifrons* and *Calypogeia sphagnicola*. Mosses such as *Drepanocladus fluitans* and *Aulacomnium palustre* are locally plentiful but often appear to indicate water movement, as does *Sphagnum recurvum*, which may be dominant in old, infilled ditches and peat cuttings. *Sphagnum cuspidatum* is also dominant in some of these artificial depressions. *Polytrichum commune*, which grows profusely in places, is probably an indicator of disturbance, and *P. alpestre* is more abundant in drier than wetter places. Tall, tussocky *Eriophorum vaginatum* and dense hummocks of *Polytrichum commune* are characteristic of ground which, though disturbed, is still very wet.

As raised bogs dry out, there is the usual reduction in cover of *Sphagnum* and increase in that of vascular plants, notably *Calluna vulgaris*, *Eriophorum vaginatum* and *Trichophorum cespitosum*, which assume a more luxuriant and tussocky habit. On heavily burned areas there may be temporary dominance of *E. vaginatum* or *Erica tetralix*, and the bare surface of the peat (often consisting of dead *Sphagnum*) is colonised by *Sphagnum tenellum* and *S. compactum*. Extreme drying can produce a complete cover of *Calluna* with little else but hypnaceous mosses and peat-encrusting lichens, mainly *Cladonia* spp. Drying usually increases the other cryptogamic component of the vegetation at the expense of *Sphagnum*; mosses such as *Hypnum cupressiforme* and *Pleurozium schreberi*, and lichens such as *Cladonia impexa* and *C. uncialis* then appear as constants. On a few bogs *Cladonia impexa* has become so abundant that there is a strong resemblance in places to the lichen-rich blanket bogs of the eastern Highlands.

Molinia caerulea is not normally found in the original Sphagnetum, but may be plentiful or even dominant on disturbed ground towards the edges of these bogs. *Dryopteris carthusiana* is a characteristic associate of these *Molinia* communities. Though locally common on the central parts of some raised bogs, *Myrica gale* is mainly a plant of the bog margins.

Another change associated with drying, typically at the bog margins but sometimes also in the centres, is colonisation by birch, usually *Betula pubescens*. This can lead to a dense growth of trees with complete modification of the bog vegetation, but much depends on wetness of the ground, and the birches may remain stunted and scattered where the water-table is high. The most frequent change is the replacement of the usual bog Sphagna by other species such as *S. palustre* and *S. fimbriatum* beneath the birches, and there may be a great increase in *Polytrichum commune*. Where drying is more pronounced, mosses such as *Dicranum scoparium*, *D. majus*, *Hypnum cupressiforme*, *Pleurozium schreberi* and *Plagiothecium undulatum* take the place of *Sphagnum*, but the shade may become so intense that the ground has little but bare litter. As the wood matures and opens out, ferns such as *Dryopteris dilatata* and *Pteridium aquilinum* often become dominant, or dense growths of *Rubus fruticosus* or *Vaccinium myrtillus* may develop.

Colonisation of raised bog by *Pinus sylvestris* occurs on Kirkconnell Flow near Dumfries, and there is the same gradual elimination of the bog flora, although some species such as *Erica tetralix* persist for a long time in closed wood. The mature stage of development under pines is a dwarf shrub layer dominated by *Vaccinium myrtillus*, and closely resembling the moss-rich *Vaccinium* communities of eastern Highland pinewoods.

This type of bog is local and occurs mainly on the coastal lands bordering the Solway Firth, on the plains of the Central Lowlands, and in scattered localities on low-lying ground along the eastern side of the Highlands. Most of the occurrences lie below 152 m. (500 ft.), although in the eastern Highlands there are examples up to 304 m. (1000 ft.). Lowland *Calluna—Eriophorum* bog is therefore characteristic of the drier parts of Scotland and, though its climatic limits are less well-defined than those of some other bog types, most examples occur in places experiencing between 175 and 230 rain days or 130 and 170 wet days (see p. 24). Bogs which have been termed "intermediate" (because they are neither true raised bog nor blanket bog) mostly have vegetation referable to the present type, though in places there are floristic transitions either to upland Calluneto—Eriophoretum or to western lowland Trichophoreto—Eriophoretum.

Although the surface of these lowland raised and intermediate bogs may have dried out, the underlying peat to a depth of at least 2 m. (and often more) is nearly always unhumified "fresh" *Sphagnum* peat, of the kind valued for "moss litter" and horticulture. Towards the edges of these bogs the shallower peat is more humified and more useful as fuel. Acidity of the surface peat is rather higher on average (pH 3·3–3·7) than in the bogs of western or upland districts, and Pearsall (1938) believes that this is associated with the greater amount of oxidation which takes place under drier climates, where periodic drying of the bog surfaces is usual.

Identical vegetation occurs on raised bogs and intermediate bogs in northern

England, around Carlisle and on the south side of the Solway Firth, on some of the lower Northumbrian moorlands, and around Morecambe Bay. There is probably also a close resemblance between the present type and the vegetation of the remaining raised bogs elsewhere in England, in drier parts of Wales, and in central Ireland.

Lowland *Trichophorum—Eriophorum* bog (Table 57, col. 2). The typical western Scottish blanket bog of the wettest ground at altitudes below 457 m. (1500 ft.) is dominated by Sphagna, notably *Sphagnum papillosum, S. capillaceum, S. rubellum, S. plumulosum* and *S. tenellum*, though *S. magellanicum* is also abundant in some areas. Some of these species commonly form hummocks and thereby give an unevenness to the surface of the bog. Two more local but very characteristic species of extensive flat bogs, *S. imbricatum* and *S. fuscum*, form pronounced tall hummocks of an orange-yellow and brown colour respectively. The *Sphagnum* carpet usually supports a subsidiary growth of bryophytes and lichens such as *Hypnum cupressiforme* var. *ericetorum, Rhacomitrium lanuginosum, Mylia anomala, M. taylori, Odontoschisma sphagni, Pleurozia purpurea, Cladonia impexa* and *C. uncialis*.

The usual vascular plants rooted in the *Sphagnum* carpet and upper peat are *Calluna vulgaris, Erica tetralix, Molinia caerulea, Eriophorum angustifolium, E. vaginatum, Narthecium ossifragum, Trichophorum cespitosum, Drosera rotundifolia* and *Potentilla erecta*. The monocotyledons are of a sparser, less tussocky form than on drier ground. Cover of vascular plants is seldom continuous or with any single dominant, but this vegetation type was named Trichophoreto—Eriophoretum by McVean and Ratcliffe (1962) after the most distinctive and abundant constants. The western character of *Trichophorum—Eriophorum* bog, and its distinctness from other types of blanket bog are marked by the presence of such species as *Myrica gale, Narthecium ossifragum, Drosera anglica, Campylopus atrovirens*, and *Pleurozia purpurea*: of these only the first two are constants and even *Myrica* is local, being absent from some quite large areas. The very rare western orchid *Spiranthes romanzoffiana*, which grows in west Inverness-shire, evidently belongs to this kind of bog.

Pools or overgrown hollows are usual on level bogs of this type, and support a different type of vegetation from the flat surface or hummocks. *Sphagnum cuspidatum* and *S. subsecundum* var. *auriculatum* occupy the pools, and there is normally an open growth of vascular plants such as *Menyanthes trifoliata, Eriophorum angustifolium, Utricularia minor* and *Carex limosa. Rhynchospora alba* is sometimes an abundant species of shallow pools or *Sphagnum* flats, and *R. fusca* is plentiful in the pools of Claish Moss in Sunart (cf. Plates 81, 82 and 83). Aligned pool systems of the kind described on p. 451 are mostly found on *Trichophorum—Eriophorum* bogs. On Rannoch Moor, believed to be its only remaining British locality, *Scheuchzeria palustris* occurs locally in this kind of habitat.

The relative dryness of taller hummocks is marked by the appearance of less hydrophilous species such as *Empetrum nigrum, Cladonia coccifera* and *C. sylvatica*, and by the greater luxuriance of *Calluna, Trichophorum, Molinia, Eriophorum vaginatum* and

Rhacomitrium lanuginosum, the last often forming a dense cap to the hummock. Disturbed and drying pool and hummock bogs in western Scotland have an abundance of large and nearly pure hummocks of *Rhacomitrium lanuginosum*, with the moss often spreading on to more level parts of the bog surface (Plate 84). A *Rhacomitrium*-dominated facies of this vegetation type, in which this moss replaces Sphagna, may thus be recognised in places.

This is one of our most distinctive oceanic vegetation types, and is confined to western areas of high rainfall and atmospheric humidity. The eastern limits of geographical distribution correspond closely to the isohyets of 235–240 rain days or 175–180 wet days. *Trichophorum—Eriophorum* bog occurs most extensively where plains or gently undulating moorlands are the prevailing topographic feature, in climatically suitable districts. This type of relief is best represented in parts of Sutherland and the Outer Hebrides, where there are huge expanses of nearly level bog ("flowe"), although in some areas the uniformity of surface is broken by innumerable lochans or bosses of bedrock. In the more mountainous country which occupies much of the western Highlands, such bogs are smaller and more dissected, though very widespread, but there is a large inland example on Rannoch Moor on the Perth-Argyll border and they reappear extensively on the moorlands of Galloway in the extreme south-west of Scotland. This type of bog extends far eastwards in the north-east, reaching Caithness, where both climate and topography are suitable, and there is an eastern bulge into the Central Highlands around Drumochter and the Laggan side of the Monadhliath.

Along the western seaboard, this vegetation extends downwards almost to sea level and has no real lower limit, but it is best developed below 305 m. (1000 ft.) and hardly occurs above 458 m. (1500 ft.); at higher levels the blanket bogs have changed sufficiently in floristics to warrant separation from the present type. It is, however, interesting that at its eastern limits in the Central Highlands, Trichophorcto—Eriophoretum is found only at about 305–458 m. (1000–1500 ft.).

At the eastern limits, there is a disappearance of the truly oceanic species (see above) and *Molinia*, and bogland below 305 m. (1000 ft.) is much less widespread, although level flowes occur locally and are not strikingly different in physiognomy and floristics from those of the west. They tend to have a higher cover of *Trichophorum* and/or *Eriophorum vaginatum* or lichens.

The peat beneath Trichophoreto—Eriophoretum is variable in depth, humification and composition. Extensive flat bogs usually have a deep upper layer of fresh *Sphagnum* peat, but on the Silver Flowe this layer is quite shallow (60–70 cm.) on average and overlies a deep deposit of well humified *Molinia—Sphagnum* peat. The shallower and more humified peats of this kind of bog are much used in the western Highlands as a source of fuel, and around crofting settlements the bogs are greatly altered by extensive peat cuttings. Acidity ranges from pH 3·6 to 4·6 and again tends to be greater in the drier, more oxidising peats.

Identical *Trichophorum—Eriophorum* bog occurs very locally in the English Lake District and North Wales, and some of the Dartmoor blanket bog is probably referable to this type. Very similar blanket bog covers huge areas of western Ireland in Donegal,

Mayo and Galway, and gives the country the same appearance as parts of the western Highlands. There is an important floristic difference, however, in that *Schoenus nigricans* is a constant, abundant and sometimes dominant component of the western Irish blanket bogs, often seeming to take the place which *Trichophorum* occupies in the Scottish equivalents. *Schoenus* is often plentiful on the western Scottish bogs, but except in a few areas, such as Rhum, it is hardly ever as generally distributed and abundant throughout the purely ombrogenous bogs as in Ireland; more usually it shows some connection with water movement through the peat and is most plentiful in obviously soligenous sites on the blanket bogs.

Calluna—Trichophorum **bog** (Table 57, col. 3). *Calluna—Trichophorum* and the succeeding *Calluna—Molinia* communities are intermediate between true ombrogenous bog and grass-heath, but since some examples are rich in *Sphagnum* and/or overlie a moderately deep peat horizon, they are treated here as bog.

Calluna vulgaris and *Trichophorum cespitosum* are co-dominant, and only two other species, *Erica tetralix* and *Cladonia uncialis*, are constantly present. Other dwarf shrubs are sparse or absent, and only a few markedly hydrophytic species such as *Eriophorum angustifolium* and *Narthecium ossifragum*, occur at all frequently, so that this vegetation type is floristically poor. Hypnaceous mosses are usually present and *Rhacomitrium lanuginosum* reaches dominance locally. Sphagna may be absent, sparse, abundant or dominant, and the *Sphagnum*-rich examples are best regarded as a separate facies. The most abundant species are *S. capillaceum* and *S. papillosum*. On dry ground where Sphagna are scarce, peat-encrusting lichens may be abundant, giving a second facies, and a third is dominated by lichens of the *Cladonia sylvatica* complex (cf. lichen-rich *Calluna—Eriophorum* bog, p. 542).

Calluna—Trichophorum bog is widely distributed and one facies or another occurs in most upland areas of Scotland, from sea level up to 914 m. (3000 ft.). The typical community, and those rich in both *Rhacomitrium lanuginosum* and crustaceous lichens, are most extensive in the west, whereas the non-crustaceous lichen facies is confined to the east. The *Sphagnum*-rich facies is also best developed in some parts of eastern Scotland, where it takes the place of the western *Trichophorum—Eriophorum* bog. Some form of *Calluna—Trichophorum* bog often occurs as a transitional stage, altitudinally and floristically, between lowland and upland *Eriophorum* bogs. It is the most prevalent type of bog in the more sharply contoured mountain districts of the western Highlands, where the ground is mostly too steep to support deep peat.

All except perhaps the *Sphagnum*- and lichen-rich facies may be regarded as derived types of vegetation, produced from woodland or other bog vegetation by forest clearance, burning and grazing. The crustaceous lichen facies is especially associated with incipient soil erosion, and both it and the *Rhacomitrium* facies appear to be produced by repeated burning. When burning is combined with heavy grazing the end product is usually a fire climax Trichophoretum with little or no *Calluna*, a community widespread in the south-west Highlands.

The soils are mostly shallow peat or mor humus horizons overlying strongly podsolised glacial drift. The humus is markedly acidic (pH 3·4–4·6) and base-deficient and, being well humified, is valued as fuel peat.

Similar vegetation occurs widely in some western hill districts of England, Wales and Ireland.

***Calluna—Molinia* bog** (Table 57, col. 4). In the second wet heath community, *Calluna vulgaris* shares dominance with *Molinia caerulea*, and *Erica tetralix*, *Potentilla erecta* and *Hypnum cupressiforme* are usually present. *Trichophorum cespitosum* is frequent and there is a complete series of intermediates linking the present type to *Calluna—Trichophorum* bog: the two may even be serally related in places. *Calluna— Molinia* bog lacks *Rhacomitrium* and lichen-rich facies, but there is a *Sphagnum*-rich type, as well as a fire climax Molinietum produced by burning and grazing.

Calluna—Molinia communities are especially characteristic of the western Highlands, and in the east occur mainly in the Cairngorms. The altitudinal range is from sea-level to about 610 m. (2000 ft.). *Molinia* grasslands with little *Calluna* are extensive in Galloway. From the frequent occurrence of *Calluna—Molinia* bog amongst pinewood and its restriction to the potential forest zone, it is clearly a kind of vegetation derived largely from woodland.

The typical situation is on gentle drift slopes, often in places where there would appear to be a minerotrophic influence, and there are transitions to the *Molinia—Myrica* mires and richer *Molinia* grasslands of definitely soligenous sites (cf. Fig. 58). The inclusion of this vegetation type amongst ombrogenous bog is therefore made on tenuous grounds, but in chemical characteristics the substrata show a greater affinity to bog than to mire. The peats are usually shallow and well humified (sometimes "pseudo-fibrous") and often show impregnation with mineral particles in the basal layer overlying the podsolised or gleyed till. In pH they range from 3·6 to 4·5 and have a low content of exchangeable bases.

Calluna—Molinia bog is very widespread in western Ireland and occurs in a few parts of western England and Wales.

REFERENCES

Conway, V. M. and Millar, A.   1960   The hydrology of some small peat-covered catchments in the North Pennines, *J. Instn. Wat. Engrs.*, **14**, 415–424.

Crampton, C. B.   1911   *The vegetation of Caithness considered in relation to the geology.* Cambridge.

Crampton, C. B. and Macgregor, M.   1913   The plant ecology of Ben Armine, Sutherlandshire. *Scot. geogr. Mag.*, **29**, 169–192; 256–266.

Durno, S. E.   1961   Evidence regarding the rate of peat growth. *J. Ecol.*, **49**, 347–351.

Durno, S. E. and McVean, D. N.   1959   Forest history of the Beinn Eighe Nature Reserve. *New Phytol.*, **58**, 228–236.

Fraser, G. K.   1933   Studies of certain Scottish moorlands in relation to tree growth. *Bull. For. Comm., (Lond.)*, **15**.

   1954   Classification and nomenclature of peat and peat deposits. *International Peat Symposium.* Dublin.

GIMINGHAM, C. H., MILLER, G. R., SLEIGH, L. M. and MILNE, L. M. 1961 The ecology of a small bog in Kinlochewe Forest, Wester Ross. *Trans. bot. Soc. Edinb.*, **39**, 125–147.

GODWIN, H. 1956 *The History of the British Flora.* Cambridge.

GODWIN, H. and CONWAY, V. M. 1939 The ecology of a raised bog near Tregaron, Cardiganshire. *J. Ecol.*, **27**, 313–363.

GORHAM, E. 1961 Water, ash, nitrogen and acidity of some bog peats and other organic soils. *J. Ecol.*, **49**, 103–106.

GORHAM, E. and PEARSALL, W. H. 1956 Acidity, specific conductivity and calcium content of some bog and fen waters in northern Britain. *J. Ecol.*, **44**, 129–141.

KUBIËNA, W. L. 1953 *The soils of Europe.* Madrid and London.

LEWIS, F. J. 1905, 1906, 1907, 1911 The plant remains in the Scottish peat mosses. Parts I–IV. *Trans. Roy. Soc. Edinb.*, **41**, 699–723; **45**, 335–360; **46**, 33–70; **47**, 793–833.

McVEAN, D. N. 1959 Ecology of *Alnus glutinosa* (L.). Gaertn. VII. Establishment of alder by direct seeding of shallow blanket bog. *J. Ecol.*, **47**, 615–618.

McVEAN, D. N. and RATCLIFFE, D. A. 1962 *Plant communities of the Scottish Highlands.* H.M.S.O., London.

OSVALD, H. 1949 Notes on the vegetation of British and Irish mosses. *Acta phytogeogr suec.*, **26**.

PEARSALL, W. H. 1938 The soil complex in relation to plant communities. III. Moorlands and bogs. *J. Ecol.*, **26**, 298–315.

 1950 *Mountains and moorlands.* London.

 1956 Two blanket-bogs in Sutherland. *J. Ecol.*, **44**, 493–516.

RATCLIFFE, D. A. and WALKER, D. 1958 The Silver Flowe, Galloway, Scotland. *J. Ecol.*, **46**, 407–445.

Second report of the Scottish Peat Committee. 1962 Edinburgh.

Second report of the Hill Farming Research Organisation. 1961 Edinburgh.

SJÖRS, H. 1948 Myrvegetation i Bergslagen. *Acta phytogeogr. suec.*, **21**.

 1961 Surface patterns in Boreal peatland. *Endeavour*, **20**, 217–224.

TANSLEY, A. G. 1949 *The British Islands and their vegetation.* Cambridge.

[See Table 56 on p. 468.

TABLE 56

Mires

Vegetation type	(1) Carex—Molinia	(2) Molinia—Myrica	(3) Juncus effusus—Sphagnum	(4) Sub-alpine Carex—Sphagnum	(5) Juncus acutiflorus—Acrocladium cuspidatum	(6) Carex panicea—Campylium stellatum	(7) Carex rostrata—Brown moss	(8) Schoenus nigricans
Number of stands	9	9	9	9	6	18	4	4
Plot size (sq. m.)	4	4	4	4	4	4	4	4
Altitudinal range (m.)	46–579	76–335	152–579	91–731	228–366	30–853	442–792	30–183
Soil type and drainage class	Peaty gley	Peaty gley	Gley podsol or peaty gley	Gley	Gley podsol or peaty gley	Gley	Hypnum peat moor	Calcareous peat or marl
Slope (degrees)	0–28	0–25	0–20	0–20	0–25	3–35	0–10	0–5
pH range	4·0–4·4	3·8–6·1	4·4–5·0*	4·5–5·7*	5·7–6·4	5·9–6·3	5·5–5·8	8·0
Total vegetation cover (%)	100	100	100	100	100	100	100	80–100
Height of vegetation (cm.)	15–30	30–60	35–70	10–25	40–60	10–20	25–35	15–35
Betula nana	2 0·8	...	...	...	...	...	...	...
B. pubescens	...	...	...	2 0·4	...	...	...	...
Betula sp.	...	...	...	...	2 0·2	...	...	...
Calluna vulgaris	9 2·8	6 1·0	1 0·2	1 0·2	...	1 0·1	...	...
Empetrum hermaphroditum	...	...	...	...	...	1 0·1	...	...
Erica tetralix	10 3·2	7 1·3	1 0·2	1 0·6	2 0·3	6 1·2	...	5 1·3
Myrica gale	1 0·3	10 5·8	...	...	...	...	...	3 0·5
Salix aurita	...	...	...	...	2 0·2	1 0·1	...	...
Salix sp.	...	...	...	...	...	...	...	...
Thelypteris limbosperma	...	...	...	...	...	...	...	...
Vaccinium myrtillus	1 0·2	...	...	...	2 0·3	...	...	...
Equisetum fluviatile	...	...	...	...	...	1 0·1	3 0·1	...
E. palustre	...	1 0·2	...	...	...	1 0·1	5 0·8	...
E. sylvaticum	...	...	...	...	...	...	...	...
E. variegatum	...	...	...	...	...	1 0·2	...	...
Selaginella selaginoides	4 1·3	2 0·4	...	...	...	9 1·5	8 1·0	5 1·3

* Water samples.

Species	1	2	3	4	5	6	7	8
Agrostis canina	3 0·8	·	3 0·7	·	3 1·0	6 1·6	4 1·0	4 1·0
A. stolonifera	·	·	·	2 0·8	2 0·9	6 2·1	·	·
A. tenuis	·	·	2 0·4	5 1·2	3 0·8	1 0·3	·	1 0·1
Anthoxanthum odoratum	·	·	4 0·6	3 0·8	6 1·7	4 0·8	·	2 0·6
Briza media	·	·	1 0·1	3 0·8	·	·	·	·
Cynosurus cristatus	·	·	1 0·2	·	·	·	·	·
Deschampsia cespitosa	·	·	·	·	2 0·6	1 0·2	1 0·1	·
D. flexuosa	·	·	·	·	6 1·6	2 0·6	3 6·7	·
Festuca ovina agg.	·	·	5 1·5	2 0·3	1 0·3	1 0·2	·	4 1·2
F. rubra	·	5 1·5	4 1·0	7 1·8	1 0·3	1 0·2	·	·
Holcus lanatus	·	·	2 0·3	8 2·7	1 0·3	3 0·9	·	·
H. mollis	·	·	·	·	·	4 1·4	·	·
Molinia caerulea	8 2·5	5 1·0	4 1·3	8 2·7	4 1·4	1 0·2	10 7·3	9 3·6
Nardus stricta	·	·	3 0·7	7 1·5	7 1·7	3 0·9	2 0·6	6 1·9
Poa annua	·	·	1 0·1	·	·	·	·	·
P. pratensis	·	·	·	·	·	·	·	·
Sieglingia decumbens	·	·	2 0·3	2 0·3	·	·	1 0·2	1 0·1
Carex aquatilis	·	3 0·5	·	·	·	·	·	·
C. bigelowii	·	·	1 0·1	·	·	·	·	·
C. capillaris	5 1·0	·	1 0·1	·	·	·	·	·
C. curta	3 0·5	5 0·8	7 2·7	·	2 0·3	·	1 0·3	1 0·3
C. demissa	3 0·8	·	3 1·1	·	1 0·2	·	·	1 0·2
C. dioica	·	·	5 2·3	·	1 0·2	·	·	·
C. echinata	·	3 1·3	2 1·2	5 1·7	9 4·9	6 1·6	4 1·0	9 3·9
C. flacca	·	·	6 2·6	·	·	·	·	·
C. hostiana	·	·	1 0·3	·	·	·	·	1 0·3
C. lepidocarpa	5 1·3	5 3·0	6 2·8	5 0·8	10 4·7	·	·	·
C. nigra	8 2·0	8 2·3	·	2 0·2	·	9 2·4	·	4 2·0
C. pallescens	·	10 4·0	10 4·9	8 2·8	·	·	·	·
C. panicea	·	·	·	3 0·7	6 1·4	·	7 1·6	9 2·6
C. pauciflora	3 0·5	5 1·0	8 2·3	·	·	·	·	·
C. pulicaris	·	10 6·0	1 0·2	·	·	·	·	1 0·2
C. rostrata	·	·	1 0·1	·	3 0·8	2 0·9	·	·
Coeloglossum viride	·	·	·	·	·	·	·	·
Dactylorchis maculata ssp. *ericetorum*	3 0·5	·	·	·	1 0·1	·	2 0·3	1 0·2
D. fuchsii	·	·	6 2·7	·	·	·	·	·
Eleocharis quinqueflora	3 0·8	5 2·5	1 0·1	·	·	·	·	·
Eriophorum angustifolium	10 2·3	5 1·0	7 1·7	2 0·3	9 3·0	8 2·3	2 0·1	10 2·8

TABLE 56—continued

Vegetation type	(1) Carex—Molinia	(2) Molinia—Myrica	(3) Juncus effusus—Sphagnum	(4) Sub-alpine Carex—Sphagnum	(5) Juncus acutiflorus—Acrocladium cuspidatum	(6) Carex panicea—Campylium stellatum	(7) Carex rostrata—Brown moss	(8) Schoenus nigricans
E. latifolium	...	1 0·1	...	...	...	2 0·6	...	...
E. vaginatum	2 1·0	...	2 0·6	2 1·0	...	...	...	...
Isolepis setacea	...	...	...	...	...	1 0·2	...	...
Juncus acutiflorus	...	1 0·2	...	...	10 8·3	1 0·2	...	...
J. alpinoarticulatus	...	...	...	...	...	2 0·4	...	...
J. articulatus	7 1·9	...	...	1 0·2	...	8 2·5	5 1·0	5 1·5
J. bulbosus	...	1 0·1	...	...	...	...	...	...
J. conglomeratus	2 0·6	...	...	...	2 0·3	1 0·1	...	...
J. effusus	...	...	10 7·1	4 0·9	2 0·5	6 1·8	8 2·0	3 0·8
J. kochii	7 2·2	1 0·4	1 0·3	7 1·6	3 0·5	1 0·4	3 0·3	...
J. squarrosus	...	...	3 0·9	...	...	1 0·1	...	...
J. triglumis	...	...	...	3 0·3	...	...	...	...
Luzula multiflora	2 0·3	1 0·2	3 0·6	...	2 0·2	...	3 0·3	...
L. sylvatica	...	...	2 0·4	...	...	...	...	...
Narthecium ossifragum	9 2·8	7 1·6	...	6 1·1	2 0·5	2 0·6	...	3 0·5
Potamogeton polygonifolius	...	...	...	...	...	...	...	5 1·5
Schoenus nigricans	...	1 0·3	...	...	...	...	...	10 8·0
Tofieldia pusilla	...	...	...	1 0·1	...	2 0·6	...	...
Trichophorum cespitosum	6 1·9	6 1·3	...	...	...	2 0·5	...	5 1·5
Triglochin palustris	...	...	...	...	...	1 0·1	...	...
Achillea ptarmica	...	...	...	...	5 1·0	1 0·1	...	...
Ajuga reptans	...	...	...	...	2 0·5	...	...	...
Alchemilla filicaulis	...	...	...	...	...	1 0·2	...	...
A. glabra	...	...	...	...	...	1 0·1	...	...
A. vestita	...	...	...	...	...	1 0·3	...	...
Angelica sylvestris	...	...	...	1 0·1	...	1 0·1	...	...
Bellis perennis	...	...	...	...	...	1 0·2	3 0·5	...
Caltha palustris	...	...	...	...	3 0·5	1 0·2	3 0·5	...
Campanula rotundifolia	...	1 0·1	...	...	...	...	...	...

Species	1	2	3	4	5	6	7	8
Cardamine hirsuta								
C. pratensis		8 0·5	1 0·2	2 0·2		2 0·2		
Centaurea nigra				2 0·1				
Cerastium holosteoides			1 0·1	2 0·2				
Cirsium palustre			1 0·1	5 1·0		1 0·1		
Crepis paludosa			1 0·1	5 1·5		1 0·1		
Digitalis purpurea								
Drosera anglica								
D. intermedia	3 0·8							
D. rotundifolia	3 0·8		2 0·3	2 0·2			3 0·2	9 1·2
Epilobium alsinifolium	3 0·5		1 0·1					
E. anagallidifolium			1 0·2					
E. palustre			1 0·1	10 1·8		4 1·3		
Euphrasia micrantha		3 0·8					1 0·2	
E. officinalis agg.			8 2·2	3 0·8				3 0·7
Filipendula ulmaria				3 0·5				
Galium palustre			1 0·1			1 0·2		
G. saxatile				3 1·0	2 0·6	9 2·3	3 0·8	
Hypericum pulchrum	3 0·5		7 1·3	3 0·8	1 0·1		2 0·2	1 0·3
Leontodon autumnalis			3 0·1			1 0·1	1 0·1	
L. hispidus		5 1·0	3 0·6					
Linum catharticum	3 0·5		1 0·1	2 0·2				
Lysimachia nemorum				2 0·5				
Menyanthes trifoliata		1 0·3						
Parnassia palustris			2 0·5	1 0·1				1 0·1
Pedicularis palustris			2 0·5	5 0·8				1 0·3
P. sylvatica	3 0·8		1 0·1					
Pinguicula lusitanica	8 1·3							
P. vulgaris		8 1·5	8 1·4	2 0·3	1 0·2		1 0·1	4 0·9
Plantago lanceolata			1 0·2					
P. maritima			1 0·2					
Polygala serpyllifolia			2 0·4		2 0·4		2 0·3	2 0·4
Polygonum viviparum	5 1·0				1 0·2			
Potentilla erecta			8 1·5	10 3·0	9 2·4	9 1·9	10 2·6	9 2·4
P. palustris				2 0·1				
Prunella vulgaris	3 0·8		3 1·0	7 1·7		1 0·3		
Ranunculus acris			3 0·6	8 1·8	1 0·3			
R. flammula			3 0·6	8 1·7	1 0·3			
Rhinanthus minor agg.			1 0·1	2 0·3				
Rumex acetosa				3 0·8		6 1·3		

TABLE 56—continued

Vegetation type	(1) Carex—Molinia	(2) Molinia—Myrica	(3) Juncus effusus—Sphagnum	(4) Sub-alpine Carex—Sphagnum	(5) Juncus acutiflorus—Acrocladium cuspidatum	(6) Carex panicea—Campylium stellatum	(7) Carex rostrata—Brown moss	(8) Schoenus nigricans
Sagina nodosa	...	...	...	...	...	1 0·1	...	...
S. procumbens	...	...	...	...	...	1 0·2	...	...
Saxifraga aizoides	...	...	...	...	...	4 0·8	3 0·5	3 0·1
S. stellaris	...	...	1 0·1	...	...	...	...	...
Stellaria alsine	...	...	1 0·1	...	...	...	...	...
Succisa pratensis	4 1·3	6 1·1	...	1 0·3	7 2·0	5 1·2	...	3 0·5
Taraxacum officinale agg.	...	...	1 0·1	...	5 1·0	3 0·4	...	...
Thalictrum alpinum	...	...	...	...	...	3 0·9	...	...
Thymus drucei	...	...	...	...	...	1 0·1	...	...
Trientalis europaea	...	...	...	1 0·1	...	...	...	...
Trifolium repens	...	...	...	...	5 0·7	2 0·2	...	...
Trollius europaeus	...	...	...	...	2 0·3	...	...	...
Utricularia intermedia	...	...	...	...	...	...	...	...
U. minor	...	...	...	...	...	...	...	...
Viola palustris	3 0·4	3 0·9	4 1·1	6 1·9	5 1·5	1 0·1	3 0·8	3 0·8
V. riviniana	...	...	2 0·1	...	...	...	3 0·5	3 0·8
Acrocladium cuspidatum	2 0·3	2 0·6	...	1 0·1	10 2·7	4 0·8	5 1·0	...
A. giganteum	...	...	...	1 0·2	...	...	3 0·8	...
A. sarmentosum	3 0·7	3 0·6	...	3 0·7	2 0·3	...	...	...
A. stramineum	...	...	3 0·6	...	...	...	...	...
A. trifarium	...	...	...	...	...	...	...	...
Atrichum undulatum	...	...	1 0·1	...	...	...	3 0·1	...
Aulacomnium palustre	6 1·4	1 0·3	4 1·0	6 1·1	3 0·3	1 0·1	...	...
Blindia acuta	...	...	...	...	...	...	...	3 0·5
Brachythecium rutabulum	3 1·1	3 0·6	...	...	...	1 0·1	...	...
Breutelia chrysocoma	...	...	...	...	2 0·3	...	...	3 0·8
Bryum pseudotriquetrum	...	1 0·3	...	...	2 0·5	6 1·3	8 2·3	3 0·8
Campylium stellatum	...	...	...	...	5 0·8	8 2·7	10 3·3	10 3·5
Campylopus atrovirens	...	1 0·1	...	...	2 0·3	...	...	3 0·3
C. flexuosus	...	...	...	...	...	...	...	...

Species	1	2	3	4	5	6	7	8
Cinclidium stygium						1 0·1		
Climacium dendroides					2 0·1			
Cratoneuron commutatum								3 1·3
C. filicinum		1 0·1						
Ctenidium molluscum	1 0·2							
Dicranum bonjeanii		2 0·2	1 0·1			7 3·0	5 2·8	
D. scoparium						1 0·2	3 0·5	
Ditrichum flexicaule						7 2·2		
Drepanocladus exannulatus				2 0·4		1 0·3		
D. fluitans		1 0·2			2 0·3	1 0·1	3 0·8	
D. revolvens	1 0·1				2 0·2	7 2·3	10 4·3	5 2·0
Eurhynchium praelongum			2 0·4					
Fissidens adianthoides							8 1·3	3 0·3
F. osmundoides				2 0·7	8 1·5	5 0·9		
Hylocomium splendens	7 1·7	8 1·7	6 1·3	1 0·1		1 0·2	3 0·3	
Hypnum cupressiforme	4 1·1	7 1·6	1 0·2			3 0·6		
Leucobryum glaucum		1 0·1				1 0·1		
Meesia uliginosa								
Mnium hornum			2 0·2				3 0·5	
M. pseudopunctatum					2 0·3	1 0·2		
M. punctatum	1 0·2		1 0·1				3 0·5	
M. seligeri					2 0·3	2 0·3	3 0·3	
M. undulatum			1 0·1		5 1·0			
Philonotis calcarea							8 1·3	3 0·8
P. fontana			1 0·1			2 0·7	3 0·5	
Plagiothecium undulatum	1 0·1	1 0·1	2 0·3		2 0·3	2 0·3		
Pleurozium schreberi	4 0·9		1 0·3					
Polytrichum alpestre	1 0·3							
P. alpinum								
P. commune	1 0·2		10 3·9	6 2·0	2 0·3	1 0·1	3 0·3	
Pseudoscleropodium purum	2 0·4	3 0·8	3 0·3	1 0·1	3 0·3	1 0·1		
Rhacomitrium lanuginosum	3 0·8	1 0·1		1 0·2				5 1·0
Rhytidiadelphus loreus		2 0·2	1 0·3	1 0·2	10 2·7	1 0·2		
R. squarrosus	3 0·4	4 0·7		2 0·4		7 1·4		
R. triquetrus		1 0·1						
Scorpidium scorpioides						4 1·5	8 3·5	3 0·8
Sphagnum compactum	1 0·3							
S. contortum					2 1·2		3 0·5	
S. cuspidatum								
S. girgensohnii	1 0·2	1 0·2		2 0·7		2 0·7		

TABLE 56—concluded

Vegetation type	(1) Carex—Molinia		(2) Molinia—Myrica		(3) Juncus effusus—Sphagnum		(4) Sub-alpine Carex—Sphagnum		(5) Juncus acutiflorus—Acrocladium cuspidatum		(6) Carex panicea—Campylium stellatum		(7) Carex rostrata—Brown moss		(8) Schoenus nigricans	
S. palustre	4	2·7	...		9	3·4	3	2·0	3	0·3	...		...		...	
S. papillosum	7	2·6	2	0·7	...		6	2·7	...		...		...		...	
S. plumulosum	6	2·1	4	0·7	...		6	1·7	...		...		...		...	
S. quinquefarium	2	0·8	...		...		...		...		...		...		...	
S. recurvum	3	1·1	1	0·1	10	6·3	9	4·9	2	0·3	...		...		...	
S. robustum	1	0·3	1	0·3	...		4	1·6	...		...		...		...	
S. rubellum †	4	1·7	3	1·1	...		1	0·4	...		...		...		...	
S. squarrosum	1	0·1	...		4	0·9	...		3	0·5	...		...		...	
S. strictum	...		1	0·2	...		...		...		...		...		3	0·8
S. subsecundum	7	2·9	...		2	0·4	7	3·2	...		1	0·3	...		...	
S. tenellum	1	0·4	...		...		...		...		...		...		...	
S. teres	...		1	0·3	2	1·1	...		2	1·2	...		...		...	
S. warnstorfianum	...		1	0·9	...		...		...		1	0·1	...		...	
Thuidium delicatulum	...		3	0·6	1	0·1	2	0·6	3	0·3	1	0·2	...		...	
T. tamariscinum	2	0·3	...		...		...		...		...		...		...	
Calypogeia muelleriana	3	0·6	2	0·3	1	0·2	2	0·2	2	0·3	1	0·1	...		...	
Cephalozia sp.	...		...		1	0·2	...		...		...		...		...	
Chiloscyphus polyanthos	...		...		...		...		3	0·5	1	0·1	...		...	

† Including Sphagnum capillaceum.

	1	2	3	4	5	6	7	8
Diplophyllum albicans	2 0·3	…	…	…	…	…	…	…
Lepidozia setacea	1 0·1	…	…	…	…	…	…	…
Lophocolea bidentata	…	2 0·2	3 0·6	1 0·2	8 1·5	1 0·2	…	…
Lophozia ventricosa	…	…	…	…	…	…	…	…
Nardia scalaris	…	…	1 0·1	…	…	…	…	…
Odontoschisma sphagni	1 0·2	…	1 0·2	…	…	…	…	…
Pellia epiphylla	1 0·1	…	…	…	…	…	…	…
P. fabbroniana	…	…	…	…	8 1·5	1 0·1	3 0·8	5 0·5
Pellia sp.	…	…	…	…	…	…	…	…
Plagiochila asplenioides	1 0·3	…	…	…	…	1 0·1	…	3 0·5
Pleurozia purpurea	…	…	…	…	…	…	…	5 0·8
Preissia quadrata	…	…	…	…	2 0·2	2 0·2	…	…
Riccardia multifida	1 0·1	…	…	…	2 0·3	1 0·2	…	…
R. pinguis	1 0·1	2 0·3	…	…	…	4 0·6	…	5 1·0
Riccardia sp.	…	…	…	…	…	…	…	…
Scapania aequiloba	…	…	…	…	…	1 0·1	…	…
S. irrigua	…	…	1 0·1	…	…	1 0·1	…	…
S. nemorosa	1 0·2	…	1 0·1	…	…	2 0·3	…	…
S. undulata	1 0·1	…	1 0·2	1 0·1	…	…	3 0·5	…
Tritomaria quinquedentata	…	…	…	…	…	…	…	…
Cladonia gracilis	1 0·2	1 0·1	…	…	…	…	…	…
C. impexa	2 0·4	…	…	…	…	…	…	…
C. mitis	1 0·1	…	…	…	…	…	…	…
C. uncialis	1 0·2	…	…	…	…	…	…	…
Peltigera canina	…	…	1 0·1	…	…	…	…	…

TABLE 57
Bogs

Vegetation type	(1) Lowland Calluna— Eriophorum	(2) Trichophorum —Eriophorum	(3) Calluna— Trichophorum	(4) Calluna— Molinia
Number of stands . . .	10	12	12	10
Plot size (sq. m.) . . .	4	4	4	4
Altitudinal range (m.) . . .	9–30	23–381	91–655	76–609
Soil type and drainage class .	Raised bog peat	Blanket bog peat	Peat or gley podsol	Peat or gley podsol
Slope (degrees) . . .	0	0–10	0–15	0–25
pH range . . .	3·3–3·7	3·6–4·6	3·4–4·6	3·6–4·5
Total vegetation cover (%) .	100	100	100	100
Height of vegetation (cm.) .	15–30	15–25	15–30	25–35
Andromeda polifolia . . .	10 3·0	...	...	...
Betula nana . . .	...	...	1 0·2	...
Calluna vulgaris . . .	10 6·1	10 4·3	10 6·3	10 6·6
Empetram nigrum . . .	3 0·8	...	...	...
Erica cinerea . . .	...	...	...	4 1·2
E. tetralix . . .	10 3·5	10 4·3	10 3·5	9 3·0
Myrica gale . . .	...	8 3·2	...	2 0·3
Vaccinium myrtillus . . .	...	...	1 0·2	2 0·4
V. oxycoccos . . .	6 1·7	...	...	...
Dryopteris carthusiana . . .	1 0·1	...	...	...
Lycopodium selago . . .	...	...	1 0·1	...
Agrostis canina . . .	...	3 0·4	...	1 0·1
A. tenuis . . .	...	...	...	1 0·1
Anthoxanthum odoratum . . .	...	...	...	1 0·1
Deschampsia flexuosa . . .	...	...	...	3 0·5
Festuca ovina agg. . . .	...	2 0·2	...	...
Molinia caerulea . . .	...	10 3·5	3 0·5	10 6·5
Nardus stricta . . .	...	2 0·5	...	2 0·3
Carex binervis . . .	...	...	...	1 0·1
C. echinata . . .	...	3 0·6	1 0·2	2 0·2
C. nigra . . .	...	1 0·2	...	...
C. panicea . . .	...	4 1·0	...	3 0·7
C. pauciflora . . .	...	3 0·6	...	...
C. pilulifera . . .	...	...	2 0·2	1 0·1
C. rostrata . . .	...	1 0·2	...	...
Dactylorchis maculata ssp. *ericetoron*	...	1 0·1	1 0·2	...
Eriophorum angustifolium . .	9 2·3	10 3·1	7 1·8	5 1·1
E. vaginatum . . .	10 5·3	10 3·2	5 1·5	1 0·2
Juncus bulbosus agg. . .	...	2 0·3	...	...
J. effusus . . .	...	1 0·3	...	...
J. squarrosus . . .	...	2 0·7	3 0·9	1 0·1
Listera cordata . . .	...	8 0·1	...	...
Luzula multiflora . . .	...	...	1 0·2	...
Narthecium ossifragum . .	5 1·2	10 3·3	7 2·0	4 1·0

TABLE 57—*continued*

Vegetation type	(1) Lowland Calluna— Eriophorum		(2) Trichophorum —Eriophorum		(3) Calluna— Trichophorum		(4) Calluna— Molinia	
Rhynchospora alba	1	0·3	...		...		...	
Trichophorum cespitosum	4	0·9	10	4·4	10	6·1	7	2·6
Drosera anglica	...		3	0·4	...		...	
D. rotundifolia	9	1·7	8	1·7	3	0·5	1	0·1
Pedicularis sylvatica	...		1	0·1	1	0·2	1	0·2
Pinguicula vulgaris	...		3	0·3	3	0·3	...	
Polygala serpyllifolia	...		3	0·4	1	0·2	4	0·8
Potentilla erecta	...		6	1·4	3	0·5	9	2·5
Succisa pratensis	...		1	0·2	...		3	0·6
Trientalis europaea	...		...		...		1	0·3
Viola riviniana	...		...		...		1	0·3
Aulacomnium palustre	4	0·9	2	0·2	...		...	
Breutelia chrysocoma	...		2	0·4	...		...	
Campylopus atrovirens	...		1	0·3	...		...	
C. flexuosus	...		1	0·1	...		1	0·1
Dicranum scoparium	4	0·8	...		2	0·2	3	0·5
Drepanocladus exannulatus	...		1	0·1	...		...	
Hylocomium splendens	...		3	0·8	4	0·7	6	1·5
Hypnum cupressiforme	7	1·3	8	1·8	8	2·2	8	2·5
Leucobryum glaucum	...		...		...		2	0·2
Mnium punctatum	...		1	0·1	...		...	
Plagiothecium undulatum	...		1	0·3	1	0·2	3	0·8
Pleurozium schreberi	7	2·0	3	0·5	4	1·1	6	1·1
Pohlia nutans	2	0·5	...		...		...	
Polytrichum alpestre	4	1·0	...		...		...	
P. commune	3	0·8	...		...		...	
Rhacomitrium lanuginosum	1	0·1	6	1·5	6	2·1	5	1·0
Rhytidiadelphus loreus	...		2	0·4	2	0·3	4	0·9
R. squarrosus	1	0·1	1	0·2	...		...	
Sphagnum compactum	...		2	0·7	1	0·3	2	0·4
S. cuspidatum	4	0·9	3	0·8	1	0·2	...	
S. fuscum	1	0·2	...		...		...	
S. imbricatum	...		1	0·3	...		...	
S. magellanicum	10	5·6	3	1·0	1	0·2	...	
S. palustre	...		...		...		1	0·2
S. papillosum	5	0·9	10	5·0	5	2·3	2	0·7
S. plumulosum	...		6	1·5	3	1·0	2	0·6
S. pulchrum	2	0·8	...		...		...	
S. recurvum	...		1	0·2	...		...	
S. robustum	...		1	0·2	...		2	0·3
S. rubellum *	10	2·3	9	5·3	8	3·3	5	1·8
S. subsecundum var. auriculatum	...		4	1·1	...		...	
S. tenellum	7	1·7	7	2·1	5	1·2	4	0·5
Thuidium tamariscinum	...		...		...		1	0·2
Anastrepta orcadensis	...		...		1	0·2	...	
Calypogeia muelleriana	2	0·2	3	0·3	1	0·1	1	0·3

* Including *Sphagnum capillaceum*.

TABLE 57—*concluded*

Vegetation type	(1) Lowland Calluna—Eriophorum		(2) Trichophorum Eriophorum		(3) Calluna—Trichophorum		(4) Calluna—Molinia	
Cephalozia sp.	1	0·1	1	0·2	2	0·2	...	
Diplophyllum albicans . . .	...		3	0·4	2	0·2	3	0·3
Lepidozia setacea . . .	...		1	0·1	...		...	
Lophocolea bidentata . .	...		...		1	0·2	...	
Lophozia floerkii . . .	...		...		1	0·2	...	
L. ventricosa	2	0·2	1	0·1	2	0·2	...	
Mylia anomala	9	2·2	3	0·4	3	0·6	...	
M. taylori	...		2	0·3	1	0·2	...	
Nardia scalaris . . .	...		...		...		1	0·2
Odontoschisma sphagni . .	10	2·9	8	1·4	3	0·8	4	0·5
Pleurozia purpurea . . .	...		4	1·4	3	0·8	1	0·2
Ptilidium ciliare . . .	...		...		2	0·2	...	
Scapania gracilis . . .	...		...		...		1	0·1
Cetraria aculeata . . .	...		...		3	0·5	...	
C. islandica	...		...		1	0·2	...	
Cladonia coccifera . . .	...		...		...		3	0·3
C. cornuta	...		...		...		1	0·1
C. floerkeana	1	0·2	...		...		...	
C. gracilis	2	0·2	...		1	0·1	1	0·2
C. impexa	7	2·0	3	0·7	8	3·0	3	1·0
C. pyxidata . . .	3	0·3	...		3	0·4	3	0·3
C. rangiferina agg. . .	...		...		3	0·7	...	
C. squamosa . . .	1	0·2	...		...		1	0·1
C. sylvatica	1	0·2	1	0·2	4	1·6	2	0·4
C. uncialis	3	0·6	5	0·8	8	2·0	2	0·3
Hypogymnia physodes . .	2	0·3	...		...		...	
Ochrolechia tartarea var. *frigida* .	...		...		1	0·1	...	
Sphaerophorus fragilis . . .	...		1	0·1	...		...	

PART II

THE MONTANE ZONE

CHAPTER 11

DWARF SHRUB HEATHS

D. N. McVEAN

In continental climates the dwarf shrub is the characteristic life form of the lowest montane or low-alpine zone. In an oceanic and deforested country such as Scotland this is not quite true as can be realised from the importance of the largely anthropogenic dwarf shrub heaths already described within the potential forest region (cf. Chapter 7). Nevertheless, completely natural dwarf shrub vegetation is characteristic of an altitudinal belt from 400 to 1000 m. in the north of Scotland and from 800 to 1200 m. in the central Highlands. This belt has been referred to the combined low- and middle-alpine zone by Poore and McVean (1957) and its vegetation falls into a lower region, with *Calluna vulgaris* as the characteristic shrub, and an upper region dominated by *Vaccinium* spp. and *Empetrum hermaphroditum*. The dominance of *Vaccinium* and *Empetrum* is largely dependent upon greater than average snow accumulation and vegetation of this kind can therefore be found above and below the altitudinal limit of *Calluna*.

The dwarf shrub heaths of the montane zone will be described roughly in order of increasing altitude, with the acidophilous members, which are by far the most abundant, being considered first (Table 58, p. 496).

Acidipholous dwarf shrub heaths

Prostrate juniper scrub association (Juniperetum nanae). Although extreme prostrate forms of the dwarf juniper (*Juniperus communis* ssp. *nana*) are found throughout the Highlands above the altitudinal limit of forest and sub-alpine scrub, the present association is confined to the western seaboard of the northern Highlands where it probably represents the remnants of a former widespread type of vegetation on the Cambrian quartzite and Torridonian sandstone. Such a prostrate juniper scrub can be regarded as marking a transition between sub-alpine scrub and low-alpine dwarf shrub heath. It was first described by Poore and McVean (1957) as the *Juniperus—Arctostaphylos* sociation.

There are eight constant species of which either *Juniperus* or *Calluna* may be locally dominant (Table 58) and a division can be made into lichen-rich and liverwort-rich facies. An undescribed species of *Herberta* is exclusive to the association and to the stands found on the Beinn Eighe Nature Reserve (Plate 85).

The juniper scrub is found from just over 305 m. to just under 610 m. on level or gently sloping quartzite moraine; occasionally on more steeply sloping screes. The liverwort facies is found only on exposures from north to east and the lichen facies on the drier south-western slopes. Stands are usually in the form of a mosaic in which areas of complete vegetation cover are developed around one or two juniper plants and amount to only a few square metres. Between these patches there is bare quartzite rubble with a sparse growth of *Molinia caerulea*, *Trichophorum cespitosum*, *Calluna vulgaris*, etc. This vegetation mosaic covers many hectares on Beinn Eighe in Ross-shire and Foinaven in Sutherland.

The soil is a ranker, consisting of a few inches of juniper and bryophyte humus directly overlying the quartzite rubble or separated from it by a thin mineral horizon.

In hollows and badly drained situations the juniper is replaced by Callunetum with much *Trichophorum*, or by a thin growth of *Narthecium ossifragum*, *Trichophorum* and *Molinia*. Vegetation intermediate between the Juniperetum and the *Arctous—Calluna* association (below) is found around 600 m. wherever finer morainic material occurs; the vegetation cover is then continuous.

Braun-Blanquet *et al.* (1939) provisionally assign the *Juniperus nana—Arctostaphylos uva-ursi* vegetation described by Praeger from Mayo and Galway to their "Juniperion nanae alliance" and it is clear that the Irish and Scottish juniper heaths represent an oceanic development of the continental "Junipereto—Arctostaphyletum".

McVean (1958) has described a juniper covered island, lying at 351 m. in the west of Ross-shire, which provides evidence of a former gradual transition from juniper-rich pine and birch forest (still to be seen on the islands of Loch Maree in Ross-shire and Loch Syre in Sutherland) to low-alpine juniper heath. Juniper-dominated vegetation is exceedingly sensitive to burning and in some places has evidently been destroyed by a single fire. In the Lewisian gneiss country of north-west Sutherland, most of the islands in the numerous lochs have at least some *Juniperus communis* ssp. *nana* but this species is absent or scarce on the surrounding burned moorlands.

Durno and McVean (1959) trace the history of the prostrate juniper scrub on the Beinn Eighe massif back to sub-Atlantic times and conclude that, as a relic of a former widespread vegetation type, they are as worthy of conservation as the nearby fragments of pine forest.

Arctous—Calluna association (Arctoeto—Callunetum). This association is closely related to the prostrate juniper scrub and was first described as the *Arctous—Loiseleuria* nodum by Poore and McVean (1957).

There are thirteen constants (Table 58) but only *Calluna vulgaris* ever attains the position of dominant. The rare northern lichen, *Platysma lacunosum*, is exclusive to the association (Plate 86).

The reduced importance of juniper and the constancy of *Empetrum hermaphroditum*,

Arctous alpinus, *Loiseleuria procumbens* and *Ochrolechia frigida* distinguish the association from that described above; differences between it and lichen-rich dwarf *Calluna* heath are dealt with on p. 484.

The association is confined to the northern Highlands and attains its finest development on the hills lying between Applecross and the Cromarty Firth. Apart from an extensive outlying stand at 275–366 m. on Whiten Head, Sutherland, the altitudinal range from 519 to 702 m. is comparatively narrow and, within this zone, it is confined to windswept crests and ridges of fine morainic material of Cambrian quartzite, Torridon sandstone or Moine schist. The ground is level or gently sloping and may be exposed in any direction.

The soil varies from a typical ranker, in which dark brown or black sandy humus passes directly to morainic debris, to podsolic types with well developed and deep (up to 20 cm.) **B** horizon. The surface humus is moder-like and well mixed with sandy and silty mineral particles (pH 4·5–5·0).

Stands vary considerably in size from fragments of only a few square metres to uniform areas of the order of 3–5 hectares. A sharp transition occurs to the *Nardus—Rhacomitrium* and *Nardus—Trichophorum* associations where snow accumulates in winter and where there is seasonal waterlogging, and also to Pennine-type blanket bog where permanent wetness leads to peat formation. On the other hand, the transition to the *Rhacomitrium*-rich dwarf *Calluna* heath (p. 485) and lichen-rich dwarf *Calluna* heath is generally a more gradual one and not associated with any obvious environmental discontinuity.

Fragments of a closely related type of vegetation not listed in Table 58 are found about 1000 m. altitude in the Cairngorms. *Calluna* is absent from this heath which lies just above its altitudinal limit and dominance is shared by *Empetrum hermaphroditum* and *Loiseleuria procumbens*. Subordinate species are similar to those of the lichen-rich dwarf *Calluna* heath at lower altitudes. McVean (1955) lists closely similar vegetation from east Iceland at an altitude of 198 m. and many similar dwarf shrub/lichen communities, mostly lacking or low in *Calluna*, have been described from Scandinavia, e.g.

1. A compact *Calluna* association locally occurring in Sylene, Torway (Nordhagen, 1927–28, p. 238) which has twenty-seven spp. in common with the *Arctous—Calluna* association.
2. A *Cetraria nivalis—Alectoria ochroleuca*-rich *Loiseleuria* association of Sylene (Nordhagen, 1927–28, p. 203) with twenty-eight spp. in common.
3. The "Alectorieto—Arctostaphyletum uvae-ursi" of Rondane, Norway (Dahl, 1956, p. 100) with twenty-five spp. in common.
4. The "Cetrarietum nivalis typicum" (a lichen heath) from Rondane (Dahl, 1956, p. 91) with twenty-seven spp. in common.

Lichen-rich dwarf *Calluna* association (Cladineto—Callunetum). The association now to be described has a wider distribution than the *Arctous—Calluna* association and occurs in both the central and northern Highlands. It includes the dwarf *Calluna* mat or mountain Callunetum of many British authors such as Metcalfe (1950) and the *Calluna*—lichen heaths of Poore and McVean (1957).

The constants consist of two dwarf shrubs and four lichens (Table 58) and either *Calluna*, or *Cladonia sylvatica*, may be dominant. There are no species exclusive to the association but *Alectoria ochroleuca* and *Cetraria nivalis* are preferential for it, although they also occur in the *Arctous—Calluna* and *Rhacomitrium—Empetrum* associations (p. 491).

Three facies have so far been distinguished: the typical one dominated by *Calluna* alone or with *Empetrum* or *Cladonia sylvatica* co-dominant; a facies in which *Arctostaphylos uva-ursi* replaces *Empetrum*, and a true lichen heath with dominant *C. sylvatica* (*C. rangiferina* occasionally co-dominant).

Floristically the association is distinguished from the *Arctous—Calluna* association by the smaller variety of dwarf shrubs (particularly the scarcity of *Loiseleuria* and absence of *Arctous*), the reduction in the number of herbs and the partial replacement of lichens such as *Platysma glaucum* and *P. lacunosum* by *Cetraria nivalis* and *Alectoria ochroleuca*.

This association occupies the same topographic position as the *Arctous—Calluna* heath but has a wider altitudinal range, from 671 to 976 m., and the greater average depth of the shrub mat shows that the exposure is probably less severe.

Soils exhibit much the same range of profile formation in both associations but the surface humus is a mor rather than moder and may be moister and unmixed with mineral particles (pH 4·3–4·4). Podsolisation is more pronounced to give either a podsol ranker or fully developed podsol with raw humus containing bleached mineral grains overlying a **B** horizon of reddish-brown, often mottled and humus-stained, sandy gravel.

The distribution centre of the association lies in the central Highlands where large areas of ground on exposed ridges and summits may be occupied by one or other of the facies. The *Arctostaphylos* facies is confined to the granite tract of the central Cairngorms where it often succeeds *Trichophorum—Calluna* bog as the peat thins out uphill and the exposed crests of the ridges are reached. The lichen-rich facies has a slightly wider distribution in the same area and is not confined to granite. It occupies more sheltered sites and slight hollows on the ridges so that it enjoys an intermittent light snow cover in winter. On the westward spurs of the Cairngorms these *Calluna*—lichen heaths are seen to occupy an intermediate position between bare erosion surface or typical lichen-rich dwarf *Calluna* heath and the *Nardus—Trichophorum* association in slight nivation hollows.

In the northern Highlands the lichen-rich dwarf *Calluna* heath has a more eastern position than the *Arctous—Calluna* heath which is widely distributed and overlaps with both this association and the *Rhacomitrium—Calluna* heath. In the districts where both associations occur either may occupy the larger area and intermediate vegetation is found. The transition from the one association to the other is always gradual.

Metcalfe (1950) divides his mountain Callunetum into a *Calluna—Arctostaphylos* community which is the equivalent of the *Arcostaphylos* facies and a *Calluna—Loiseleuria* community, the equivalent of the typical facies.

South of the Highlands, lichen-rich dwarf *Calluna* heath is now evidently confined to a limited area of the Southern Uplands, where good stands occur on the ranges of White Coomb and Dollar Law. Fragments remain on Skiddaw in the English Lake District and the association has evidently been eradicated on many southern hills by moor burning and sheep grazing.

Small stands are also found fairly near sea-level on Hirta of the St. Kilda island group.

The closest relationship that can be found in the continental literature is with the *Calluna-* and *Empetrum*-rich birchwoods of the Sylene National Park in Norway (Nordhagen, 1927–28, p. 107). If the birches are ignored, which are in open and park-like stands, there are three constants, and twenty-two species in all, common to the association described here and Nordhagen's Table (p. 108–109). Nordhagen's (p. 218) "*Cladonia sylvatica—Rangiferina*-rich *Calluna* association" has twenty-four species and three constants in common with the lichen-rich dwarf *Calluna* heath and the large homogeneous stand of a *Betula nana*-rich—*Cetraria nivalis—Cladonia sylvatica* association also described from Sylene (p. 198) makes another interesting comparison. In the last association *B. nana* appears to replace *Calluna vulgaris* of the Scottish association. It is significant that Sylene lies in a relatively oceanic area of Norway whereas the normal lichen heath of continental areas, such as Rondane, is dominated by *Cladonia alpestris*. Knaben (1950) records that in the district of middle Sogn in western Norway communities in which lichens obscure phanerogams are absent but that dense patches of chionophobous, brown and yellow lichens are found on the tops of the easternmost ridges, with localised patches on the rising tops of crags and crests further west. The puzzling, disjunct distribution of lichen heath in Scotland is typical of a vegetation type, or a species, on the edge of its range. Poore and McVean (1957, p. 427) are of the opinion that its potential habitat at the junction of the low-alpine and middle-alpine zones is occupied by *Rhacomitrium* heath and *Juncus trifidus* communities in our oceanic climate.

Rhacomitrium-rich dwarf Calluna association (Rhacomitreto—Callunetum). Vegetation of this association consists of a wind clipped heather mat in which *Rhacomitrium lanuginosum* replaces the lichens of the lichen-rich heaths. The constants are somewhat similar (Table 58), with *Calluna* and *Rhacomitrium* the usual dominants, and *Empetrum hermaphroditum*, *Cladonia uncialis* and *C. sylvatica* sometimes approaching co-dominance. An unsatisfactory division can be made into an *Empetrum* facies, corresponding to the lichen-rich heaths, and an *Arctostaphylos* facies in which *A. uva-ursi* and *Arctous alpinus* replace *Empetrum* to some extent and which is the equivalent of the *Arctous—Calluna* heath. The *Arctostaphylos* facies is confined to the northern Highlands while the *Empetrum* facies covers the entire range of the association.

Floristically the association is distinguished from the two previous ones by the abundance of *Rhacomitrium lanuginosum* and *Hypnum cupressiforme* and occasionally by a wide range of oceanic hepatics. The lichens *Alectoria ochroleuca* and *Cetraria nivalis* are absent.

The association is markedly western in its distribution in both the northern and central Highlands and is not found to the east of a line from Ben Clibreck to Ben Alder. It has a wider altitudinal range and a lower limit than the other two dwarf *Calluna* heaths (300–760 m.) but occupies the same range of exposed habitats. It appears to be differentiated from the *Arctous—Calluna* association by less extreme exposure and so tends to replace that type of heath on windswept shoulders and the tops of morainic knolls at lower levels. It owes its existence, even at the comparatively low altitude of 300 m., to repeated exposure to moist, gale-force winds. It may form extensive stands passing uphill to *Rhacomitrium* heath and below, to various bog and heath communities such as the *Trichophorum—Calluna* association and *Trichophorum—Eriophorum* bog. With increasing snow cover and drainage impedance it often shows a sharp transition to the *Trichophorum—Nardus* association or to patches of *Trichophorum*, *Nardus* and *Juncus squarrosus* on deeper peat.

Soils too are similar to those of the other dwarf Calluneta, ranging from rankers to podsols and grey-brown podsolic types, but there is a tendency for less mineral matter to be incorporated in the humus. Raw *Calluna* and *Rhacomitrium* humus may directly overlie large rock fragments, a feature not found in either the lichen-rich or *Arctous—Calluna* heath. The pH of the surface soil again lies in the neighbourhood of 4·5.

Corresponding associations have not been described from Iceland, the Faroes or the Continent.

Vaccinium snow bed association (Vaccinetum chionophilum). All the dwarf shrub associations described so far are blown clear of snow in winter so that they are frequently exposed to frost and there is no reduction in the length of the growing season due to late snow lie. In contrast to this state of affairs the present association owes its existence to the accumulation and persistence of winter snow fall. There are eight constants (Table 58) and the dominants are *Vaccinium myrtillus*, *V. uliginosum* and *Pleurozium schreberi*, while *Dicranum scoparium*, *Hylocomium splendens* and *Rhytidiadelphus loreus* may come close to co-dominance in the moss mat; *Chamaepericlymenum suecicum* is selective for this association.

Separate facies have not been distinguished so far but the collection of further data should make possible the separation of the *Sphagnum*-rich stands in wetter localities.

The association is distinguished floristically from the chionophobous, dwarf shrub heaths by the near absence of *Calluna*. The closest relationship seems to be with the *Vaccinium*-rich birchwood association (p. 151).

Distribution of this type of snow bed vegetation is predominantly central and eastern. There are only fragmentary stands north of the Great Glen. The altitudinal range of the community is also restricted, from 610 to 763 m. on moderate to steep slopes generally with a northern or eastern aspect.

Stands are not generally extensive and vary in size from a few square metres to one or two hectares. There may be a central patch of the *Nardus—Pleurozium* association where snow lies longer, or the *Vaccinium* may give way to the *Nardus—Trichophorum* association down-slope, where there is an intermittent flow of melt water. There may be an intermediate zone of the *Vaccinium—Empetrum* association between the Vaccinetum and the surrounding vegetation but the transition may also be direct to Callunetum or to *Calluna—Eriophorum* bog.

In many places, stands of the *Vaccinium* snow bed association appear to have extended, and to be extending still, due to the burning and grazing of surrounding Callunetum. This anthropogenic Vaccinetum lacks many of the chionophilous indicators such as *Blechnum*, *Oxalis* and *Chamaepericlymenum* but it is difficult to tell where the transition lies. Trampled and fouled patches in the *Vaccinium* beds sometimes show where groups of sheep have survived below the winter snow and it is suspected that a tendency for *Agrostis—Festuca* grassland to develop in these situations may be due primarily to this.

Another unclassified Vaccinetum which may also be anthropogenic in origin, like those of the Southern Uplands, Wales and the English Lake District, occupies substantial areas of ground between 600 and 750 m. (locally below 600 m.) on the calcareous schists between Glen Shee and Glen Tilt. There is a sharp boundary between the Vaccinetum and the Callunetum on the adjacent quartzite although both types of vegetation have a raw humus soil. The Vaccinetum passes over to *Agrostis—Festuca* and *Nardus* grassland below, and where the slope is ridged tongues of Vaccinetum descend into the grassland on the tops of the ridges.

Vaccinium—Empetrum **association** (Vaccineto—Empetretum). The range of vegetation now distinguished as *Vaccinium—Empetrum* heath was included with *Vaccinium* snow beds in the *Vaccinium—Chamaepericlymenum* nodum by Poore and McVean (1957). The constants are similar to those of the last association (Table 58) and the vegetation may be dominated by *Empetrum hermaphroditum*, *Vaccinium myrtillus*, *V. uliginosum*, *Hylocomium splendens* and *Pleurozium schreberi*. *Phyllodoce caerulea* is exclusive to the association but so far it has been recorded only from the one stand on a mountain in Atholl.

The association is distinguished floristically from the *Vaccinium* snow beds by the abundance of *Empetrum* and parallel reduction of *Vaccinium* spp., the reduced amount of *Blechnum* and *Chamaepericlymenum* and the increase in *Carex bigelowii*, *Rhacomitrium lanuginosum* and the variety and abundance of hepatics and lichens. From *Vaccinium*-rich Callunetum it is distinguished by the virtual absence of *Calluna*, the dominance of *Empetrum* and the increase in *Carex bigelowii*. *Listera cordata* is a good differential species, absent in the *Vaccinium—Empetrum* association and of fairly high constancy in the other.

The association is more widely distributed in the central and northern Highlands than the *Vaccinium* snow beds but it occupies similar habitats. The altitudinal range is greater, from 610 m. in the northern Highlands to 914 m. in the central Highlands, on less steep slopes with a greater variety of aspect. Stands of many hectares in area are found in association with large, shallow snow beds in the central Highlands. Smaller stands, measurable in square metres, occur around *Vaccinium* beds in nivation hollows as indicated above. In the north-west Highlands the average size of the stands is much smaller, the association is less dependent on snow cover and it is found at lower altitudes where it is usually rich in *Sphagnum* and hepatics. A local variant in the north-west is exceptionally rich in hepatics and is confined to vegetated, block screes on north to east-facing corrie slopes.

A heath of *Empetrum hermaphroditum* and hypnaceous mosses is a relatively rare type of vegetation whose affinities lie with *Vaccinium—Empetrum* heath as well as with *Rhacomitrium—Empetrum* heath (p. 491). It is northern in distribution and is found as patches in the *Rhacomitrium heath* of summit ridges, where the change in moss dominance can generally be seen to coincide with the edge of the *Empetrum* mat, or in especially sheltered hollows of *Rhacomitrium—Empetrum* heath on boulder slopes.

The soils of the *Vaccinium* snow bed and *Vaccinium—Empetrum* associations are similar and consist either of deep, wet, raw humus (up to 50 cm.) resting directly on stony detritus and boulders, or well developed podsols which may show signs of mottling in the **B** horizons. The humus may contain mineral particles almost to the surface but is usually purely organic in content. Thin raw humus over stones is found only in the *Vaccinium—Empetrum* association and one profile that was examined consisted of a moss mat and thin skin of peat (5 cm.) over a deep, undifferentiated mudstone soil. The soils of the *Vaccinium* snow beds tend to be drier and with more typical podsols. Both the typical and mossy facies of the Empetreto—Vaccinetum of Burges (1951) seem to belong to the *Vaccinium—Empetrum* association although the more lichen-rich stands from high levels might be referred more appropriately to the *Empetrum* facies of the lichen-rich *Vaccinium* heaths (p. 489). Part of the Highland Vaccinieta described by R. Smith (in Tansley, 1949) might be the *Vaccinium* snow bed association.

Many similar communities have been described from Scandinavia. Dahl (1956, p. 117) says that his "Phyllodoco—Vaccinetum myrtilli" (Myrtilletum) is one of the most characteristic communities of Rondane (central Norway) and covers appreciable areas. It compares most closely with the drier, lichen-rich lists of the *Vaccinium* snow bed association. On the other hand Nordhagen (1943, p. 133) lists an oceanic *Vaccinium myrtillus* heath with *Chamaepericlymenum* and *Hylocomium splendens* from Myrdal in western Norway which has twenty-four species and four constants in common with the *Vaccinium—Empetrum* association. There is also a close resemblance between the *Vaccinium* snow beds and the *V. myrtillus*-rich birchwoods of Sylene (Nordhagen, 1927–28, p. 122), particularly the *Chamaepericlymenum* variant.

Lichen-rich *Vaccinium myrtillus* association (Cladineto—Vaccinetum). Another *Vaccinium myrtillus* association of somewhat similar distribution to the *Vaccinium* snow beds is this lichen-rich *Vaccinium* heath (including *Vaccinium*-lichen heath). There are eleven constants (Table 58) and *Vaccinium myrtillus*, *Empetrum hermaphroditum*, *Cladonia rangiferina* and *C. sylvatica* may each attain dominance or co-dominance. There are no characteristic species and the species list is a short one.

Three facies have been distinguished: a typical one which is lichen-rich but not

PLATE 85. Prostrate *Juniper* scrub association, Beinn Eighe Nature Reserve, Wester Ross, 518·5 m. A mixed dwarf shrub heath dominated by *Juniperus communis* ssp. *nana* and *Calluna vulgaris* and forming a discontinuous patchwork on quartzite morainic debris. Other dwarf shrubs such as *Arctostaphylos uva-ursi*, *Arctous alpinus* and *Vaccinium* spp. are typically present and the bryophyte layer is dominated by mats of an unnamed species of *Herberta*.

PLATE 86. *Arctous—Calluna* association, Glen Cannich, Inverness-shire, 732 m. In this close view of the vegetation on a windswept spur, the reticulate leaves of *Arctous alpinus* are mixed with *Calluna* (whose completely flattened branches show up clearly due to over-growth by the pale coloured lichen *Ochrolechia frigida*), *Vaccinium uliginosum* and the distinctive foliose lichen, *Platysma lacunosum*.

PLATE 87. *Dryas—Salix reticulata* stand, Ben Lui, Argyll, 701·5 m. This community covers several square metres of a steep bank of broken cliffs. *Saxifraga oppositifolia, Carex flacca, F. ovina* agg., *Pinguicula vulgaris, Vaccinium uliginosum* and *Rhacomitrium lanuginosum*, are also present.

lichen-dominated; a *Cladonia sylvatica* facies which is dominated either by this species or occasionally by *C. rangiferina*; and an *Empetrum* facies which is again lichen-rich but is dominated by *E. hermaphroditum*.

The association as a whole is distinguished from *Vaccinium—Empetrum* heath by the prominence of *Cladonia* spp. combined with scarcity of the hypnaceous mosses. Some lichen-rich lists of *Vaccinium—Empetrum* heath come very close to the *Empetrum* facies of the present association but these always have considerable quantities of *Pleurozium schreberi* or *Rhytidiadelphus loreus* in addition. The floristic differences from *Festuca ovina*-rich *Vaccinium* heath are described under that association (p. 490). Intermediates between lichen-rich *Vaccinium* heath and the *Dicranum fuscescens—Carex bigelowii* association are encountered in the Clova area.

All three facies are east-central in distribution; the type has a more western spread than the other two. The type and the *C. sylvatica* facies range from 702 to 960 m. on level to moderately sloping ground of any aspect on the tops of spurs and ridges, while most of the stands of the *Empetrum* facies are rather higher, all but two lying above 914 m. and one reaching an altitude of 1129 m.

The stands of this association are seldom large, although the typical facies occupies an area of many hectares on the south-west facing slopes of Meall Odhar (Loch Lochy) between 750 and 760 m., and again in Clova and the White Mounth at about 914 m. It is more usual to find a mosaic of lichen-rich *Vaccinium* heath with lichen-rich dwarf *Calluna* heath or the *Dicranum fuscescens—Carex bigelowii* association, the individual patches ranging from a few square metres to hundreds of square metres in size. Patches of *Pleurozium*-rich *Vaccinium—Empetrum* heath often occur within the lichen-rich *Vaccinium* association.

The snow cover regime has been observed directly upon the *Empetrum* facies only, where duration of snow lie was found to vary between that experienced by *Rhacomitrium* heath and that experienced by the outer fringes of the middle-alpine *Nardus* association. The typical facies can often be seen forming a zone between the low-alpine *Nardus* associations and lichen-rich dwarf *Calluna* heath. In other sites the intimate mosaic of lichen heaths belonging to this, and the lichen-rich dwarf *Calluna* heath, would suggest that their snow regimes are identical.

The *Cladonia sylvatica* facies of the lichen-rich *Vaccinium* association is a true lichen heath and in it the dominance of lichens over dwarf shrubs is generally more complete than in any stands of the corresponding dwarf *Calluna* heath. *Vaccinium* spp. and *Empetrum hermaphroditum* are seldom vigorous, even in the typical facies, and *Deschampsia flexuosa* and *Carex bigelowii* are physiognomically as prominent.

The *Empetrum* facies, on the other hand, forms a dense, springy shrub and lichen mat, up to 10 cm. deep, often in the sheltered angle of a solifluction lobe or among large boulders.

The soils of all facies are podsolic, occasionally with a distinct A_2 horizon but more often showing a composite **A** horizon of black or dark grey, sandy peat with pH 3·7 to 4·3.

The *Cladonia sylvatica* and *Empetrum* facies of the association are confined to the Highlands but patchy stands resembling the type have been observed on the Dollar Law range in the Southern Uplands and on Skiddaw in the English Lake District. A similar type of vegetation occurs on the northern part of the Crossfell range in the Pennines but is distinguished by a patchy dominance of lichens and by an unusual abundance of *Cetraria islandica*.

The *Cladonia sylvatica*-rich *Vaccinium myrtillus* association of Sylene (Nordhagen, 1927–28, p. 224) has twenty-seven species in common with lichen-rich *Vaccinium* heath and seven of these are constants. There is thus a close floristic resemblance between the two although *Vaccinium* is more vigorous in the Norwegian association. The Norwegian soil profiles are also similar, with a better development of the A_2, and surface humus pH of 4·1–4·2. The Norwegian heaths have a reliable winter snow cover and melt out comparatively late in the season. The Scottish *Empetrum* facies compares better with Nordhagen's (p. 210) *C. sylvatica*-rich *Empetrum* association which is also floristically close to his (pp. 102, 107) *Empetrum*-rich birchwoods. The Norwegian *Empetrum* heaths have a thinner winter snow cover than the *Vaccinium* heaths and melt out sooner in spring but the snow cover is fairly reliable. Knaben (1950, pp. 69–71) describes similar *Empetrum*—lichen heaths from Middle Sogn and ascribes their brown and withered appearance on crag tops in 1942 to a deficiency of snow in the previous winter.

In general it should be pointed out that the continental *Vaccinium* heath of Norway combines the floristics of this association with the physiognomy and snow regime of our snow bed *Vaccinium* association.

Festuca ovina-rich *Vaccinium myrtillus* association (Festuceto—Vaccinetum). The lichen-rich *Vaccinium*—*Festuca* association of Ben Lawers and Cairn Mairg (Poore, 1955, p. 639) forms the basis of this association.

There are ten constants and a wide variety of possible dominants, the most common being *V. myrtillus*, *F. ovina*, *Alchemilla alpina*, *Pleurozium schreberi*, *Rhacomitrium lanuginosum* and *Cladonia sylvatica*, with *Carex bigelowii* and *Nardus stricta* attaining co-dominance in one or two stands. There are no characteristic species.

The association is floristically richer than the closely related lichen-rich *Vaccinium* heath. Two facies have been distinguished, one rich in lichens and rather poor in herbs and mosses, and one which may be dominated by *R. lanuginosum* or *P. schreberi* and which is richer in herbs and grasses and poorer in lichens than the first. A further division of the lichen-rich facies could be made according to whether the dominant vascular species is *Vaccinium myrtillus* or *Alchemilla alpina*.

The association, as a whole, is distinguished from the previous one by the presence of *A. alpina* and the abundance of grasses, especially *Festuca ovina*. *V. myrtillus* is more abundant and vigorous, lichens are generally less important and mosses, especially *P. schreberi* and *R. lanuginosum*, play a more prominent role. The association is distinguished from *Vaccinium*—*Empetrum* heath by the scarcity of *Empetrum*, the absence of species of moist habitats, such as Sphagna and *Oxalis acetosella*, and the abundance of grasses and *A. alpina*.

In the central and south-west Highlands the occurrences of the lichen-rich facies closely follow the line of the Dalradian limestones. This is in accordance with the observation that, where limestone or calcareous schist is in juxtaposition with quartzite, this facies of the association is found on the calcareous rock replacing lichen-rich *Vaccinium* heath on the siliceous rock. A particularly sharp transition can be seen on the summit ridge of Carn a' Chlarsaich to the south-west of The Cairnwell. Only lichen-rich *Vaccinium* heath is found on the Cairngorm granite.

The mossy facies has a more western distribution and, apart from a few fragments of the lichen-rich facies, is the only representative of the association north of the Great Glen. It is not obviously associated with calcareous rocks.

In altitude the association ranges from 732 to 1068 m. but the lichen-rich facies has not been recorded from over 885 m. In aspect too the lichen-rich facies appears to be more restricted to moderately steep, southern to eastern slopes while the mossy facies is largely indifferent.

Stands may be quite extensive but there is often a lack of homogeneity and transitions to *Rhacomitrium* heath, *Alchemilla*-rich grasslands, *Vaccinium—Empetrum* heaths and the *Dicranum fuscescens—Carex bigelowii* association are frequent.

Soils are typically brownish-black, peaty loams, 10–30 cm. deep, micaceous or with a high silt and sand content. Podsolisation is well marked in the **A** horizon but occasional reddish-brown colourations below this indicate that some leaching of sesqui-oxides has taken place. Recorded pH of surface soil varies from 3·8 to 4·8.

Poore (1955) has already pointed out that this vegetation corresponds in part to the Arctic-Alpine grassland of W. G. Smith, but his comparison with the *Empetrum—Vaccinium* zone of the Cairngorms is now invalid. It also compares well with Nordhagen's *A. alpina*-rich *Vaccinium myrtillus* heath and has a certain amount in common with the *Festuca ovina—Cladonia sylvatica* sociation of Sikilsdalen (Nordhagen, 1943, p. 193), particularly in physiognomy.

***Rhacomitrium—Empetrum* association** (Rhacomitreto—Empetretum). The last of the acidophilous dwarf shrub associations to be considered is a rather unsatisfactory one since it lacks sharp delimitation from true *Rhacomitrium* heath and is floristically similar. It might well be considered a facies of the moss heath were it not that well developed stands have obviously as much in common with the present group of associations.

There are eight constants and *Empetrum hermaphroditum*, *Rhacomitrium lanuginosum* and *Juncus trifidus* are the possible dominants. There are no characteristic species and separate facies have not been distinguished since even the *Juncus trifidus*-rich stands have no other differences in common.

Floristically the association is distinguished from *Vaccinium—Empetrum* heath and from the *Empetrum* facies of lichen-rich *Vaccinium* heath by the dominance of *Rhacomitrium* coupled with low values for lichens and hypnaceous mosses. While it has already been noted that a change in moss dominance may take place at the edge of an *Empetrum* mat the very existence of the present association shows that this is not necessarily so.

The association is constant and widespread throughout the Highlands from 671 to 1098 m. but it has its distribution centre in the north-west, where it may occupy substantial areas. There are two main habitats either (*a*) on steep block scree, bedrock or summit block detritus or, (*b*) on level or gently sloping ridges and summits where it generally occurs below true *Rhacomitrium* heath and sometimes in a mosaic with it.

It may also occur at lower levels in the north-west Highlands on rock ledges or among isolated boulder fields where north exposures may give a wide variety of oceanic liverworts. There is no preference for any particular aspect.

Rhacomitrium—Empetrum heath may pass abruptly to *Rhacomitrium* heath especially where a litter of boulders or angular detritus gives way to smooth ground. Slight hollows may contain the *Empetrum*—hypnaceous moss heath, although this is generally found only in association with true *Rhacomitrium* heath and, where the topography encourages larger amounts of snow accumulation, *Nardus* communities take over. There is frequently a gradual transition to *Vaccinium—Empetrum* heath downslope as shelter and moisture encourage *Vaccinium* and hypnaceous mosses at the expense of *Rhacomitrium*.

The soils are rankers, with moist and greasy raw humus resting directly on angular fragments of siliceous rocks, or they are shallow, well developed podsols. Buried humus horizons are sometimes encountered.

This association has been developed from the *Empetrum hermaphroditum* facies of the *Rhacomitrium—Carex* nodum of Poore and McVean (1957). Comparable vegetation has not been described from Norway but Steindorsson (1951) lists several sociations containing *E. hermaphroditum* under the Icelandic *Rhacomitrium* heath. Wace and Holdgate (1958, p. 610) describe comparable heaths of *E. rubrum* and *R. lanuginosum* from 914 to 1524 m. on Tristan da Cunha.

Calcicolous dwarf shrub heath

Dryas octopetala communities. Calcicolous dwarf shrub heath is rare and fragmentary in Scotland but, after Poore and McVean (1957) listed a number of *Dryas* heaths from shell sand and coastal limestone in Sutherland, further localities have been examined and a greater number of lists are available for discussion. All are essentially heaths of *Dryas octopetala*, showing the fragments of three overlapping associations, namely, (*a*) *Dryas—Salix reticulata* (list 1), (*b*) *Dryas—Carex rupestris* (list 2) and (*c*) *Dryas—Carex flacca* (list 3) (Table 59, p. 498).

Each is too sparsely represented to bear any discussion of separate constants and characteristic species. The *Dryas—Salix reticulata* stands are the most consistently species-rich.

The *Dryas—Salix reticulata* stands are confined to mountain rock ledges and the edges and inclined faces of cliffs from 702 to 914 m. (Plate 87). The *Dryas—Carex rupestris* stands are only well developed on outcrops of the Durness dolomite from near sea-level on the north coast, to 519 m. in the foothills of Ben More Assynt. Stands of the *Dryas—Carex flacca* group occur mainly on coastal shell sand but also on coastal limestone and on calcareous rocks at two inland stations. The stands of all three are generally small and measurable in square metres, but those of the last two associations may occupy areas of one or two hectares.

One stand of the *Dryas—Carex rupestris* association that has been examined could also be described as a *Dryas—Empetrum hermaphroditum* heath, a type of vegetation which is also found in Iceland (Steindorsson, 1951). It forms a level sward on rotten and eroding sugar limestone and passes quickly into *Vaccinium—Empetrum* heath around the outcrop.

On sites unprotected from grazing animals *Dryas* heath generally gives way to herb-rich grassland or to dwarf herb vegetation, the dwarf shrubs being quickly eliminated by the intense grazing pressure to which such fertile sites are exposed.

Where there are suitable soils, *Dryas* heaths are likely to have covered wider areas before the advent of sheep farming, but the limited distribution of the species, even in ungrazed places, suggests that they have never been extensive in the Highlands during the recent past. *Dryas* appears to need highly calcareous substrata in Britain and it has a predilection for dry or, at least, well drained sites; the combination of these conditions occurs only locally. Although *Dryas* heaths may have been widespread in parts of the British Isles during the Late-glacial Period (Godwin, 1956) there is, as yet, no evidence to show that they were ever present on the non-calcareous mountains of the Highlands. Even within the calcareous areas the rapid leaching of the soils in a wet climate is likely to have caused a considerable restriction of suitable habitats within the Post-glacial Period. The same probably applies to *Salix reticulata*, *Carex rupestris* and other strongly calcicolous montane species.

Soils of the *Dryas* heaths are rendzina-like (cf. Brown Rendzina of Kubiëna, 1953, p. 188) or moist loams, owing their high calcium content to irrigation from calcareous rock close at hand. The dry limestone or dolomite soils are usually bright red loams whose pedology has not yet been investigated but which are probably relict in origin. The soil profile of the *Dryas—Carex rupestris—Empetrum* stand referred to above was as follows with pH of the surface soil 7·5:—

Dark brownish-black sandy loam	0–8 cm.
Light brown sandy loam	8–14 cm.
Dark brown sandy loam	14–24 cm.
Reddish-brown sandy loam	24–34 cm.
White, sandy, disintegrating limestone	34 cm. →

Other pH values determined for the surface soils of *Dryas* heaths range from 6·8 to 7·8.

The *Dryas—Salix reticulata* stands belong without question to the species-rich *Dryas* association of Nordhagen (1927–28, p. 242). Besides the two dwarf shrubs they have a number of species in common including *Astragalus alpinus*, *Bartsia alpina*, *Carex rupestris*, *C. atrata*, *C. capillaris* and *Solorina saccata*. The range of intermediates from these to stands of the *Dryas—Carex flacca* association establishes the claim made by Poore and McVean (1957) that the coastal *Dryas* heaths of Scotland belong to the alliance "Kobresio—Dryadion". The *Dryas—Carex flacca* heaths seem to be similar to the extensive *Dryas* heaths of the Burren district in western Ireland (Praeger, 1909).

Arctostaphylos—**grass heath**, which is fairly extensive on the Blair Atholl limestone at Edintian, Perthshire, is also referable to the "Kobresio—Dryadion". The heath occupies the level tops of limestone ridges at 397 m. where the soil consists of 10 cm. of brown, calcareous loam (pH 7·79) over sugar limestone debris. Between the ridges various types of Calluneta grow on deeper, leached soil and a sample from below a nearby stand of *Arctostaphylos—Calluna* heath gave a pH of 4·9.

The species list from a plot of 4 sq. m. of the limestone heath was as follows (summarised in Table 59):—

Arctostaphylos uva-ursi	7	*Galium verum*	2
Helianthemum chamaecistus	2	*Linum catharticum*	1
Thymus drucei	3	*Plantago lanceolata*	1
Vaccinium vitis-idaea	+	*Senecio jacobaea*	+
		Taraxacum officinale, agg.	1
Agrostis canina	1	*Dicranum scoparium*	2
Briza media	3	*Ditrichum flexicaule*	1
Festuca ovina	4	*Hypnum cupressiforme*	2
Helictotrichon pratense	3	*Rhacomitrium lanuginosum*	1
Koeleria cristata	2	*Rhytidium rugosum*	3
Carex flacca	2	*Tortella tortuosa*	1
Anthyllis vulneraria	+	*Cladonia impexa*	1
Campanula rotundifolia	2		

The tops of the ridges are certainly exposed but it is likely that scrub growth during the Post-glacial climatic optimum eliminated *Dryas* and other montane species which subsequently failed to recolonise the site. It seems probable that *Arctostaphylos* is a life-form replacement of the *Dryas* at this locality and the situation should be compared with the survival of *Dryas* heath at 519 m. on Cronkley Fell in Yorkshire (cf. Pigott, 1956). Praeger (1909) records *Arctostaphylos* communities along with *Dryas* heaths on the coastal limestones of County Clare in western Ireland, but in Scotland *Arctostaphylos* is normally a plant of non-calcareous substrata.

REFERENCES

Braun-Blanquet, J., Sissingh, G. and Vlieger, J.   1939   *Prodromus der Pflanzengesellschaften. 6. Klasse der Vaccinio-Piceetea.* Montpellier.

Burges, N. A.   1951   The ecology of the Cairngorms. III. The *Empetrum-Vaccinium* zone. *J. Ecol.*, **39**, 271–284.

Dahl, E.   1956   *Rondane: mountain vegetation in south Norway and its relation to the environment.* Oslo.

Durno, S. E. and McVean, D. N.   1959   Forest history of the Beinn Eighe Nature Reserve. *New Phytol.*, **58**, 228–236.

Godwin, H.   1956   *The history of the British flora.* Cambridge.

Knaben, G.   1950   *Botanical investigation in the middle districts of western Norway.* Bergen.

KUBIËNA, W. L.	1953	*The soils of Europe*. Madrid and London.
McVEAN, D. N.	1955	Notes on the vegetation of Iceland. *Trans. bot. Soc. Edinb.*, **36**, 320-338.
	1958	Island vegetation of some west Highland freshwater lochs. *Trans. bot. Soc. Edinb.*, **37**, 200-208.
METCALFE, G.	1950	The ecology of the Cairngorms. II. The mountain Callunetum. *J. Ecol.*, **38**, 46–74.
NORDHAGEN, R.	1927–28	*Die Vegetation und Flora des Sylenegebeites*. Oslo.
	1943	*Sikilsdalen og Norges Fjellbeiter*. Bergen.
PIGOTT, C. D.	1956	The vegetation of Upper Teesdale in the north Pennines. *J. Ecol.*, **44**, 545–586.
POORE, M. E. D.	1955	The use of phytosociological methods in ecological investigations. III. Practical applications. *J. Ecol.*, **43**, 606–651.
POORE, M. E. D. and McVEAN, D. N.	1957	A new approach to Scottish mountain vegetation. *J. Ecol.*, **45**, 401–439.
PRAEGER, R. L.	1909	*A tourist's flora of the west of Ireland*. Dublin.
STEINDORSSON, S.	1951	*Skra um Islensk grodurhverfi* (*A list of Icelandic plant sociations examined and defined*). Akureyri.
TANSLEY, A. G.	1949	*The British Islands and their vegetation*. Cambridge.
WACE, N. M. and HOLDGATE, M. W.	1958	The vegetation of Tristan da Cunha. *J. Ecol.*, **46**, 593–620.

TABLE 58

Acidophilous montane dwarf shrub heaths.

Association No.	(1)	(2)	(3)	(4)	(5)	(6)	(7)	(8)	(9)
Average number of species	24	26	19	23	25	20	19	25	23
Number of stands	10	11	18	13	13	18	23	24	11
Plot area (sq. m.)	4	4	4	4	4	4	4	4	4
Altitude (m.)	305–610	519–732	671–976	305–763	549–763	610–914	702–1129	732–1068	671–1098
Aspect (degrees)	Various	Various	Various	Various	0–180	0–180	0–180	Various	Various
Slope (degrees)	0–20	0–5	0–23	0–30	8–50	2–50	0–15	3–35	2–35
Soil	Ranker	Podsol ranker	Podsol ranker	Podsol ranker	Podsol	Podsol	Podsol	Brown podsolic	Ranker
pH	...	4·3–4·9	4·4	4·5	3·8–4·1	4·4–4·7	3·7–4·3	4·1–4·9	...
Cover (%)	75–100	50–100	80–100	70–100	100	80–100	100	70–100	90–100
Height of vegetation (cm.)	5–20	1–5	2–8	2–9	12–20	5–15	1–8	4–20	2–12
Arctostaphylos uva-ursi	9 3	4 +	2 1	3 1	...	...	...	...	...
Arctous alpinus	6 1	10 4	...	4 2	...	...	...	...	...
Calluna vulgaris	10 6	10 7	10 7	10 7	4 1	1 +	1 +	5 2	10 6
Empetrum hermaphroditum	4 1	10 4	9 3	8 3	10 2	10 7	10 4	...	...
Erica cinerea	7 3	1 1	...	2 1	...	...	...	...	...
Juniperus communis ssp. *nana*	10 6	4 1	...	3 1	...	...	...	...	...
Loiseleuria procumbens	...	10 3	3 1	4 1	10 8	10 5	1 1	10 5	10 3
Vaccinium myrtillus	3 1	6 1	4 1	4 1	3 1	3 1	10 4	...	2 1
V. uliginosum	1 1	2 +	1 1	1 1	5 1	5 1	3 1	8 2	1 +
V. vitis-idaea	...	4 1	3 +	1 +		...	6 2	...	...
Blechnum spicant	...	...	...	...	10 2	3 1	...	1 1	2 1
Lycopodium selago	5 1	8 1	4 +	6 +	1 1	1 +	2 +	1 1	1 1
Agrostis canina	1 1	2 1	...	3 1	2 1	2 1	1 1	7 2	1 1
A. tenuis	1 1	1 1	...	...	2 +	...	...	6 1	...
Deschampsia flexuosa	9 2	7 1	6 1	5 1	9 3	7 2	9 2	6 2	7 2
Festuca ovina	2 1	6 1	...	3 1	1 1	3 1	2 1	9 5	4 1
Nardus stricta	1 1	2 +	...	3 +	8 1	3 1	2 +	5 1	5 +
Carex bigelowii	...	8 1	7 2	4 1	5 1	6 1	10 3	10 3	10 3
C. pilulifera	2 1	2 1	1 1	1 +	1 1	1 1	...	7 2	...

	(1)	(2)	(3)	(4)	(5)	(6)	(7)	(8)	(9)
Juncus trifidus	...	...	2 1	1 1	...	...	...	1 1	7 3
Trichophorum cespitosum	8 1	3 +	3 +	...	...	...	...	...	...
Alchemilla alpina	...	...	...	2 +	4 1	3 1	...	10 4	2 1
Chamaepericlymenum suecicum	...	...	...	...	7 1	1 +	...	...	1 +
Galium saxatile	...	2 1	2 1	1 1	10 2	4 1	3 1	9 2	1 1
Dicranum fuscescens	...	1 1	2 +	1 1	2 1	1 1	6 2	4 1	4 1
D. scoparium	3 1	1 1	1 1	5 1	6 1	6 1	4 1	5 1	5 1
Hylocomium splendens	4 1	...	...	4 1	8 4	8 3	1 1	6 1	3 1
Hypnum cupressiforme	10 2	2 1	3 1	9 2	1 1	1 1	...	3 1	5 1
Pleurozium schreberi	4 1	3 +	2 1	5 1	10 5	9 4	6 1	9 3	4 1
Polytrichum alpinum	...	2 1	7 1	3 1	3 1	4 1	4 1	7 1	4 1
Rhacomitrium lanuginosum	10 3	10 3	...	10 6	1 1	6 1	9 2	9 3	10 8
Rhytidiadelphus loreus	3 1	...	4 1	4 1	7 3	9 3	2 1	6 1	3 1
Pleurozia purpurea	7 2	2 1	4 1	2 1	...	1 1	...	...	3 1
Ptilidium ciliare	1 1	1 1	...	3 1	7 1	9 1	7 1	8 1	5 1
Alectoria nigricans	...	7 1	5 1	2 1	...	...	5 +	1 1	1 +
A. ochroleuca	...	3 +	2 1	...	...	1 +	...	...	...
Cetraria aculeata	2 1	8 2	8 2	5 2	3 +	5 1	7 1	5 1	6 1
C. islandica	1 1	10 2	10 2	8 2	...	5 1	10 3	8 1	10 3
C. nivalis	...	3 1	3 1	3 1	3 1	2 1	2 1	...	1 1
Cladonia bellidiflora	6 1	3 1	4 1	4 1	3 +	2 1	6 1	3 1	4 1
C. gracilis	7 2	5 1	6 2	7 1	1 1	1 +	10 2	7 1	8 1
C. impexa	4 1	...	...	4 1	1 1	3 1	...	1 1	1 1
C. rangiferina	6 2	2 1	7 2	9 4	1 1	9 2	10 5	7 2	7 +
C. sylvatica	9 2	9 4	10 5	10 3	4 1	4 1	10 6	9 3	9 2
C. uncialis	...	9 3	10 3	6 1	2 1	2 1	10 3	8 2	10 3
Ochrolechia tartarea var. *frigida*	...	9 2	6 1	4 1	...	...	9 1	2 1	...
Platysma glaucum	...	10 3	2 +	2 +	...	...	...	...	5 +
P. lacunosum	...	6 +	...	...	...	...	...	...	...
Sphaerophorus globosus	6 1	10 2	3 +	9 2	...	...	...	3 1	3 +

(1) Prostrate juniper scrub association.
(2) Arctous—Calluna association.
(3) Lichen-rich dwarf Calluna association.
(4) Rhacomitrium-rich dwarf Calluna association.
(5) Vaccinium snow bed association.
(6) Vaccinium—Empetrum association.
(7) Lichen-rich Vaccinium myrtillus association.
(8) Festuca ovina-rich Vaccinium myrtillus association.
(9) Rhacomitrium—Empetrum association.

2 I

TABLE 59
Calcicolous montane dwarf shrub heaths.

Association No.	(1)		(2)		(3)		(4)
Average number of species . .	49		32		31		24
Number of stands . . .	6		6		6		1
Plot area (sq. m.) . . .	4		4		4		4
Altitude (m.)	660–900		510		450		397
Aspect (degrees) . . .	Various		Various		Various		...
Slope (degrees)	15–50		0–50		2–40		...
Soil	Brown earth		Brown earth —Rendzina		Brown earth		Rendzina
pH	6·2–6·8		7·5–7·9		...		7·8
Cover (%)	80–100		75–100		100		100
Height of vegetation (cm.) . .	5		4		5–8		...
Arctostaphylos uva-ursi . .	...		...		...		7
Dryas octopetala . .	10	5	10	6	10	7	...
Helianthemum chamaecistus .	...		...		...		2
Salix reticulata . . .	10	4	...		...		...
Selaginella selaginoides . .	10	1	9	2	5	1	...
Deschampsia cespitosa . .	8	2	...		1	+	...
Festuca ovina . . .	10	3	10	4	8	3	4
Helictotrichon pratense . .	1	1	...		1	1	3
Koeleria cristata . . .	...		1	1	1	+	2
Carex capillaris . . .	7	1	2	1	1	+	...
C. flacca	1	1	5	1	10	5	2
C. rupestris . . .	1	1	10	4	...		...
Alchemilla alpina . .	6	2	5	1	1	1	...
Linum catharticum . . .	...		8	1	8	2	...
Plantago lanceolata . .	1	1	1	1	10	2	1
P. maritima . . .	...		6	2	8	2	...
Polygonum viviparum . .	8	3	6	2	1	1	...
Saxifraga aizoides . .	6	1	8	1	1	+	...
Silene acaulis . . .	10	4	...		1	1	...
Thalictrum alpinum . .	6	2	3	1	3	1	...
Thymus drucei . . .	8	2	10	3	10	3	3
Viola riviniana . . .	1	1	8	1	10	1	...
Ctenidium molluscum . .	9	3	8	2	3	1	...
Ditrichum flexicaule . .	8	3	6	1	5	1	1
Hylocomium splendens . .	10	3	5	1	1	1	...
Rhacomitrium lanuginosum .	6	2	6	1	1	1	1
Rhytidiadelphus triquetrus .	8	2	...		5	1	...
Rhytidium rugosum . .	1	1	...		5	1	3
Tortella tortuosa . . .	6	1	10	3	...		1
Solorina saccata . . .	...		5	1	...		...

(1) *Dryas—Salix reticulata* association.   (3) *Dryas—Carex flacca* association.

(2) *Dryas—Carex rupestris* association.   (4) *Arctostaphylos—*grass heath.

CHAPTER 12

GRASS HEATHS

D. N. McVEAN

In mountain country, with vegetation unmodified by man, grass heaths belong mainly to a zone lying above the dwarf shrub heaths, the Middle-Alpine Zone of Du Rietz and Nordhagen. Grass heaths extend to the limit of growth of vascular plants and are replaced beyond this by open communities of bryophytes and lichens. In Scotland, grass heaths and grassland are found at all levels from the Forest Zone to the highest summits but, apart from maritime swards, all those lying below about 763 m. are evidently anthropogenic in origin. The obviously anthropogenic grasslands have already been described (Chapter 6) and their relation to forest and dwarf shrub heath discussed.

In the present chapter the term grass heath is used in a wide sense to include vegetation dominated by sedges and rushes as well as by the Gramineae.

Alpine *Deschampsia cespitosa* association (Deschampsietum cespitosae alpinum). Low-level stands of the first montane grassland association to be described exhibit intermediates to the *Agrostis—Festuca* grasslands already dealt with (cf. p. 188 *et seq.*). On the whole, however, these *D. cespitosa* grasslands appear to be confined to the Highlands and are quite distinct from the sub-montane and definitely anthropogenic vegetation dominated by this species in northern England, southern Scotland and some southern parts of the Highlands.

The association has twelve constants (Table 60, p. 512) and *D. cespitosa* is the usual dominant although the other constant grasses taken together have a moderate cover in most stands. It is convenient to distinguish species-poor and species-rich facies which are listed separately. *Phleum commutatum* is selective for the association but there are no other characteristic species.

The species-poor facies is distributed over the whole of the Highlands and is particularly common and extensive in the west. It occurs between 488 and 914 m. The species-rich facies is more localised on calcareous rocks and the stands tend to be smaller, their size depending on the area of ground receiving calcareous drainage water (Plate 88).

The association occurs mainly on steep slopes of 30–40 degrees, facing between north and east, and the typical situation is on the sides of a deep corrie, often below cliffs.

Soils are variable with a tendency towards podsolic types under the species-poor facies. There is usually slight surface humus accumulation but a separation into well developed **A** and **B** horizons has not been observed. The species-rich soils are non-podsolic, dark brown, silty loams, loose textured and nearly always stony, with surface mull humus. Chemical analysis shows a higher calcium content than for soils of the species-poor facies.

Snow cover is moderate so that there is an increase in effective precipitation without the solifluction movements associated with extreme exposure or the latest snow lie. Snow melt water seems to play an important part in the hydrology of the sites and when the snow has gone the slopes remain damp, if not distinctly wet, throughout the rest of the year. Although drainage is rapid there is usually a great deal of water seepage, especially from below rock faces. Thus, although the association is dependent on late snow lie its predominantly western distribution suggests a connection with wetness of climate in summer. Typical stands are not found in the Cairngorms, although *D. cespitosa* vegetation occurs around springs (see below), and this could mean that the association requires soils which are neither too base deficient nor too porous.

Here and there in the mountains *D. cespitosa* grasslands may be found which cannot be assigned to the present association. These are mostly distinguished by the overwhelming dominance of *Deschampsia*, and, consequently, by floristic poverty. They are mostly to be found either on the plateau or in the corries of the Cairngorms around perennial springs of icy water, or on other high plateaux such as those of Ben Alder, Creag Meagaidh and Aonach Beag of the Nevis range.

In most places the species-poor facies is not obviously derived from a different type of vegetation by grazing. However, if comparison is made between corrie slopes bearing poor *D. cespitosa* grassland and large, ungrazed cliff ledges above, where other conditions appear comparable, it is usually found that the ledge communities show a greater abundance and luxuriance of *Vaccinium myrtillus*, *Luzula sylvatica*, *Rumex acetosa*, *Ranunculus acris* and ferns.

On Beinn Bhan, Applecross, part of a corrie slope about 300 by 50 m. in size is protected from grazing by cliffs above and below and its vegetation provides a striking contrast to that of the grazed slopes at the foot of the cliffs. This ledge is sufficiently large to duplicate the habitat conditions of the slope below so that differences in its vegetation are attributable mainly to absence of grazing. Except where irrigation from moderately calcareous beds of the Torridon sandstone gives richer soils and a lush growth of tall herbs the vegetation consists either of luxuriant fern beds or dense *Vaccinium—Luzula*. The soil is generally shallow, often consisting of a thin layer of fern humus over blocks, but the vegetation cover is complete. By way of contrast the grazed slopes below the cliffs are largely composed of unstable scree, with a patchy development of species-poor *Deschampsia cespitosa* grassland. It would seem that where grazing has not reduced the original fern—*Vaccinium—Luzula* vegetation to bare scree there has been a change to grassland. This is, however, a markedly oceanic district and it is perhaps unjustifiable to imply that this interpretation can be applied widely in the Highlands.

PLATE 88. Species-rich, alpine *Deschampsia cespitosa* association, Caenlochan Glen, Angus, 823·5 m. The luxuriant growth of *D. cespitosa* prevents recognition of the other herbs. Below, the stand passes into block scree, above, to tall herb ledges on the broken cliffs (cf. Plate 90).

PLATE 89. *Juncus trifidus—Festuca ovina* association, Am Faochagach, Easter Ross, 915 m. This vegetation is developed on a windswept erosion surface which is still losing soil, the finer material accumulating to leeward on the stable *Rhacomitrium* heath. As the slope increases, patches of erosion surface form strips along the outer edge of solifluction terraces, as on the spur behind. These particular terraces, their sinuous edges picked out by the shadowed bank below, are unusual in running obliquely down the slope rather than across it. The whole length of the summit of the massive ridge of Ben Wyvis, in the distance, is covered by continuous *Rhacomitrium* heath.

On the other hand, there is less doubt that the species-rich facies is often the biotic-ally produced equivalent of tall herb vegetation (p. 514) and owes its existence to grazing by sheep and deer. These two communities are nearly always found in the same corrie without any apparent difference in habitat except that tall herb stands are confined to ungrazed cliff ledges and the species-rich grassland covers the grazed slopes adjoining. Many tall herbs survive in the grassland but they are dwarfed and *D. cespitosa* has clearly increased at their expense for it is considerably less abundant on the ledges.

Both facies pass into other types of vegetation as drainage and snow cover alter. Wherever block screes occur on the same corrie slopes they usually carry stands of *Vaccinium—Empetrum* heath and, in the north-west Highlands, this is usually the hepatic-rich facies. The porous block scree has the effect of buffering its vegetation against the irrigation which affects the rest of the slope and this again suggests that *Deschampsia* grassland depends particularly upon irrigation. As snow cover increases on the upper slopes the grassland gives way to chionophilous moss heath (*Deschampsia—Rhytidiadelphus* association) in the west, or to stands of the *Dicranum fuscescens—Carex bigelowii* association in the central Highlands. The species-rich facies passes into species-rich *Juncus squarrosus* or *Nardus stricta* vegetation as the ground becomes wetter on decreasing slopes. The factors governing the transition from species-rich *Deschampsia cespitosa* heath to dwarf herb vegetation are not clear but the amount of irrigation and snow cover and the extent to which calcium enrichment takes place may all be involved.

Deschampsia cespitosa meadows are local in Fennoscandia but the "Deschampsietum caespitosae alpicolum" of Nordhagen (1943, p. 33), including the *D. cespitosa—Geranium sylvaticum* association and the sub-alpine *D. cespitosa* meadow of Sylene (Nordhagen, 1927–28, pp. 344, 348), has much in common, both floristically and in its ecological relationships, with the Scottish association.

Low-alpine *Nardus* associations. *Nardus stricta* communities which are obviously influenced by snow-lie more than by grazing animals begin to appear around 610 m., generally in association with the chionophilous Vaccinieta and they extend to the summits of the hills at over 1220 m. The three low-alpine *Nardus* associations will be considered together since they are related so closely floristically and physiognomically to one another and to the sub-alpine *Nardus* grasslands.

The ***Nardus—Pleurozium* association** is based on the high altitude *Nardus stricta* sociation of Poore (1955a) with the addition of data from outside the Breadalbane district. There are five constants (Table 60) and *Nardus* is the sole dominant.

This association is distinguished from the other two by the abundance of hypnaceous mosses, *Rhytidiadelphus squarrosus* and *Hylocomium splendens* in addition to the two constants, *Pleurozium schreberi* and *Rhytidiadelphus loreus*, and the small amounts of dwarf shrubs and lichens.

In distribution it is the most widespread of the group. Although Poore recorded it as occurring indifferently on sericite and quartzite schists or quartzite in Breadalbane there does seem to be a general tendency for it to avoid wholly siliceous rocks and especially sites liable to more than seasonal irrigation. It is entirely absent from the Cairngorm granite.

The next most widespread type is the **Nardus—Trichophorum association** which is characterised by the abundance of dwarf shrubs and *Trichophorum cespitosum*, with the partial or complete replacement of hypnaceous mosses by *Rhacomitrium lanuginosum*. *Trichophorum*, *Rhacomitrium*, and *Loiseleuria procumbens* may be co-dominant with *Nardus*, and lichens may be quite abundant. On the wetter sites, where deep peat is able to form, *Trichophorum cespitosum* may become completely dominant, a feature noted by Poore and McVean (1957) in their brief survey of *Nardus* snow beds. Gjaerevoll (1956) also comments upon the existence of *Trichophorum* "fen" below *Nardus*-dominated snow beds in the oceanic regions of Scandinavia.

The distribution of the association is predominantly north-western with an important subsidiary centre in the Cairngorms. The stands are well irrigated by both rain and melt water and may occupy many hectares on the sides and bottoms of large corries.

In many respects the last of the group, the **Nardus—Rhacomitrium association**, is intermediate between *Nardus—Trichophorum* and *Rhacomitrium* heath so that its status must be regarded as provisonal. There are six constants and either *Nardus* or *Rhacomitrium* may be dominant.

The typical stand has co-dominant *Nardus* and *Rhacomitrium* with a little *Vaccinium myrtillus* and *Empetrum hermaphroditum* but no other dwarf shrubs. *Trichophorum*, if present, is in small amounts, the mosses and lichens are those of *Rhacomitrium* heath and there may be a number of oceanic liverworts such as *Anastrepta orcadensis*. Species numbers per stand are low.

Apart from one record from the Loch Laggan area, vegetation of this type has been seen only in the north-west Highlands where it generally occupies sites equivalent in snow cover and drainage to those of the *Nardus—Pleurozium* association. In several places such as the foothills of Ben More Assynt the *Nardus—Pleurozium* association has been found as a patch in the centre of a *Nardus—Rhacomitrium* hollow where snow-lie is presumably longest. Even the more exposed stands tend to collect snow among the dead grass leaves so that effective precipitation and protection from wind and frost are greater than on the adjacent *Rhacomitrium* heath.

Both the *Nardus*—moss associations may be found as a strip along either side of drystone dykes built across *Rhacomitrium* heath to mark estate boundaries. A visit to these localities in winter reveals that the *Nardus* strips coincide with the main snow accumulations on the heath. The dykes are generally 50–90 years old so that the change in vegetation must have taken place within that period.

Middle-alpine Nardus association (Nardetum medio-alpinum), Although the foregoing *Nardus* associations exhibit a wide range of altitude the stands are found mainly within the low-alpine zone and represent a downward extension of grass heaths into the zone of dwarf shrubs due to prolonged snow cover in winter and spring. The present association, on the other hand, is confined to a narrow zone from 1068 to 1220 m.

There are eight constants (Table 60) and *Nardus* is always completely dominant with only *Dicranum fuscescens* and *D. scoparium* ever attaining dominance among the cryptogams. The chionophilous lichens *Cetraria hiascens* and *Cladonia delessertii* are strongly selective for the association. Species numbers per stand are low due to the dense growth of the *Nardus*.

Middle-alpine *Nardus* heath is confined to the Cairngorm massif where it is associated with the extensive complexes of late snow vegetation on the 1220 m. plateaux of Braeriach, Cairngorm and Ben Macdhui with outliers on Beinn Bhrotain and Ben a'Bhuird.

The soils of all the chionophilous *Nardus* associations are podsolic and similar to those described by Poore (1955b) except that the A_2 horizon is generally less distinct than he describes. The middle-alpine association shows least peat accumulation and the following profile is typical:

Humose sandy gravel, pH 5·0	0–7·5 cm.
Grey, non-humose sandy gravel	7·5–11·5 cm.
Dark reddish brown gravel	11·5–24·0 cm.
Boulders	24·0 cm.→

The other associations may have up to 15 cm. peat resting directly on rocks, detritus, or forming the A_1 horizon of a podsol profile. Sand grains may be present all the way to the surface and the peat sometimes shows signs of having been redistributed. Mottling is common in the A and B horizons and buried A_1 and A_2 horizons are sometimes encountered. Under the *Trichophorum*-dominated vegetation the peat varies from 20 to 60 cm. in depth. The pH of the surface peat ranges from 4·4 to 5·4.

The occurrence of *Nardus* vegetation in the centre, or at the bottom, of a *Vaccinium* or *Vaccinium—Empetrum* snow bed has already been mentioned (p. 486). The transition may be gradual or abrupt according to the gradient in the controlling habitat factor. Transitions from windswept erosion surface through Callunetum and Vaccinetum to sheltered *Nardus* hollow may take place within a few metres.

Above 800 m. the *Nardus* associations give way to moss heath rather than to dwarf shrub with decrease in snow-lie and these transitions will be described later. In the Cairngorms a vertical distance of only 90–150 m. sometimes separates the highest stand of the *Nardus—Trichophorum* association from the lowest stand of the middle-alpine association, the two types being separated by moss heaths of semi-permanent snow beds.

Where snow-lie is of intermediate duration there are sometimes communities transitional between *Vaccinium—Empetrum* heath and the three low-alpine *Nardus* associations. These mixed shrub and grass heaths occur mainly in the Cairngorms and western Highlands and they are extensive on some hills in the north-west where pure stands are poorly represented.

Mice and voles often congregate on *Nardus* beds below the winter snow and the heaps of chopped grass and droppings are revealed at the spring thaw. In Norway lemmings behave in the same way in snow bed vegetation (Nordhagen, 1927-28, pp. 361-2).

Comparisons between the chionophilous *Nardus* associations of British authors have been made by Poore (1955a, b) and Poore and McVean (1957). These can be summarised as follows:—

High altitude *Nardus* soc. (Poore, 1955a, b)   ≡*Nardus—Pleurozium* assoc.

Nardetum of *Calluna* zone (Metcalfe, 1950) ⎫
Nardetum of *Empetrum—Vaccinium* zone   ⎪
   (Burges, 1951)   ⎬ ≡*Nardus—Trichophorum*
Nardus snow beds, Table 8 (in part) (Poore and ⎪   assoc.
   McVean, 1957)   ⎭

Nardetum of *Juncus* zone (not described) (Watt ⎫
   and Jones, 1948; Burges, 1951; Ingram, 1958) ⎪
Poore (1955b) list from Cairngorms on p. 624   ⎬ ≡Middle-alpine *Nardus* assoc.
        list from Ben Lawers on p. 622   ⎪
Poore and McVean (1957), Table 8 (in part)   ⎭

There is no continental equivalent of the *Nardus—Pleurozium* association. The *Nardus—Trichophorum* association has little in common with Norwegian Nardeta except the dominance of *Nardus*, and the closest floristic equivalents must be sought among the associations of the "Phyllodoco—Vaccinion myrtilli" rather than the "Nardeto—Caricion bigelowii". In habitat and physiognomy, if not in floristics, it bears some resemblance to the "Cetrarietum delisei loiseleurietosum" of Rondane (Dahl, 1956).

Poore (1955b) compares his high altitude *Nardus* sociation with the alpine *Nardus* association of Sylene (Nordhagen, 1927–28, p. 317), which is the equivalent of the "Nardetum chionophilum" of Rondane (Dahl, 1956, p. 166), but the middle-alpine *Nardus* association seems to be closer to these in its lack of hypnaceous mosses and the presence of more chionophilous species although it is less species-rich. The high altitude *Nardus* and the *Nardus—Pleurozium* association resemble rather the sub-alpine *Nardus* association of Sylene (Nordhagen, 1927–28, p. 321) in the abundance of hypnaceous mosses, floristic poverty and snow regime. Sub-alpine *Nardus* grassland (pp. 186 & 192), on the other hand, is not influenced by snow-lie and lacks many mountain species, but is otherwise also similar to the Sylene association.

The closest correspondence of all is found between Scottish middle-alpine *Nardus* and several of the lists in the Alpine *Nardus stricta* sociation of Gjaerevoll (1956, Table 8). Gjaerevoll's species-impoverished lists, especially I and V from Torne Lappmark and Vågå are particularly like the Cairngorm lists.

Polytrichum alpinum—Carex bigelowii association (Polytricheto—Caricetum bigelowii). This and the following association can be regarded as either moss or grass heaths according as to whether mosses or grasses are dominant. The present association incorporates the *Polytrichum alpinum* nodum of Ben Lawers (Poore, unpublished) as a distinct local facies. There are only two constants (Table 60) and either of these may be dominant. *Anthoxanthum odoratum*, *Cherleria sedoides* and *Rhytidiadelphus loreus* may approach co-dominance in the Ben Lawers facies. *Cetraria hiascens* is selective for the type as well as for the middle-alpine *Nardus* association. The type is distinguished by the dominance of *Carex bigelowii* and abundance of lichens while the Ben Lawers facies has a greater variety of grasses and other herbs with dominance of *P. alpinum* and scarcity of *C. bigelowii*.

The association is confined to the central Highlands and forms a band stretching from Ben Nevis in the west to Clova in the east, with a southern outlier on Ben Lawers. The altitudes of the stands range from 610 m. in Clova and on Ben Lawers to over 1220 m. in the Cairngorms and the Nevis area. The ground is generally level or gently sloping and there is a preponderance of northern and eastern exposures, as with most communities of late snow-lie.

The stands are neither extensive nor particularly homogeneous, except on Lochnagar, and they are usually found in mosaic with Nardeta, the *Dicranum fuscescens—Carex bigelowii* association and chionophilous moss heaths around the margins of large snow fields. The ecology of the association is not clear and while many stands are obviously associated with melt water channels and wet hollows others occupy well drained and un-irrigated sites, or even raised soil patches on stony erosion surfaces. There is reason to believe that many dry stands are relics from a fairly recent regime of locally impeded drainage.

Stands of this association in the Cairngorms may not melt out until the month of June if winter snow fall has been heavy.

Soils are podsolic and gleying is frequent, although downwash of fine sand and silt may mask the tendency to leaching. In the Cairngorms wet, sandy peat overlying mottled gravel gives way to a deeper peat with less sand under neighbouring *Nardus* vegetation. On Ben Lawers the more base and clay-rich soils show less sign of podsolisation and this is reflected in the greater floristic variety of the local facies. The pH of the surface soil varies from 4·4 to 5·1, considerably less than the values given by Poore (1955b).

The "Polytricheto—Caricetum bigelowii" of Rondane in Norway (Dahl, 1956) is similar to this association in many ways. They have thirty-five species and two constants in common and they occupy closely similar habitats. The Rondane association is seasonally wet and may be covered by ice in winter although snow cover is variable. Where there is little snow cover the ground is thrown into hummocks by frost action; this has been observed in Scotland only on the 1000 m. plateaux of Lochnagar, Ben Alder and the Glas Maol. The Rondane soils too have well developed podsol profiles and the pH of the surface humus or sandy humus has a mean value of 4·4.

Gjaerevoll (1956, p. 67) also lists several stands of his "Caricetum bigelowii-lachenalii" in which *Carex bigelowii* and *Polytrichum alpinum* are the prominent species. The stands are from Torne Lappmark and Beiarn and the habitat is similar to that of "Polytricheto—Caricetum bigelowii" in Rondane and Scotland. On the other hand the facies from Ben Lawers has more in common with the *Deschampsia flexuosa—Polytrichum alpinum* sociation of Torne Lappmark and the Borgefjell Mountains (pp. 42–44) in the dominance of *Polytrichum*, the higher constancy of *Salix herbacea* and the greater abundance of grasses and other herbs.

Dicranum fuscescens—Carex bigelowii association (Dicraneto—Caricetum bigelowii). The second mixed moss and grass heath has been based on the *D. fuscescens—C. bigelowii* sociation of Breadalbane (Poore, 1955b).

There are five constant species (Table 60) and either *D. fuscescens* or *C. bigelowii* may be dominant. Species numbers per stand of 1–4 m. are exceptionally low and range from 8 to 24 with an average of 13·5.

The distribution of the association is similar to that of the previous one but there are two fragmentary outliers in the northern Highlands on Ben Wyvis and the Glen Cannich Sgurr na Lapaich. The altitudinal range is from 793 to 1159 m. on level or gently sloping terrain of NW to SE aspect. The tendency for the association to be missing from the areas of "poorer" rocks is surprising since none of the constituent species can be described as eutrophic. In the south-west Cairngorms its presence on Moine schists and absence from the granite area is most striking.

Outside Breadalbane there is not the difficulty, described by Poore (1955b), of drawing the line between this association and *Rhacomitrium* heath although intermediates are encountered here and there. *Carex bigelowii* attains greater dominance in this association than in any stands of the *Rhacomitrium* heath and this is a useful distinguishing feature when both mosses are present in abundance; otherwise there can be little to distinguish the two associations floristically.

Actual records for the snow regime of *D. fuscescens—C. bigelowii* heath are scanty but in its topographical position, in hollows of the *Rhacomitrium* heath or on sheltered slopes above late snow beds, it corresponds to the *Deschampsia cespitosa—Rhytidiadelphus loreus* association which is known to be chionophilous and weakly hygrophilous. Its close juxtaposition with the *Nardus—Pleurozium* association in vegetation mosaics signifies a similar snow cover and it can be seen to form both sharp and gradual transitions to *Festuca ovina*-rich *Vaccinium* heath and the *Polytrichum alpinum—Carex bigelowii* association. Mixed vegetation consisting of intermediates with the last two associations are common in the Clova-Caenlochan area where the *D. fuscescens—C. bigelowii* heath forms some of its most extensive stands of many hectares on the 900 m. plateau.

As Poore has pointed out, the soils are invariably podsolic with considerable humus accumulation and gleying of the **B** horizon is commonly present. Exceptionally, one stand on the summit of Glas Maol was found to have only a few centimetres of black, wet, badly humified moss humus over large boulders. The pH of the surface soil varies from 3·6 to 4·4.

Records of comparable Scandinavian vegetation are few. Gjaerevoll (1949) describes a *C. bigelowii* sociation, with *D. fuscescens* dominant, from the Oviksfjällen Mountains of central Sweden and Dahl (1956) describes a *Deschampsia flexuosa—D. fuscescens* association rich in *C. bigelowii* from Rondane. Apart from these one must look among the lists of Nardetum, "Caricetum bigelowii-lachenalii" and "Anthoxantho—Deschampsi-etum flexuosae" (*Lycopodium alpinum* sociation) for vegetation with abundant *C. bigelowii* and *D. fuscescens*.

Lichen-rich *Juncus trifidus* association (Cladineto—Juncetum trifidi). In Scotland, as elsewhere throughout its range, the rush *Juncus trifidus* exhibits a wide ecological amplitude. It has already been described as abundant in some stands of the *Rhacomitrium—Empetrum* heath (p. 491) and a *J. trifidus—Rhacomitrium* heath will be described later (p. 524) but in this, and the following association, it plays its most important phytosociological role.

The present association is decidedly chionophilous. It is confined to a small area of the east-central Highlands centred upon the granite mass of the Cairngorms where it is confined to level or gently sloping summit plateaux above 900 m. Stands are developed as a network on loose erosion surfaces, with an increasing amount of ground cover as the shallow basins with middle-alpine *Nardus* stands are approached. It is difficult to select a sample plot of more than 4 sq. m. which excludes bare granite gravel or the hepatic crust of a different association.

There are eight constants (Table 60) and *J. trifidus* is the only dominant, although several species of *Cladonia* and *Rhacomitrium lanuginosum* may almost reach co-dominance.

The relationships of the *J. trifidus* communities of the high Cairngorm plateaux to exposure and snow cover can be summed up as follows:—

Moderately exposed site which does not form a collecting ground for snow . . . *Rhacomitrium* heath with *J. trifidus* (p. 524).
Moderately exposed site with intermittent snow cover of up to 50 cm. . . . lichen-rich *J. trifidus* association.
Severely exposed site where snow never lies and where *Rhacomitrium* cannot form a carpet . . . *J. trifidus* tussocks with a few chionophobous lichens and a little *Rhaco-mitrium* (probably the equivalent of the *J. trifidus—F. ovina* association, p. 508).

There is a gradual transition from the one habitat to the next so that it is difficult to say where the lichen-rich *Juncus* heath ends and the isolated *Juncus* tussock ground begins. The edge of the *Rhacomitrium* heath is usually well defined. On aerial photographs, the last two associations described above show up as a dark reticulum or stipple against the pale background of erosion surface while the *Rhacomitrium* heaths, Nardeta and late snow communities form areas of uniform colour.

Outside the Cairngorms the present association has only been seen in fragmentary form on the Dalradian quartzite of An Socach, south of Braemar, and on part of the Clova plateau.

Most of the soils examined were uniform mixtures of humus and sandy gravel with a surface crust (= Alpine rawmark of Kubiëna?) but one stand was developed on a podsol profile.

The *Juncus trifidus* communities of the Cairngorms have been described by Ingram

(1958, pp. 707–737) but he considers all vegetation of which *J. trifidus* is the most prominent vascular constituent to be one association; hence his conclusion that the minimal area of the "Juncetum trifidi scoticum" must have a size of many square metres.

The "Juncetum trifidi nudum" of Rondane (Dahl, 1956, p. 165) has a total list of forty-one species; twenty species and three constants in common with the lichen-rich *Juncus trifidus* association. In the more oceanic region of Sylene the "*Cetraria crispa— Cladonia sylvatica—Juncus trifidus* association" (Nordhagen, 1928, p. 289) has a list of forty-nine species of which twenty-six species, including six constants, are shared with the Scottish association. When comparable associations are matched there seems to be little justification for Ingram's contention that the Scottish Juncetum trifidi reveals a pronounced paucity in species compared with similar European communities, at least so far as Scandinavia is concerned.

The Norwegian Junceta are found between 1100 and 1400 m. and they experience a regular, but only moderately deep, winter snow cover which disappears before that on the *Deschampsia—Anthoxanthum* and *Nardus* communities. They remain moister in summer than the Scottish *Juncus* heath and occur on deeper soils with humus accumulation but no podsolisation, over boulders.

Juncus trifidus—Festuca ovina association. The second of the *Juncus trifidus* associations is markedly chionophobous and occupies some of the most exposed ground of the Scottish mountains (Plate 89).

The constant species are *Juncus trifidus, Festuca ovina, Alchemilla alpina* and *Rhacomitrium lanuginosum* and there are eleven other species of near constancy. It is rather misleading to speak of dominants in such open vegetation but *Salix herbacea, Alchemilla alpina, Cherleria sedoides, Thymus drucei* and *Steriocaulon vesuvianum* reach the highest cover-abundance values in addition to the four constants. *Solorina crocea* is highly selective for this association as well as for the *Gymnomitrium—Salix herbacea* association (p. 529). Two recent additions to the vascular flora of Scotland, *Diapensia lapponica* and *Artemisia norvegica* have their stations in this type of vegetation.

The association is confined to the north-west Highlands and is found from just under 610 to 1129 m. on exposed ridges and cols. Stands from Ben Lawers are intermediate in composition between this and the *Gymnomitrium—Salix herbacea* association and lack several constants of both. Transitional stands are also frequent in the north-west Highlands. The merging of the two types in certain places is almost certainly due to the similar selective effects of extreme exposure and late snow-lie, which encourage species sensitive to competition from less hardy plants. The ground is level, or with a moderate slope of any aspect, and consists of a typical wind erosion surface with small and large stones firmly set in a matrix of finer particles as though rolled in. Vegetation cover varies from 20 to 60 per cent. of the total area.

Soils are often surprisingly deep and fertile in appearance below the surface armour of stones (= Alpine hamada Rawmark of Kubiëna, 1953, p. 150). Ferreira (1958) records more than 60 cm. of friable light brown micaceous soil of pH 4·3–4·8 under the stones of the Ben Hope summit plateau in north-west Sutherland and remarks that this soil apparently lacks grains of felspar and quartz. However, soils are generally less than 25 cm. deep with pH values of around 4·7–4·9. There may be an ill-defined and crusted layer of humus accumulation at the surface while the loam immediately below is reddish or orange brown and becomes brighter in colour with depth. These soils often appear to be truncated types which originally formed beneath a rather different vegetation, probably closed *Rhacomitrium* heath.

Solifluction phenomena are common on this exposed ground. The level and homogeneous pavement often passes to terracing as the slope increases, with *Rhacomitrium* heath on the bank and the present association occupying the strip of level ground. Stone polygons and stripes can sometimes be distinguished and flat slabs may be tilted on end to give the so-called "gravestones".

There may be abrupt or gradual transitions from stands of the *J. trifidus—F. ovina* association to either rich or poor *Rhacomitrium* heath according to the rate of wind erosion or deposition. Raised and relict patches of moss heath are common in the midst of the erosion surface and moss heath may also be seen to build up from the *J. trifidus— F. ovina* heath where soil is being deposited.

The corresponding vegetation of the central Highlands is the exposed ground variant of the *Gymnomitrium—Salix herbacea* association or the *J. trifidus* tussock community of the Cairngorms.

Similar erosion surfaces or "fell field" have been described under various names from the Faeroes by Ostenfeld (1908), from Iceland by Hansen (1930) and from Shetland by Spence (1957).

REFERENCES

Burges, N. A.   1951   The ecology of the Cairngorms. III. The *Empetrum—Vaccinium* zone. *J. Ecol.*, **39**, 271–284.

Dahl, E.,   1956   *Rondane: mountain vegetation in south Norway and its relation to the environment*. Oslo.

Ferreira, R. E. C.   1958   *A comparative ecological and floristic study of the vegetation of Ben Hope, Ben Loyal, Ben Lui and Glas Maol in relation to the geology*. Ph.D. Thesis, University of Aberdeen.

Gjaerevoll, O.   1949   Snøleievegetasjonen i Oviksfjellene. *Acta phytogeogr. suec.*, **25**.

     1956   *The plant communities of the Scandinavian alpine snow beds*. Trondheim.

Hansen, H. M.   1930   *Studies on the vegetation of Iceland*. Copenhagen.

Ingram, M.   1958   The ecology of the Cairngorms. IV. The *Juncus* zone: *Juncus trifidus* communities. *J. Ecol.*, **46**, 707–737.

Kubiëna, W. L.   1953   *The soils of Europe*. Madrid and London.

Metcalfe, G.   1950   The ecology of the Cairngorms. II. The mountain Callunetum. *J. Ecol.*, **38**, 46–74.

Nordhagen, R.   1927–28   *Die Vegetation und Flora des Sylenegebeites*. Oslo.

     1943   *Sikilsdalen og Norges Fjellbeiter*. Bergen.

Ostenfeld, C. H.   1908   "The land-vegetation of the Faeroes", in *Botany of the Faeroes*, III. Copenhagen.

POORE, M. E. D.   1955*a* The use of phytosociological methods in ecological investiga-
                           tions. II. Practical issues involved in an attempt to apply the
                           Braun-Blanquet system. *J. Ecol.*, **43**, 245–269.

                   1955*b* The use of phytosociological methods in ecological investiga-
                           tions. III. Practical applications. *J. Ecol.*, **43**, 606–651.

POORE, M. E. D. and 1957   A new approach to Scottish mountain vegetation. *J. Ecol.*, **45**,
  McVEAN, D. N.   401–439.

SPENCE, D. H. N.   1960   Studies on the vegetation of Shetland. I. The serpentine debris
                           vegetation in Unst. *J. Ecol.*, **45**, 917–945.

WATT, A. S. and   1948   The ecology of the Cairngorms. I. The environment and the
  JONES, E. W.   altitudinal zonation of the vegetation. *J. Ecol.*, **36**, 283–304.

TABLE 60

Montane "grass" heaths

Association No.	(1)	(2)	(3)	(4)	(5)	(6)	(7)	(8)	(9)	(10)
Average number of species	27	50	23	20	18	16	19	13	19	25
Number of stands	8	8	8	5	8	6	11	19	8	12
Plot area (sq. m.)	4	4	4	2–4	4	4	4	1–4	1–4	2–12
Altitude (m.)	480–900	570–840	600–1080	900	600–900	1050–1200	840–1200	780–1010	900–1010	570–990
Aspect (degrees)	0–135	0–270	Various	Various	Various	0–180	Various	Various	Various	Various
Slope (degrees)	35	40	2–5	2–10	0–2	0–5	0–12	0–12	5–10	2–12
Soil	Incipient podsol	Brown earth	Podsol	Podsol	Podsol	Podsol	Podsol	Podsol	Rawmark	Rawmark
pH	5·2–5·3	5·4	5·0	4·4	...	5·2	4·5	3·7–4·2	4·3	4·7–4·9
Cover (%)	100	90–100	90–100	100	100	95–100	100	90–100	90–100	20–60
Height of vegetation (cm.)	15	20–40	2–10	8–12	3–12	5–10	2–5	2–12	12–15	6
Empetrum hermaphroditum	··	··	10 2	2 +	7 2	··	1 +	··	2 1	4 +
Salix herbacea	7 2	··	1 +	··	··	··	1 1	··	1 1	9 2
Vaccinium myrtillus	··	7 2	9 2	6 1	9 3	2 1	··	5 1	5 +	5 1
V. uliginosum		··	8 2	··	2 +	··	··	··	··	1 +
Lycopodium alpinum	··	··	8 1	2 1	5 1	··	··	··	3 +	··
Selaginella selaginoides	··	6 1	··	··	··	··	··	··	··	··
Agrostis canina	8 2	9 2	4 +	2 +	2 +	··	2 1	1 +	1 +	7 2
A. tenuis	10 5	9 4	··	··	··	··	··	4 1	1 +	1 1
Anthoxanthum odoratum	10 6	7 3	··	··	··	··	··	1 +	1 1	··
Deschampsia cespitosa	10 6	10 6	··	6 2	··	1 +	5 1	1 +	1 1	9 2
D. flexuosa	7 3	9 3	4 +	8 1	2 +	5 1	6 2	5 3	4 1	10 3
Festuca ovina agg.	5 1	9 3	··	4 1	2 +	··	2 1	5 2	4 1	1 1
F. rubra	1 1	7 2	··	··	··	··	··	1 1	3 1	··
Nardus stricta	8 3	3 1	10 6	10 8	10 7	10 10	2 1	10 8	10 3	7 2
Carex bigelowii	6 1	5 1	8 2	8 3	10 3	10 3	10 8	10 6	10 3	7 +
Juncus trifidus	··	3 1	··	··	··	2 +	2 1	··	10 7	10 3
Luzula spicata	··	3 1	··	··	··	··	2 1	··	3 1	7 +
L. sylvatica	5 1	7 2	10 4	2 +	3 +	··	··	··	··	··
Trichophorum cespitosum	1 1	··	··	··	··	··	··	··	··	··
Alchemilla alpina	9 2	10 3	··	2 +	3 +	4 1	··	1 1	2 +	10 2
Antennaria dioica	··	··	··	··	··	··	··	··	··	8 2
Armeria maritima	2 +	2 +	··	··	··	··	··	··	··	8 1
Cerastium holosteoides	··	7 1	··	··	··	··	··	··	··	··
Cherleria sedoides	··	··	··	··	··	··	··	··	··	6 1

Species	1	2	3	4	5	6	7	8	9	10
Galium saxatile	10 3	·	2 +	2 +	10 3	·	1 1	1 1	2 1	6 1
Geum rivale	6 2	6 2	·	·	·	·	·	·	·	·
Gnaphalium supinum	·	·	·	·	·	6 2	·	·	·	1 +
Oxalis acetosella	6 2	7 2	·	·	·	·	·	·	·	·
Potentilla erecta	5 1	4 +	·	·	·	·	·	·	·	·
Ranunculus acris	4 1	9 2	·	·	·	·	·	·	·	·
Rumex acetosa	8 3	10 3	·	·	·	·	·	·	1 1	7 1
Silene acaulis	·	·	·	·	·	·	·	1 +	·	8 2
Thymus drucei	1 1	3 1	·	·	·	·	·	·	·	·
Viola riviniana	6 1	9 2	·	·	·	·	·	·	·	·
Dicranum fuscescens	·	·	2 +	·	·	·	10 3	6 2	10 7	1 +
D. scoparium	4 1	3 +	3 +	·	8 1	4 +	3 1	5 1	1 +	1 1
Hylocomium splendens	10 3	10 4	10 4	·	7 3	3 1	1 1	1 1	1 1	·
Hypnum callichroum	·	6 1	6 1	4 +	2 +	5 1	·	·	·	·
H. cupressiforme	7 1	4 1	4 1	3 1	10 3	3 +	5 1	1 1	2 1	1 1
Pleurozium schreberi	9 2	1 1	1 1	10 4	6 1	2 +	·	10 6	8 2	1 1
Polytrichum alpinum	·	·	·	·	·	·	5 1	·	·	2 1
P. piliferum	·	·	·	4 +	·	·	7 1	6 1	8 1	8 1
Rhacomitrium lanuginosum	8 3	1 1	1 1	10 4	8 2	10 6	·	1 1	·	10 3
Rhytidiadelphus loreus	10 3	9 3	9 3	4 +	10 3	5 1	·	1 1	·	·
R. squarrosus	10 3	9 2	9 2	·	6 2	·	·	·	·	·
R. triquetrus	1 1	6 2	6 2	·	·	·	·	·	·	·
Thuidium tamariscinum	3 1	7 2	7 2	·	·	·	·	·	·	·
Lophocolea bidentata	1 1	7 1	7 1	·	·	·	·	7 2	·	·
Ptilidium ciliare	4 1	·	·	·	10 2	4 +	9 2	·	3 1	1 1
Cetraria hiascens	·	·	·	·	·	·	·	·	·	·
C. islandica	1 1	·	·	·	6 1	8 2	10 1	5 1	7 1	2 1
Cladonia bellidiflora	·	1 1	1 1	·	6 1	4 1	10 2	7 1	7 1	2 +
C. delessertii	1 1	·	·	·	·	·	10 3	6 2	·	·
C. gracilis	·	·	·	6 1	2 +	4 1	8 1	1 1	4 1	1 1
C. pyxidata	2 +	·	·	4 +	·	·	7 1	2 1	3 1	1 1
C. rangiferina	1 1	·	·	7 1	·	2 +	3 +	6 1	·	·
C. sylvatica	·	·	·	5 1	6 1	5 1	10 2	8 2	7 1	7 1
C. uncialis	·	1 1	1 1	10 2	2 +	8 1	5 1	6 1	5 1	4 1
Ochrolechia tartarea var. frigida	·	·	·	3 +	·	·	2 1	1 1	1 +	8 2

(1) Species-poor alpine Deschampsia cespitosa association.
(2) Species-rich alpine Deschampsia cespitosa association.
(3) Nardus—Trichophorum association.
(4) Nardus—Pleurozium association.
(5) Nardus—Rhacomitrium association.
(6) Middle-alpine Nardus association.
(7) Polytrichum alpinum—Carex bigelovii association.
(8) Dicranum fuscescens—Carex bigelovii association.
(9) Lichen-rich Juncus trifidus association.
(10) Juncus trifidus—Festuca ovina association.

CHAPTER 13

HERB AND FERN MEADOWS

D. N. McVEAN

In Scandinavia, herb and fern-dominated vegetation is described from sub-alpine birchwoods and willow scrub and from areas of deep snow-lie in the low alpine zone. In Scotland there are fragmentary examples of all these communities, some of which have already been mentioned in previous chapters, but the ones to be described here are those that can be grouped conveniently under the term "montane herb meadow".

For various reasons, both biotic and climatic, natural montane meadows are a rarity in the Scottish Highlands, grazing by wild and domestic animals being everywhere responsible for the restriction of such vegetation to precipitous or otherwise protected ground. Poore recognised the existence in Breadalbane of a Tall Herb Nodum (1954) on inaccessible rock ledges and two of his three lists have been incorporated in the summary presented in Table 61. His *Sibbaldia* nodum (Poore, 1955), a heavily grazed herb mat on calcium-rich soils was the first published example of this kind of British vegetation.

Tall Herb Association. This association provides the best introduction to the group. There are six constants and a wide variety of possible dominants (Table 61, p. 522). *Heracleum sphondylium* and *Leptodontium recurvifolium* are exclusive to the association and *Rubus saxatilis*, *Angelica sylvestris*, *Geranium sylvaticum*, *Saussurea alpina*, *Sedum rosea* and *Trollius europaeus* are selective or preferential. *Leptodontium* is an extremely oceanic moss and appears in stands in the north-west Highlands only. The total list of species is a long one.

It has not been possible to divide this association into local or floristic facies. There are, however, distinct central and north-west Highland variants due to differences of geographical plant distribution, for example, *Heracleum sphondylium* and *Geranium sylvaticum* are confined to stands south of the Great Glen. A floristic series from oligotrophic to eutrophic can also be made out, evidently corresponding to the calcium content of the bedrock or the irrigating water, but the vegetation at the acid end of the series, dominated by *Vaccinium myrtillus* and *Luzula sylvatica*, is closer to woodland and scrub.

It is quite likely that the apparent lack of differentiation within the association is due to the restricted size of the habitats available and hence of the stands themselves. Small and isolated ledges have also come to be dominated by one species at the expense of floristic variety.

Nevertheless, the tall herb association is a widespread one and is found wherever the mountains above the present limit of woodland offer a reasonable exposure of calcareous rock and a sufficient number of crags and areas of broken ground to provide protection from grazing animals. Tall herb communities may be present at altitudes well below potential or even actual forest limit. The total altitudinal range is from under 305 to 854 m. Good examples can be seen on Meall Cumhan of Ben Nevis, Ben Lui, Ben Lawers, Seana Bhraigh and at the head of Caenlochan (Plate 90).

The size of the stands varies from a few square metres to several hundred square metres, the larger ones (more suitable for floristic analysis), tending to be on steep or precipitous slopes in inaccessible situations.

Soils vary considerably in depth and moisture content but all are fertile brown loams of moderate acidity (pH 4·8–5·4) and the rate of nitrification is obviously high. Fertility results either from the continual enrichment by fragments of soft, calcareous rocks, or from intermittent irrigation with drainage water from soft or hard calcareous rocks. Where the enrichment fails *Vaccinium* and *Luzula* become dominant, as mentioned above.

Tall herb ledges are also to be found in Lakeland and North Wales. Pigott (1956) describes mowing meadow with related vegetation from upper Teesdale and Poore (unpublished) notes the same affinities in the riverbank vegetation of the Tay.

Individual stands are encountered which provide floristic lists that would fit into one or other of a number of Scandinavian associations of the order "Lactucion". The Scottish association is, therefore, best regarded as an unorganised or fragmentary order. *Cicerbita* (*Lactuca*) *alpina* itself is a rare species in Scotland but has been found in analysable stands on the rocks of Coire Kander.

In the Rondane district of central Norway tall herb vegetation has a distribution which recalls the situation in Scotland since it is restricted to steep slopes in areas of better rocks. Dahl (1956, p. 192), distinguishes two associations in this area, the "Geranietum sylvatici alpicolum", which he compares with the *Deschampsia flexuosa* variant of Nordhagen's association of the same name, and the "Chamaenerietum angustifolii nudum". The soils of the tall herb meadows are similar in Scotland and Norway.

There are no direct records of the snow cover experienced by the Scottish tall herb ledges but circumstantial evidence indicates a fairly deep accumulation in most winters, melting out early in spring. On the other hand, it has been established (see below) that communities of *Athyrium alpestre* and *Cryptogramma crispa* are completely dependent on the protection that a snow cover provides against winter frost and records show that there is early accumulation of a considerable depth of snow reaching its maximum in March and melting out quickly thereafter.

***Cryptogramma crispa—Athyrium alpestre* association** (Cryptogrammeto—Athyrietum chionophilum). There are six constants of this association (Table 61) and the field layer may be dominated by either *Athyrium* or *Cryptogramma*. *Rhytidiadelphus loreus* is the only bryophyte found dominating the ground layer. Apart from isolated occurrences in moss-dominated snow beds (p. 529) *Cryptogramma crispa* is exclusive to this association.

Low level screes in which *Cryptogramma* may also be abundant (Leach, 1930) are found in the west Highlands but not to the same extent as in England, Wales and the Southern Uplands. This may be due in part to the scarcity of suitable habitats but it is more likely to reflect the incidence of damaging frosts. *Cryptogramma* is abundant from 100 m. upward on the screes of Applecross, a markedly oceanic district of the west Highlands.

Floristically the association cannot easily be confused with any other but its limits are occasionally ill defined. *Thelypteris limbosperma* stands and tall herb communities may contain a little *Athyrium alpestre*, and *Cryptogramma*-dominated fern beds sometimes pass gradually to the *Polytrichum norvegicum—Dicranum starkei* association.

The stands are found on stablised block screes as small patches of vegetation among tumbled boulders, or on ledges between 824 and 1098 m. and they vary in size from one or two to several hundred square metres. These larger stands are neither continuous nor particularly homogeneous but there is seldom any difficulty in obtaining a plot of 4 sq. m. for analysis (Plate 91).

Soils may consist of almost pure humus up to 14 cm. deep resting on boulders, or be composed of humus, sand and silt intermixtures over smaller rock fragments. The pH of pure *Athyrium* humus was found to be 4·1.

There is insufficient representation of the association in the Highlands to attempt floristic separation of the *Athyrium* from the *Cryptogramma*-dominated stands. Gjaerevoll (1956) follows Nordhagen (1943) in dividing the Scandinavian chionophilous fern communities into two separate associations, the "Athyrietum alpestre" and the "Cryptogrammetum crispi". While the "Athyrietum alpestre" is represented in all parts of Scandinavia it forms a greater proportion of the vegetation in western Norway; in contrast, the second association is confined to the west. A further subdivision is sometimes made within the Athyrietum according as to whether tall herbs or species of later snow-lie such as *Salix herbacea* and *Sibbaldia procumbens* accompany the fern. The Cryptogrammetum is floristically closer to the second group.

The present association, which also exhibits the tall herb and late snow elements, has twenty-two species in common with the "Athyrietum alpestre" of Gjaerevoll (1956, Table 17) and twenty-five species in common with his Cryptogrammetum (loc. cit. Table 18). Snow regime and soils also appear to be similar. Nordhagen (1927-28) describes a distinct podsol profile from Athyrietum in Sylene.

Knaben (1950) emphasises the importance of ferns in the vegetation of mid-west Norway both in sub-alpine woods and scrub and in the low-alpine snow beds. She finds that "the development of fern meadows (*Athyrium* spp., *Dryopteris* spp., *Thelypteris* spp., etc.) depends on precipitation and moisture" and that within her study area of the Middle Sogn, "they concentrate in the districts with the highest precipitation".

PLATE 90

Tall herb association, Caenlochan Glen, Angus, 854 m. This luxuriant vegetation occurs on an ungrazed cliff ledge and includes *Angelica sylvestris, Cirsium heterophyllum, Trollius europaeus, Sedum rosea, Valeriana officinalis, Luzula sylvatica, Filipendula ulmaria, Rubus saxatilis, Geranium sanguineum* and *Polystichum lonchitis*. Some ledges on the same cliff have montane willow scrub.

PLATE 91. Fern community, Beinn Bhan, Applecross, Wester Ross, 732 m. The dominant fern on this ungrazed "ledge" of Torridon Sandstone cliff (c. 300 × 50 m.), is *Athyrium alpestre* but *Dryopteris abbreviata* and *D. dilatata* are also abundant. Where the soil is irrigated by seepage lines the fern, or *Vaccinium—Luzula* communities are replaced by broad strips of tall herb vegetation, one of which can be seen in the middle of the bed of ferns.

Dwarf Herb association. While the meadow communities dealt with so far have a relatively luxuriant growth the remainder contrast with them in dwarfness of stature, the herbs forming a dense low sward. The first of these can most conveniently be identified as the dwarf herb association since none of the many species of herbs present is in outstanding abundance. This is a floristically rich vegetation with nine constants (Table 61) and an average of thirty-nine species per stand. *Silene acaulis* is the most frequent dominant and forms a discontinuous carpet in which its associates are rooted. Grasses and other small herbs are usually abundant and together they may replace *Silene* entirely. *Cherleria sedoides* is often plentiful and may replace *Silene* as the carpet former. Bryophytes are numerous but, apart from *Rhacomitrium lanuginosum* and *R. canescens*, usually have a low cover. *Sagina saginoides* and *Myosotis alpestris* are exclusive and *Cerastium alpinum* is selective or preferential for the association. Montane species in general are particularly well represented and some are rarities otherwise confined to rock ledges.

The dwarf herb association is similar to many stands of species-rich *Rhacomitrium* heath and differs mainly in the lesser abundance of *Rhacomitrium* and the greater variety of other mosses. It is also closely related to the *Deschampsia cespitosa—Rhytidiadelphus loreus* association, but this has a higher cover of hypnaceous mosses. Another dwarf herb community which often occurs in close proximity to the present one in Breadalbane is distinguished by the dominance of *Alchemilla vulgaris* agg. This could probably rank as a distinct association but insufficient data are available.

The dwarf herb association has a widespread western distribution north of the Highland line but is confined to calcareous rocks throughout its range. Although present on all the rich mica-schist hills of Breadalbane it is represented by only one or two small patches on the equally calcareous rocks of Caenlochan and Clova. In the Ben Nevis and Ben Alder massifs there are fine examples on Dalradian limestone while all occurrences north of the Great Glen are on lime-bearing rocks of the Moine and Lewisian series. In some of the northern localities the associated rock appears to be less calcareous than is usual in the south.

The association is distinctly montane with an altitudinal range of 710–1050 m. and does not occur on calcareous rocks at lower levels, e.g. in the Glen Tilt area. Stands may be sited almost anywhere on stable ground regardless of aspect and slope provided there is good drainage accompanied by intermittent irrigation. Steep ground below cliffs is the usual situation but stands often occur on gently inclined summit slopes.

The soils are fertile brown loams of high base status (pH 4·8–5·8) with, or without, some surface accumulation of mull humus and they commonly contain earthworms. Some sites are enriched by the downwash of mineral particles or by the gravitational addition of material from disintegrating rock and unstable banks.

Stands vary in size from a few square metres to several hundred square metres. The largest ones occur on hills where there are extensive areas of highly calcareous rock, as on the upper south-east slopes of Ben Lawers. On some Breadalbane hills the total area occupied by dwarf herb vegetation amounts to many hectares.

Snow cover is moderate on most sites but its significance for the distribution of the association has not been studied. Some other factor would appear to lie at the root of the western bias in distribution and it may be that the greater rainfall of the west leads to more frequent irrigation than in the drier east. Since calcareous rocks are much scarcer in the east a lack of suitable parent materials for the soils may also be partly responsible for the biased distribution.

The dwarf herb association is the high level equivalent of species-rich and sub-montane *Agrostis—Festuca* grasslands (p. 189); edaphic conditions show close similarity and there is a good deal of floristic overlap. Like the grasslands the dwarf herb vegetation may have been produced by heavy grazing in some places. A few stands contain tall herbs which have been dwarfed by grazing so that there are affinities with the tall herb association also. Where there is a little *Dryas* in the turf and this species is plentiful on adjacent cliff faces the dwarf herb association is almost certainly a biotic derivative of *Dryas* heath, except where there is also evidence of late snow-lie. Nevertheless, the *Silene* carpets give an impression of complete "naturalness" in many places, especially on the high tops, and many seem to be climatically controlled. Moreover, the association shows great similarity to certain rock face communities, not subject to repeated grazing, in which banks of *Silene* are conspicuous and in which there is a mixed growth of small herbs and mosses.

On steep slopes facing to the north and east the dwarf herb association often passes into *Deschampsia cespitosa* grassland, evidently in response to a change in irrigation and snow cover. On the gentler inclines of high watersheds and summits it often merges imperceptibly into species-rich *Rhacomitrium* heath or the *Deschampsia cespitosa— Rhytidiadelphus loreus* association. Where stands occur amongst species-poor *Rhaco- mitrium* heath they usually mark the site of an intermittent spring.

The dwarf herb community dominated by species of the *Alchemilla vulgaris* aggregate is a more local type and usually occupies more strongly irrigated sites alongside stands of the present association. The relationships between the two have also been discussed by Poore (1955), the dwarf herb association being based upon Poore's *Sibbaldia procumbens* nodum.

Alchemilla alpina—Sibbaldia procumbens association. The constants of this association are *Agrostis tenuis, Deschampsia cespitosa, Alchemilla alpina* and *Sibbaldia procumbens. Alchemilla* and *Sibbaldia* are the usual dominants but grasses may be abundant and moss cover, mainly of *Rhacomitrium* spp., is high. There are no characteristic species.

The *Alchemilla—Sibbaldia* association differs from the last in its lack of *Silene acaulis* and many other species of herbs and mosses. The average number of species per stand is lower (22).

A closely related type of vegetation, dominated by *Alchemilla alpina*, is distinguished by an abundance of *Potentilla erecta* instead of *Sibbaldia procumbens* and a still more restricted list of species (an average total of 16). Intermediates do occur. Some stands of the *Rhacomitrium*-rich—*Dicranum starkei* association (p. 529) contain abundant

Sibbaldia but they differ from the present association in the greater abundance of chionophilous species and the higher cover of mosses.

The geographical distribution is rather similar to that of the last association but it is more widespread in the east, probably because its dependence on snow cover, rather than soil base status, gives it an important niche in the Cairngorms. Like the dwarf herb association it depends on intermittent irrigation but, more particularly, on irrigation by meltwater or permanent springs issuing from late snow beds. The stands are usually situated in hollows and corries which hold snow readily, and a north to east aspect is particularly favoured. The position of a moderately late snow cornice around the steep rim of a corrie is sometimes marked by an interrupted band of *Alchemilla—Sibbaldia* patches. Stands may also occur in the floor of the corries below, or on the summit slopes above, so that the overall altitudinal range varies from 640 to 1068 m. Individual stands seldom exceed 100 sq. m. in area and are usually much less.

In the west this type of vegetation occurs on all but the poorest rocks whereas in the east it is found chiefly on calcareous substrata. Although stands occur most frequently on soils with some lime the soils tend to show incipient podsolisation, sometimes with mottling of the **B** horizon. There is usually a surface humus layer but profiles vary greatly, some being shallow peats up to 24 cm. deep passing quickly to rock debris whereas others are silty or sandy loams with only a few centimetres of surface humus. The pH of the surface soil lies in the range 4·8–5·4.

The *Alchemilla—Sibbaldia* association usually occurs among other late snow communities and may be irrigated by melt water from sites with chionophilous Nardeta or the moss-dominated associations of the latest snow beds. The *Rhacomitrium*-rich—*Dicranum starkei* association is often in close proximity but appears to be differentiated from the *Alchemilla—Sibbaldia* patches by drier soil and a longer snow cover.

The *Alchemilla—Potentilla* communities belong chiefly to the western Highlands but although they also depend on intermittent irrigation this does not come so often from melting snow. Stands may occupy sites exactly equivalent to those of the *Alchemilla—Sibbaldia* association but more often they are found below intermittent springs or solifluction lobes. The widespread occurrence of *Alchemilla—Potentilla* vegetation on non-calcareous rocks such as Torridon sandstone and Moine granulite suggests that low soil-calcium status is responsible for the floristic differentiation from *Alchemilla—Sibbaldia* vegetation. On the whole, *Sibbaldia* is a reliable indicator of soils which have a rather higher calcium status than those formed from the poorest rocks.

Typical *Alchemilla—Sibbaldia* vegetation is confined to the Highlands but in the English Lake District there are equivalents of the *Alchemilla—Potentilla* communities of the west Highlands.

In floristics and habitat the association can be compared with the "Alchemilletum alpinae" of Rondane (Dahl, 1956, p. 184) and either the "Sibbaldietum procumbentis" or the "*Alchemilla alpina* sociation" of the "Anthoxantho—Deschampsietum flexuosae" (Gjaerevoll, 1956, pp. 53, 177). The first two Norwegian associations occur in sites resembling those of irrigated stands of the *Alchemilla—Sibbaldia* association while the third is closer in habitat to the snow cornice stands mentioned above.

Saxifraga aizoides **association**. There are twelve constants in this association and *Saxifraga aizoides* is the usual dominant, although *S. oppositifolia* may occasionally be co-dominant. *Cystopteris montana* is exclusive. In a closely related, but less hydrophytic type of vegetation, *S. aizoides* more frequently shares dominance with *S. oppositifolia* as well as with *S. hypnoides* and hypnaceous mosses.

The association is confined to cliff faces, steep banks at the base of cliffs or other steep, rocky ground. It has been found only on calcareous mountains and mainly on those lying between Breadalbane and Clova. Ferreira (1958) has described the same type of vegetation on Ben Hope, Ben Lui and elsewhere and believes that it is a more reliable indicator of highly calcareous rocks than any other community.

A copious seepage of water down the rock face is as essential as the high lime content of the rock. The association occurs most often on north-facing cliffs since these tend to be the wettest but it has been found on sites of all aspects. The altitudinal range is from 564 to 793 m. The necessary habitat conditions occur over limited areas only, so that the largest continuous stands are not usually more than 20 sq. m. Where this vegetation occurs on steep banks there is usually a moderate depth, up to 30 cm., of wet, silty soil containing variable amounts of humus. Some sites show a definite accumulation of mull humus. On cliff faces the vegetation may overlie the rock surface almost directly with hardly any soil between.

Mixed saxifrage communities also occur on steep, earthy banks at the base of calcareous cliffs but they are drier than the typical *Saxifraga aizoides* association and tend to be found at higher elevations. Sometimes these stands appear to be intermediate between the present association and the dwarf herb association. Both types of vegetation show transitions to various open rock face communities and, on the cliffs of Ben Lui, the *Saxifraga aizoides* association passes into *Dryas* heath as the flow of water fails. There are other transitions to the tall herb association on more stable ledges and to heavily grazed, saxifrage grassland on the slopes below.

Small fragments of a similar *S. aizoides* vegetation occur on a few calcareous crags in the English Lake District but the association otherwise seems to be confined to the Highlands.

The equivalent Norwegian associations are not found on such steep ground and they experience a deep winter snow cover. They are the "species-rich *Saxifraga* association" of Sylene (Nordhagen, 1927–28, p. 352) and the "Oppositifolietum" (Gjaerevoll, 1956, p. 303) which is dominated by *Saxifraga oppositifolia* rather than *S. aizoides*.

REFERENCES

DAHL, E.   1956   *Rondane: mountain vegetation in south Norway and its relation to the environment.* Oslo.

FERREIRA, R. E. C.   1958   *A comparative ecological and floristic study of the vegetation of Ben Hope, Ben Loyal, Ben Lui and Glas Maol in relation to the geology.* Ph.D. Thesis, University of Aberdeen.

GJAEREVOLL, O.   1956   *The plant communities of the Scandinavian alpine snow beds.*
                             Trondheim.

KNABEN, G.   1950   *Botanical investigation in the middle districts of western Norway.*
                             Bergen.

LEACH, W.   1930   A preliminary account of the vegetation of some non-
                             calcareous British screes. *J. Ecol.*, **18**, 321–332.

NORDHAGEN, R.   1927–28   *Die Vegetation und Flora des Sylenegebeites.* Oslo.

                      1943   *Sikilsdalen og Norges Fjellbeiter.* Bergen.

PIGOTT, C. D.   1956   The vegetation of Upper Teesdale in the north Pennines. *J.
                             Ecol.*, **44**, 545–586.

POORE, M. E. D.   1954   *Phytosociology of the Breadalbane district of Perthshire.* Ph.D.
                             Thesis, University of Cambridge.

                      1955   The use of phytosociological methods in ecological investiga-
                             tions. III. Practical applications. *J. Ecol.*, **43**, 606–651.

TABLE 61

Montane herb and fern meadows

Association No.	(1)		(2)		(3)		(4)		(5)	
Average number of species	47		31		39		22		47	
Number of stands	22		10		20		12		9	
Plot area (sq. m.)	4–16		4		4		1–4		4	
Altitude (m.)	450–840		710–1050		690–1170		630–990		540–780	
Aspect (degrees)	Various		0–135		Various		Various		Various	
Slope (degrees)	35–80		0–50		0–40		2–20		25–70	
Soil	Brown earth		Skeletal		Brown earth		Incip. podsol		Skeletal	
pH	4·8–5·4		4·1		4·8–5·8		4·8–5·4		6·8–7·4	
Cover (%)	100		50–100		80–100		75–100		100	
Height of vegetation (cm.)	20–60		8–35		2–10		1–6		...	
Rubus saxatilis	6	1	...		...		...		...	
Vaccinium myrtillus	8	2	4	+	2	+	3	1	...	
Athyrium alpestre	1	+	9	4	...		...		...	
Cryptogramma crispa	...		8	5	...		...		...	
Selaginella selaginoides	4	+	...		9	2	2	+	9	2
Agrostis canina	5	1	...		3	1	3	1	1	+
A. tenuis	3	1	4	1	9	3	10	2	5	1
Anthoxanthum odoratum	5	1	2	1	4	1	1	+	8	2
Deschampsia cespitosa	9	3	8	2	9	3	10	3	10	3
D. flexuosa	4	1	9	2	1	+	3	1	1	+
Festuca ovina	7	2	2	+	10	4	6	1	9	2
F. rubra	2	1	...		2	1	1	+	10	4
Nardus stricta	2	+	6	1	6	2	7	2	2	1
Carex bigelowii	2	+	6	1	6	2	6	1	...	
Luzula spicata	...		2	+	6	1	2	+	1	+
L. sylvatica	10	4	...		1	+	...		5	1
Alchemilla alpina	6	1	9	2	10	4	10	4	7	2
A. glabra	6	2	...		1	+	...		9	3
Angelica sylvestris	9	3	...		1	+	...		3	1
Cherleria sedoides	...		...		6	2	...		...	
Galium saxatile	3	1	10	2	5	1	6	2	5	+
Geranium sylvaticum	6	2	...		...		...		4	+
Geum rivale	9	3	...		1	+	...		7	1
Gnaphalium supinum	...		...		3	+	7	2	...	
Heraclium sphondylium	3	1	...		...		...		...	
Parnassia palustris	...		...		...		...		9	2
Pinguicula vulgaris	...		...		1	+	...		9	1
Polygonum viviparum	2	+	...		6	2	2	1	10	2
Ranunculus acris	5	1	...		4	1	...		9	2
Saussurea alpina	5	2	...		1	+	...		...	
Saxifraga aizoides	2	+	...		2	+	...		10	7
S. oppositifolia	1	+	...		3	1	...		9	2
Sedum rosea	10	3	...		2	+	...		3	+
Sibbaldia procumbens	...		2	+	8	2	10	4	...	

TABLE 61—*continued*

Association No.	(1)		(2)		(3)		(4)		(5)	
Succisa pratensis . . .	6	2	1	+	2	+	...		2	+
Silene acaulis . . .	...		...		8	4	1	+	...	
Thalictrum alpinum . .	3	1	...		7	1	...		6	1
Thymus drucei . . .	3	1	...		9	3	5	2	8	2
Trollius europaeus . .	6	2	...		1	+	...		...	
Acrocladium cuspidatum .	3	+	...		...		...		6	1
Bryum pseudotriquetrum .	...		...		1	+	...		7	1
Cratoneuron commutatum .	...		...		...		...		6	2
Ctenidium molluscum . .	6	1	...		4	1	1	+	9	2
Fissidens adianthoides . .	1	+	...		...		...		6	1
Hylocomium splendens . .	9	3	6	2	6	2	3	+	7	1
Hypnum callichroum .	1	+	8	3	...		...		1	+
Leptodontium recurvifolium .	1	+	...		...		...		...	
Polytrichum alpinum . .	2	+	8	3	8	2	6	1	1	+
Rhacomitrium lanuginosum .	1	+	4	1	5	2	6	2	1	+
Rhytidiadelphus loreus . .	8	2	8	3	4	1	3	1	2	1
R. squarrosus . . .	7	2	5	1	5	1	2	+	2	+
R. triquetrus . . .	8	2	...		2	+	...		8	2
Thuidium tamariscinum .	8	3	...		1	+	1	1	4	1
Barbilophozia floerkii . .	...		9	3	...		2	1	...	
Plagiochila asplenioides . .	4	1	...		1	+	...		5	1
Cladonia bellidiflora . .	...		8	1	...		1	+	...	

(1) Tall herb association.
(2) *Cryptogramma crispa—Athyrium alpestre* association.
(3) Dwarf herb association.
(4) *Alchemilla alpina—Sibbaldia procumbens* association.
(5) *Saxifraga aizoides* association.

CHAPTER 14

MOSS HEATHS

D. N. McVEAN

Moss-dominated vegetation is characteristic of oceanic climates throughout the world and is well represented in Scotland in the low and middle alpine zones above 610 m. The accompanying vascular plants may be either grasses or dwarf shrubs, according to the altitude and the length of snow-lie.

Heaths dominated by the moss *Rhacomitrium lanuginosum* are one of the most prominent features of Scottish mountain vegetation and there are numerous references to them in the literature from R. Smith (1900) to the present day. *Rhacomitrium* heath represents the chionophobous end of the moss heath series at the other end of which lie the substantially smaller areas of bryophyte-dominated vegetation of late snow beds or "schneetälchen", which are found in oceanic and continental climates alike.

Species-poor *Rhacomitrium* heath association (Cariceto—Rhacomitretum lanuginosi). This is essentially the species-impoverished *Rhacomitrium* heath of Poore (1955) and the *Rhacomitrium—Carex bigelowii* nodum of Poore and McVean (1957) with the atypical facies omitted.

A wide range of floristic lists is available from all parts of the Highlands and in the eleven that have been summarised in Table 62 (p. 534) there are six constants *Rhacomitrium lanuginosum* is always the physiognomic dominant but *Carex bigelowii*, *Deschampsia flexuosa* and *Armeria maritima* may attain co-dominance locally (Plate 92). There are no characteristic species. The species list is almost as restricted as that of the *Dicranum fuscescens—Carex bigelowii* association (p. 506).

Separate facies have not been recognised but a variant, rich in *Juncus trifidus*, should be mentioned. This differs from *Rhacomitrium—Empetrum* heath containing *J. trifidus* only in the absence of *Empetrum* itself but, in practice, it is exceptional to encounter intermediate stands. This variant has been seen forming a zone between the *Juncus trifidus—Festuca ovina* association and the *Rhacomitrium—Nardus* association on both Beinn Eighe and Ben More Assynt. Another variant differs only in having an abundance of cushion herbs, which may be *Silene acaulis, Cherleria sedoides, Armeria maritima,* or all three together.

Typical *Rhacomitrium* heath has been recorded from most parts of the Highlands with the most extensive stands on Creag Meagaidh, the Drumochter hills and Ben Wyvis, where it occupies many square kilometres of summit ridges and plateaux. The cushion herb variant is equally extensive on high ground in the west-central and north-west Highlands, particularly in Fannich Forest and the Beinn Dearg group. It descends to a little under 610 m. and extends to the highest summits at 1159 m. in the west and north-west. In the central Highlands the *Rhacomitrium* heaths are not found much below 914 m. and probably the highest extensive stand lies at 1190 m. in the Ben Nevis range, while small stands extend to over 1220 m. in the Cairngorms wherever there is a little shelter from the prevailing winds without deep winter snow cover. On the east side of the Cairngorms the lower limit lies about 100 to 250 m. higher than on the exposed western spurs.

The ground is level or gently sloping as a rule and there is no restriction to any particular aspect. Steeper ground is usually terraced, and an eroded form of heath, richer in species, passes to *J. trifidus—F. ovina* stands on the terrace flats.

Where dwarf shrub or grass heaths pass over to the *Rhacomitrium* heath association the transition generally takes place through a mosaic ecotone. This is beautifully illustrated on Ben Wyvis and in the Dalnaspidal Forest. The transition to the *J. trifidus—F. ovina* association is often abrupt, in this case along an eroding edge. Gradual transitions take place to the species-rich *Rhacomitrium* heath on some hills in the west Highlands. Increasing depth of snow accumulation and increasing wetness of soil lead to replacement of *Rhacomitrium* heath by *Nardus* patches, the *Dicranum fuscescens—Carex bigelowii* association, the *Deschampsia cespitosa—Rhytidiadelphus loreus* association, *Trichophorum* or *Juncus squarrosus* bogs and the *Eriophorum* bog association.

An interesting variant can be seen at 1220 m. on the summit of Aonach Mor near Ben Nevis. Over an area of some tens of square metres *Rhacomitrium lanuginosum* is replaced by *R. canescens*, apparently because of frequent additions of wind blown sand from a neighbouring erosion surface. This is a frequent occurrence on a smaller scale around the margins of "blow outs" in *Rhacomitrium* heath and *Alchemilla alpina* is another frequent species of these areas, although it may be absent from the surrounding heath. The soil profiles at the Aonach Mor site confirmed that fresh sand is continually being added.

R. canescens is often the dominant species in Icelandic moss heaths (McVean, 1955, p. 333) and in the moss mat of Jan Mayen (Warren Wilson, 1952).

Since moss heath is a characteristic oceanic formation and lichen heath an equally characteristic continental one any juxtaposition of the two is of considerable interest. On the ridge of Carn Ban Mor, a western spur of the Cairngorms, *Calluna*—lichen heath passes to *Rhacomitrium* heath at 914 m. Little difference in habitat can be detected for the lichen heath patches in the moss heath but the moss patches in the lichen heath usually occupy damp hollows, sometimes with distinct water seepage. The constituents of the two associations do not mingle to any extent. Fifteen miles to the south-east, the summit ridge of Carn a'Gheoidh and Carn nan Sac in the Cairnwell hills is remarkable for the extent of a lichen-rich *Rhacomitrium* heath which has also been seen in small patches elsewhere. True lichen heath can also be seen occupying sheltered hollows in the *Rhacomitrium* heath of Carn nan Sac, a curious reversal of the usual situation.

In Continental Norway, *Rhacomitrium* heath has been found occupying small depressions, or localities with slightly impeded drainage, and apparently depending upon some supply of soil water (Nordhagen, 1943, p. 205 and Dahl, 1956, p. 101).

Soils are either shallow rankers or there is an incipient, or well developed, podsol. The floristically poorest heaths are frequently found on a few centimetres of un-decomposed moss and humus over siliceous rock debris. The wet moss peat may also be found resting directly on stony brown loams over more basic, but still non-calcareous, rock which appear to be more fertile but which have little effect on the floristics of the vegetation. Gleyed and mottled profiles have never been observed and the pH of the surface humus varies from 4·2 to 4·8.

The similarity of *Rhacomitrium* heaths in Britain, Scandinavia, Iceland and the Faeroes has been established by many authors. The "Rhacomitreto—Caricetum bigelowii" of Rondane (Dahl, 1956, Table 18) has twenty species and two constants in common with the Scottish association. In general, the Icelandic and Scandinavian heaths have a eutrophic floristic element found only in Scottish species-rich heaths (see below). The quantities of *Silene acaulis*, *Cherleria sedoides* and *Armeria maritima* present in the Scottish species-poor heaths increase with distance north and west, quite irrespective of the base status of the parent material of the soil.

Species-rich *Rhacomitrium* heath association (Polygoneto—Rhacomitretum lanuginosi). The species-rich heath has twelve constants (Table 62) and four species—*Deschampsia flexuosa*, *Cherleria sedoides*, *Salix herbacea* and *Silene acaulis*—may reach co-dominance with the *Rhacomitrium*. *Plagiothecium striatellum*, *Aulacomnium turgidum* and *Hypnum hamulosum* are strongly selective for the association. The rare foliose lichen, *Nephromium arcticum*, has been recorded from stands of this association but it does not appear in Table 62.

Species numbers per stand range from 20 to 48, so that there is no overlap with the species numbers of the species-poor heath and intermediate stands are surprisingly rare, although there is a physiognomic similarity between this association and the cushion herb variant of the last.

The species-rich heath is also distinguished floristically from the species-poor one by the presence of *Polygonum viviparum*, *Thymus drucei* and *Aulacomnium turgidum* as well as by the occurrence of a wide variety of species of lower constancy. Other species, such as *Sphaerophorus globosus*, are more often present in the one than in the other. The principal distinction from the dwarf herb association is the dominance of *R. lanuginosum* instead of hypnaceous mosses, but intermediates can be found where the dwarf herb vegetation occupies intermittently irrigated channels through the rich moss heath. The species-rich *Agrostis—Festuca* grasslands are separated by the replacement of moss as dominants by grass.

The species-rich heath is a distinctly northern type with outliers in west Perthshire, and it tends to follow the general increase of *Silene, Cherleria* and *Armeria* in moss heath towards the north and west which has been remarked upon above. The restriction of the association to outcrops of Cambrian dolomite pointed out by Poore and McVean (1957) cannot now be maintained, since rich heath has been recorded from a wide-variety of lime-rich rocks in the northern Highlands and from the calcareous schists of Perthshire. The contrast between poor moss heath on quartzite and rich heath on the dolomitic mudstone of Beinn Eighe, Foinaven and elsewhere remains the most striking feature of such vegetation.

The altitudinal range of the rich moss heath is more restricted than that of the species-rich heath, from 763 m. to just over 914 m., although the terrain on which the two heaths are developed is similar. Slopes are generally steeper and more exposed so that there is a greater tendency to incomplete plant cover and liability to solifluction. The stands of species-rich heath are less extensive and tend to lack homogeneity in the larger examples. Nevertheless, they can vary in size from patches of a few square metres to areas of many hectares where situation and soil allow.

The soil profile may be almost completely undifferentiated as on dolomitic mudstone, or may show signs of distinct podsolisation with, or without, some mottling of the **B** horizon. The pH values of the surface soil vary from 4·6 to 5·9 so that there is little overlap with values from the species-poor heath. The processes counteracting the leaching of nutrients appear to be intermittent irrigation, to a lesser extent than in the dwarf herb association, or the stirring of the soil by frost movement. On some of the high-lying mudstone outcrops, periodic soil flows take place with gradual recolonisation of the exposed surface. The pH of one mudstone soil flow was found to be 7·1 in contrast to 5·9 under the adjacent mat of unbroken moss heath.

At 793 m. on Sgurr na Feartaig in west Ross-shire species-rich *Rhacomitrium* heath occurs in a mosaic with *Empetrum—Rhacomitrium* heath on irregular stone polygons, the species-rich heath occupying the fine materials between the lines of stones. The commonest transitions are to species-poor heath, the *Deschampsia cespitosa—Rhytidiadelphus loreus* association, or to the *Juncus trifidus—Festuca ovina* association on erosion surface.

The species-rich *Rhacomitrium* heath association was first described as the *Polygonum viviparum—Salix herbacea* facies of the *Rhacomitrium—Carex bigelowii* nodum (Poore and McVean, 1957).

While the Icelandic and Faeroese *Rhacomitrium* heaths bear a closer resemblance to this association than to the species-poor heaths, those of Norway are insufficiently described for it to be possible to decide if they cover as wide a range of floristics as the two Scottish moss heaths. The "Hygro—Festucetum ovinae" of Rondane (Dahl, 1956) is quite close, floristically, to Scottish rich heath (they have forty-five species in common) and in its relationship to snow-lie and soil enrichment; but *Rhacomitrium lanuginosum* is only sparsely present in it. None of the other *Festuca ovina* associations of Norway have this close resemblance except perhaps the "moss-rich *F. ovina* association" of Nordhagen (1927–28).

***Deschampsia cespitosa—Rhytidiadelphus loreus* association** (Deschampsi-
eto—Rhytidiadelphetum). Increasing snow cover on moss heaths leads to vegetation
dominated by hypnaceous mosses. There are five constants of this association (Table 62)
and the physiognomic dominants are all mosses: *Rhytidiadelphus loreus*, *R. squarrosus*,
R. triquetrus and *Pleurozium schreberi*. *Deschampsiu cespitosa* and *Carex bigelowii* may
sometimes attain co-dominance with one of the mosses. There are no characteristic
species.

Two facies have been recognised, the typical, species-poor variety with six constants
and a rarer, species-rich one with twelve constants. Although there may be some overlap
in the species numbers of the two facies many good differentials such as *R. triquetrus*,
Silene acaulis and *Ranunculus acris* separate them.

The present association is distinguished floristically from *Rhacomitrium* heaths by
the change in dominant mosses and from the more closely related alpine *Deschampsia
cespitosa* association by the substitution of mosses for grasses as the dominant (p. 524).

The distribution of the association (both facies) is distinctly western with only
fragmentary stands developed east of Creag Meagaidh and Ben Heasgarnich in the
central Highlands. With the exception of an extensive area of the species-rich facies in
Coire Heasgarnich it is a local type of vegetation south of the Great Glen and it can be
regarded as the northern Highland equivalent of the *Dicranum fuscescens—Carex
bigelowii* association, so far as snow-lie is concerned.

Stands may be only a few square metres in area where they occur in the damper
hollows of *Rhacomitrium* heath, or they may extend over many hectares as a zone
surrounding late snow bed vegetation. The transition from *Rhacomitrium* to hypnaceous
moss heath may be gradual or abrupt according to change in slope of the ground in
relation to snow-lie and moisture regime. On some summits, such as that of Fionn
Bheinn near Achnasheen, extensive soil-hummock systems show a mosaic pattern of
these two associations, with *Rhacomitrium* heath occupying the exposed hummock tops
and *Rhytidiadelphus* heath the sheltered hollows between. The relationships with the
Polytrichum alpinum—Carex bigelowii association and the low alpine *Nardus* associations
are not clear; the hypnaceous moss heath may occasionally be found as a zone around
one of the others, separating them from chionophobous vegetation. In large corries the
hypnaceous moss heaths pass gradually to *Deschampsia cespitosa* grasslands with decrease
in altitude, and the transition is never abrupt.

The association ranges altitudinally from 702 m. in the extreme north to a maximum
of 1068 m. in the central Highlands. Slopes are generally moderate to steep with a
northerly or easterly aspect.

On Ben Lawers, vegetation intermediate in some respects between the present
association and the *P. alpinum—C. bigelowii* association is quite abundant. This has been
described on p. 505 as the Ben Lawers facies of the latter.

Soils are well developed podsols with strongly gleyed **B** horizons, mostly under the
typical facies, or deep sandy loams with little profile development except for traces of
mottling below, mostly under the species-rich facies. The typical facies has also been seen

occupying deep, redistributed peat on Sgurr a'Ghlas Leathaid, Ross-shire. The pH of the surface soil varies from 4·1 to 4·9 (typical) and from 4·5 to 5·4 (species-rich).

The association was first described as the *Rhytidiadelphus—Deschampsia cespitosa* nodum and the hypnoid moss facies of the *Rhacomitrium—Carex bigelowii* nodum (Poore and McVean, 1957, p. 429).

Hylocomium splendens may be an important constituent, or even dominant, in Icelandic moss heaths (McVean, 1955, p. 333) but *Rhytidiadelphus* spp. seem to be absent. The corresponding vegetation in Scandinavia appears to be the "Ranunculetum acris acidophilum" of Gjaerevoll (1956), a series of "hydrophilous low-herb meadows poor in calciphile species". There are twenty-nine species and three constants *Sibbaldia procumbens*, *R. acris* and *Polygonum viviparum* common to the *Ranunculus acris— Anthoxanthum odoratum* sociation of the Ranunculetum and the Scottish association.

Late snow bed heaths. The moss-dominated vegetation of late snow areas or "schneetälchen" have proved rather troublesome to classify floristically. To some extent the situation resembles that of the tall herb ledge vegetation where we find a complex that can only be referred to an entire Continental alliance. More data on the snow bed areas is available, however, and by rejecting many analyses that appear to have been made in intermediate stands, three separate associations can be recognised. These three floristic groups can be shown to possess distinct habitat preferences and different geographical distributions.

The first of these, the **Polytrichum norvegicum—Dicranum starkei** association, has six constants (Table 62). *Dicranum starkei* is the usual dominant but other species such as *D. falcatum*, *Pohlia ludwigii*, *Barbilophozia floerkii* and *Gymnomitrium concinnatum* may take over or be co-dominant. *D. falcatum* is exclusive to the association.

Species numbers per stand range from 12 to 26 with an average of 19 while a total of sixty-four species was recorded from the ten lists. In making these lists, areas with some variety of both vascular plants and cryptogams were chosen. Where snow lies particularly late *D. starkei* may form an almost pure carpet.

This is the most widely distributed of the late snow bed group and it is found in all the principal mountain areas of the Highlands. Only fragmentary stands are to be seen north of Beinn Dearg in Ross-shire.

The **Rhacomitrium-rich—Dicranum starkei** association has a closely similar range of six constants (Table 62). No single species stands out as the principal dominant and *Gnaphalium supinum*, *Sibbaldia procumbens*, *Dicranum starkei*, *Rhacomitrium canescens*, *R. fasciculare* and *R. heterostichum* can each be dominant or co-dominant from time to time. *Gnaphalium supinum* is preferential for the association (Plate 93).

The species list is longer than that of the previous association; there are seventy-one species on record from nine lists and numbers range from 14 to 30 with an average of 22.

This association does not extend so far to the south as the previous one but, within the central and northern Highlands, it is the more widely distributed of the two.

The third schneetälchen association, the **Gymnomitrium concinnatum—Salix**

2 L

herbacea **association** (Plate 94) could also have been considered along with the dwarf shrub heaths but it is more convenient to deal with it here for the sake of floristic and other comparisons.

There are seven constants and the usual dominants are *Salix herbacea* and/or *Gymnomitrium concinnatum*, while *Dicranum starkei* and *Rhacomitrium fasciculare* may occasionally become co-dominant. A number of species, all of low constancy, are exclusive to the association:—*Ochrolechia geminipara, Gymnomitrium varians, G. alpinum, Luzula arcuata, Diplophyllum taxifolium* and *Lecidea alpestris. Solorina crocea* appears only in this association and in the *Juncus trifidus—Festuca ovina* association. There is a variant in which *Gymnomitrium varians* replaces *G. concinnatum* and becomes completely dominant. Species numbers and averages are almost exactly the same as in *Rhacomitrium—Dicranum starkei* association.

Stands of the present association are not found north of the Achnashellach Forest in Ross-shire, but they have a more general distribution than stands of the other two associations in the south-west Highlands.

All three late snow bed associations have a similar altitudinal range from just under 900 m. to about 1220 m. The *Gymnomitrium—Salix herbacea* heath is largely indifferent to aspect and occupies gentle to moderate slopes, while the other two are confined to steeper slopes of northerly and easterly aspect. Vegetation cover is more often complete in the last association.

The edaphic situation is confusing and only general tendencies can be indicated at this stage. The profile under stands of *Polytrichum norvegicum—Dicranium starkei* generally shows incipient podsolisation with marked surface humus accumulation and sometimes traces of mottling in the **B** horizon. Buried humus horizons are quite common. Under stands of *Rhacomitrium—Dicranum starkei*, mottling and the occurrence of buried horizons are more frequent, and there is less accumulation of surface humus. *Gymn-mitrium—Salix herbacea* stands have undifferentiated soils or incipient podsols without banding or mottling.

Other observations on the stand habitats are mostly in keeping with soil characteristics although there are a few anomalies. The *Polytrichum norvegicum—Dicranum starkei* association favours situations that are relatively stable and not liable to solifluction or the downwash of sand or gravel, while the *Rhacomitrium—D. starkei* association is generally to be found where there is intermittent irrigation by melt water and rain water and where downwash may completely bury the vegetation from time to time. The surface of *Gymnomitrium—Salix herbacea* stands indicates a continually high water content with considerable amorphous solifluction taking place either on exposed ground or areas of deep snow accumulation.

Stands of all three associations may be found together in a large snow bed, each occupying the appropriate habitat as described above, or they may occur in an intimate mosaic with little apparent relation to topography. Much Scottish snow bed vegetation consists of intermediate stands which defy classification and it is obvious that this is the result of habitat instability.

Apart from the general climatic shift, which seems to be causing a withdrawal of snow bed vegetation everywhere, there are great variations in depth and length of snow-lie in the Scottish Highlands from year to year. Individual plants may be killed by frost at a time when they would normally experience a deep snow cover and others may be damaged or killed by unusually prolonged snow-lie in spring. The winter of 1961–62 was remarkable for the extent to which *Calluna vulgaris* suffered both from frosting and prolonged snow cover.

The abundance of melt water produced at any time of the year from the larger snow fields, combined with frequent heavy rain storms, disrupts the feeble vegetation cover of such areas and causes much erosion and deposition. This is particularly well seen on parts of the Cairngorm plateau.

Another factor of importance to all the snow-influenced moss heaths is the deposition of wind-blown plant and mineral debris. This may be found in wind rows over the ground when the snow has disappeared or it may completely bury the vegetation over an area of many square metres so that the mechanical effect must be considerable apart from any nutritional effect of the top dressing (cf. Warren Wilson, 1958).

Poore (1955) reviewed the literature on Scottish snow beds up to that time and he noted that Smith's (1912) Anthelietum "occupies stony localities irrigated by melt water rather than snow beds *per se*". *Anthelia* spp. are frequent constituents of both the *Dicranum starkei* associations but they cannot be regarded as "pioneers" nor can Anthelietum be regarded as standing in successional relationship to Polytrichetum and Salicetum as Tansley (1949) maintained.

In Poore's Table 5 (1955, p. 630) lists 1–5 seem to correspond to the *Gymnomitrium concinnatum—Salix herbacea* association, lists 6 and 7 to the *Polytrichum norvegicum—Dicranum starkei* association and lists 8–11 to the *Rhacomitrium*-rich—*Dicranum starkei* association but his soil data for these lists are not what would have been expected. Here, as in other situations, the Ben Lawers area appears to be somewhat anomalous and difficult to reconcile with the rest of the Highlands.

There is a wealth of Scandinavian literature to compare with the scanty Scottish data. The "Dicranetum starkei" of Rondane (Dahl, 1956, p. 169) has nine species and two constants in common with the Scottish *Polytrichum—D. starkei* association. It occurs in Norway in moist depressions in snow beds of the low-alpine zone and is characteristic of relatively stable ground. The "*Kiaeria (Dicranum) starkei* sociation" of "Polytrichetum norvegici" (Gjaerevoll, 1956, p. 224) is similar and has fifteen species and two constants in common with the Scottish association. Gjaerevoll describes it as occurring in places not subject to irrigation and sedimentation and remarks that it is more abundant in the west of Norway.

The "*Rhacomitrium fasciculare* sociation" of the "Weberetum commutatae acidophilum" occurs in Torne Lappmark and the Sognefjell mountains (Gjaerevoll, 1956, p. 246). It is almost devoid of phanerogams but has nine species and one constant in common with the *Rhacomitrium*-rich—*D. starkei* association. An even better comparison can be made between the "*Gnaphalium supinum—Dicranum starkei* sociation" of the "Salicetum herbaceae" (Gjaerevoll, 1956, p. 129) and the *Rhacomitrium*-rich—*D. starkei* association which have twenty-two species and three constants in common.

While the *R. fasciculare* sociation occurs on stony ground subject to periodic melt water irrigation, the *G. supinum* sociation occupies steep and well drained slopes in the snowfields where it receives seasonal irrigation and sedimentation but dries out quickly in summer.

The "Lophozieto—Salicetum herbaceae" of Rondane (Dahl, 1956, p. 168) has thirty-six species and two constants in common with the *G. concinnatum*—*D. starkei* association. It occupies wet slopes subject to considerable movement, due to amorphous solifluction, and the soil is a sandy humus in which buried humus horizons are frequent. Dahl regards it as a continental type of snow bed vegetation. His (p. 169) "Luzuleto—Cesietum" has more in common with Scottish lists of the *G. concinnatum*—*D. starkei* association from exposed ground. There are eighteen species and one constant common to both lists. The "Luzuleto—Cesietum" is a high-alpine association and the ground may sometimes be without winter snow cover. It is characteristic of the unstable fine soil in the centre of stone polygons.

The "*Salix herbacea—Anthelia juratzkana—Gymnomitrium varians* sociation" of the "Salicetum herbaceae" and the "*Anthelia juratzkana—Gymnomitrium varians* sociation" of the "Anthelietum juratzkanae" of Gjaerevoll (1956, pp. 116, 229) are also related to the *G. concinnatum*—*S. herbacea* association in Scotland and particularly to the *Gymnomitrium varians* facies. Gjaerevoll makes a fundamental distinction between snow bed communities with some vascular plant cover and those with none but, as Dahl found in Rondane, this cannot be maintained in the Scottish Highlands, since vascular plants appear to drop out gradually with increasing duration of snow cover.

Deschampsia flexuosa may be the dominant vascular plant locally in some of the large Cairngorm snowfields but the stands are too fragmentary for analysis. This appears to be the only Scottish representative of a series of *D. flexuosa* sociations of late snow beds on acid soil in Norway.

REFERENCES

DAHL, E.   1956   *Rondane: mountain vegetation in south Norway and its relation to the environment.* Oslo.

GJAEREVOLL, O.   1956   *The plant communities of the Scandinavian alpine snow beds.* Trondheim.

McVEAN, D. N.   1955   Notes on the vegetation of Iceland. *Trans. bot. Soc. Edinb.,* **36**, 320–338.

NORDHAGEN, R.   1927–28   *Die Vegetation und Flora des Sylenegebeites.* Oslo.
                                  1943   *Sikilsdalen og Norges Fjellbeiter.* Bergen.

POORE, M. E. D.   1955   The use of phytosociological methods in ecological investigations. III. Practical applications. *J. Ecol.,* **43**, 606–651.

POORE, M. E. D. and   1957   A new approach to Scottish mountain vegetation. *J. Ecol.,* **45**, 401–439.
   McVEAN, D. N.

PLATE 92

Species-poor *Rhacomitrium* heath association, An Sgulan, Dalnaspidal Forest, Perthshire, 870 m. *R. lanuginosum* covers the ground continuously although the depressions, between the solifluction hummocks and ridges, have a greater abundance of *Carex bigelowii*. When the difference between hummocks and hollows is enhanced the vegetation may assume a striking mosaic pattern.

PLATE 93

Rhacomitrium-rich—*Dicranum starkei* association, Sgurr na Lapaich, Glen Cannich, Easter Ross, 1007 m. A late snow-bed association dominated by the mosses especially *R. canescens* and other species with a sparse representation of vascular plants such as *Gnaphalium supinum*, *Saxifraga stellaris*, *Alchemilla alpina*, *Viola palustris*, *D. cespitosa* and *C. bigelowii*.

PLATE 94

Gymnomitrium concinnatum—Salix herbacea association, Ben Heasgarnich, Perthshire, 1037 m. There is a particularly dense mat of *S. herbacea* but the dark crust of *G. concinnatum* is visible in places. This late snow-bed vegetation has developed on ground subject to amorphous solifluction.

SMITH, R.   1900 Botanical survey of Scotland. II. North Perthshire district. *Scot. geogr. Mag.*, **16**, 441–467.

SMITH, W. G.   1912 *Anthelia:* an arctic-alpine plant association. *Scot. Bot. Rev.*, 1, 81–89.

TANSLEY, A. G.   1949 *The British Islands and their vegetation.* Cambridge.

WILSON, J. WARREN   1952 Vegetation patterns associated with soil movements on Jan Mayen Island. *J. Ecol.*, **40**, 249–264.

                     1958 Dirt on snow patches. *J. Ecol.*, **46**, 191–198.

TABLE 62
Moss heaths

Association No.	(1)	(2)	(3)	(4)	(5)	(6)	(7)
Average number of species	16	35	21	32	19	22	21
Number of stands	11	11	13	7	10	9	9
Plot area (sq. m.)	2–10	4	4	1–4	4	4	4
Altitude (m.)	660–930	720–1050	780–1050	840–960	900–1050	900–1170	900–1080
Aspect (degrees)	Various	Various	0–270	0–270	0–135	0–135	Various
Slope (degrees)	0–25	5–15	3–35	2–40	5–45	10–35	3–20
Soil	Ranker, podsol	Skeletal	Gley podsol	Brown earth	Incip. podsol	Mult. podsol	Skeletal
pH	4·2–4·8	4·6–5·9	4·1–4·9	4·5–5·4	...	...	...
Cover (%)	75–100	95–100	100	100	75–100	80–100	70–100
Height of vegetation (cm.)	3–12	2	5–20	2–8	...	...	1–5
Salix herbacea	3 1	8 3	...	7 1	...	4 +	10 4
Vaccinium myrtillus	9 3	7 2	5 1	2 +	...	1 +	...
Agrostis canina	6 1	8 3	4 1	6 2	1 +	...	4 1
A. tenuis	1 +	4 1	9 3	4 1	1 +	5 1	...
Deschampsia cespitosa	2 +	8 2	9 4	10 5	10 2	9 2	4 1
D. flexuosa	9 3	7 3	7 2	2 +	1 +	2 +	5 2
Festuca ovina	7 2	8 3	3 1	9 2	1 +	2 +	7 2
Nardus stricta	...	2 +	3 1	1 1	4 1	5 1	1 +
Carex bigelowii	10 5	10 4	9 3	10 2	7 1	9 2	4 1
Juncus trifidus	4 1	8 3	...	1 +	...	3 1	1 +
Luzula spicata	3 1	7 1	...	3 +	...	1 +	2 +
Alchemilla alpina	3 +	9 3	4 +	8 2	2 +	4 1	4 +
Armeria maritima	4 1	10 3	1 +	7 1	...	...	...
Galium saxatile	9 2	5 1	10 3	9 2	1 +	6 2	1 +
Gnaphalium supinum	...	2 +	...	3 1	6 1	10 4	5 1
Polygonum viviparum	...	9 3	...	9 2	...	...	...
Ranunculus acris	...	2 1	1 +	9 2	1 +	1 +	...
Rumex acetosa	...	1 +	8 2	9 2	9 2	...	...
Saxifraga stellaris	...	...	1 +	...	9 2	5 1	1 +
Sibbaldia procumbens	...	3 1	1 +	9 2	1 +	4 2	1 +

Species	(1)	(2)	(3)	(4)	(5)	(6)	(7)
Silene acaulis	2 1	9 4		8 1		2 +	1 +
Thymus drucei		9 3		8 2			
Aulacomnium turgidum		8 2		2 1	4 1	6 1	9 2
Conostomum tetragonum							1 +
Dicranum fuscescens	8 2	4 1	2 +	3 1			
D. scoparium	1 +	4 1	4 1	1 +			
D. starkei				1 +	10 7	10 3	10 3
Hylocomium splendens	2 1	7 2	8 3	10 4		1 +	
Hypnum cupressiforme	2 +	7 1	2 +	3 +			
H. hamulosum		6 1		2 +			
Oligotrichum hercynicum		1 +		2 +	9 2	9 1	9 2
Pleurozium schreberi	4 1	6 1	8 2	4 1	1 +	1 +	3 1
Polytrichum alpinum	7 2	9 2	10 3	10 2	9 1	4 1	3 1
P. norvegicum					10 4	9 3	
Rhacomitrium canescens		2 +	2 +	2 1	2 1	6 3	
R. fasciculare					6 1	5 1	3 2
R. heterostichum			5 1	4 1	3 +	7 3	6 2
R. lanuginosum	10 9	10 8	10 6	9 4	2 +	3 1	9 1
Rhytidiadelphus loreus	3 1	9 2		9 3	4 1	1 +	
R. triquetrus							
Barbilophozia floerkii			3 +	1 +	6 3	7 2	2 1
Gymnomitrium concinnatum					2 1	1 +	10 6
Lophozia alpestris		1 +		1 +	5 1	4 1	7 1
Nardia scalaris	2 1	1 +	9 2	3 +	6 2	6 1	9 2
Ptilidium ciliare	1 +	7 1		2 +		1 +	2 +
Cetraria aculeata	3 1	6 1		2 +			
C. islandica	8 2	9 2	6 1	3 +	2 +	3 +	1 +
Cladonia bellidiflora	2 +	3 1	1 +	1 +	4 1	3 1	
C. uncialis	9 2	9 2			1 +	1 +	6 1
Ochrolechia tartarea var. *frigida*	4 1	8 2		2 +			4 1
Sphaerophorus globosus	2 +	9 2					

(1) Species-poor Rhacomitrium heath association.
(2) Species-rich Rhacomitrium heath association.
(3) Deschampsia cespitosa—Rhytidiadelphus loreus association.
(4) Species-rich D. cespitosa—R. loreus association.
(5) Polytrichum norvegicum—Dicranum starkei association.
(6) Rhacomitrium-rich—Dicranum starkei association.
(7) Gymnomitrium concinnatum—Salix herbacea association.

CHAPTER 15

MONTANE MIRES AND BOGS

D. A. RATCLIFFE

Oligotrophic, mesotrophic and eutrophic mires occur in the montane regions and many are evidently equivalent too, or replace, lowland mires of a similar type, e.g. there is a high level *Carex—Sphagnum* mire which is equivalent to the low level type; at high levels, *Carex-saxatilis* dominated mires replace the lowland *C. panicea—Campylium stellatum* mire. In addition, bog vegetation occupies many square miles of montane country and, indeed, mountain *Empetrum—Eriophorum* bog is restricted to the Scottish Highlands in the British Isles. A further type of vegetation, not dealt with in Chapter 10, is that of springs and flushes. Such vegetation is highly characteristic of high level country and, ecologically, is closely related to mire vegetation. Accordingly these vegetation types are treated after the mires but before the bogs. Many of these vegetation types have already been described by McVean and Ratcliffe (1962).

MIRE VEGETATION

Oligotrophic mires

Alpine Carex—Sphagnum mire (Table 63, col. 1, p. 545). This is the high level equivalent of the sub-alpine *Carex—Sphagnum* oligotrophic mire (cf. p. 436). *Carex echinata* and *C. nigra* are again dominant among the vascular plants and there is a carpet of *Sphagnum. Eriophorum angustifolium, Nardus stricta, Viola palustris, Polytrichum commune, Sphagnum papillosum* and *S. robustum* are constant, but the alpine mire differs from its sub-alpine counterpart mainly in the presence of northern or montane species such as *Carex curta, Carex bigelowii, Saxifraga stellaris* and, very locally, *Sphagnum lindbergii.*

Alpine *Carex—Sphagnum* mires are naturally less widespread than the sub-alpine type; for they are restricted to altitudes above 732 m. (2400 ft.) and so occur most frequently on the high mountains of the central Highlands. They are found on a wide variety of acidic parent rocks and occupy similar habitats to the sub-alpine mires, although they are often associated with late snow vegetation. Soils are again peaty gleys, similar in acidity and base status to low level types.

536

Carex aquatilis—rariflora **mire** (Table 63, col. 2). Another montane mire which has a *Sphagnum* carpet similar to the previous type, but the sedges are replaced by *Carex aquatilis*, *C. rariflora* and *C. curta*.

This is a very local community, confined to a few high massifs of the east-central Highlands, above 732 m. (2400 ft.). On the whole it occupies more definite hollows, with a more stagnant water-table and deeper peat, than the other alpine *Carex—Sphagnum* mire, but the two often occur close together.

Mesotrophic to eutrophic mires

Carex rostrata—Sphagnum warnstorfianum **mire** (Table 63, col. 3). *Carex rostrata* is the physiognomic dominant, and there is a *Sphagnum* carpet composed principally of the relatively basiphilous species *S. warnstorfianum*, *S. contortum*, *S. teres*, *S. subsecundum* (*sens. strict.*) and *S. squarrosum*. Other characteristic species include *Selaginella selaginoides*, *Festuca ovina* agg., *Viola palustris*, *Aulacomnium palustre*, *Mnium pseudopunctatum*, *Hylocomium splendens* and, occasionally, *Camptothecium nitens*. The flora is fairly rich, with a wide variety of sedges and herbs. Locally there are similar mires in which *Carex rostrata* is replaced by *C. nigra*, *Juncus acutiflorus* or *J. squarrosus*, while the *Sphagnum* carpet and other associates remain the same.

This vegetation type is very local and occurs only in the central Highlands and in a few places in the Southern Uplands, between 427 m. (1400 ft.) and 824 m. (2700 ft.). It usually occupies basins or level ground where drainage is more or less stagnant. The drainage water is calcareous, but less markedly so than in *Carex rostrata*—brown moss, mires, into which the present type sometimes intergrades. The pH values of water samples range from 5·8 to 6·0 and those of peats from 5·5 to 5·7, and this mire is mesotrophic rather than eutrophic. The peat has a high *Sphagnum* content, with little or no mineral matter.

Similar vegetation occurs in some lowland fens in Scotland, and in one or two places on the hills of northern England. In Scandinavia, comparable mires are widespread, but they usually have a shrub layer with willows such as *Salix lapponum* and a greater number of montane plants.

Alpine *Carex—Hypnum* mire (Table 63, col. 4). The *Carex—Sphagnum* mires of base-poor soils have a mesotrophic counterpart in which Sphagna are replaced by a wide selection of other mosses, particularly those of the old genus *Hypnum*. These *Carex —Hypnum* mires usually lie at moderate elevations and so have been included in the montane group.

There are numerous constants—*Selaginella selaginoides*, *Festuca ovina* agg., *Nardus stricta*, *Carex nigra*, *C. panicea*, *C. pulicaris*, *Eriophorum angustifolium*, *Leontodon autumnalis*, *Polygonum viviparum*, *Thalictrum alpinum*, *Acrocladium cuspidatum*, *Hylocomium splendens*, *Philonotis fontana* and *Rhytidiadelphus squarrosus*. There is seldom any single dominant, and any one stand usually contains a number of other basiphilous herbs and mosses which reflect soil conditions better than some of the base-tolerant sedges. *Carex panicea—Campylium stellatum* mires (cf. p. 437), and species-rich *Nardus stricta* and *Juncus squarrosus* communities (cf. p. 192) all have some floristic similarity to alpine *Carex—Hypnum* mire, and all may occur together in places.

Alpine *Carex—Hypnum* mires occur on most hills where calcareous rocks outcrop at moderate elevations, but are most frequent in Breadalbane and Clova. The altitudinal range is 305–976 m. (1000–3200 ft.), and in range of habitat and size of stands there is again great similarity to the *Carex—Sphagnum* mires. The soils (pH 5·3–5·6) vary widely in humus content, but when a definite peat horizon is present, it is usually well humified. The basal mineral soil is strongly gleyed.

Carex saxatilis mire (Table 63, col. 5). At high levels, the *Carex panicea— Campylium stellatum* mires (cf. p. 437) are replaced in corresponding situations by a type in which *Carex saxatilis* is dominant. The usual associates include several other species of *Carex*, *Eriophorum angustifolium*, *Drepanocladus revolvens*, *Hylocomium splendens*, *Riccardia pinguis* and *Scapania undulata*. Montane species are usually well represented, and there are transitions to the open *Saxifraga aizoides* flushes with which the mire is often associated.

Carex saxatilis mires occur between 763 m. (2500 ft.) and 976 m. (3200 ft.), on calcareous mountains of the Scottish Highlands, and usually in places where snow lies late. They are frequent only in the Perthshire district of Breadalbane, and elsewhere occur on a few scattered mountains in the central and western Highlands. *Carex saxatilis* itself can grow on base-poor soils, so that the accompanying species are better indicators of soil conditions. Soils are peaty muds with a very variable humus content, and show a pH range of 4·6–5·7 and fairly high exchangeable calcium content.

There is an extremely close resemblance between Scottish and Norwegian *Carex saxatilis* mires, but such vegetation does not occur elsewhere in the British Isles. This is the most montane of the mires on base-rich soils.

SPRINGS AND FLUSHES

Springs and flushes are closely related to mires, both edaphically and floristically. They are soligenous sites where the flow of water is more localised and rapid than in mires, and so usually cover a smaller area. Springs are separated from flushes on purely arbitrary grounds: they mark the emergence at the ground surface of a concentrated, more or less permanent flow of free drainage water, and are often sharply delimited from the surrounding non-irrigated vegetation and soils, except on their downslope side. Spring water is often canalised below into a small rill, and either habitat may grade into a flush where the irrigation water spreads out, giving a more diffuse and less rapid flow.

Springs are covered with dense, spongy mats of bryophytes and have little or no bare ground; but in flushes a good deal of the mineral substratum is usually exposed, giving a stony or gravelly appearance, and vascular plants are prominent in the open vegetation. Springs and flushes may be classed as oligotrohpic, mesotrophic and eutrophic, using the same criteria as for mires (p. 432), into which they often grade spatially and floristically. As with mires, the mesotrophic and eutrophic types are best represented on the calcareous Dalradian mountains from Breadalbane to Clova, and elsewhere are more localised, due to the patchy distribution of major occurrences of lime-bearing rock. The substrata vary a good deal in humus content but are usually silty muds rather than peats.

Flushes vary in size from a few square metres to hundreds of square metres, but the larger examples usually form mosaics with other communities. Springs seldom exceed a few square metres in area, except in places fed by melt water from late snow beds. Both categories occur at all altitudes, but they are most characteristic of the higher levels and, as only one or two types occur in association with woodland or within the potential Forest zone, the group as a whole has been treated with montane vegetation. Springs and flushes are often rich in montane species and some rarities are more or less confined to these habitats and the closely related mires.

Oligotrophic springs and flushes

Philonotis—Saxifraga stellaris **spring** (Table 64, col. 1, p. 550). The most common type of spring vegetation is dominated either by any one of several calcifuge bryophytes, or by a mixture of these species in varying abundance. There appears to be some connection between prominence of certain species and mineral content of the spring water. For instance, *Sphagnum subsecundum* var. *auriculatum* is usually the predominant species on the most acidic mountains, whereas *Solenostoma cordifolium* and *Philonotis fontana* dominate springs where the drainage water is slightly richer. In between these are types containing one or more of these species, with the addition of others such as *Scapania undulata*, *S. uliginosa*, *Dicranella palustris*, *Drepanocladus exannulatus* and *Acrocladium sarmentosum*.

Associated plants vary in abundance, too, but there are several characteristic species such as *Agrostis stolonifera*, *Deschampsia cespitosa*, *Poa trivialis*, *Caltha palustris* ssp. *minor*, *Chrysosplenium oppositifolium*, *Epilobium anagallidifolium*, *Montia fontana*, *Stellaria alsine* and *Saxifraga stellaris*. In some high level stands, distinctive montane species such as *Deschampsia alpina*, *Veronica serpyllifolia* ssp. *humifusa*, *Alopecurus alpinus* and *Splachnum vasculosum* are present locally. While it would be possible to define separate facies according to the different dominants, or to floristic richness, this has not been done and the complex has been named after its most constant and characteristic species.

Flushes of this kind occur on nearly all the higher mountains of Scotland, chiefly above 457 m. (1500 ft.), but are replaced by mesotrophic or eutrophic types where the parent rock is strongly calcareous. They are also well represented on the hills of northern England and Wales, and closely comparable communities are widespread in Norway.

Pohlia "glacialis" **spring** (Table 64, col. 2). This type of spring is completely dominated by the moss *Pohlia albicans* var. *glacialis*, which forms soft, spongy carpets of a bright apple-green colour. The associates, which are few, include *Deschampsia cespitosa* and montane species such as *Saxifraga stellaris*, *Cerastium cerastoides* and *Epilobium anagallidifolium*. There are transitions to the *Philonotis* springs.

Pohlia "glacialis" springs occur on ground fed by melt water from the longest lasting snow beds, and so are found only on the highest hills of the Highlands, above 854 m. (2800 ft.). They are usually associated with the moss-heath snow bed communities described in Chapter 14. Virtually identical vegetation occurs on some of the Norwegian mountains.

Anthelia—Deschampsia cespitosa **flush** (Table 64, col. 3). Like the *Pohlia "glacialis"* springs, this type has only one dominant, which may be *Anthelia julacea* or *A. juratzkana*, forming a more or less continuous greyish carpet. Vascular plant associates are few, the most constant being *Deschampsia cespitosa*, but there is usually a wide selection of other bryophytes, such as *Scapania undulata*, *Marsupella emarginata*, *Pohlia ludwigii* and *Philonotis fontana*.

Anthelia flushes are found mainly in areas where snow lies late, above 854 m. (2800 ft.), and are affected by snow melt water for much of the year, although their soils appear to be less completely waterlogged than those of the two springs described above. They are more widespread and frequent than *Pohlia "glacialis"* springs and occur on most of the higher hills of the central Highlands. Comparable vegetation is widespread in Norway.

Narthecium—Sphagnum **flush** (Table 64, col. 4). *Narthecium ossifragum* is the most abundant of the vascular plants, although its growth is rather depauperate compared with that in bogs. *Trichophorum cespitosum*, *Nardus stricta* and *Lycopodium selago* are usually present and there is a rather open growth of *Sphagnum*, mainly *S. tenellum*, *S. compactum*, or *S. subsecundum* var. *auriculatum*.

Such flushes are apparently confined to highly acidic rocks, and although widespread in Scotland, are nevertheless local. They occur most frequently above 610 m. (2000 ft.) but may be seen as low as 305 m. (1000 ft.) in some places, so that there is no connection with prolonged snow-cover. They are often indistinct, occupying very small areas and grading rapidly into oligotrophic mire, wet heath or grassland. Similar communities have been seen in a few hills in northern England.

Mesotrophic to eutrophic springs and flushes

Cratoneuron—Saxifraga aizoides **spring** (Table 64, col. 5). *Cratoneuron commutatum* is dominant, often forming a large mound or bank, and supporting an open growth of vascular plants such as *Saxifraga aizoides*, *Festuca rubra*, *Cardamine pratensis* and *Epilobium alsinifolium*. Other bryophytes are rather poorly represented although *Philonotis fontana* is usually present.

This is a strongly eutrophic spring depending on water draining from calcareous rocks, and there is often tufa formation within the moss cushions. It occurs in all areas where there are lime-bearing rocks and has a wide altitudinal range, from 305 to 915 m. (1000–3000 ft.). *Cratoneuron* dominated springs may sometimes be found in woods, and they occur in most upland parts of the British Isles. Counterparts are found in Norway.

Carex—Saxifraga aizoides **flush** (Table 64, cols. 6 and 7). *Cratoneuron* springs often grade into open, stony flushes with a very sparse plant cover, which nevertheless contains a distinctive assemblage of plants. The most abundant and constant species are

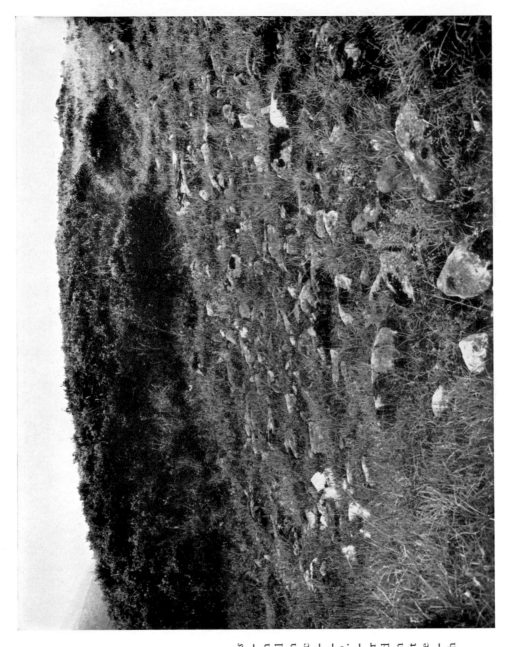

PLATE 95

Carex — Saxifraga aizoides flush. The seepage of calcareous drainage water down a slight hollow in the glacial drift produces base-rich muddy soils with a eutrophic vegetation containing *Saxifraga aizoides, Eriophorum latifolium, Carex panicea, C. demissa, Festuca rubra, Scorpidium scorpioides* and other calcioles. This is in marked contrast to the Callunetum on podsolised drift soils just beyond the influence of the flush water. The bare, stone-littered appearance of the flush is very characteristic.

PLATE 96. Lichen-rich facies of upland *Calluna—Eriophorum* bog, Ladder Hills, Banffshire, 793 m. The patchy dominance of *Cladonia sylvatica* and *C. rangiferina* shows up as lighter patches on the undisturbed blanket bog with *Calluna vulgaris*, *Eriophorum vaginatum*, *Rubus chamaemorus* and *Sphagnum capillaceum*.

Carex demissa, C. panicea, Festuca ovina agg., *Juncus triglumis, Pinguicula vulgaris, Saxifraga aizoides, Thalictrum alpinum* and *Blindia acuta.* Most of these have a low cover, and the total plant cover in sample plots is often less than 50 per cent. The brown mosses of calcareous mires are usually represented, sometimes with moderate cover but often sparingly. This type of flush is nevertheless floristically rich, and many rare montane species find their optimum habitat here or in the related mesotrophic and eutrophic mires. A distinctive high level facies, with such plants as *Carex atrofusca, C. microglochin, Kobresia simpliciuscula, Juncus biglumis* and *J. castaneus,* may be recognised.

Flushes of this type, still containing montane species, are well developed in open places among the birch-juniper woods at Braemar, Aberdeenshire; but there is a low level facies, occurring nearly always in deforested country, in which the montane species are replaced by others such as *Schoenus nigricans, Drosera anglica, Pinguicula lusitanica, Eriophorum latifolium* and *Carex hostiana* (Table 64, col. 7).

Carex—Saxifraga aizoides flushes are widely distributed in Scotland, wherever there are calcareous rocks, and in some western districts even occur where the rocks are not markedly rich in lime. *Saxifraga aizoides* does not grow in the Southern Uplands, but flushes otherwise similar in floristics occur there locally. The low level facies is especially characteristic of the western Highlands, at altitudes up to 366 m. (1200 ft.), while the montane facies is best represented in Breadalbane from 763 to 914 m. (2500–3000 ft.).

These flushes have a water-scoured appearance (Plate 95), and it may be that the open cover is maintained partly by the mechanical effect of strong irrigation. Calcareous flushes sometimes develop in the residual mineral soil of recently eroded peat haggs. Humus content is usually low, and the soils or muds are saturated mixtures of silt, sand and gravel, with a high content of exchangeable calcium and pH range of 5·6–7·0. Although this type of flush is frequently associated with complexes of other calcicolous vegetation, especially on limestone, it occurs just as often amongst oligotrophic communities and grades suddenly into these. It is quite usual to find *Carex—Saxifraga aizoides* flushes amongst shallow bog or oligotrophic mire, with hummocks of the poorer vegetation occurring as islands within the flush.

Carex—Saxifraga aizoides flushes occur in the English Lake District and Upper Teesdale, but elsewhere in northern England and Wales they lack *Saxifraga aizoides.* Again, similar types are present in some parts of Norway.

BOG VEGETATION

Upland *Calluna—Eriophorum* bog (Table 65, cols. 1–3, p. 556). The most widespread kind of upland blanket bog is dominated by *Calluna vulgaris* and *Eriophorum vaginatum,* but differs in associated species from the lowland type described on p. 459. *Rubus chamaemorus* is perhaps the most characteristic species of the upland bogs, growing in great profusion on most peaty moorlands from the Cheviots northwards, except in south-west Scotland. Although, conversely, *Myrica gale* is absent, the upland bogs tend to be richer in dwarf shrubs than those of the lowlands. *Vaccinium myrtillus* is a constant, and *V. vitis-idaea* very abundant in many sites. *Empetrum hermaphroditum* is constant in most parts of the Highlands, but is replaced by *E. nigrum* on some lower moorlands of the region and in the Southern Uplands. Very locally there is an abundance of montane dwarf shrubs such as *Betula nana, Arctous alpinus* and *Arctostaphylos uva-ursi*, which give the vegetation a sufficiently distinctive character to allow recognition of a shrub-rich facies (Table 65, col. 1). In Scotland, *Betula nana* appears to find its optimum habitat in such bogs, although it occurs less frequently in other types. *Vaccinium microcarpum* is another characteristic but very local dwarf shrub.

Sphagnum species are usually present, but only on very wet, level ground do they form a continuous carpet and, as such ground is local and seldom extensive on the uplands, the vascular plant component is more important than in many low level bogs. There is again evidence, however, that the extent of *Sphagnum*-dominated bog in the uplands has been greatly reduced in recent times. Hummock forming *Sphagnum* species such as *S. rubellum, S. capillaceum* and *S. papillosum* are the most abundant. Small, shallow hollows or channels occur in many upland bogs which are usually overgrown with *S. cuspidatum*, or *S. recurvum* where there is lateral water movement. Pool complexes of the type described on p. 451 are rare on the plateau bogs, but an extensive system of enlarged pools occurs on the Knockfin Heights, on the Sutherland-Caithness border, where the vegetation is referable to the present type.

Hypnaceous mosses, particularly *Hylocomium splendens, Rhytidiadelphus loreus* and *Pleurozium schreberi* are abundant whereas the first two species are absent from lowland *Calluna—Eriophorum* bog. *Rhacomitrium lanuginosum* occurs locally in sufficient quantity to justify the separation of a *Rhacomitrium*-rich facies, especially where the bogs are drying through channel erosion, but also as an extensive undisturbed bog community of Shetland. In yet another facies (Table 65, col. 2, and Plate 96) the cryptogamic component of the vegetation is dominated by lichens of the *Cladonia sylvatica—C. rangiferina* complex, which occur in dense carpets and impart a pale grey or cream colour to the bog (cf. lichen-rich dwarf shrub heath, p. 483).

Although typical upland Calluneto—Eriophoretum occurs in many parts of western Scotland, it is far more extensive and generally distributed in the east. Since the altitudinal range is mainly between 305 and 768 m. (1000–2500 ft.), the tendency to an eastern distribution might be explained, in part, by the greater extent of suitable elevated plateaux and gentle slopes in the east than in the west, but there is also likely to be some connection with the more continental climate. The shrub-rich and lichen-rich facies, which often occur together, certainly appear to depend on a relatively continental climate, for they have a markedly eastern distribution, apart from anomalous local occurrences on the coastal moorlands of north-west Sutherland. Both are fire sensitive and their original areas may have been greatly reduced.

Calluna—Eriophorum bogs occupy many square miles of upland in the Cheviots, and eastern half of the Southern Uplands, and in certain districts of the eastern Grampians such as the Monadhliath, the Forest of Atholl and Clova. Together with the Callunetum of the drier slopes they form the predominant vegetation of many grouse moors. In the east they may be replaced, in some apparently suitable situations, by *Calluna—Trichophorum* bogs, and it is not yet clear what determines whether *Eriophorum vaginatum* or *Trichophorum* shall be dominant. In any one locality there is altitudinal separation between the present type of bog and lowland *Calluna—Eriophorum* or *Trichophorum—Eriophorum* bog, with transitional communities at intermediate elevations but in different districts the last type overlaps altitudinally with upland Calluneto—Eriophoretum. Spatial separation between upland and lowland types is sometimes due to steepness of the ground and absence of bog at intermediate elevations. Transitional communities also occur widely in some areas, such as Shetland, where one or both true types are absent or poorly represented.

Some upland *Calluna—Eriophorum* bogs occur within the present tree limits and their treeless character may be due partly to human disturbance but, as a whole, they belong to an altitudinal zone above that of the forests. The shrub-rich and lichen-rich facies, in particular, could be regarded as montane. The whole group has, therefore, been treated with the high-level types of vegetation.

Upland bogs are severely gullied or affected by sheet erosion in many places, but this process makes examination of the peat stratigraphy possible without boring. The basal layer of tree remains overlying the mineral soil is usually of pine, birch or juniper, and where an upper buried forest layer is present it shows the same species. The remains of *Eriophorum vaginatum* and *Calluna*, as well as *Sphagnum*, are frequent throughout many deposits, but recent workers have been unable to find the "arctic plant beds" reported by Lewis from many bogs (1905–11). The depth of peat in upland blanket bogs varies greatly, but on extensive plateaux reaches 4–5 m. or even more. The deeper deposits naturally contain a good deal of "fresh" *Sphagnum* peat. Acidity is fairly high, with a pH range of 3·6–4·2 for peats. Despite the poverty of this kind of peat in available nutrients, wherever peat from eroding blanket bog is redistributed on steeper slopes below there is usually an abundance of *Nardus stricta* and other grasses with low nutrient requirements which have clearly been encouraged by the process so that slight enrichment is evidently involved.

Identical *Calluna—Eriophorum* bogs are extensive in the Pennines of northern England and the "Eriophoretum vaginati" described by Tansley (1949) for this region is merely a local facies in which *Calluna* has been destroyed by burning and grazing. The same vegetation occurs on many of the Welsh mountains and on some Irish uplands, especially in the east. The *Rhacomitrium*-rich facies occurs very locally in Ireland and the lichen-rich facies in the eastern Southern Uplands and northern Pennines, but the shrub-rich facies is confined to the Highlands in the British Isles. Both the dwarf shrub and lichen facies show a strong resemblance to a type of ombrogenous bog widespread in Norway, but there *Calluna* is a much more local species.

Mountain *Empetrum—Eriophorum* bog (Table 65, col. 4). *Calluna vulgaris* has an upper altitudinal limit of about 1007 m. (3300 ft.) in the Cairngorms and 702 m. (2300 ft.) in the north-west Sutherland hills, so that it is absent from the really high-level bogs. Its place as co-dominant with *Eriophorum vaginatum* is then taken by *Empetrum* *hermaphroditum.* The high mountain bogs are otherwise similar in floristics to the upland *Calluna—Eriophorum* type, but show a greater emphasis on certain species, such as the other dwarf shrubs, *Vaccinium myrtillus, V. vitis-idaea* and *V. uliginosum,* and lichens such as *Cladonia sylvatica.* The montane sedge *Carex bigelowii* becomes constant and *Rubus chamaemorus* remains so. In average number of species the *Empetrum—Eriophorum* bogs are richer than the *Calluna—Eriophorum* type, with twenty-five against twenty-one. *Sphagnum* species are locally dominant, notably *S. papillosum* and *S. capillaceum,* but *S. fuscum* is a characteristic species. Lichens are usually abundant and become dominant locally.

Empetrum—Eriophorum bog occurs widely above 763 to 914 m. (2500–3000 ft.), but mainly in the central and eastern Highlands where plateaux and broad watersheds are frequent at high levels. Stands are never as extensive as those of *Calluna—Eriophorum* bog, but the total area covers several square kilometres on some elevated table lands, such as that between Caenlochan and the head of Glen Clova. In this locality the high level bogs are severely eroded, but some examples show little or no disturbance or wastage. The peat is shallower, on average, than that of the lower bogs, with a usual maximum depth of 2–3 m. The maximum altitude for this bog appears to be about 1068 m. (3500 ft.). Above this level, severe wind, prolonged snow cover, and solifluction movement probably inhibit peat formation, and aquatic vegetation consists of springs, flushes and small mires. *Empetrum—Eriophorum* bogs are typically associated either with chionophilous vegetation such as the high level *Vaccinium, Nardus* or *Carex bigelowii* communities, or with types depending on severe wind exposure, such as *Rhacomitrium* heath (cf. Chapter 14).

This type of bog does not occur outside the Scottish Highlands in Britain, and its northern, montane character is confirmed by the strong floristic similarity which it bears to certain types of Scandinavian ombrogenous bog. The only important difference in a widespread type of Norwegian bog is the constancy and abundance of *Betula nana,* which occurs in Scotland mainly in *Calluna—Eriophorum* bogs at an intermediate elevation.

REFERENCES

LEWIS, F. J. 1905–07, 1911   The plant remains in the Scottish peat mosses. *Trans. Roy. Soc. Edinb.,* **41,** 699–723; **45,** 335–360; **46,** 33–70; **47,** 793–833.

McVEAN, D. N. and RATCLIFFE, D. A. 1962   *Plant communities of the Scottish Highlands.* H.M.S.O., London.

TANSLEY, A. G. 1949   *The British Islands and their vegetation.* Cambridge.

TABLE 63

Montane mires

Vegetation type	(1) Alpine Carex— Sphagnum		(2) Carex aquatilis— rariflora		(3) Carex rostrata —Sphagnum warnstorfianum		(4) Alpine Carex— Hypnum		(5) Carex saxatilis	
Number of stands . .	11		9		10		12		15	
Plot size (sq. m.) . .	4		4		4		4		4	
Altitudinal range (m.) .	731–960		731–1051		457–838		305–838		792–975	
Soil type and drainage class	Gley		Peaty gley		Peaty gley		Gley		Gley	
Slope (degrees) . .	0–15		0–10		0–25		5–25		0–35	
pH range . . .	...		...		5·5–5·7		5·3–5·6		4·6–5·7	
Total vegetation cover (%)	100		100		100		100		80 (mean)	
Height of vegetation (cm.) .	10–25		10–30		25–45		15–25		10–20	
Betula sp. . . .	...		...		1	0·1	...		...	
Calluna vulgaris . .	...		...		1	0·1	...		...	
Empetrum hermaphroditum	...		...		2	0·3	2	0·2	...	
E. nigrum . . .	1	0·1	...		1	0·3	1	0·2	...	
Erica tetralix . . .	...		...		4	1·1	...		...	
Salix aurita . . .	...		...		2	0·1	1	0·1	...	
S. herbacea . . .	1	0·2	1	0·3	...		1	0·1	1	0·1
S. lapponum × cinerea ssp. atrocinerea	1	0·1	...		...		...		...	
Vaccinium myrtillus . .	2	0·3	1	0·3	...		...		...	
V. vitis-idaea . . .	1	0·1	...		...		...		...	
Equisetum arvense .	...		1	0·1	...		...		...	
E. palustre . . .	...		...		1	0·3	2	0·6	2	0·6
E. variegatum . . .	...		...		...		1	0·2	...	
Lycopodium selago . .	...		...		...		1	0·2	4	0·5
Selaginella selaginoides .	2	0·2	...		9	1·4	9	1·9	5	1·0
Agrostis canina . .	6	1·5	2	0·9	3	0·7	5	1·5	5	1·3
A. stolonifera . . .	2	0·6	1	0·4	5	0·8	...		...	
A. tenuis . . .	1	0·2	1	0·2	1	0·4	4	0·9	3	0·7
Alopecurus alpinus . .	...		...		...		...		1	0·1
Anthoxanthum odoratum .	2	0·2	1	0·3	3	0·7	3	0·7	...	
Briza media . . .	...		...		...		2	0·5	...	
Deschampsia alpina . .	1	0·3	1	0·4	...		...		...	
D. cespitosa . . .	...		1	0·1	1	0·3	3	0·7	3	1·0
D. flexuosa . . .	1	0·2	...		...		...		...	
Festuca ovina agg. . .	6	1·2	3	0·7	8	2·6	9	2·8	6	1·1
F. rubra . . .	1	0·3	...		1	0·3	6	1·8	3	0·6
Holcus lanatus . . .	...		...		...		2	0·4	...	
Molinia caerulea . .	...		...		...		2	0·5	...	
Nardus stricta . . .	8	2·0	1	0·2	7	2·3	8	2·3	4	1·2
Phleum alpinum . .	...		...		...		1	0·2	...	
Sesleria albicans . .	...		...		...		1	0·1	...	
Sieglingia decumbens . .	...		...		...		1	0·2	...	
Carex aquatilis . .	...		7	3·4	1	0·1	1	0·5	4	1·3
C. bigelowii . . .	5	1·3	7	1·6	1	0·4	1	0·6	...	

2 M

TABLE 63—continued

Vegetation type	(1) Alpine Carex— Sphagnum		(2) Carex aquatilis— rariflora		(3) Carex rostrata —Sphagnum warnstorfianum		(4) Alpine Carex— Hypnum		(5) Carex saxatilis	
C. capillaris	...		...		...		...		1	0·1
C. curta	6	1·6	6	2·8	2	0·5	...		6	1·4
C. demissa	...		...		4	1·1	5	1·2	4	1·1
C. dioica	...		...		...		3	0·7	5	1·6
C. echinata	9	4·5	2	0·9	7	2·9	6	2·3	...	
C. lachenalii	...		1	0·4	...		...		...	
C. nigra	4	1·6	3	1·0	6	1·9	9	5·3	5	1·6
C. panicea	...		...		7	2·2	9	3·1	...	
C. pulicaris	...		...		3	0·8	9	3·3	1	0·3
C. rariflora	...		7	2·6	...		...		...	
C. rostrata	1	0·5	...		10	6·9	...		...	
C. saxatilis	1	0·3	...		1	0·1	3	0·7	10	6·9
C. vaginata	...		...		...		1	0·2	1	0·2
Coeloglossum viride	...		...		...		1	0·1	...	
Dactylorchis maculata ssp. ericetorum	...		...		...		1	0·2	...	
Eriophorum angustifolium	10	3·4	8	1·7	7	1·6	8	2·3	7	2·6
E. vaginatum	6	1·8	3	0·3	...		...		...	
Juncus acutiflorus	...		...		1	0·2	3	0·3	...	
J. articulatus	...		...		4	0·6	3	1·4	1	0·1
J. biglumis	...		...		...		...		1	0·1
J. castaneus	...		...		...		...		3	0·5
J. effusus	...		...		1	0·2	1	0·2	...	
J. kochii	4	0·9	...		5	1·4	3	1·1	...	
J. squarrosus	1	0·1	...		...		5	1·3	...	
J. triglumis	...		...		...		3	0·3	5	1·4
Luzula multiflora	2	0·3	3	0·4	3	0·4	4	0·9	1	0·1
L. spicata	...		...		...		...		1	0·2
L. sylvatica	...		...		1	0·1	...		...	
Narthecium ossifragum	1	0·3	...		...		3	0·6	1	0·1
Potamogeton polygonifolius	...		...		1	0·1	...		...	
Tofieldia pusilla	...		...		...		...		1	0·1
Trichophorum cespitosum	2	0·4	1	0·2	...		1	0·3	...	
Triglochin palustris	...		...		...		2	0·3	1	0·1
Alchemilla alpina	...		...		...		...		1	0·1
A. filicaulis	...		...		...		...		1	0·2
A. glabra	...		...		...		4	1·3	2	0·1
A. vulgaris agg.	...		...		3	0·4	...		...	
A. wichurae	...		...		...		...		1	0·2
A. xanthochlora	...		...		...		3	0·6	...	
Anemone nemorosa	...		...		...		1	0·1	...	
Angelica sylvestris	...		3	0·7	...		...		...	
Armeria maritima	...		...		...		...		1	0·3
Bellis perennis	...		...		...		...		5	1·1
Caltha palustris	...		...		2	0·5	4	0·8	5	1·1
Campanula rotundifolia	...		...		...		2	0·3	...	
Cardamine pratensis	...		...		2	0·3	2	0·3	1	0·2
Cerastium holosteoides	...		...		2	0·2	3	0·3	1	0·1
Cirsium palustre	...		...		1	0·2	...		...	

TABLE 63—*continued*

Vegetation type	(1) Alpine Carex— Sphagnum		(2) Carex aquatilis— rariflora		(3) Carex rostrata —Sphagnum warnstorfianum		(4) Alpine Carex— Hypnum		(5) Carex saxatilis	
Cochlearia officinalis ssp. *alpina*	...		...		...		...		1	0·1
Crepis paludosa . .	...		...		1	0·2	2	0·6	...	
Drosera rotundifolia . .	...		...		1	0·1	...		...	
Epilobium anagallidifolium .	1	0·1	1	0·2	1	0·1	...		2	0·3
E. palustre . . .	1	0·2	...		6	0·6	3	0·4	...	
Euphrasia officinalis agg. .	...		...		2	0·6	7	1·8	1	0·1
E. scottica . . .	...		...		...		...		2	0·5
Filipendula ulmaria . .	...		...		...		1	0·1	...	
Galium saxatile . .	3	0·4	2	0·8	6	1·0	2	0·4	...	
Geum rivale . . .	...		...		...		4	0·9	1	0·1
Leontodon autumnalis .	...		1	0·1	3	0·5	8	1·5	3	0·3
Linum catharticum . .	...		...		1	0·1	4	0·8	...	
Lysimachia nemorum . .	...		...		...		2	0·5	...	
Oxalis acetosella . .	...		...		...		1	0·1	...	
Parnassia palustris . .	...		...		1	0·3	3	0·8	...	
Pedicularis palustris . .	...		...		2	0·1	...		...	
P. sylvatica . . .	...		...		...		1	0·1	...	
Pinguicula vulgaris . .	2	0·2	...		2	0·3	7	1·1	5	0·9
Plantago lanceolata . .	...		...		...		2	0·4	...	
Polygonum viviparum . .	2	0·5	1	0·4	4	1·1	9	2·5	7	1·9
Potentilla erecta . .	...		1	0·2	6	1·3	6	1·8	...	
P. palustris . . .	1	0·3	...		4	1·2	...		...	
Prunella vulgaris . .	...		...		...		4	0·9	...	
Ranunculus acris . .	1	0·1	...		1	0·4	5	1·4	1	0·2
R. flammula . . .	...		...		...		3	0·4	...	
Rhinanthus minor agg. .	...		...		...		3	0·2	...	
Rubus chamaemorus . .	...		2	0·4	...		...		...	
Rumex acetosa . .	...		2	0·6	...		3	0·3	1	0·3
Sagina procumbens . .	...		...		...		1	0·1	...	
Saxifraga aizoides . .	...		...		...		2	0·3	3	0·7
S. oppositifolia . .	...		...		...		1	0·1	...	
S. stellaris . . .	5	0·6	1	0·1	...		1	0·1	2	0·4
Succisa pratensis . .	...		...		1	0·2	3	0·8	...	
Taraxacum officinale agg. .	...		...		...		4	0·6	1	0·1
Thalictrum alpinum . .	1	0·3	...		4	1·0	8	2·9	6	1·7
Thymus drucei . .	...		...		...		2	0·4	...	
Trientalis europaea . .	...		1	0·3	1	0·3	...		...	
Trifolium repens . .	...		...		...		3	0·7	...	
Viola palustris . .	8	2·4	4	1·2	9	2·9	5	1·5	4	0·5
Acrocladium cuspidatum .	...		...		6	0·9	8	2·4	1	0·1
A. giganteum . . .	...		...		1	0·1	...		1	0·3
A. sarmentosum . .	4	0·7	2	0·4	2	0·4	...		5	1·7
A. stramineum . .	5	0·5	3	0·6	6	1·0	...		1	0·1
A. trifarium . . .	...		...		...		...		5	1·4
Aulacomnium palustre .	2	0·5	1	0·1	9	3·1	3	0·3	...	
Blindia acuta . .	...		...		...		...		4	0·7
Brachythecium rivulare .	...		...		...		2	0·4	...	

TABLE 63—continued

Vegetation type	(1) Alpine Carex—Sphagnum		(2) Carex aquatilis—rariflora		(3) Carex rostrata—Sphagnum warnstorfianum		(4) Alpine Carex—Hypnum		(5) Carex saxatilis	
B. rutabulum	...		...		2	0·5	...		...	
Breutelia chrysocoma	...		...		...		3	0·6	...	
Bryum pseudotriquetrum	...		...		3	0·5	6	1·8	5	1·4
Camptothecium nitens	...		...		3	1·3	3	0·7	...	
Campylium stellatum	...		...		3	0·9	4	1·2	3	0·3
Cinclidium stygium	...		...		...		5	0·8	...	
Climacium dendroides	...		...		2	0·3	1	0·3	1	0·1
Cratoneuron commutatum	...		...		...		4	1·4	2	0·9
C. filicinum	...		...		...		1	0·2	...	
Ctenidium molluscum	...		...		1	0·2	5	1·3	...	
Dicranella palustris	...		...		2	0·4	...		3	0·5
Dicranum bonjeanii	...		...		2	0·4	1	0·3	...	
D. scoparium	3	0·6	...		...		2	0·3	2	0·2
Drepanocladus exannulatus	4	0·6	1	0·2	...		...		2	0·5
D. fluitans	...		...		4	0·7	...		...	
D. revolvens	...		2	1·1	4	1·0	6	1·9	10	4·7
D. uncinatus	...		...		...		1	0·2	...	
Fissidens adianthoides	...		...		2	0·4	4	0·8	1	0·1
F. osmundoides	...		...		...		...		3	0·5
Hylocomium brevirostre	...		...		...		1	0·2	...	
H. splendens	4	0·7	...		8	2·1	9	3·0	9	1·7
Hypnum cupressiforme	...		...		1	0·3	...		...	
Mnium hornum	...		...		...		2	0·2	1	0·2
M. pseudopunctatum	...		...		8	1·9	5	0·7	1	0·1
M. punctatum	...		1	0·1	...		2	0·3	...	
M. seligeri	...		...		...		1	0·2	...	
M. undulatum	...		...		...		6	1·4	...	
Philonotis calcarea	...		...		...		1	0·3	...	
P. fontana	4	0·6	...		3	0·7	8	1·6	3	0·4
Plagiothecium undulatum	...		1	0·3	...		...		...	
Pleurozium schreberi	...		...		2	0·3	...		...	
Pohlia nutans	1	0·1	...		...		...		...	
Polytrichum alpestre	3	0·6	3	1·2	...		...		...	
P. alpinum	...		...		...		2	0·2	1	0·1
P. commune	9	2·4	8	2·0	6	1·0	1	0·1	5	0·7
P. juniperinum	...		...		...		...		1	0·1
Pseudoscleropodium purum	...		...		2	0·1	3	0·7	...	
Ptilium crista-castrensis	...		...		1	0·2	1	0·3	...	
Rhacomitrium lanuginosum	3	0·4	...		...		2	0·5	3	0·4
Rhytidiadelphus loreus	3	0·5	...		2	0·3	3	0·7	3	0·3
R. squarrosus	...		1	0·3	7	1·1	8	2·2	2	0·3
R. triquetrus	...		...		...		7	1·6	1	0·1
Scorpidium scorpioides	...		...		...		...		3	0·4
Sphagnum compactum	...		4	1·4	...		...		...	
S. contortum	...		...		2	0·5	...		...	
S. cuspidatum	1	0·3	...		...		...		1	0·3
S. girgensohnii	4	1·3	4	2·1	4	0·3	1	0·1	...	
S. lindbergii	6	3·1	2	0·8	...		...		...	
S. magellanicum	1	0·2	1	0·4	...		...		...	
S. palustre	1	0·5	1	0·1	4	0·7	1	0·3	...	

TABLE 63—*concluded*

Vegetation type	(1) Alpine Carex—Sphagnum		(2) Carex aquatilis—rariflora		(3) Carex rostrata—Sphagnum warnstorfianum		(4) Alpine Carex—Hypnum		(5) Carex saxatilis	
S. papillosum	9	4·5	6	2·6	3	1·1	...		...	
S. plumulosum	5	1·6	4	1·1	3	0·5	3	0·8	...	
S. recurvum	6	2·6	6	3·2	5	2·0	1	0·1	...	
S. riparium	1	0·6	...		...		...		...	
S. robustum	8	2·0	2	0·3	2	0·3	1	0·1	...	
S. rubellum *	2	0·6	2	1·1	3	0·9	1	0·3	1	0·1
S. squarrosum	...		1	0·8	4	1·4	...		...	
S. subsecundum	6	3·3	3	1·6	4	1·9	1	0·3	3	0·9
S. tenellum	1	0·2	1	0·3	...		...		...	
S. teres	2	0·6	2	1·1	10	3·0	...		...	
S. warnstorfianum	1	0·3	...		9	4·7	3	0·8	...	
Tayloria lingulata	...		...		...		...		1	0·1
Thuidium delicatulum	...		...		...		1	0·1	...	
T. tamariscinum	...		...		4	0·8	3	0·8	...	
Anthelia julacea	...		...		...		...		1	0·1
Barbilophozia lycopodioides	...		...		...		...		1	0·1
Calypogeia muelleriana	...		...		4	0·7	2	0·2	...	
Chiloscyphus polyanthos	...		...		2	0·3	1	0·2	...	
Diplophyllum albicans	1	0·3	...		...		...		...	
Harpanthus flotovianus	...		...		1	0·2	...		...	
Leiocolea bantriensis	...		...		1	0·1	1	0·2	...	
Lophocolea bidentata	...		...		3	0·7	3	0·4	...	
Lophozia ventricosa	1	0·2	2	0·4	...		...		...	
Odontoschisma elongatum	...		...		...		...		1	0·1
Pellia epiphylla	4	0·5	...		...		...		...	
P. fabbroniana	...		...		5	1·3	3	0·3	1	0·1
Plectocolea obovata	...		...		...		...		1	0·1
Ptilidium ciliare	2	0·4	1	0·1	3	0·4	2	0·3	...	
Riccardia multifida	...		...		1	0·2	...		1	0·1
R. pinguis	...		...		4	0·9	3	0·4	9	2·0
R. sinuata	...		...		...		3	0·4	1	0·2
Scapania irrigua	...		1	0·2	...		1	0·1	1	0·1
S. nemorosa	...		...		4	0·8	1	0·1	...	
S. uliginosa	2	0·7	...		1	0·1	...		2	0·3
S. undulata	2	0·4	...		1	0·3	...		8	2·1
Tritomaria polita	...		...		...		...		1	0·1
T. quinquedentata	...		...		2	0·4	2	0·3	1	0·2
Cladonia sylvatica	1	0·2	1	0·1	...		1	0·1	...	
C. uncialis	1	0·1	...		...		...		...	
Peltidia aphthosa	...		...		...		1	0·1	...	
Stereocaulon evolutoides	...		...		...		...		1	0·1

* Including *Sphagnum capillaceum*.

TABLE 64

Springs and flushes

Vegetation type	(1) *Philonotis—Saxifraga stellaris*	(2) *Pohlia albicans*	(3) *Anthelia—Deschampsia cespitosa*	(4) *Narthecium—Sphagnum*	(5) *Cratoneuron—Saxifraga aizoides*	(6) *Carex—Saxifraga aizoides*	(7) *Low level facies*
Number of stands .	23	8	4	3	11	18	7
Plot size (sq. m.) .	2·0 (mean)	4	4	4	4	4	4
Altitudinal range (m.) .	518–975	868–1097	975–1051	746–823	328–914	335–883	30–427
Soil type and drainage class	Skeletal mud	Skeletal mud	Skeletal mud	Skeletal mud	Skeletal mud	Skeletal mud	Skeletal mud
Slope (degrees) .	...	...	...	...	...	0–30	2–25
pH .	5·7–6·1 *	...	...	...	7·3–7·4 *	5·6–7·0	...
Total vegetation cover (%)	90–100	90–100	90–100	90–100	80–100	65 (mean)	70 (mean)
Calluna vulgaris .	...	...	...	...	...	2 0·2	3 0·6
Empetrum hermaphroditum	...	...	...	...	...	1 0·1	...
Erica tetralix .	...	...	...	3 0·7	...	1 0·1	7 1·9
Equisetum arvense .	1 0·1	...	...	...	...	...	...
E. hyemale .	...	...	...	...	...	1 0·1	...
E. palustre .	...	1 0·1	...	...	5 0·9	1 0·2	...
E. variegatum .	...	...	...	...	1 0·2	1 0·2	...
Lycopodium alpinum .	...	...	...	...	...	...	...
L. selago .	...	...	...	3 0·1	...	1 0·1	...
Selaginella selaginoides	...	...	8 1·0	10 1·7	1 0·2	7 1·5	4 0·9
Agrostis canina .	2 0·4	...	...	3 0·3	2 0·4	4 0·7	...
A. stolonifera .	5 1·4	...	...	...	4 1·0	1 0·1	...
A. tenuis .	2 0·6	1 0·4	3 0·8	...	4 1·0	1 0·2	...
Anthoxanthum odoratum .	3 0·6	...	...	...	...	2 0·2	...
Briza media .	1 0·1	...	...	...	...	1 0·1	...
Deschampsia alpina .	...	...	...	...	...	...	...
D. cespitosa .	8 2·5	10 2·4	10 3·3	...	6 1·3	5 0·9	...
D. flexuosa .	...	...	...	...	...	1 0·1	...
Festuca ovina agg.	1 0·2	...	...	3 0·3	2 0·6	8 2·1	1 0·3
F. rubra .	4 1·3	1 0·3	...	7 1·3	8 2·2	2 0·6	1 0·3
Molinia caerulea .	...	...	...	7 1·3	...	3 0·8	9 2·1
Nardus stricta .	1 0·1	...	8 1·0	10 3·0	...	4 0·7	...

* Water samples.

Species	1	2	3	4	5	6	7	8
Poa alpina	...	...	1 0·1	...	...	...	...	...
P. annua	...	...	...	...	...	3 0·6	...	...
P. pratensis	...	...	5 1·3	...	...	...	1 0·1	...
P. trivialis	...	1 0·1	...	...	...	1 0·3	1 0·1	...
Sieglingia decumbens	...	1 0·1	...	...	...	...	...	...
Carex atrofusca	...	1 0·2	...	...	...	1 0·3	2 0·4	...
C. bigelowii	...	1 0·1	...	7 1·3	5 1·3	1 0·3	...	...
C. curta	3 0·7	10 3·8	1 0·1	...	...	...	1 0·1	...
C. demissa	4 1·1	6 1·4	3 0·8	...	...	...	1 0·1	...
C. dioica	3 0·6	1 0·2	...	...	...	...	...	...
C. echinata	...	1 0·4	...	...	...	...	1 0·4	...
C. flacca	...	2 0·8	...	...	...	...	...	...
C. hostiana	9 3·0	1 0·1	3 0·6	...	...	...	...	...
C. nigra	3 0·4	9 3·1	4 0·9	...	...	...	...	...
C. panicea	7 1·9	7 1·7	1 0·2	...	...	...	1 0·1	...
C. pulicaris	...	1 0·3	1 0·1	...	...	...	1 0·1	...
C. saxatilis	...	...	...	...	3 2·0	...	...	...
Eleocharis multicaulis	1 0·3	...	...	...	...	...	...	...
E. quinqueflora	6 2·1	3 0·9	...	7 2·0	...	1 0·4	1 0·2	...
Eriophorum angustifolium	7 1·4	4 0·6	...	...	...	...	...	...
E. latifolium	7 1·3	1 0·2	...	...	...	...	...	...
Juncus alpinoarticulatus	...	2 0·5	2 0·4	...	...	...	...	...
J. articulatus	6 1·9	6 1·6	1 0·3	7 2·0	...	...	...	...
J. kochii	7 1·4	4 0·8	1 0·1	...	...	...	3 0·6	...
J. squarrosus	1 0·1	1 0·1	1 0·1	...	...	...	1 0·1	...
J. triglumis	...	8 1·6	...	...	...	...	...	...
Luzula multiflora	...	1 0·1	...	...	...	...	...	...
L. spicata	...	2 0·2	...	...	...	...	...	...
L. sylvatica	...	1 0·1	...	10 7·1	...	...	...	...
Narthecium ossifragum	7 1·7	2 0·2	...	...	...	...	...	...
Platanthera bifolia	1 0·1	...	...	...	...	...	...	...
Potamogeton polygonifolius	1 0·1	...	...	...	...	...	...	...
Schoenus nigricans	6 3·3	...	...	...	...	...	...	...
Tofieldia pusilla	3 0·4	6 0·9	...	...	...	...	...	...
Trichophorum cespitosum	7 2·7	4 0·4	...	10 4·0	...	...	...	...
Triglochin palustris	3 0·1	1 0·1	...	...	...	...	...	...
Alchemilla alpina	2 0·3	...	...	...	...	...	1 0·1	...
A. filicaulis	2 0·4	...	...	...	...	...	1 0·1	...
A. glabra	...	1 0·1	2 0·4	...	...	...	...	...
A. vestita	...	1 0·1	...	...	...	...	...	...

TABLE 64—continued

Vegetation type	(1) Philonotis— Saxifraga stellaris	(2) Pohlia albicans	(3) Anthelia— Deschampsia cespitosa	(4) Narthecium— Sphagnum	(5) Cratoneuron— Saxifraga aizoides	(6) Carex— Saxifraga aizoides	(7) Low level facies
Armeria maritima	2 0·5	...	...	...	...	2 0·5	...
Caltha palustris	...	1 0·4	...	...	2 0·5	...	...
Campanula rotundifolia	1 0·1	...	...	...	...	1 0·1	...
Cardamine pratensis	...	...	...	...	7 1·7	...	...
Cerastium cerastoides	1 0·2	6 1·1	...	...	...	...	...
C. holosteoides	...	...	...	...	...	1 0·1	...
C. arcticum	...	...	...	...	...	1 0·2	...
Cherleria sedoides	2 0·7	...	...	...	...	...	...
Chrysosplenium oppositifolium	...	4 1·1	...	...	3 0·8	...	...
Cochlearia officinalis ssp. alpina	...	...	...	...	1 0·3	...	...
Drosera anglica	...	...	...	...	...	...	9 1·7
D. rotundifolia	...	...	...	...	...	1 0·1	4 0·6
Epilobium alsinifolium	1 0·2	5 1·5	...	...	6 2·0	...	...
E. anagallidifolium	3 0·7	...	...	...	...	1 0·1	...
E. palustre	1 0·3	...	...	...	1 0·2	...	...
Euphrasia officinalis agg.	...	...	...	...	...	6 1·2	3 0·9
Galium boreale	...	...	...	...	...	1 0·1	...
G. saxatile	...	...	...	...	...	1 0·1	...
Geum rivale	1 0·1	...	...	...	1 0·2	2 0·3	...
Hypericum pulchrum	...	...	...	...	...	1 0·1	3 0·1
Leontodon autumnalis	...	...	...	...	...	3 0·4	...
Linum catharticum	...	...	...	...	...	3 0·4	...
Lotus corniculatus	...	...	...	...	...	1 0·1	...
Montia fontana ssp. fontana	2 0·5	1 0·5	...	...	2 0·6	...	...
Oxyria digyna	...	...	...	...	...	1 0·1	...
Pedicularis palustris	...	...	...	...	...	1 0·1	1 0·1
P. sylvatica	...	...	...	...	...	1 0·2	3 0·1
Pinguicula lusitanica	...	...	...	...	...	...	6 0·7
P. vulgaris	...	...	...	...	2 0·3	8 1·6	10 1·4
Plantago maritima	...	...	...	...	...	4 1·1	1 0·3
Polygonum viviparum	...	...	...	...	4 0·7	2 0·2	...
Potentilla erecta	...	...	...	...	...	2 0·2	3 0·4
Ranunculus acris	...	...	...	...	1 0·2	2 0·3	...
R. flammula	1 0·2	...	...	...	...	2 0·6	1 0·3

Species	1	2	3	4	5	6	7
Rhinanthus minor agg.							
Rumex acetosa	1 0·2	1 0·1			2 0·3	1 0·1	
Sagina nodosa						1 0·1	
S. procumbens	1 0·2				1 0·1	1 0·2	
Saussurea alpina							
Saxifraga aizoides					8 1·6	1 0·1	6 1·6
S. oppositifolia	10 3·0	8 2·0				10 3·9	
S. stellaris		4 1·1	5 0·8		1 0·3	4 1·1	
Silene acaulis						2 0·3	
Stellaria alsine	4 1·0					1 0·3	
Succisa pratensis							
Taraxacum officinale agg.	1 0·1		3 0·5		3 0·5	2 0·2	6 0·7
Thalictrum alpinum					2 0·4	3 0·6	1 0·1
Thymus drucei					2 0·4	8 2·1	
Tussilago farfara						4 0·4	
Veronica serpyllifolia ssp. humifusa						1 0·2	
Viola palustris	1 0·2	1 0·3	5 1·0			3 0·3	
V. riviniana	1 0·3					1 0·1	
Acrocladium cuspidatum					1 0·1	1 0·2	
A. sarmentosum	2 0·6	1 0·8					
A. stramineum		3 1·0				1 0·2	
A. trifarium						1 0·4	
Anomobryum filiforme							
Blindia acuta	1 0·1	1 0·1					1 0·3
Brachythecium rivulare	1 0·3					8 2·8	6 1·4
B. rutabulum						1 0·1	
Breutelia chrysocoma						1 0·1	
Bryum alpinum	1 0·1						1 0·3
B. pseudotriquetrum	1 0·3						
B. weigelii		4 0·4	3 0·5			2 0·3	3 0·4
Camptothecium lutescens						1 0·1	
Campylium stellatum						6 1·4	10 3·7
Campylopus atrovirens							3 0·4
Catoscopium nigritum						1 0·1	
Cratoneuron commutatum			10 9·3			6 1·4	
Ctenidium molluscum	7 2·8	3 1·0				4 0·9	4 0·7
Dicranella palustris						2 0·3	6 1·4
Dicranum starkei			3 0·8		2 0·4		
Ditrichum flexicaule						1 0·1	
Drepanocladus exannulatus	3 1·9	3 0·8	3 0·8				1 0·1

Table 64—concluded

Vegetation type	(1) Philonotis—Saxifraga stellaris	(2) Pohlia albicans	(3) Anthelia—Deschampsia cespitosa	(4) Narthecium—Sphagnum	(5) Cratoneuron—Saxifraga aizoides	(6) Carex—Saxifraga aizoides	(7) Low level facies
Drepanocladus revolvens						7 2·2	6 1·6
Fissidens adianthoides						2 0·3	1 0·1
F. osmundoides						2 0·4	
Gymnostomum recurvirostrum						1 0·2	
Hygrohypnum luridum		3 0·6				3 0·3	1 0·1
Hylocomium splendens						1 0·1	
Meesia uliginosa						1 0·1	
Mnium seligeri							
Oligotrichum hercynicum	1 0·1					1 0·3	
Orthothecium rufescens						1 0·1	
Philonotis calcarea			5 1·0		7 1·6	1 0·1	
P. fontana	9 3·3	6 2·0				1 0·1	
P. seriata	1 0·1		5 1·5				
Pohlia glacialis var. glacialis		10 8·6	3 0·5				
P. ludwigii		5 1·0					
P. mutans							
Pohlia sp.			3 0·5				
Polytrichum alpinum	3 0·4					1 0·1	
P. commune							
P. norvegicum			5 1·3				
Pseudoscleropodium purum							
Rhacomitrium aquaticum	1 0·1					1 0·1	
R. fasciculare			3 0·8				
R. heterostichum			3 0·5			1 0·1	3 0·7
R. lanuginosum			3 0·5	7 2·0		1 0·1	
Rhytidialelphus loreus							
R. squarrosus		1 0·3				1 0·1	
R. triquetrus						4 2·2	
Scorpidium scorpioides				10 3·3			10 4·7
Sphagnum compactum				3 0·7			
S. cuspidatum				3 1·3			
S. girgensohnii		1 0·3		3 1·0			
S. papillosum							
S. robustum							

Species	1	2	3	4	5	6	7
S. squarrosum . .	1 0·2	1 0·4					
S. subsecundum .	6 2·3	1 0·4	3 0·8	3 2·0			1 0·1
S. tenellum . .							
S. teres . .	1 0·1		3 0·3	10 4·7			
Splachnum vasculosum	1 0·2	1 0·4					
Tortella tortuosa .						1 0·1	
Anastrepta orcadensis							
Anthelia julacea			10 8·5			1 0·1	
Barbilophozia floerkii			3 0·8			1 0·1	
Blepharostoma trichophyllum							
Calypogeia fissa .	1 0·2					1 0·1	
Chiloscyphus polyanthos .						1 0·1	
Diplophyllum albicans				3 0·3			
Gymnomitrium concinnatum			3 0·5				
Leiocolea bantriensis						1 0·1	
Lophozia quadriloba						1 0·1	
Marchantia polymorpha		3 0·8					
Marsupella emarginata			8 3·5			2 0·3	
Moerckia blyttii .			3 0·5				
Mylia taylori .				3 0·3		1 0·1	
Nardia scalaris .	1 0·1		3 1·0		1 0·1	1 0·1	
Pellia cf. *epiphylla*	1 0·5				1 0·1	1 0·1	
P. fabbroniana .						1 0·1	
Plagiochila asplenioides						1 0·1	
P. spinulosa .		1 0·3				1 0·1	
Plectocolea obovata		1 0·3					
P. paroica .						1 0·1	
Pleurozia purpurea	1 0·2						
Riccardia pinguis		1 0·5			2 0·3	6 1·0	1 0·3
Scapania nemorosa							6 1·0
S. uliginosa .	4 2·8	4 2·0	3 0·5			2 0·3	
S. undulata .	7 2·7	4 0·7	10 3·0				
Solenostoma cordifolium	1 0·4	1 0·1			2 0·3		
S. sphaerocarpum .	1 0·1						
S. triste .	1 0·1						
Cetraria islandica .				3 0·7			
Cladonia bellidiflora .				3 0·7			
C. uncialis .				7 1·3			

TABLE 65

Montane bogs

Vegetation type	(1) Upland *Calluna—Eriophorum*		(2) Lichen-rich facies		(3) Shrub-rich facies		(4) *Empetrum—Eriophorum*	
Number of stands . . .	10		3		8		9	
Plot size (sq. m.) . . .	4		4		4		4	
Altitudinal range (m.) . .	457–762		579–731		457–853		762–914	
Soil type and drainage class .	Blanket bog peat		Blanket bog peat		Blanket bog peat		Blanket bog peat	
Slope (degrees) . . .	0–25		0–10		0–10		0–15	
pH range	3·6–4·2		...		...		...	
Total vegetation cover (%) .	100		100		100		100	
Height of vegetation (cm.) .	10–30		6–12		12–30		5–10	
Arctous alpinus . . .	...		...		6	1·8	...	
Betula nana . . .	...		3	1·3	10	3·3	...	
Calluna vulgaris . . .	10	6·5	10	4·3	10	7·3	2	0·2
Empetrum hermaphroditum .	8	2·4	10	3·3	8	2·3	10	5·1
E. nigrum	2	1·0	...		6	2·0	...	
Erica tetralix . . .	1	0·2	3	1·3	5	0·6	...	
Vaccinium microcarpum .	...		7	2·0	1	0·4	1	0·1
V. myrtillus . . .	9	2·4	10	0·7	9	2·0	9	2·5
V. uliginosum . . .	2	0·2	...		...		8	2·4
V. vitis-idaea . . .	7	1·5	7	0·7	4	0·6	8	2·4
Deschampsia flexuosa . .	2	0·4	...		...		3	0·6
Festuca ovina agg. . .	...		...		...		2	0·3
Nardus stricta . . .	1	0·1	...		...		2	1·0
Carex bigelowii . . .	5	1·6	3	0·7	1	0·1	10	2·1
C. binervis . . .	1	0·1	...		1	0·1	...	
C. nigra	...		...		...		1	0·1
Dactylorchis maculata ssp. *ericetorum*	1	0·1	...		...		...	
Eriophorum angustifolium .	4	1·0	...		5	1·1	8	2·4
E. vaginatum . . .	10	5·3	10	5·0	8	4·0	10	5·3
Juncus squarrosus . .	9	2·7	3	1·7	6	2·3	3	0·2
Listera cordata . . .	4	0·7	...		3	0·3	...	
Luzula multiflora . .	...		...		...		2	0·1
Narthecium ossifragum .	1	0·4	...		...		...	
Trichophorum cespitosum .	4	1·2	...		3	0·4	6	1·7
Chamaepericlymenum suecicum .	4	0·8	...		1	0·1	2	0·2
Galium saxatile . . .	1	0·1	...		...		2	0·3
Melampyrum pratense . .	2	0·3	...		1	0·1	...	
Pinguicula vulgaris . .	5	0·4	...		...		1	0·1
Potentilla erecta . . .	5	0·7	...		3	0·3	2	0·3
Rubus chamaemorus . .	8	2·6	10	3·7	9	2·0	10	2·9
Solidago virgaurea . .	1	0·2	...		...		...	
Trientalis europaea . .	...		...		...		1	0·1
Viola palustris . . .	...		...		...		1	0·1

TABLE 65—*continued*

Vegetation type	(1) Upland Calluna— Eriophorum		(2) Lichen-rich facies		(3) Shrub-rich facies		(4) Empetrum— Eriophorum	
Aulacomnium palustre . . .	2	0·3	...		4	0·6	6	1·4
Campylopus flexuosus . . .	1	0·1	...		3	0·3	1	0·2
Dicranum fuscescens . . .	...		...		...		2	0·2
D. majus	1	0·2	...		...		1	0·2
D. scoparium	4	0·5	3	0·3	4	0·8	4	1·1
Eurhynchium praelongum . .	...		...		1	0·1	...	
Hylocomium splendens . .	9	4·6	10	1·0	9	3·8	4	1·1
Hypnum cupressiforme . .	4	0·8	...		4	1·0	...	
Plagiothecium undulatum . .	4	0·8	...		5	0·9	...	
Pleurozium schreberi . .	8	2·2	7	0·7	9	2·5	9	2·2
Pohlia nutans	...		3	0·3	...		2	0·2
Polytrichum alpestre . . .	...		3	0·7	...		8	1·9
P. alpinum	...		...		...		3	0·7
P. commune	5	0·9	...		1	0·1	4	0·8
Rhacomitrium lanuginosum .	6	1·8	3	1·0	1	0·5	8	1·7
Rhytidiadelphus loreus . .	8	2·5	3	0·3	8	2·0	6	1·6
R. squarrosus	...		...		1	0·4	...	
Sphagnum fuscum . . .	2	0·1	7	1·3	4	0·1	3	0·4
S. magellanicum . . .	...		...		...		3	1·4
S. palustre	1	0·4	...		...		...	
S. papillosum	1	0·7	...		...		6	4·0
S. plumulosum	4	1·4	...		...		4	1·4
S. quinquefarium . . .	4	1·6	...		...		...	
S. recurvum	...		...		1	0·6	...	
S. robustum	...		...		3	1·3	3	1·1
S. rubellum * . . .	8	4·0	10	5·3	9	4·3	9	4·3
S. tenellum	1	0·2	7	1·7	...		2	0·1
Thuidium tamariscinum . .	...		...		...		...	
Anastrepta orcadensis . .	3	0·7	...		...		2	0·6
Barbilophozia floerkii . .	2	0·5	...		1	0·1	1	0·2
Calypogeia muelleriana . .	1	0·2	7	0·7	3	0·3	...	
Diplophyllum albicans . .	2	0·4	...		3	0·3	1	0·2
Lepidozia pearsonii . . .	1	0·1	...		...		...	
L. setacea	...		...		1	0·1	...	
Lophozia cf. *porphyroleuca* .	...		...		...		1	0·1
L. ventricosa	...		3	0·7	4	0·6	6	0·8
Mylia anomala . . .	2	0·2	7	0·7	1	0·1	4	1·0
M. taylori	1	0·2	3	1·0	1	0·1	1	0·3
Odontoschisma sphagni . .	1	0·2	...		...		...	
Ptilidium ciliare . . .	6	1·0	10	1·3	5	1·3	7	1·6
Scapania gracilis . . .	1	0·1	...		...		...	
Cetraria aculeata . . .	1	0·2	3	0·7	...		3	0·2
C. islandica	1	0·2	7	1·3	1	0·3	4	1·0
Cladonia bellidiflora . .	2	0·2	...		...		2	0·2
C. coccifera	1	0·1	...		...		...	
C. cf. *deformis* . . .	...		...		1	0·3	...	
C. gracilis	1	0·1	...		...		3	0·4
C. impexa	1	0·3	...		6	1·3	...	
C. pyxidata	...		...		...		1	0·1

* Including *Sphagnum capillaceum*.

TABLE 65—*concluded*

Vegetation type	(1) Upland *Calluna—Eriophorum*		(2) Lichen-rich facies		(3) Shrub-rich facies		(4) *Empetrum—Eriophorum*	
C. rangiferina agg. . . .	2	0·4	10	4·3	3	0·3	3	0·7
C. squamosa	...		3	0·3	3	0·3	...	
C. sylvatica	6	1·5	10	7·0	4	0·6	9	2·6
C. tenuis	...		3	0·3	...		...	
C. uncialis	5	0·8	7	1·3	3	0·4	4	0·8
Ochrolechia tartarea var. *frigida* .	...		...		...		1	0·2
O. tartarea	1	0·1	3	0·7	...		...	

PART III

HISTORY AND PATTERN OF SCOTTISH VEGETATION

CHAPTER 16

PRE-HISTORY AND ECOLOGICAL HISTORY

D. N. McVEAN

The Pleistocene glaciation of Scotland provides a convenient starting point for any discussion of the history of present-day vegetation in the area. Knowledge of this period, and of the various stages of the advance and retreat of the ice sheets and glaciers in relations to those of Scandinavia and central Europe, continues to increase and Charlesworth (1956) has recently published the result of a life's work on the later stages of the ice retreat in the Highlands.

Botanical opinion has now hardened against any possibility of the survival of vascular plants in Scotland during the period of maximum glaciation and Godwin (1949) has shown that most, if not all, the facts of species distribution can be explained in terms of the Post-glacial history of our flora without the necessity of postulating periglacial survival as Wilmott (1935) had done.

Nevertheless, there is some geomorphological evidence that limited areas such as the summit plateau of the Cairngorms and many headlands along the western seaboard escaped at least the later stages of the glaciation (Dahl, 1954). Whether these localities provided a refuge for any sort of vegetation or plant life is not known.

The presence of macroscopic plant remains and pollen grains in peats and fine grained, or organic, sediments has provided that basis for these studies on vegetational history. The techniques used and the interpretation of the pollen analytical results have been discussed by many authors, notably Faegri and Iversen (1950) and Godwin (1956). Classification of the Post-glacial period is based on the varying composition of the forest, as revealed by remains of the tree species, both micro- and macro-scopic, throughout this time. For this reason the recent outline by Steven and Carlisle (1959) of the forest history of Scotland covers much of the ground of this chapter.

Few Late-glacial sites have been discovered in Scotland and those that have been described have been mostly from south of the Highland line. Donner (1957) lists these and describes the probable composition of Scottish vegetation in Late-glacial times on the basis of his own, and other, published evidence. (cf. also Donner, 1958; Mitchell, 1948, 1952).

Immediately following the withdrawal of the main ice sheet about 15,000 years ago, vegetation was thinly distributed and consisted of grasses, sedges and a few dwarf shrubs, with possibly a fair number of mosses and lichens although no records of these remain. Much rock debris was exposed and this was continually on the move in many places due to frost action (solifluction and cryoturbation) and washing about by rain and melt water. Only on the high Cairngorm plateau, and in one or two other high level sites in the Scottish mountains, does such a regime persist into the present day in this country. In Iceland, Greenland, Spitzbergen and Jan Mayen, however, large areas of country remain at such a periglacial stage.

After the passage of some further 2000–3000 years, those parts of Scotland free from ice were still covered by a largely treeless tundra which already showed the influence of proximity to the sea in the abundance of *Calluna* and other ericaceous species. Donner (1957) considers that the tree pollen content of the deposits (10–20 per cent. of the total pollen) is too low to indicate even so-called "park tundra", in which groves and thickets of scrubby trees and shrubs are scattered about the landscape, except possibly in the extreme south of the country. For the rest, the vegetation most probably consisted of wide stretches of *Empetrum—Calluna* and *Empetrum—Vaccinium* heath, interspersed with heaths and meadows rich in grasses, sedges and forbs on the finer-grained, moister and more base-rich soils. *Dryas octopetala* heaths would certainly have existed on the calcareous rock debris and, in addition, might possibly have been widespread on freshly exposed, less basic substrata. Dwarf birch (*Betula nana*) and dwarf willows (including *Salix herbacea*) entered the composition of the heaths and mires as they still do in sub-arctic lands today. Sea buckthorn (*Hippophaë rhamnoides*) has been recorded from one site near the coast and it might have been fairly widespread inland in Scotland at this time, as it appears to have been further south.

To obtain a picture of the vegetation at this time (Allerød interstadial) the best that can be done is to examine the present vegetation at intermediate altitudes on the hill slopes above the tree line and above the zone of tall heather moor. In particular, the more species-rich dwarf shrub heaths on exposed shoulders and spurs and the *Calluna— Eriophorum* bogs rich in dwarf birch give some impression of an oligotrophic, late glacial vegetation. The plant communities on areas with greater than average snow accumulation must have been quite similar to those of the present day.

The climate then became colder again for 1000 years or so, after this interstadial, and there seems to have been a return to extremely open vegetation with much frost movement of the soil. The end of this period, some 10,000 years ago, marks the beginning of the true Post-glacial epoch, with a rapid amelioration of the climate and rapid vegetation changes, so that a second tundra/heath period, if it existed at all, has not been recorded. Instead, there was a rapid colonisation of the open vegetation by a rather sparse forest of birch and pine, with birch as the dominant tree species. Scottish deposits from this period are no more numerous than those of Late-glacial times but it would appear that the non-woodland element of the vegetation returned to what it had been at the height of the Late-glacial climatic amelioration.

During the succeeding 2000 years or so, the stands of birch and pine thickened to form a closed forest, and gradually increasing quantities of pine over the low ground largely excluded the ericaceous and grassy heaths of earlier times. Around 7000 B.C. there was a spectacular increase in the amount of hazel (*Corylus avellana*) which had been a subordinate species up till then although generally more abundant than in the south. Closed forest and abundant flowering hazel are difficult to reconcile in view of the known ecological requirements of that species and several suggestions have been put forward to explain the pollen spectrum of the period. The best hypotheses seems to be that the closing of the forest canopy and the parallel exclusion of heath that took place were brought about by colonising hazel which came in under a canopy of birch and pine open enough to allow abundant production of hazel pollen. Pure hazel scrub probably developed in many places. Dense hazel thicket under a thin stand of pine and spruce can be seen at one or two places on sandy eskers in southern Finland at the present day but otherwise there are no examples of such vegetation.

According to the evidence from pollen analysis, pine was at its maximum post-glacial extent about this time and was a particularly important forest constituent in north and east Scotland as well as in the south and east of England. Both elm (*Ulmus* spp.) and oak (*Quercus* spp.) were present and spreading through the Scottish forests of the period, with perhaps the formation of small areas of mixed oak forest toward the south.

Like hazel, alder appears to have played a more important role in Scotland during early post-glacial times than it did in the south of Britain. A rapid increase in the proportion of alder about 5000 B.C. is general, except in north-east Scotland (Durno, 1956, 1957, 1958), and has been used to mark the transition from Boreal to Atlantic times.

Both the increasing prominence of alder and the sudden acceleration of bog growth that took place at this time indicate increasing wetness of climate. Independent evidence of a change from a continental climate to a marked oceanic tendency in the vigour of the north Atlantic atmospheric circulation is given by a peat profile on the island of St. Kilda recently re-investigated (McVean, 1961). At an exposed cliff top site, over 100 m. above the sea, the horizon to which this transition would be assigned on the evidence of the tree pollen is also marked by the replacement of grass pollen by that of *Plantago maritima*, the species which dominates the present day sward at this site. This seems to indicate a sudden increase in frequency of gale force winds with consequent inundation of the vegetation by sea spray.

In spite of the supposed climatic wetness of this phase Durno and McVean (1959) have demonstrated that forest and moor fires did occur at that time in the neighbourhood of Beinn Eighe in west Ross-shire, and that they have continued to play an important part in vegetation development up to the present day. Superficial observations elsewhere in the Highlands indicates that this was not merely a local feature and, even on the island of St. Kilda, McVean (1961) found small fragments of charcoal, probably of *Calluna*, in peat of this age, although the most convincing fire horizon lay somewhat lower and may have belonged to the drier late-Boreal period.

Short spells of dry spring weather, such as form a feature of our present climate, may also have occurred in Atlantic times and rendered the vegetation dry enough to catch fire from lightning strikes. The Highland forests that were burned at this date appear to have consisted largely of pine, juniper and birch, with alder in the wetter places.

After about 2000 years (3000 B.C.) the climatic pendulum appears to have swung in the opposite direction once again and more continental conditions brought about some drying of the Scottish bogs. Pine stumps, and, more rarely, fallen pine logs, are particularly abundant in peat of this age throughout the Highlands. In the northern Highlands at least, however, it is difficult to detect any division between an Atlantic phase of treeless blanket bog and the sub-Boreal phase in which pine colonised the drying surface. Pine stumps scarred by fire and zones of pine charcoal are abundant in peat which shows little sign of there having been a check in bog growth. Pollen analysis of the same peats fails to show a pine pollen peak corresponding to the remains of the burned forests but in view of the widespread occurrence of such remains it is difficult to accept altogether the opinion expressed by Godwin (1956) that these pine forests on bogs failed to influence the general pollen rain because they were strictly localised.

The general pollen spectrum then indicated a preponderance of birch/alder forest with subordinate pine and oak and decreasing small amounts of elm. In the north-west Highlands pine remained more abundant than elsewhere, as in earlier times.

From 500 B.C. bog growth, where it had been interrupted, was resumed and there was a steady reduction in the proportion of forest cover extending into historical times. After the appearance of man upon the scene it is difficult to decide which of the changes in forest extent and composition were due to climatic change and which to man's direct and indirect influence. Pollen analysis reveals little significant change in the composition of the diminishing forests until the surface of the peat deposits is reached. Here, the marked increase in the proportion of pine pollen has been set down as due to the increased planting of pine over the last two centuries. In fact, Steven and Carlisle (1959) are of the opinion that the percentage of Scots Pine forest, both planted and natural, at the present day is probably as high as it has ever been in the Post-glacial period.

The overall picture of the Scottish forests that emerges from pollen analytical studies is one that changes little throughout the Post-glacial period compared with that of southern England and the Continent. The changes seem to become less with increasing distances north and west, although the paucity of suitable sites where the record extends back beyond Atlantic times makes it difficult to be sure of this. Certainly it is more difficult to zone diagrams from the Scottish peats using the criteria worked out in southern and Continental regions. Birch appears to have been the dominant species throughout with alder, hazel and pine next in order of importance. The species of mixed oak forest are never prominent, although there is a distinct possibility of their being under-represented in the pollen rain due to low pollen production and any fluctuation is too inconsistent for the purposes of diagram zonation. Beech (*Fagus sylvatica*), ash (*Fraxinus excelsior*), lime (*Tilia cordata*) and holly (*Ilex aquifolium*) are noted too infrequently to have any significance as indicators.

Archaeological evidence indicates that man had little or no influence on the Scottish forests until Bronze Age times (*c.* 1000 B.C.) when progressive clearance and crop cultivation began together with the use of forest grazing. In Roman times the tempo of exploitation increased throughout the lowlands and Steven and Carlisle (1959) point out that dispossessed native tribes may have extended grazing and cultivation into the formerly sparsely populated Highland region.

Later, historical records are conflicting about the extent of forest at any particular time but it seems reasonably certain that accessible resources were exhausted by the fifteenth century and the story from then on is concerned with the discovery and exploitation of the Highland forests, of oak and pine, for timber and for charcoal burning. Graphic accounts of the destruction are given by Ritchie (1919) and Darling (1947). The remains of the native pine forests were used to meet the need for timber in two world wars, and surviving areas of oak scrub of doubtful status are being cleared to make way for new coniferous plantations.

There have been few attempts anywhere in Britain to link Post-glacial vegetation history, as revealed by pollen analysis and peat stratigraphy, to the existing vegetation of a region and to the available historical records. Durno and McVean (1959), working in the neighbourhood of the Beinn Eighe Nature Reserve, have traced the continuity of the local pine forest from Boreal times to the present day and have shown that the dwarf juniper scrub lying above the forest is also of respectable antiquity. One of the most important features of the local peat deposits was the widespread occurrence of charcoal horizons, which represented the destruction of at least four successive forests in Boreal, Atlantic and modern times, the last forest extending to about 350 metres above sea-level and giving way to a juniper and heather scrub which was also burned. The modern fire was probably contemporaneous with the exploitation of the oak forest on the opposite side of Loch Maree to provide charcoal for the local iron works of the late eighteenth century. This fire consumed the shallow raw humus of the forest as well as standing trees over a large area. Durno and McVean could find no evidence of the period at which the oak stands became established and the pollen record did not suggest that oak had ever been more widespread in the district than today, even at the climatic optimum.

The lack of a peak in pine pollen, corresponding with extensive remains of pine in blanket peat, has already been mentioned. In the same way, substantial quantities of oak stumps and timber found, for example, in the bog of Buchan (Aberdeenshire) and the Carse of Stirling do not agree with the generally low levels of oak pollen in diagrams from these areas. There are other reasons for not accepting too uncritically the evidence of pollen statistics which may present a somewhat distorted picture of forest composition. Until more experimental evidence has been obtained concerning the distances that pollen can be transported and until the composition of a mixed forest can be compared with the pollen rain resulting from it, the findings of pollen analysis must continue to be interpreted in the light of present knowledge of the ecology of the various species involved.

Autecological investigations are most useful in elucidating vegetation changes within recent times. McVean (1955) has shown that alder trees (*Alnus glutinosa*) above about 300 m. in the Highlands fail to set good seed at the present day and that the moribund, open alderwood extending above this altitude in some places must, therefore, have become established during a more continental climatic phase about the middle of the nineteenth century. Mackenzie (1924) writes of the minor climatic optimum obtaining in the west Highlands about this time when abundant crops of wild fruits and nuts, not now abundant, were obtained. It appears, therefore, that the continental fluctuations of wider amplitude in pre-historical times may have resulted in the upward extension of alderwood on the hills, although the oceanic phases were more favourable for the growth of alder on the low ground.

There is little evidence concerning the general level of the forest limit during the various climatic phases mentioned above. The remains of pine, birch and juniper in blanket peat indicate that the forest limit lay at a maximum of just over 1000 m. during the post-glacial climatic optimum and it can only be supposed that it ascended and descended according to the continentality and oceanicity of the various phases. The potential tree limit may lie not far short of 1000 m. in sheltered places even today, although 600 m. on a windswept ridge is the highest observable limit.

Of the history of non-forest vegetation very little is known. There are a few promising sites where pollen and macroscopic remains of mountain plants may have been preserved in lake muds and peats (as in the Cwm Idwal locality in Wales described by Godwin (1955)) but none have been investigated. The sites from which Lewis (1905–11) described "arctic beds" containing *Betula nana, Salix arbuscula* and other arctic-alpine species intercalated with forest layers have not been re-discovered and doubt has been thrown upon the identification of the species (Samuelsson, 1910; Erdtman, 1928; Poore and McVean, 1957). Examination of the peats underlying *Calluna—Eriophorum* bog with *Betula nana* and *Arctous alpinus*, as recommended by Poore and McVean (1957), has so far failed to reveal fragments of anything but the dominant species. Since *B. nana* and mountain willows may be found well below the actual, or potential, tree line at the present day, their remains could conceivably alternate with those of forest trees at intermediate altitudes with changes in local habitat unconnected with major climatic fluctuations. In general, the identifiable remains of dwarf shrub and herbaceous species in Scottish bog peats show that there has been little or no change in floristic composition of the bog vegetation since Boreal times.

REFERENCES

CHARLESWORTH, J. K.   1956   The late-glacial history of the Highlands and Islands of Scotland. *Trans. Roy. Soc. Edinb.*, **62**, 769–928.

DAHL, E.   1954   Weathered gneisses at the island of Runde, Sunnmøre, western Norway and their geological interpretation. *Nytt Magasin for Botanikk*, **3**, 5–23.

DARLING, F. FRASER   1947   *Natural History in the Highlands and Islands.* London.

DURNO, S. E.   1956   Pollen analysis of peat deposits in Scotland. *Scot. geogr. Mag.*, **72**, 177–187.

                   1957   Certain aspects of vegetational history in north-east Scotland. *Scot. geogr. Mag.*, **73**, 176–184.

DURNO, S. E.   1958 Pollen analysis of peat deposits in eastern Sutherland and Caithness. *Scot. geogr. Mag.*, **74**, 127–135.

DURNO, S. E. and   1959 Forest history of the Beinn Eighe Nature Reserve. *New Phytol.*, **58**, 228–236.
  McVEAN, D. N.

DONNER, J. J.   1958 Loch Mahaick, a late-glacial site in Perthshire. *New Phytol.*, **57**, 183–186.

                         1957 The geology and vegetation of late-glacial retreat stages in Scotland. *Trans. Roy. Soc. Edinb.*, **63**, 221–264.

ERDTMAN, G.   1928 Studies in the post-arctic history of the forests of north-western Europe. I. Investigations in the British Isles. *Geol. Foren. Stockh. Forh.*, **50**, 123–192.

FAEGRI, K. and   1950 *A textbook of modern Pollen Analysis*. Copenhagen.
  IVERSEN, J.

GODWIN, H.   1949 The spreading of the British Flora considered in relation to conditions of the Late-glacial period. *J. Ecol.*, **37**, 140–147.

                         1955 Vegetational History at Cwm Idwal: a Welsh plant refuge. *Svensk. bot. Tidskr.*, **49**, 1–2; 35–43.

                         1956 *The History of the British Flora*. Cambridge.

LEWIS, F. J.   1905–07, 1911 The plant remains in Scottish peat mosses. *Trans. Roy. Soc. Edinb.*, **41**, 699–723: **45**, 335–360: **46**, 33–70: **47**, 793–833.

MACKENZIE, O. H.   1924 *A Hundred Years in the Highlands*. London.

McVEAN, D. N.   1955 Ecology of *Alnus glutinosa* (L.) Gaertn. I. Fruit formation. *J. Ecol.*, **43**, 46–60.

                         1961 Flora and vegetation of the islands of St. Kilda and North Rona in 1958. *J. Ecol.*, **49**, 39–54.

MITCHELL, G. F.   1948 Late-glacial deposits in Berwickshire. *New Phytol.*, **47**, 262–264.

                         1952 Late-glacial deposits at Garscadden Mains, near Glasgow. *New Phytol.*, **50**, 277–286.

POORE, M. E. D. and   1957 A new approach to Scottish mountain vegetation. *J. Ecol.*, **45**, 401–439.
  McVEAN, D. N.

RITCHIE, J.   1919 *The influence of man on animal life in Scotland*. Cambridge.

SAMUELSSON, G.   1910 Scottish peat mosses. A contribution to the knowledge of the late-quarternary vegetation and climate of North-Western Europe. *Bull. Geol. Inst. Univ. Uppsala*, **10**, 197–260.

STEVEN, H. M. and   1959 *The native pinewoods of Scotland*. Edinburgh.
  CARLISLE, A.

WILMOTT, A. J.   1935 Evidence in favour of survival of the British Flora in glacial times. *Proc. Roy. Soc.*, **B118**, 215–222.

CHAPTER 17

REGIONAL PATTERN OF THE VEGETATION

D. N. McVEAN

In Chapters 4 to 15 the vegetation types of Scotland have been described and arranged, firstly according to altitudinal zones and secondly according to the predominant life form of the constituent species. Some indication has been given for each type of its relative abundance and its approximate distribution throughout the country.

The purpose of the present chapter is to consider Scottish vegetation on a regional basis and to examine the extent to which the abundance of particular types and their occurrence in association with one another vary from district to district. This topic has already been touched upon to some extent in previous chapters so that only the broad outline of the quantitatively important vegetation need by considered here.

If the information available under each type of vegetation is related to existing maps, such as that of Geddes and Stamp, it is obvious that regional differences do exist and that these are determined, on the large scale, by climatic and geomorphological variation and, in detail, by differences in geology both solid and superficial. The regional boundaries can be drawn in a great variety of ways based on different, valid criteria so that the arrangement of boundaries adopted here is largely an arbitrary one.

Apart from cultivated and urban land, four main regions have been distinguished and outlined on the accompanying map (Fig. 61): north Highland; east-central Highland; west-central Highland; southern. The islands off the western seaboard from Arran to Lewis and the northern isles of Orkney and Shetland form a separate group for descriptive purposes but not a natural region. A similar consideration applies to the cultivated land of the eastern and southern central parts of the country; they are not discussed here.

EAST-CENTRAL HIGHLANDS

The east-central Highland area stretches from the Highland Boundary Fault in the south-east to Huntly and Inverness in the north and as far west as Rannoch Moor; it also includes a small portion north of the Great Glen from Drumnadrochit to Oykell Bridge and Helmsdale.

KEY

North region		West central region	
South region		Islands	
East central region		Cultivated land	

Fig. 61. Map showing the principal vegetational regions of Scotland and the main tendencies of woodland distribution.

In this area heather dominated vegetation is the most important feature of the plant cover and from 150 to 450 m. heather moor occupies the largest share of the free-draining morainic terrain on slopes of all aspects. In some places such as Dinnet and Newtonmore, where the raw humus layer is thin or absent, *Arctostaphylos uva-ursi* becomes co-dominant with the heather and certain other species (*Lathyrus montanus*, *Pyrola media*, *Genista anglica*), which are otherwise sparse or absent in heather moor, become prominent. Badly drained hollows and flats have deeper peat with *Sphagnum*—*Eriophorum* bog containing an abundance of *Erica tetralix*, *Carex pauciflora* and *Narthecium ossifragum*. Where there is water movement poor fens of *Carex rostrata*, *Eriophorum angustifolium*, *Menyanthes trifoliata* and *Equisetum* spp. are developed.

Above 450 m. the pure heather moors pass over to *Calluna*—*Trichophorum* communities, even on well drained slopes, and this transition appears to be encouraged by heather burning in most areas. *Calluna*—*Trichophorum* communities may also be found in the heather moor below 300 m. where the ground is slightly wetter.

Calluna—*Eriophorum* bog also occupies large areas of flat or gently undulating ground at all levels up to about 900 m. in this region. The underlying peat is deeper than under *Calluna*—*Trichophorum* moor but not so charged with water as that of the *Sphagnum*—*Eriophorum* bogs in the hollows. Cloudberry (*Rubus chamaemorus*) is generally abundant in this vegetation and *Cladonia* lichens are co-dominant in some places such as the Ladder Hills.

These three heathery types of vegetation between them occupy most of the terrain and the distinctive linear mosaic pattern of systematic heather burning lies over them all. On steep, sunless slopes which are difficult to burn a tall *Vaccinium*—*Calluna* vegetation, closely related to the woodland floor vegetation of open pine stands, may be developed between 300 and 800 m. On the exposed ground of hill ridges and summits the heather becomes dwarfed and mixed with other prostrate shrubs to form lichen-rich dwarf *Calluna* heath from about 670 m. to the altitudinal limit of *Calluna* at about 970 m. In one or two places around the flanks of the Cairngorms and the Monadhliath this vegetation becomes completely dominated by shrubby *Cladonia* spp. to form a true lichen heath.

The two principal peat types of the region are the fibrous, rubbery peat of *Calluna* and *Calluna*—*Trichophorum* moors and the soft, fibrous and stringy peat of *Eriophorum* dominated areas.

Above the *Calluna* limit the most abundant vegetation type of the summits is *Rhacomitrium* moss heath. This is a type common to the high ground of the three Highland regions and it is particularly well developed on Ben Wyvis. The bogs of the high plateaux belong to the *Empetrum*—*Eriophorum* association which is better represented in this region than elsewhere in the Highlands.

Other communities of minor importance in the region are snow bed *Vaccinium* and *Vaccinium*—*Empetrum* heaths, species-poor *Agrostis*—*Festuca* grassland, low and middle alpine *Nardus* grassland, *Juncus trifidus* heaths and montane communities of springs, flushes and late snow beds.

Although the central Cairngorm block is hardly typical of the region it is probably the best area in the country for demonstrating altitudinal zonation and its vegetation has been more extensively studied than any other part of the Highlands.

Altitudinal zonation of the vegetation on ridges and spurs differs from that in the glens and corries and there are also minor variations according to the aspect of the slope. Typical ridge zonation is as follows:—

Pure heather moor or pine forest with patches of bog extends to 500 m. followed by *Trichophorum—Calluna* communities to the heather limit at 950 m. Within the upper half of the *Trichophorum—Calluna* belt exposed areas carry the lichen-rich dwarf *Calluna* heath and, where wind speeds are particularly great, the vegetation cover is broken into a pattern of continuous or broken waves. The lichens sometimes attain dominance where vegetation cover is complete. Heather moor without *Trichophorum* sometimes extends uphill to where the stunting of the *Calluna* begins. Above the heather limit comes *Rhacomitrium* heath which may extend to the summits if these are lower than 1150 m. If the ridge continues above this altitude the unbroken moss heath gives way to an increasing proportion of bare ground with *Juncus trifidus* tussocks and more abundant lichens. Roughly circular patches of *Calluna—Eriophorum* bog are found throughout the moss heath where seepage water emerges.

In the corries, zonation follows a different course: *Vaccinium—Calluna* vegetation or *Calluna—Eriophorum* bog, or a mixture of these two, extends to about 800 m. This is followed by mossy *Vaccinium—Empetrum* heath, perhaps with patches of pure Vaccinetum where snow lies longer, or by an intimate mosaic of low alpine *Nardus* grassland and *Vaccinium—Empetrum*. Pure *Rhacomitrium* or *Rhacomitrium—Empetrum* heath then appears and continues in mosaic with *Nardus* patches and lichen-rich *Vaccinium—Empetrum* heath to about 1100 m. Lichen-rich *Vaccinium* heath also occurs with both dwarf *Calluna* and moss heath between 700 and 1000 m. There may be extensive areas of deep peat with *Empetrum—Eriophorum* vegetation from 800 to 1100 m. where slopes are gentle. Above this altitude the typical plateau complex of the Cairngorms is developed. This is a mosaic of *Juncus trifidus* heath, middle alpine *Nardus* grassland, *Carex bigelowii—Polytrichum alpinum* heath and late snow bed moss heaths dominated by *Dicranum starkei* or *Rhacomitrium heterostichum* and *R. fasciculare*. Patches of *Agrostis—Festuca* grassland may be encountered up to 1000 m. but, above this level, comparable sites are dominated by *Deschampsia cespitosa*. *D. cespitosa* is also abundant around springs and irrigated areas in the high corries and on the plateaux. Local patches of vegetation in the late snow beds may be dominated by *Deschampsia flexuosa*.

Springs and flushes, and the banks of torrents between 500 and 1000 m. have a mossy vegetation dominated by *Philonotis fontana, Dicranella palustris, Sphagnum subsecundum, Scapania undulata* and *S. uliginosa*. Above 1000 m. *Pohlia albicans* var. *glacialis* or *P. ludwigii* become increasingly common in the same habitat and wet stony areas adjacent are dominated by the liverworts *Anthelia juratzkana* and *A. julacea*.

The Clova-Caenlochan-Glen Shee area is atypical of the region as a whole. Here, an extensive development of floristically rich *Agrostis—Festuca, Nardus* and

Vaccinium grasslands occurs in the glens and on the steep hill slopes due to the occurrence of soft calcareous rocks. Montane willow scrub, *Dryas octopetala* heath, tall herb and dwarf herb vegetation and floristically rich montane mires are relatively common. To some extent the *Dicranum fuscescens—Carex bigelowii* moss heath replaces *Rhacomitrium* heath as on the Glas Maol plateau.

Calcareous rock outcrops are also responsible for the rich assemblage of mountain species in such famous botanical localities as the head of Glen Clova and Caenlochan, and Creag an Dail Bheag.

The region corresponds roughly to the area of predominant pine forest (cf. Fig. 61), especially that with a floor of *Vaccinium*—moss species, and to a large extent the heather moors have been derived from such forest by burning and felling. The process can still be seen in operation between the valleys of the Dee and Don. Pure heather moor can be regarded as replacing dense, tall pine forest, while *Calluna—Trichophorum* and *Calluna—Eriophorum* bogs probably carried more open stands of stunted trees with juniper scrub up to the forest limit at 600–800 m.

Juniper is the characteristic tall shrub of the region in natural, open pine stands and on heather moor wherever burning has been moderate. On some moors the juniper is now confined to irrigated and grassy areas where there has been some protection from fire. Broom (*Sarothamnus scoparius*) is equally characteristic of the fringes of cultivation at lower elevations.

The land use of the region varies from deer forest and hill sheep, with subsidiary grouse interest, in the central area, to grouse moors and hill farms towards the peripheral cultivation of the south and east. There are natural forests of birch and pine and planted forests of conifers in the Dee and Spey valleys, Nairnshire and Morayshire and north of the Great Glen. As an important constituent of natural birch populations, *Betula pendula*, is virtually confined to this region. Scots pine is used extensively in re-afforestation and larch (*Larix decidua* and *L. leptolepis*) is important in some areas such as Dunkeld.

Northern Highlands

The northern Highland region comprises the Scottish mainland north of Loch Carron and Strathfarrar but excluding the south-east portion already considered in the east-central region.

In this region the prevailing vegetation is blanket bog, consisting of *Trichophorum—Eriophorum* bog at the lower levels (up to 450 m.) and *Calluna—Eriophorum* bog above. The *Calluna—Eriophorum* bogs of the north often contain appreciable quantities of *Betula nana* and *Arctous alpinus* in addition to cloudberry except in the extreme west where stands are more restricted in size. The proportion of ground covered by bog increases towards the north and the cover is finally broken only by the isolated summits of Ben Hope, Ben Loyal, Ben Klibreck, Ben More Assynt and one or two other peaks. Both the typical and sedge-rich facies of *Trichophorum—Eriophorum* bog occur and on many hill slopes there is a gradual transition to the western phase of *Trichophorum—Calluna* moor which has more abundant *Sphagnum* and other moisture-demanding species than the eastern phase. The dominance of bog vegetation is probably a response both to climatic wetness and to the impermeable glacial drifts of the region. The peat type is typically colloidal or pseudo-fibrous and formed mainly of the remains of *Trichophorum cespitosum.*

Along with the *Calluna—Trichophorum* moor goes a moorland type with co-dominant *Molinia* and *Calluna* which replaces it wherever there is a moderate rate of water movement through the peat, especially if the water originates in bedrock or glacial debris rather than in bog. This vegetation in turn grades into *Molinia—Myrica* mire with increase in both water amount and movement, and into pure *Molinia* grassland where there is periodic irrigation combined with good drainage. (cf. pp. 194-196). Flushes and mires containing *Schoenus nigricans* are also a characteristic associate of the blanket bog of the region, especially on the coast and along the line of the Durness dolomite, but *Juncus acutiflorus* and *J. effusus* mires are by no means common.

In none of these communities is *Calluna* a vigorous constituent but to some extent its lack of physiognomic prominence can be ascribed to moor burning. In this part of the country burning tends to depress *Calluna* and encourage competitors such as *Trichophorum, Molinia* and *Erica tetralix*, while the burning itself has been carried out in a more haphazard and harmful fashion than in the east.

Steep, north-facing slopes between 300 and 700 m. that have escaped recent moor fires again carry the *Vaccinium—Calluna* association as in the east-central region but the vegetation tends to be richer in bryophytes, particularly oceanic liverworts. The total area covered by this type is greater than in the east-central region.

Pure heather moor is of only fragmentary occurrence in the northern region, being confined to sunny, well drained slopes. Patches rich in *Arctostaphylos uva-ursi* occur but these are confined to exposed sites with coarse soils lacking surface raw humus. *Lathyrus, Pyrola* and *Genista* are absent and *Rhacomitrium lanuginosum* is generally abundant.

Heather becomes dwarfed by exposure at lower elevations in this region than in the central Highlands; as low as 300 m. in the extreme north, but at about 500 m. on the average hill ridge. Lichen-rich dwarf *Calluna* heath does occur, as in the east-central region, but only east of a line from Whiten Head to Loch Cluanie, and the characteristic dwarf shrub heath of the northern Highlands is the *Arctous—Calluna* association which is richer in species and also differs in some other aspects. To the west of the Whiten Head-Loch Cluanie line *Rhacomitrium*-rich dwarf *Calluna* heath occurs along with stands of the *Arctous—Calluna* association where exposure is less severe and deeper, wetter raw humus has accumulated.

Above the altitudinal limit of *Calluna*, at about 750–800 m., the most widespread vegetation type is again the *Rhacomitrium* moss heath which is particularly well developed on the hills of the Fannich Forest. Associated with the moss heath are stands of the *Juncus trifidus—Festuca ovina* association on the wind-eroded surfaces of spurs, ridges and summits from 600 to 1100 m. This association is virtually confined to the northern Highlands but it has its equivalent in the more exposed of the central Highland *Juncus trifidus* heaths.

A second moss heath, the *Deschampsia cespitosa—Rhytidiadelphus loreus* association is well developed in this region, while occurring only on Ben Wyvis and Clova in the east-central region. It requires a greater amount of winter snow protection than the *Rhacomitrium* heath and, therefore, has a more restricted total cover although present in appreciable quantities on all the high tops of the north.

Communities of minor importance in the northern region are the prostrate juniper scrub of the Cambrian quartzite, *Vaccinium—Empetrum* heath, *Rhacomitrium—Empetrum* heath, *Festuca ovina* and *Rhacomitrium*-rich *Vaccinium* heath, montane *Deschampsia cespitosa* grassland, low alpine *Nardus* grassland and various sedge-dominated flushes. Late snow bed vegetation is confined to the higher summits in the south of the region.

The Durness, Inchnadamph, Elphin and Loch Kishorn areas are not typical of the region because of the substantial outcrops of Cambrian dolomite occurring there. The calcareous soil parent materials, combined with intensive grazing of the vegetation, has produced an *Agrostis—Festuca* sward which may be floristically rich locally and which is often swamped by a dense growth of bracken. *Dryas* heath and patches of scrub with tall herbs have survived where there is shallow, stony soil, deeply dissected limestone pavement or long-standing protection from grazing. Other outcrops of dolomite, with associated mudstones, along the line of the Moine Thrust are too restricted in area to produce more than strictly local effects on the vegetation, although they are of great importance floristically and ecologically. Coastal shell sand deposits in the neighbourhood of Bettyhill have produced a similar effect where the sand blows inland and the locality is well known for its rich assemblage of mountain plants at sea-level.

The region corresponds roughly to the mainland area of predominantly birch forest and scrub (Fig. 61) and while much of the drier "flowe" country of Sutherland may have been derived from birch scrub within the last 1200 years it is likely that the region always contained extensive unforested areas corresponding to the wetter bogs of today. Practically all the tree birches are *Betula pubescens* spp. *odorata* especially in the far north. Pine woodland is confined to the southern part of the region and has a floor vegetation belonging to the *Vaccinium—Calluna* association.

The present restriction of tall juniper scrub to islands in the lochs of Sutherland and Ross-shire indicates a reduction of juniper by fires from which it has failed to recover to the same extent as in the drier climate of the east-central Highlands. Prostrate juniper scrub above the forest limit seems to have suffered in the same way so that little remains except for a few patches on the quartzite of Beinn Eighe and the Foinaven range. Whin (*Ulex europeus*) is now the characteristic tall shrub, especially in the west.

Bracken is rampant in many of the natural birch and oak scrubs and on the drier hill slopes as well as occupying many of the sites of former crofts and shielings. Heather burning on the drier slopes is leading to rapid spread of the bracken just as it encourages the increase of *Trichophorum* on the wetter ground. The fern *Thelypteris limbosperma* behaves rather like bracken among the long heather of north facing slopes.

The land use of the region is predominantly deer forest and hill sheep farming with some forestry in the glens of the southern half and a discontinuous fringe of crofting around the coast. Afforestation is being extended to districts where it has not been regarded as practicable hitherto, the main species planted being lodgepole pine (*Pinus contorta*) and Sitka spruce (*Picea sitchensis*) which are better adapted to deep acid peat than the native Scots pine (*Pinus sylvestris* ssp. *scotica*). Even these tolerant exotics require drainage, ploughing and fertilisation with ground rock phosphate or basic slag for their successful establishment. Hill cattle enterprises are also springing up in many places and multiple land use (sheep, cattle, forestry) is practised by the Westminster Estates in Sutherland.

West-central Highlands

The west-central Highland region comprises the rest of the mainland Highlands. It is not sharply delimited from the two regions already described and many of the characteristic vegetation types of these regions extend for some distance into this region also. On the whole it is an area of mixed grass and dwarf shrub communities with the grasslands predominating.

The associations of greatest extent are *Calluna—Molinia* heath, *Molinia—Myrica* bog, *Molinia*, *Agrostis—Festuca* and sub-alpine *Nardus* and *Juncus squarrosus* grasslands with many intermediate types. *Trichophorum—Eriophorum* and *Trichophorum—Calluna* bogs are still important, particularly north of the Great Glen and on Rannoch Moor, but *Calluna—Eriophorum* and *Empetrum—Eriophorum* bogs are of local occurrence only. Altitudinal zonation of the vegetation is not well marked in the absence of abundant *Calluna* since the most prominent species are those of wide tolerance.

The *Vaccinium—Calluna* association is confined mainly to the border with the east-central region from Ben Alder to Monar Forest while the dwarf *Calluna* heaths are not important outside the Affric-Cannich district.

A good development of tall *Calluna*, *Empetrum* and *Vaccinium* is seen only on inaccessible crag ledges, rather like tall herb vegetation which is also confined to such sites where there is calcareous rock. There can be little doubt that *Calluna* has been eliminated as a physiognomic dominant within this region by the combination of burning and sheep grazing. In some districts such as Lochaber the process can still be seen in action but in mid-Argyll the period of rapid change has passed and dominant heather is confined to the most favourable and protected spots.

On the higher ground (above about 600 m.) all three low alpine *Nardus* associations are found but there is a tendency for the *Nardus* grasslands to be less closely associated with snow-lie than in the other regions and to merge imperceptibly with the sub-alpine *Nardus* vegetation below. *Rhacomitrium* heath is less well developed than in the other regions, probably because of the sharper peaks and ridges. *Vaccinium—Empetrum* heath and *Vaccinium* snow beds are important only in the Affric-Cannich district and in Breadalbane but both the *Rhacomitrium* and *Cladonia* facies of *Festuca ovina*-rich *Vaccinium* heaths are quite common in western and eastern districts respectively.

Species-rich montane grasslands and mires and dwarf herb communities are more numerous and cover larger areas in this region than elsewhere although they also extend eastward to the Tay Valley and Clova. Breadalbane is the principal centre for them. Montane mires dominated by *Carex saxatilis* are practically confined to the region while sub-montane *Juncus* mires are confined to its southern edge.

The most famous localities for mountain plants in Scotland lie on the calcareous sericite schists of Breadalbane from Ben Lui to Ben Lawers.

The region corresponds approximately with the north-westward extension of the main oak forest region into the Highlands (Fig. 61), and relict oak scrub with associated hazel is still more important here than elsewhere in Scotland. On the steep slopes of the Tertiary basalt escarpments of Morvern, hazel scrub with ash standards is a characteristic type of vegetation; it extends also to the basalt areas of Skye and Mull. Whin is again a characteristic thicket-forming tall shrub. The west-central region is the only part of the Highlands where *Betula pubescens* spp. *pubescens* is found.

Land use is essentially similar to that of the northern and east-central Highlands but sheep stocking rates are higher and hill cattle more numerous. Forestry is extensive and more varied than in the other Highland regions and, while Sitka spruce (*Picea sitchensis*) is probably the commonest of the planted trees, a wide variety of conifers from the Pacific coast of North America can be grown successfully. There are some large farms of lowland style in the south-west.

Bracken is perhaps a greater menace in this region than anywhere else in Scotland. On deep, fertile soils in sheltered, frost-free districts along the western seaboard it can assume complete dominance and reaches a phenomenal height.

Southern Region

The southern region comprises the Ochil Hills, Kilpatrick and Campsie Fells, the Renfrewshire uplands, the Pentlands, Moorfoots and Lammermuirs and the main block of the Southern Uplands.

These are all essentially grassland areas or grassland-bog mosaics, and dwarf shrubs play an even less important role than in the west-central Highlands. The granite areas of Galloway have a greater intermixture of *Calluna* in their vegetation. The Campsies, Renfrewshire uplands, the hills of Galloway and the Lowthers are on the whole wetter than the eastern ranges and have more *Molinia*, *Molinia—Myrica* and deep peat communities.

The important vegetation types of the region are sub-alpine *Nardus* and *Juncus squarrosus* grassland, species-poor *Agrostis—Festuca* and *Molinia* grassland, *Calluna—Eriophorum*, *Trichophorum—Eriophorum* and *Molinia—Myrica* bog. There are localised examples of heather moor, species-rich *Agrostis—Festuca*, *Nardus* and anthropogenic *Deschampsia cespitosa* grassland. The sub-alpine grasslands mostly extend to the summits of the hills but there is a small amount of dwarf Callunetum on White Coomb and Dollar Law along with grassy patches of lichen-rich *Vaccinium*-dominated vegetation on the latter. Anthropogenic *Vaccinium* heath is quite widespread with local patches of

Vaccinium—Empetrum. There is no *Rhacomitrium* heath and there are no examples of vegetation definitely influenced by snow anywhere. The principal peat types of the region are fibrous *Eriophorum—Sphagnum* and amorphous *Molinia*.

Juncus acutiflorus—Acrocladium cuspidatum and *Juncus effusus—Sphagnum* mires are quite common as they are in the southern and eastern Highlands. Sedge mires with brown mosses are found in Moffat and Tweedsmuir and *Carex panicea—Campylium stellatum* mires occur on calcareous sites. Vegetation of the hill springs is similar to that in the Highlands and examples of both *Philonotis fontana—Saxifraga stellaris* and *Cratoneuron commutatum* dominated types are found.

This region corresponds to the higher lying parts of the main oak forest region (Fig. 61) although there is little natural scrub, even of birch, hazel and juniper, left today. There are a few semi-natural oakwoods left in Glen Trool, around Thornhill, near Selkirk and elsewhere but the largest and oldest trees are those preserved in policy woodland and parkland as at Dalkeith and Lanark. Fragments of mixed scrub survive in some of the steeper cleuch of the Pentlands, Tweedsmuir and Ettrick.

The region has a longer history of hill sheep farming than the other three regions and this is the key to the principal vegetation contrasts that it offers with them. A full discussion has already been given in Chapter 6. There can be little doubt that both deciduous scrub and heather have been virtually eliminated by this form of land use. Large areas of the uplands have been, and are being, planted with conifers, mainly spruce, pine and larch.

THE ISLANDS

As stated earlier, the islands do not form a natural region and each really merits a separate description. In general terms the affinities of the Long Island, Skye and Rhum are with the northern Highlands while the remainder could be grouped with the west-central region.

Lewis, the Uists and Barra have the largest proportion of *Calluna—Eriophorum* and *Trichophorum—Eriophorum* bog land although there are also sizeable patches in Islay and Jura and on the basalt plateaux of Skye and Mull. *Molinia—Calluna* moor is an important type of vegetation throughout the islands from St. Kilda to Arran and there are generally some small patches of pure *Calluna* moor associated with it. Lewis and Harris, Jura and north Arran have probably the most heathery vegetation of the group. *Agrostis—Festuca* grasslands are at their best and cover the greatest area on the steep basalt slopes of Skye and Mull but they are found everywhere from North Rona to Islay and Arran as maritime grasslands with much *Festuca rubra* or sub-montane grasslands which may have abundant *Anthoxanthum odoratum* or *Deschampsia flexuosa*.

Montane vegetation (mainly *Rhacomitrium* heath, low-alpine *Nardus* grassland and the associated open plant cover of erosion surfaces) is restricted to the Cuillins of Skye and Rhum, Ben More in Mull and the north Arran peaks.

Fragments of oak and hazel scrub remain on Arran, Islay, Eigg, Raasay, Mull and Skye with mixed, mainly birch, scrub in numerous other places. On the steep slopes of

20

the basalt escarpments in Skye, Mull and one or two of the smaller isles hazel scrub with scattered stunted ash trees is a characteristic feature. There is a small ashwood on the Sleat peninsula of Skye. Small patches of *Dryas octopetala* heath occur on the calcareous rocks of Raasay and Rhum and the species is also found on Eigg and Mull.

Crofting is the principal land use in the islands, with the moorland utilised as common grazing for cattle and sheep. Cattle are most numerous in Islay, Coll, parts of Skye, the Uists and Barra. Reclamation of moorland, both by skinning the peat and the more recent technique of fertilising and reseeding the cultivated or unworked surface is most active in Lewis. There are some larger holdings and farms in Mull, and Islay and small areas of deer forest in Harris and Mull. Re-afforestation is of importance only in Mull.

INDEX OF AUTHORS

(Bibliographical entries are in italics)

INDEX OF PLACE NAMES

Mentioned in text only (*Places outwith Scotland are in italics*)

INDEX OF PLANT NAMES

which occur in the text.

GENERAL INDEX

(Tabular matter is indicated by italics)

ass. = association; com. = community; soc. = sociation.

Adaptations, hydrophytes, 30, 371–375.
Advance growth, pine, 149.
Afforestation, of bogs, 454, 457–458.
  of dunes, 103, 107.
  of heaths, 236, 270–271, 275–277.
Agropyron junceiforme stands, 86, 92, 93–95.
Agrostis—Festuca grassland, 172, 173, 174, 181, 195, 198, 199, 200, 271, 438, 487, 499, 518, 570, 571, 574, 575, 577.
  type 10, 192–193, 195, 196, *219–223*.
Agrostis—Festuca—Poa type 4; 193, 196, *216–218*, *223*.
Agrostis stolonifera stands, 118.
Agrosto—Festucetum, species-poor, 188–189, 195, 196, *224–231*, 570, 576.
  species-rich, 189, 190, 195, 198, *224–231*, 526, 571, 574, 576.
Alchemilla alpina—Sibbaldia ass., 518–520, *522–523*.
Achemilleto—Agrosto—Festucetum, 190, 195, 196, 197, *224–231*.
Alder carr, 106, 339, 348, 350, 351, *354*, 355, 356, *420–423*.
Alderwood, 160–161, 563, 565–566.
Algal communities, of cliffs, 71–72.
  of salt marsh, 113, 116, 117, 118.
  of lochs (see plankton).
Alkalinity (see water).
Allerød Period, 562.
Alliances, aquatic plant, 356.
Altitude, and vegetation zones, 5, 145, 168, 246.
Ammophila arenaria stands, 95–97, *134–138*.
Anthelia—Deschampsia cespitosa flush, 430, 540, *550–555*, 571.
Anmoor, warp, 316, 348, 351, 353, 380.
Anthropogenic grasslands, 168–209.
  heaths, 234, 269–270.
  influence (see man).
Apposition beaches, 80, 84–85, *133*.
Aquatic vegetation (see communities).
  grazing, 337–340, 347–348, 349, 352–354.
Arctostaphyleto—Callunetum, 263.
Arctostaphylos grass heath, 494, *498*.
Arctoeto—Callunetum, 482.

Arctous—Calluna ass., 482–483, 484, 485, 486, *496–497*, 573.
Armeria—Cochlearia stand, 73, 75, 79, *128–129*.
Armeria sward, 74, 83, 85, *128–129*.
Arrhenatherum elatius stand, of shingle, 84–85, *133*.
Aspect, and climate, 28, 29.
  effect on soil, 58.
  of slope and heaths, 246–247.
  and turbulence of water, 365–367.
Association, plant, 8, 318.
  between species, 326, 341, 344–345.
Atlantic Period, 269, 270, 443, 444, 445, 448, 563–564.
Atriplex glabriuscula—Polygonum raii ass., 83.
Atriplex—Silene maritima—Tripleurospermum stand, 81–84, *133*.
Atriplicion littoralis, 87.

Bacillariophyceae, distribution in lochs, 297, *305*.
Basc status, 91, 145, 164, 182, 188, 189, 195, 200, 201, 234, 247–248, 256, 262, 264, 271, 437, 439, 538.
Bathymetric Survey of Scottish Lochs, 290, 306, 314, 359, 369–370, 377, 378.
Beech wood, 4, 146.
Biomass, 204–205, 380.
Biotic factor (see grazing, man).
Birch wood, 150–158, *166–167*, 563–564, 576.
Bird cliff, 79–80.
Black mud (see mud).
Blanket peat (see peat).
Blanket bog (see bog).
Block scree, 153.
Bog, 8, 439, 445, 448.
  blanket, 428, 442–444.
  climate, 445–446.
  conservation, 458–459.
  cyclical change, 450–451.
  distribution of, *430*.
  erosion, 454.
  flush, 427.
  grazing on, 449.

'White Diamond' is said to be considerably hardier than the type *S. cineraria*, the leaves less divided and the silver-grey colouration more intense.

Exhibited by Mr. S. M. Gault, M.B.E., V.M.H., New Lodge, Regents Park, N.W.1.

June, 1965.

BOOK NOTES

"The Vegetation of Scotland." Edited by J. H. Burnett. 613 pp. Illus. (Oliver & Boyd, Edinburgh and London.) 1964. 126s.

This book is the first comprehensive treatment of the vegetation of Scotland. Since the pioneer work of Robert and W. G. Smith at the turn of the century, little was published on Scottish vegetation until the late 'thirties. This book is largely the fruit of the post-war revival of interest which led first to the publication of the Plant Communities of the Scottish Highlands (H.M.S.O., London, 1962). Much of the material of this work is included in the present volume, but there is also much that is new.

The book is divided into four parts. In an introductory chapter Professor Burnett reviews the history of plant ecology in Scotland and explains the methods which have been adopted for describing and classifying Scottish vegetation in this book. Two chapters on environment follow, on climate and on soils. The former lays particular stress on periods of "potential water deficit" and their influence in controlling the distribution of vegetation; the latter, all too briefly, provides a description and classification of Scottish soils well illustrated by block diagrams and excellent colour photographs.

The main body of the book comprises eight chapters describing in detail the terrestrial and freshwater vegetation of Scotland. Man-made communities and those below the high tide level are not included.

For this description the vegetation is divided into four zones. First there is a detailed treatment of the Maritime and Sub-maritime zone which brings together much scattered or previously unpublished information. Under the heading of the Forest zone, there are chapters on woodland and scrub, and the grasslands and dwarf-shrub heaths which have been derived from them by grazing and burning. There is much new material in the treatment of the Lowland Aquatic zone which deals with the planktonic and macrophytic vegetation of the Scottish lochs, swamps, fens, mires and bogs. Lastly the Montane zone includes dwarf-shrub heaths, herb and fern meadows, moss heaths and mountain mires and bogs.

Each community is described in detail with full floristic lists; and there is ample discussion of the causal factors determining their presence, their dynamics and their relationship with similar vegetation elsewhere in N.W. Europe. Fascinating glimpses of social history appear from time to time in the discussion of the origin of certain types of vegetation.

Seven authors have contributed to this part of the book, each very experienced in the topics with which he has dealt.

Finally there are two synoptic chapters, one discussing prehistory and ecological history, and the other the regional pattern of vegetation. These serve to set the details of the preceding chapters in perspective and leave the reader with a satisfying overall picture.

The book is well illustrated with maps, line drawings and excellent photographs, some of the most fascinating of which are pairs taken of certain lochs, showing the change, or lack of it, between West's survey in 1904–5 and the present day.

The book is exceptionally well indexed. For, as well as a general index, there are special indices to authors and to plant and place names.

Although specialized and authoritative, this is not a book for the specialist only, as much of the text is very readable. For this reason it is perhaps unfortunate that there is no glossary and that slightly more concession had not been made to the general reader in some of the more technical passages.

Like the first edition of Tansley's *British Islands and Their Vegetation*, it is too heavy and bulky for its binding and for convenient handling. It would be better for a future edition to be in two volumes.

The Editor and authors are to be congratulated on a magnificent production which makes the vegetation of Scotland among the best described in Europe.

M. E. D. POORE